HANDBOOK OF ENVIRONMENTAL ANALYSIS

FOURTH EDITION

Authored by

Roy-Keith Smith, PhD
Apichemical Consultants

Genium Publishing Corporation

One Genium Plaza., Schenectady, NY 12304-4690   (518) 377-8854

FOREWORD

Environmental analysis is the fundamental technology of the whole environmental industry. It is a combination of traditional and modern chemistry techniques and civil engineering materials characterizations, mixed together with a hefty dose of legalistic regulatory jargon. The majority of the users of the information produced by environmental laboratories, and for that matter the majority of the people performing the analyses, have little or no formal training in chemistry. The writers of analytical methods in both the EPA and the *Standard Methods* manuals have sought to simplify the procedures to the greatest extent possible and present each method as a recipe, which, if followed exactly, will produce an acceptable answer. This results in situations where seemingly anomalous results cannot be explained because an in-depth chemical understanding of the test procedure is lacking.

While teaching environmental chemistry as a course to civil engineering students, I found that the most profitable approach was to present the chemical and biological background information as an adjunct to understanding the individual analytical procedures. I have always felt that a fundamental understanding of how the procedure worked led to better performance of the test by the technician. Unfortunately, the explanations for many of the tests used in environmental analysis are difficult to find, being scattered in many texts. This text is a collection of all the explanations for all the questions I have asked while working as an environmental analyst.

Another reason for writing this handbook is to gather together in one convenient place the miscellaneous facts and figures necessary in performing environmental analysis. Having this handbook nearby will be appreciated by those who, like me, keep misplacing the tables for Langelier's index and the *t*-statistic, and can't remember the COD value for KHP.

Finally, this handbook was written as a general guide to what information is important in environmental analysis and where to find it. Every year the environmental business changes with new programs, new regulations, and new methods. It's a daunting task for the newcomer to assimilate enough information to get up to speed and function, let alone appear literate.

What's new in the Fourth Edition

The Internet has become the key resource within the environmental analytical industry. The amount of information available to be down-loaded is staggering. Almost everything that has been or is being published from Federal and State government agencies is available. Simply keeping up-to-date with the major regulatory programs as they change and evolve is a fulltime job. However, because of the instant availability of information, the excuse that, "we didn't know'" is less and less tenable to clients and regulators.

With this Fourth Edition, the entire book has been revised. Section 3, Organic Parameters, has undergone a complete re-write to include detailed discussions of both Updates III and IV to SW-846, and other evolving methodologies. Other major revisions include discussions of the AFCEE QAPP version 3.0, and *Standard Methods* 20th Edition. A discussion of Natural Attenuation is added. The FIFRA program has published a consolidated methods manual which is described. The EPA has established a workgroup to prepare a biosolids analytical manual and the progress to date is reviewed. An expanded discussion of toxicity testing for both EPA and OECD is included. Groundwater and site-remediation evaluations using the Appendix IX list of analytes are discussed in Section 4. A discussion of Water Quality Criteria is added in Section 1. The commercialized PE replacement program for the WS and WP studies is examined and contacts into NELAP are presented. Many new and revised analytcial methods have been added to the lists in Section 1.II. References to and discussion of over 30 new or revised testing manuals have been included. The Regulatory Contact directory has been up-dated to the most current information, particularly with regards to telephone numbers.

Although EPA has been debating and preparing for agency-wide implementation of Performance Based Methods Systems (PBMS) for several years, the final versions for most of the regulatory programs have not been promulgated. Even the Office of Solid Waste's RCRA program testing manual (SW-846), which is written as guidance, has yet to be implemented as PBMS. However PBMS is coming. Successful utilization of PBMS by laboratories requires operation from a broad-based analytical knowledge base. Over the years this *Handbook* has evolved as my own personal set of references into that knowledge base. My own copy is dog-eared and filled with sticky notes. I am always open to suggestions as to how I can make it more useful. If you have a question or comment, just send an e-mail to me at r-ksmith@asi-lab.com.

I thank and acknowledge the contributions and suggestions from all my friends and colleagues in the industry and my editor at Genium Publishing.

Roy-Keith Smith, PhD
May, 1999

Table of Contents

Section 2   Physical, Biological and General Chemical Parameters, *continued*

Appendices

Illustrations

Tables

Table No.	Table Titles, *continued*	Page No.

Introduction to Environmental Analysis

No plant manager wakes up in the morning and on the spur of the moment decides to go down to the plant wastewater outfall, take a sample of the effluent and send it off to an environmental laboratory for testing. The testing is expensive and adds directly to the cost of manufacturing products without creating any additional value in the product. The only reason that the plant manager takes the sample is because he is directed to do so by a federal or state government regulation. The environmental industry is a regulated industry in the sense that it exists solely because it services government requirements for monitoring, remediation and pollution prevention. Persons in the industry who refuse to recognize this fundamental motivating force and fail to keep themselves informed of changes in the regulations are deluding themselves and will eventually run into the reality of what it means to be ignorant of government directives.

I. APPLICABLE FEDERAL AND STATE REGULATIONS

A. Title 40, Code of Federal Regulations: Protection of Environment

Titles in the Code of Federal Regulations (CFR) are compilations of the rules and regulations promulgated by the federal government to define, implement, and enforce the laws enacted by the Congress of the USA and signed into effect by the President. They are the ultimate authority (other than the Supreme Court) of federal requirements. Many commercial (and municipal) laboratories miss this point. It is against the Federal law of the land not to follow explicitly the methods listed in the CFR. Every laboratory should have a copy of 40 CFR on hand and a competent legal firm, which specializes in environmental issues, under retainer to interpret the laws. New editions of 40 CFR are published annually, and the most recent edition should be in the lab's collection of reference materials. 40 CFR is available on-line from the Government Printing Office, See Appendix F of this book for the address.

Table 1–1. Contents of Title 40, Code of Federal Regulations

Chapter I - Environmental Protection Agency (Parts 1-799)		
Subchapter	**Part**	**Title**
Subchapter A	1-29	General
	1	Statement of organization and general information
	2	Public information
	4	Uniform relocation assistance and real property acquisition for Federal and federally assisted programs
	6	Procedures for implementing the requirements of the Council on Environmental Quality on the National Environmental Policy Act
	7	Nondiscrimination in programs receiving Federal assistance from the Environmental Protection Agency
	8	Environmental impact assessment of nongovernmental activities in Antarctica
	9	OMB approvals under the Paperwork Reduction Act
	10	Administrative claims under Federal Tort Claims Act
	11	Security classification regulations pursuant to Executive Order 11652
	12	Nondiscrimination on the basis of handicap in programs or activities conducted by the Environmental Protection Agency
	13	Claims collection standards
	14	Employee personal property claims
	16	Implementation of Privacy Act of 1974
	17	Implementation of the Equal Access to Justice Act in EPA administrative proceedings
	19	Adjustment of civil monetary penalties for inflation
	20	Certification of facilities
	21	Small business
	22	Consolidated rules of practice governing the administrative assessment of civil penalties and the revocation or suspension of permits
	23	Judicial review under EPA--Administered statutes
	24	Rules governing issuance of and administrative hearings on interim status corrective action orders
	25	Public participation in programs under the Resource Conservation and Recovery Act, the Safe Drinking Water Act, and the Clean Water Act
	26	Protection of human subjects
	27	Program fraud civil remedies
	29	Inter-governmental review of Environmental Protection Agency programs and activities
Subchapter B	30-49	Grants and other Federal Assistance
	30	Grants and agreements with institutions of higher education, hospitals, and other non-profit organizations
	31	Uniform administrative requirements for grants and cooperative agreements to State and local governments
	32	Governmentwide debarment and suspension (nonprocurement) and government-wide requirements for drug-free workplace (grants); Clean Air Act and Clean Water Act ineligibility of facilities in performance of Federal contracts, grants and loans
	34	New restrictions on lobbying

Table 1–1. Contents of Title 40, Code of Federal Regulations, *continued*

Chapter I - Environmental Protection Agency (Parts 1-799)		
Subchapter	**Part**	**Title**
	35	State and local assistance
	40	Research and demonstration grants
	45	Training assistance
	46	Fellowships
	47	National Environmental Education Act grants
	49	Tribal Clean Air Act authority
Subchapter C	50-95	Air Programs
	50	National primary and secondary ambient air quality standards
	51	Requirements for preparation, adoption, and submittal of implementation plans
	52	Approval and promulgation of implementation plans
	53	Ambient air monitoring reference and equivalent methods
	54	Prior notice of citizen suits
	55	Outer continental shelf air regulations
	56	Regional consistency
	57	Primary nonferrous smelter orders
	58	Ambient air quality surveillance
	60	Standards of performance for new stationary sources
	61	National emission standards for hazardous air pollutants
	62	Approval and promulgation of State plans for designated facilities and pollutants
	63	National emission standards for hazardous air pollutants for source categories
	64	Compliance assurance monitoring
	66	Assessment and collection of noncompliance penalties by EPA
	67	EPA approval of State noncompliance penalty program
	68	Chemical accident prevention provisions
	69	Special exemptions from requirements of the Clean Air Act
	70	State operating permit programs
	71	Federal operating permit programs
	72	Permits regulation
	73	Sulfur dioxide allowance system
	74	Sulfur dioxide opt-ins
	75	Continuous emission monitoring
	76	Acid rain nitrogen oxides emission reduction program
	77	Excess emissions
	78	Appeal procedures for Acid Rain Program
	79	Registration of fuels and fuel additives
	80	Regulation of fuels and fuel additives
	81	Designation of areas for air quality planning purposes
	82	Protection of stratospheric ozone
	85	Control of air pollution from mobile sources

Table 1–1. Contents of Title 40, Code of Federal Regulations, *continued*

Chapter I - Environmental Protection Agency (Parts 1-799)		
Subchapter	**Part**	**Title**
	86	Control of air pollution from new and in-use motor vehicles and new and in-use motor vehicle engines: Certification and test procedures
	87	Control of air pollution from aircraft and aircraft engines
	88	Clean-fuel vehicles
	89	Control of emissions from new and in-use nonroad engines
	90	Control of emissions from nonroad spark-ignition engines
	91	Control of emissions from marine spark-ignition engines
	92	Control of air pollution from locomotives and locomotive engines
	93	Determining conformity of Federal actions to State or Federal implementation plans
	95	Mandatory patent licenses
Subchapter D	104-149	Water Programs
	104	Public hearings on effluent standards for toxic pollutants
	108	Employee protection hearings
	109	Criteria for State, local and regional oil removal contingency plans
	110	Discharge of oil
	112	Oil pollution prevention
	113	Liability limits for small onshore storage facilities
	116	Designation of hazardous substances
	117	Determination of reportable quantities for hazardous substances
	121	State certification of activities requiring a Federal license or permit
	122	EPA administered permit programs: The national pollutant discharge elimination system
	123	State program requirements
	124	Procedures for decisionmaking
	125	Criteria and standards for the national pollutant discharge elimination system
	129	Toxic pollutant effluent standards
	130	Water quality planning and management
	131	Water quality standards
	132	Water quality guidance for the Great Lakes System
	133	Secondary treatment regulation
	135	Prior notice of citizen suits
	136	Guidelines establishing test procedures for the analysis of pollutants
	140	Marine sanitation device standard
	141	National primary drinking water regulations
	142	National primary drinking water regulations implementation
	143	National secondary drinking water regulations
	144	Underground injection control program
	145	State UIC program requirements
	146	Underground injection control program: Criteria and standards
	147	State underground injection control programs
	148	Hazardous waste injection restrictions

Table 1–1. Contents of Title 40, Code of Federal Regulations, *continued*

Chapter I - Environmental Protection Agency (Parts 1-799)		
Subchapter	Part	Title
	149	Sole source aquifers
Subchapter E	152-186	Pesticide Programs
	152	Pesticide registration and classification procedures
	153	Registration policies and interpretations
	154	Special review procedures
	155	Registration standards
	156	Labeling requirements for pesticides and devices
	157	Packaging requirements for pesticides and devices
	158	Data requirements for registration
	159	Statements of policies and interpretations
	160	Good laboratory practice standards
	162	State registration of pesticide products
	163	Certification of usefulness of pesticide chemicals
	164	Rules of practice governing hearings under FIFRA arising from refusal to register, cancellation of registrations, changes of classifications, suspensions of registrations and other hearings called pursuant to section 6 of the Act
	166	Exemption of Federal and State agencies for use of pesticides under emergency conditions
	167	Registration of pesticide and active ingredient producing establishments, submission of pesticide reports
	168	Statements of enforcement policies and interpretations
	169	Books and records of pesticide production and distribution
	170	Worker protection standard
	171	Certification of pesticide applicators
	172	Experimental use permits
	173	Procedures governing the rescission of State primacy enforcement responsibility for pesticide use violations
	177	Issuance of food additive regulations
	178	Objections and request for hearings
	179	Formal evidentiary public hearings
	180	Tolerances and exemptions from tolerances for pesticide chemicals in food
	185	Tolerances for pesticides in food
	186	Pesticides in animal feed
Subchapter F	190-195	Radiation Protection Programs
	190	Environmental radiation protection standards for nuclear power operations
	191	Environmental radiation protection standards for management and disposal of spent nuclear fuel, high-level and transuranic radioactive wastes
	192	Health and environmental protection standards for uranium and thorium mill tailings

Table 1–1. Contents of Title 40, Code of Federal Regulations, *continued*

Chapter I - Environmental Protection Agency (Parts 1-799)		
Subchapter	**Part**	**Title**
Subchapter F, *continued*	194	Criteria for the certification and re-certification of the Waste Isolation Pilot Plant's compliance with the 40 CFR 191 disposal regulations
	195	Radon proficiency programs
Subchapter G	201-211	Noise Abatement Programs
	201	Noise emission standards for transportation equipment: interstate rail carriers
	202	Motor carriers engaged in interstate commerce
	203	Low-noise-emission products
	204	Noise emission standards for construction equipment
	205	Transportation equipment noise emission controls
	209	Rules of practice governing proceedings under the Noise Control Act of 1972
	210	Prior notice of citizen suits
	211	Product noise labeling
Subchapter H	220-238	Ocean Dumping
	220	General
	221	Applications for ocean dumping permits under section 102 of the Act
	222	Action on ocean dumping permits under section 102 of the Act
	223	Contents of permits; revision, revocation, or limitation of ocean dumping permits under section 104(d) of the Act
	224	Records and reports required of ocean dumping permittees under section 102 of the Act
	225	Corps of Engineers dredged material permits
	227	Criteria for the evaluation of permit applications for ocean dumping of materials
	228	Criteria for the management of disposal sites for ocean dumping
	229	General permits
	230	Section 404(b)(1) guidelines for specification of disposal sites for dredged or fill material
	231	Section 404(c) procedures
	232	404 program definitions; exempt activities not requiring 404 permits
	233	404 State program regulations
	238	Degradable plastic ring carriers
Subchapter I	240-282	Solid Wastes
	240	Guidelines for the thermal processing of solid wastes
	243	Guidelines for the storage and collection of residential, commercial, and institutional solid waste
	244	Solid waste management guidelines for beverage containers
	246	Source separation for materials recovery guidelines
	247	Comprehensive procurement guideline for products containing recovered materials
	254	Prior notice of citizen suits
	255	Identification of regions and agencies for solid waste management

Table 1–1. Contents of Title 40, Code of Federal Regulations, *continued*

Chapter I - Environmental Protection Agency (Parts 1-799)		
Subchapter	**Part**	**Title**
Subchapter I, *continued*	256	Guidelines for development and implementation of State solid waste management plans
	257	Criteria for classification of solid waste disposal facilities and practices
	258	Criteria for municipal solid waste landfills
	260	Hazardous waste management system: General
	261	Identification and listing of hazardous waste
	262	Standards applicable to generators of hazardous waste
	263	Standards applicable to transporters of hazardous waste
	264	Standards for owners and operators of hazardous waste treatment, storage, and disposal facilities
	265	Interim status standards for owners and operators of hazardous waste treatment, storage, and disposal facilities
	266	Standards for the management of specific hazardous wastes and specific types of hazardous waste management facilities
	268	Land disposal restrictions
	270	EPA administered permit programs: The Hazardous Waste Permit Program
	271	Requirements for authorization of State hazardous waste programs
	272	Approved State hazardous waste management programs
	273	Standards for universal waste management
	279	Standards for the management of used oil
	280	Technical standards and corrective action requirements for owners and operators of underground storage tanks (UST)
	281	Approval of State underground storage tank programs
	282	Approved underground storage tank programs
Subchapter J	300-374	Superfund, Emergency Planning and Community Right-to-Know Programs
	300	National oil and hazardous substances pollution contingency plan
	302	Designation, reportable quantities, and notification
	303	Citizen awards for information on criminal violations under superfund
	304	Arbitration procedures for small superfund cost recovery claims
	305	CERCLA administrative hearing procedures for claims against the superfund
	307	CERCLA claims procedures
	310	Reimbursements to local governments for emergency response to hazardous substance releases
	311	Worker protection
	350	Trade secrecy claims for emergency planning and community right-to-know
	355	Emergency planning and notification
	370	Hazardous chemical reporting: Community right-to-know
	372	Toxic chemical release reporting: Community right-to-know

Table 1–1. Contents of Title 40, Code of Federal Regulations, *continued*

Chapter I - Environmental Protection Agency (Parts 1-799)		
Subchapter	**Part**	**Title**
Subchapter J, *continued*	373	Reporting hazardous substance activity when selling or transferring Federal real property
	374	Prior notice of citizen suits
Subchapter N	401-471	Effluent Guidelines and Standards
	401	General provisions
	403	General pretreatment regulations for existing and new sources of pollution
	405	Dairy products processing point source category
	406	Grain mills point source category
	407	Canned and preserved fruits and vegetables processing point source category
	408	Canned and preserved seafood processing point source category
	409	Sugar processing point source category
	410	Textile mills point source category
	411	Cement manufacturing point source category
	412	Feedlots point source category
	413	Electroplating point source category
	414	Organic chemicals, plastics and synthetic fibers
	415	Inorganic chemicals manufacturing point source category
	417	Soap and detergent manufacturing point source category
	418	Fertilizer manufacturing point source category
	419	Petroleum refining point source category
	420	Iron and steel manufacturing point source category
	421	Nonferrous metals manufacturing point source category
	422	Phosphate manufacturing point source category
	423	Steam electric power generating point source category
	424	Ferroalloy manufacturing point source category
	425	Leather tanning and finishing point source category
	426	Glass manufacturing point source category
	427	Asbestos manufacturing point source category
	428	Rubber manufacturing point source category
	429	Timber products processing point source category
	430	The pulp, paper and paperboard point source category
	431	The builder's paper and board mills point source category
	432	Meat products point source category
	433	Metal finishing point source category
	434	Coal mining point source category
	435	Oil and gas extraction point source category
	436	Mineral mining and processing point source category
	439	Pharmaceutical manufacturing point source category
	440	Ore mining and dressing point source category
	443	Paving and roofing materials (tars and asphalt) point source category

Table 1–1. Contents of Title 40, Code of Federal Regulations, *continued*

Chapter I - Environmental Protection Agency (Parts 1-799)		
Subchapter	**Part**	**Title**
Subchapter N, *continued*	446	Paint formulating point source category
	447	Ink formulating point source category
	454	Gum and wood chemicals manufacturing point source category
	455	Pesticide chemicals point source category
	457	Explosives manufacturing point source category
	458	Carbon black manufacturing point source category
	459	Photographic point source category
	460	Hospital point source category
	461	Battery manufacturing point source category
	463	Plastics molding and forming point source category
	464	Metal molding and casting point source category
	465	Coil coating point source category
	466	Porcelain enameling point source category
	467	Aluminum forming point source category
	468	Copper forming point source category
	469	Electrical and electronic components point source category
	471	Nonferrous metals forming and metal powders point source category
	501	State sludge management program regulations
	503	Standards for the use or disposal of sewage sludge
Subchapter Q	600-610	Energy Policy
	600	Fuel economy of motor vehicles
	610	Fuel economy retrofit devices
Subchapter R	702-799	Toxic Substances Control Act
	700	General
	702	General practices and procedures
	704	Reporting and recordkeeping requirements
	707	Chemical imports and exports
	710	Inventory reporting regulations
	712	Chemical information rules
	716	Health and safety data reporting
	717	Records and reports of allegations that chemical substances cause significant adverse reactions to health or the environment
	720	Premanufacture notification
	721	Significant new uses of chemical substances
	723	Premanufacture notification exemptions
	725	Reporting requirements and review processes for microorganisms
	745	Lead-based paint poisoning prevention in certain residential structures
	747	Metalworking fluids
	749	Water treatment chemicals

Table 1–1. Contents of Title 40, Code of Federal Regulations, *continued*

Chapter I - Environmental Protection Agency (Parts 1-799)		
Subchapter	**Part**	**Title**
Subchapter R, *continued*	750	Procedures for rulemaking under section 6 of TSCA
	761	PCB manufacturing, processing, distribution in commerce, and use prohibitions
	763	Asbestos
	766	Dibenzo-para-dioxins/dibenzofurans
	790	Procedures governing testing consent agreements and test rules
	791	Data reimbursement
	792	Good laboratory practice standards
	795	Provisional test guidelines
	796	Chemical fate testing guidelines
	797	Environmental effects testing guidelines
	798	Health effects testing guidelines
	799	Identification of specific chemical substance and mixture testing requirements
Chapter V - Council on Environmental Quality (Parts 1500-1599)		

B. Government Regulations Administered By EPA

1. RCRA – Resource Conservation and Recovery Act

The original Federal Act was the Solid Waste Disposal Act of 1965. With the creation of the EPA, expanded legislative frameworks were needed to enable the EPA to perform its mission. Passage of RCRA in 1976 gave EPA the authority to oversee waste disposal and hazardous waste management. Integral to the law is the definition of what is a hazardous waste. The identification of a waste as hazardous relies on either the results of specific analytical tests or its being on a list of recognized hazardous wastes. The analytical methods are compiled in SW-846. Important subtitles to RCRA are:

    a. Subtitle C. Hazardous Waste Management - Introduces the "cradle-to-grave" concept of hazardous waste accounting. The originator or manufacturer of the hazardous waste is the cradle, and the treatment, storage and disposal facility (TSD) is the grave. The law requires traceability through the *Uniform Hazardous Waste Manifest* of the waste as it moves from the originator to the transporter to the TSD, with the federal or state EPA serving in the oversight role. Subtitle C also defines and regulates the construction, operation, and closure of hazardous waste TSD's. As far as environmental analysis is concerned this subtitle specifies the responsibility of the waste originator to characterize the waste, and the groundwater and other analytical monitoring responsibilities of the TSD. The Hazardous Substance List (HSL) analytes are located in 40 CFR Part 261, Appendix VIII. The groundwater monitoring target analytes are located in 40 CFR Part 264, Appendix IX and make-up the so-called Appendix IX analyses.

    b. Subtitle D. Solid Waste Management - This is the subtitle that regulates your local municipal landfill. It details the construction, operation, maintenance, monitoring, and closure of municipal landfills. The newest version of this regulation establishes two sets of extensive monitoring lists, 40 CFR 258, Appendix I and Appendix II, in addition to construction specifications for impermeable liners and leacheate collection and treatment systems with all facilities required to come into full compliance by 1996.

    c. Subtitle E. Underground Storage Tanks - These are defined as storage tanks with at least 10% of the volume underground. There are 1.5 million existing in the US. Over 15% are estimated to be leaking and spreading their contents into the soil and groundwater. Petroleum tanks make up the bulk of leaking storage tanks, although they may not be the most significant as illustrated by videos from remote-controlled cameras in the radioactive waste storage tanks at the Hanford, Washington and Savannah River, South Carolina atomic energy plants. Under the Leaking Underground Storage Tank (LUST) program, individual states with general environmental responsibility, establish the proper methods of analysis and require some sort of laboratory certification. The most common analytical requests under this program are for benzene, toluene, ethyl benzene and xylene (BTEX), and total petroleum hydrocarbons (TPH), both from soil matrix. A variety of methods are in use to determine these groups.

2. CERCLA – Comprehensive Environmental Response, Compensation and Liability Act (Superfund)

The EPA is given two powers under this legislation, passed in 1980. The first is the authority to take any necessary short-term or emergency steps to cope with hazardous situations that affect health. A representative situation could be an explosion and fire that results in contamination of the environment, the food chain, and drinking water supplies. The second power is the ability to enter into long-term (greater than six months) projects to clean-up hazardous sites that are listed on the National Priority List (NPL). The EPA further has the authority to investigate the origins of waste found in hazardous sites and force the generators and other responsible parties to pay for the remediation (clean-up). Analytical support for investigations and remediations under CERCLA is provided through the Contract Laboratory Program (CLP), with the detailed methods contained in the contract Statements of Work, which are updated almost annually.

3. Drinking Water and Wastewater

These two programs cover all aspects of drinking water and wastewater under the below two legislations. Both programs are administered by the individual states. States with primacy offer a range of laboratory certifications for submitting sample results in support of required periodic monitoring. They may range from simple certification of a lab for only microbiology (fecal coliform), to complete certification of micro, chemistry, and toxicology testing.

    a. SDWA - Safe Drinking Water Act - Last amended in 1996, this Act gives the EPA the ability to regulate drinking water quality. This is done through two tiers of analytes. The first is the National Primary Drinking Water Standards. These compounds directly affect human health, and all drinking water systems are required to reduce their presence to below the Maximum Contaminant Levels (MCL), set for each compound by the federal government. Any Primary Contaminant that assays above the MCL in a drinking water system sets off an escalating chain of regulatory actions. In general method detection limits must be lower than 1/5 of the MCL for tested parameters, however some methods have required MDL that are listed in 40 CFR 141, and reproduced below in Table 1-2. The second tier of analytes consists of the National Secondary Drinking Water Standards. They include materials that affect the taste, odor, color and other non-health related qualities of water and collectively serve as a suggested list for states to act upon. The same material may appear on both lists but generally at different action levels, for example, copper and fluoride. Almost all states have accepted primacy for administration of the Act.

The scheduled introduction (Phases I, II, & V) of 25 new drinking water analytes every 3 years by EPA was abolished by the Safe Drinking Water Act of 1996. New analytes are now added as needed by EPA according to risk based criteria. The required analytes along with proper sampling procedures and approved analytical methodologies are found in 40 CFR 141 (National Primary Drinking Water Standards), 40 CFR 143 (National Secondary Drinking Water Standards), and the Manual for Certification of Laboratories Analyzing Drinking Water. These analytes are listed in Tables 1-2 and 1-3.

Table 1-2. Primary Drinking Water Monitoring Requirements[1]

Contaminant	MCL mg/L	MDL mg/L[2]	Method[3]
Inorganics			
Antimony	0.006	.0008-.003	EPA 200.8, 200.9, SM 3113B
Arsenic	0.05		EPA 200.7A, 200.8, 200.9, SM 3120B, 3113B, 3114B
Asbestos	7 mf/L[4]	.01	EPA[5] 100.1, 100.2
Barium	2	.001-.1	EPA 200.7, 208.1, 200.8, SM 3120B, 3111D, 3113B
Beryllium	0.004	.00002-.0003	EPA 200.7, 200.8, 200.9, SM 3120B, 3113B
Cadmium	0.005	.0001-.001	EPA 200.7, 200.8, 200.9, SM 3113B
Chromium	0.1	.001-.007	EPA 200.7, 200.8. 200.9, SM 3120B, 3113B
Copper[6]	1.3	.001-.05	EPA 200.7, 200.8, 200.9, SM 3120B, 3113B, 3111B
Cyanide	0.2	.005-.02	EPA 335.4, SM 4500-CN C, E, F, & G
Fluoride	4		SM 4500-F B, C, D, & E, 4110B

Continued on next page.

---

[1] Approved methods are from the CFR, 1 July, 1996

[2] MDL will vary with the particular method.

[3] EPA: Environmental Protection Agency; *SM: Standard Methods for the Examination of Water and Wastewater*, 18th Edition, 1992.

[4] Million fibers per liter exceeding 10 μm in length.

[5] Analytical method for the determination of asbestos fibers in water, EPA 600/4-83-0433, Jan 1983 NTIS PB83-260471; Determination of asbestos structure over 10 μm in length in drinking water, EPA 600/R-94-134, NTIS PB94-201902

[6] Found in the Lead and Copper Rule, 40 CFR 141.89.

Table 1-2. Primary Drinking Water Monitoring Requirements[7], *continued*

Contaminant	MCL mg/L	MDL mg/L[8]	Method[9]
Inorganics, *continued*			
Lead[10]	0.015	.001	EPA 200.8, 200.9, SM 3113B
Mercury	0.002	.0002	EPA 245.1, 245.2, 200.8, SM 3112B
Nickel	0.1	.0006-.005	EPA 200.7, 200.8, 200.9, SM 3120B, 3113B, 3111B
Nitrate-N	10	.01-1	EPA 300.0A, 353.2, SM 4110B, 4500-NO3 D & F
Nitrite-N	1	.004-.05	EPA 300.0A, 353.2, SM 4110B, 4500-NO2 B, 4500-NO3 E & F
Selenium	0.05	.002	EPA 200.8, 200.9, SM 3114B, 3113B
Sodium	20		EPA 200.7, SM 3113B
Thallium	0.002	.0007-.001	EPA 200.8, 200.9
Synthetic organic compounds (SOC)			
Adipates (Di[ethylhexyl]adipate)	0.4	.0006	EPA 506, 525.2
Alachlor	0.002	.0002	EPA 505, 507, 525.2, 508.1
Atrazine	0.003	.0001	EPA 505, 507, 525.2, 508.1
Carbofuran	0.04	.0009	EPA 531.1, SM 6610
Chlordane	0.002	.0002	EPA 505, 508, 525.2, 508.1
Dalapon	0.2	.001	EPA 515.1, 552.1
Dibromochloropropane (DBCP)	0.0002	.00002	EPA 504.1, 551
2,4-D	0.07	.0001	EPA 515.2, 515.1, 555
Dinoseb	0.007	.0002	EPA 515.1, 515.2, 555
Diquat	0.02	.0004	EPA 549.1
Endothall	0.1	.009	EPA 548.1
Endrin	0.002	.00001	EPA 505, 508, 525.2, 508.1
Ethylene dibromide (EDB)	0.00005	.00001	EPA 504.1, 551
Glyphosate	0.7	.006	EPA 547, SM 6651
Heptachlor	0.0004	.00004	EPA 505, 508, 525.2, 508.1
Hepatchlor epoxide	0.0002	.00002	EPA 505, 508, 525.2, 508.1
Hexachlorobenzene	0.001	.0001	EPA 505, 508, 525.2. 508.1
Hexachlorocyclopentadiene	0.05	.0001	EPA 505, 525.2, 508.1, 508
Lindane	0.0002	.00002	EPA 505, 508, 525.2, 508.1
Methoxychlor	0.04	.0001	EPA 505, 508, 525.2, 508.1
Oxamyl (Vydate)	0.2	.002	EPA 531.1, SM 6610

Continued on next page.

---

[7] Approved methods are from the CFR, 1 July, 1996
[8] MDL will vary with the particular method.
[9] EPA: Environmental Protection Agency; *SM: Standard Methods for the Examination of Water and Wastewater*, 18th Edition, 1992.
[10] See footnote 5.

Table 1-2. Primary Drinking Water Monitoring Requirements[11], *continued*

Contaminant	MCL mg/L	MDL mg/L[12]	Method[13]
Synthetic organic compounds (SOC), *continued*			
(PAHs) Benzo[a]pyrene	0.0002	.00002	EPA 525.2, 550, 550.1
Pentachlorophenol	0.001	.00004	EPA 515.2, 525.2, 555, 515.1
Phthalates (di[ethylhexyl]phthalate)	0.006	.0006	EPA 506, 525.2
Picloram	0.5	.0001	EPA 515.1, 515.2, 555
Polychlorinated biphenyls (PCB)	0.0005	.0001	EPA 508A, 505, 508
Simazine	0.004	.00007	EPA 505, 507, 525.2, 508.1
Toxaphene	0.003	.001	EPA 505, 508, 525.2
2,3,7,8-TCDD (Dioxin)	3×10^{-8}	5×10^{-9}	EPA 1613
2,4,5-TP (Silvex)	0.05	.0002	EPA 515.1, 515.2, 555
Total Trihalomethanes[14]	0.10	.0005	EPA 502.2, 524.2, 551
Volatile organic compounds (VOC)[15]			
Benzene	0.005	.0005	EPA 502.2, 524.2
Carbon tetrachloride	0.005	.0005	EPA 502.2, 524.2, 551
Chlorobenzene	0.1	.0005	EPA 502.2, 524.2
p-Dichlorobenzene	0.075	.0005	EPA 502.2, 524.2
o-Dichlorobenzene	0.6	.0005	EPA 502.2, 524.2
1,2-Dichloroethane	0.005	.0005	EPA 502.2, 524.2
1,1-Dichloroethylene	0.007	.0005	EPA 502.2, 524.2
c-1,2-Dichloroethylene	0.07	.0005	EPA 502.2, 524.2
t-1,2-Dichloroethylene	0.1	.0005	EPA 502.2, 524.2
Dichloromethane	0.005	.0005	EPA 502.2, 524.2
1,2-Dichloropropane	0.005	.0005	EPA 502.2, 524.2
Ethylbenzene	0.7	.0005	EPA 502.2, 524.2
Styrene	0.1	.0005	EPA 502.2, 524.2
Tetrachloroethylene	0.005	.0005	EPA 502.2, 524.2, 551
Toluene	1	.0005	EPA 502.2, 524.2
1,2,4-Trichlorobenzene	0.07	.0005	EPA 502.2, 524.2
1,1,1-Trichloroethane	0.2	.0005	EPA 502.2, 524.2, 551
1,1,2-Trichloroethane	0.005	.0005	EPA 502.2, 524.2
Trichloroethylene	0.005	.0005	EPA 502.2, 524.2, 551
Vinyl chloride	0.002	.0005	EPA 502.2, 524.2
Total Xylene	10	.0005	EPA 502.2, 524.2
Microbiological			
Total coliform	Zero	Zero	MPN, MF, P-A, MMO-MUG
Fecal coliform	Zero	Zero	MPN, MF, MMO-MUG
Legionella	Zero	Zero	SM_{18} 9260J
Giardia lamblia	Zero	Zero	SM_{18} 9711B

Continued on next page.

---

[11] Approved methods are from the CFR, 1 July, 1998

[12] MDL will vary with the particular method.

[13] EPA: Environmental Protection Agency; *SM: Standard Methods for the Examination of Water and Wastewater*, 18th Edition, 1992.

[14] These methods are also included as Parts I and II of 40 CFR 141.30, Appendix C.

[15] The required detection limits for the VOCs are found in 40 CFR 141.24.

Table 1-2. Primary Drinking Water Monitoring Requirements, *continued*

Contaminant	MCL mg/L	MDL mg/L	Method
Microbiological, *continued*			
Heterotrophic Bacteria	-	-	HPC
Viruses	Zero	Zero	SM_{18} 9510
Radiological[16]			
Gross alpha	15 pCi/L	3 pCi/L	EPA 900, SM_{18} 7110
Gross beta	4 millirem/yr[17]	4 pCi/L	EPA 900.0, SM_{18} 7110
Radium 226 + Radium 228	5 pCi/L	1 pCi/L	EPA 903.0, SM_{18} 7500-Ra
Tritium	20,000 pCi/L	1000 pCi/L	EPA 906.0, SM_{18} 7500-^{3}H
Strontium 90	8 pCi/L	2 pCi/L	EPA 905.0, SM_{18} 7500-Sr
Strontium 89	4 millirem/yr[17]	10 pCi/L	EPA 905.0, SM_{18} 7500-Sr
Iodine 131	4 millirem/yr[17]	1 pCi/L	EPA 902.0, SM_{18} 7500-I
Cesium 134	4 millirem/yr[17]	10 pCi/L	EPA 901.0, SM_{18} 7500-Cs

Table 1-3. Secondary Drinking Water Monitoring Requirements

Contaminant	Level mg/L	Method[18]
Aluminum	0.05 to 0.2	EPA 200.7, 200.8, 202.1, 202.2, 200.9
Chloride	250	SM_{14} 408C
Color	15 color units	EPA 110.2
Copper	1.0	EPA 200.7, 200.8, 200.9, 220.1, 220.2
Corrosivity	Noncorrosive	SM_{14} 203
Fluoride	2.0	EPA 340.1, 340.2, 340.3
Foaming agents	0.5	EPA 425.1
Iron	0.3	EPA 200.7, 236.1, 236.2
Manganese	0.05	EPA 200.7, 243.1, 243.2
Odor	3 TON	EPA 140.1
pH	6.5-8.5	EPA 150.1
Silver	0.1	EPA 200.7, 200.8, 200.9, 272.1, 272.2
Sulfate	250	EPA 375.4
Total dissolved solids (TDS)	500	EPA 160.1
Zinc	5	EPA 200.7, 289.1

---

[16] EPA methods are found in *Prescribed Procedures for Measurement of Radioactivity in Drinking Water*, EPA-600/4-80-032, USEPA EMSL Cincinnati, OH. Other radiological methods were approved for use by EPA on 5 March, 1997 in *Federal Register* 62(43):10167-10174.

[17] The 4 millirem/year exposure MCL is based upon consumption of 2 L/day of water.

[18] EPA: Environmental Protection Agency; *SM: Standard Methods for the Examination of Water and Wastewater*, 18th Edition, 1992.

b. CWA – Clean Water Act - Last amended in 1987, the Act provides for grants to POTW (publicly owned treatment works) to build and upgrade treatment facilities, and establishes a permitting system NPDES (National Pollutant Discharge Elimination System), for discharge of water to natural water bodies by industry and municipalities. Over two thirds of the states have accepted primary responsibility for administration of the Act. The Act also mandates the EPA to collect data about environmental pollutants and make decisions about treatment based on water quality goals and best available technology (BAT). The following precepts are established in the Act and its amendments:

1. No one has the right to pollute the navigable waters of the United States.

2. Permits shall limit the composition of a discharge and the concentrations of pollutants in it.

3. Some permit conditions require the best controls technology can produce, regardless of the receiving water's ability to purify itself naturally.

4. Any limits or control higher than the minimum federal requirements must be based on receiving water quality.

Wastewater effluents are monitored through the NPDES, quite probably the number one money maker for commercial analytical laboratories. Each industry and wastewater treatment facility (Publicly Owned Treatment Works, POTW) that directly discharges into a receiving stream or river has either a Federal or State NPDES permit. Industries that discharge in a municipality to a sewer system are permitted through the wastewater treatment plant at the end of the sewer system (Industrial Pre-treatment Program), and the POTW holds the Federal or State permit. For industries not specifically listed in the CFR, the federal EPA or state environmental agency will set allowable limits for contaminant levels in wastewaters discharged by the particular plant, based on submitted analysis of the wastewaters generated by the commercial operation. A permit is given to the industrial location allowing release of certain maximum limits of target parameters based on either the limits in 40 CFR Subchapter N, or on historical records and local environmental concerns, or on watershed Water Quality considerations, and specifying regular analysis for target analytes in the waste stream to back-up the allowable limits. Often a time-frame for collection and analysis of wastewater samples is specified, which may or may not coincide with actual releases of contaminants. The approved methods of analysis along with approved sampling containers, preservatives, and holding times are found in 40 CFR 136.3 (the most current version, 1 July, 1998, is reproduced in Appendix I of this book). Consult the most recent edition for specific approved methods as these do change over time.

Three classes of pollutants are recognized.

1) Conventional Pollutants: BOD, COD, pH, total suspended solids, bacteria, oil & grease, and fecal coliforms.

2) Non-conventional Pollutants: nitrogen, phosphorous, ammonia, chloride, sulfate, and other pollutants that may endanger water quality. Not listed as toxic pollutants, most are what are considered nutrients.

3) Toxic Pollutants: The so-called 129 priority pollutants are listed in Table 1-4.

The origin of the toxic pollutant list is a Committee Report from the House Committee of Public Works and Transportation, which was adopted into the CWA by specific reference in section 301(a)(1) of the Act. The list is transcribed in 40 CFR 401.15 and is reproduced in Table 1-4. Quality control check samples (DMR, discharge monitoring report) are issued to facilities holding Federal or State NPDES permits for analysis by the contracted laboratories on an annual basis to back-up the analytical results submitted by the plant.

Table 1-4. Toxic Pollutant list from 40 CFR 401.15

Analyte
1. Acenaphthene
2. Acrolein
3. Acrylonitrile
4. Aldrin/Dieldrin
5. Antimony and compounds
6. Arsenic and compounds
7. Asbestos
8. Benzene
9. Benzidine
10. Beryllium and compounds
11. Cadmium and compounds
12. Carbon tetrachloride
13. Chlordane (technical mixture and metabolites)
14. Chlorinated benzenes (other than dichlorobenzenes)
15. Chlorinated ethanes (including 1,2-dichloroethane, 1,1,1-trichloroethane and hexachloroethane)
16. Chloroalkyl ethers (chloroethyl and mixed ethers)
17. Chlorinated naphthalene
18. Chlorinated phenols (other than those listed elsewhere; includes trichlorophenols and chlorinated cresols)
19. Chloroform
20. 2-Chlorophenol
21. Chromium and compounds
22. Copper and compounds
23. Cyanides
24. DDT and metabolites
25. Dichlorobenzenes (1,2-, 1,3-, and 1,4-dichlorobenzenes)
26. Dichlorobenzidine
27. Dichloroethylenes (1,1- and 1,2-dichloroethylene)
28. 2,4-Dichlorophenol
29. Dichloropropane and Dichloropropene
30. 2,4-Dimethylphenol
31. Dinitrotoluene
32. Diphenylhydrazine
33. Endosulfan and metabolites
34. Endrin and metabolites
35. Ethylbenzene
36. Fluoranthene
37. Haloethers (other than those listed elsewhere; includes chlorophenylphenyl ethers, bromophenyl-phenyl ether, bis(dichloroisopropyl) ether, bis(chloroethoxy) methane and polychlorinated diphenyl ethers

Continued on next page.

Table 1-4. Toxic Pollutant list from 40 CFR 401.15, *continued*

	Analyte
38.	Halomethanes (other than those listed elsewhere; includes methylene chloride, methyl chloride, methyl bromide, bromoform, dichlorobromomethane, trichlorofluoromethane and dichlorodifluoromethane)
39.	Heptachlor and metabolites
40.	Hexachlorobutadiene
41.	Hexachlorocyclohexane
42.	Hexachlorocyclopentadiene
43.	Isophorone
44.	Lead and compounds
45.	Mercury and compounds
46.	Naphthalene
47.	Nickel and compounds
48.	Nitrobenzene
49.	Nitrophenols (includes 2,4-dinitrophenol, dinitrocresol)
51.	Pentachlorophenol
52.	Phenol
53.	Phthalate esters
54.	Polychlorinated biphenyls (PCBs) (chrysenes, dibenzoanthracenes and indenopyrenes)
56.	Selenium and compounds
57.	Silver and compounds
58.	2,3,7,8-Tetrachlorodibenzo-*p*-dioxin (TCDD)
59.	Tetrachloroethylene
60.	Thallium and compounds
61.	Toluene
62.	Toxaphene
63.	Trichloroethylene
64.	Vinyl chloride
65.	Zinc and compounds

A number of states have accepted primacy from EPA for administration of NPDES permits. In general the state is required to establish permit limits that would be at least as stringent as those of the federal government. States often establish priority pollutant lists based on the EPA lists and add required analysis detection limits as a structure within which monitoring must be conducted by the reporting facility. As Table 1-5 indicates, there can be considerable variation among states in their priority pollutant lists. A study was conducted by the General Accounting Office in 1995 in response to a specific request by Senator Max Baucus for information concerning State differences in permitting, the causes of the differences and how EPA was overseeing the program. Although the study limited itself to examination of the permitting of five metals (cadmium, copper, lead, mercury and zinc) in municipal wastewater treatment facilities, the results were interesting. In general it was found that "in some states, the permitting authorities consistently established numeric limits on the discharges, while in other states, the authorities consistently required monitoring. In some states no controls were imposed. In addition, the numeric discharge limits for specific pollutants differed from state to state and even within the same state for facilities of similar capacity."[19] What is allowable in one state can and often is specifically prohibited in another state.

In March, 1994, EPA issued a draft memorandum that set forth guidelines for establishment of effluent limits below analytical detection limits that are achievable using current technology. Some states have jumped on this program and have issued modified permit limits to affected industries. Other states have taken a wait-and-see attitude.

Table 1-5.   Priority Pollutant lists and required reportable detection limits for monitoring

Parameter	GA[20] DL μg/L	SC[21] DL μg/L	NC[22] DL μg/L
Acrolein	50	-	100
Acrylonitrile	50	-	100
Benzene	2	2	5
Bromodichloromethane	10	2	5
Bromoform	10	2	5
Bromomethane	10	2	10
Carbon tetrachloride	2	2	5
Chlorobenzene	10	2	6
Chloroethane	5	2	10
2-Chloroethylvinyl ether	10	2	10
Chloroform	2	2	5
Chloromethane	10	2	10
Dibromochloromethane	10	2	5
1,1-Dichloroethane	2	2	5
1,2-Dichloroethane	2	2	5
1,1-Dichloroethylene	2	2	5
trans-1,2-Dichloroethylene	2	2	5
1,2-Dichloropropane	2	2	6
cis-1,3-Dichloropropene	2	2	5
trans-1,3-Dichloropropene	2	2	5
Ethylbenzene	2	2	8
Methylene chloride	10	2	5
1,1,2,2-Tetrachloroethane	2	2	7
Tetrachloroethylene	2	2	5
Toluene	2	2	6
1,1,1-Trichloroethane	2	2	5
1,1,2-Trichloroethane	2	2	5
Trichloroethylene	2	2	5
Trichlorofluoromethane	-	2	10
Vinyl chloride	10	2	10
4-Chloro-3-methylphenol	10	10	10
2-Chlorophenol	10	10	10
2,4-Dichlorophenol	10	10	10

Continued on next page.

19   United States General Accounting Office, January, 1996. Water pollution: Differences among the states in issuing permits limiting the discharge of pollutants. GAO/RCED-96-42.
20   GA EPD 13 January, 1994.
21   SC DEHC January, 1994.
22   NC DEHNR June, 1990.

Table 1-5. **Priority Pollutant lists and required reportable detection limits for monitoring,** *continued*

Parameter	GA[23] DL µg/L	SC[24] DL µg/L	NC[25] DL µg/L
2,4-Dimethylphenol	10	10	10
2,4-Dinitrophenol	50	-	50
2-Methyl-4,6-dinitrophenol	50	10	50
2-Nitrophenol	50	10	10
4-Nitrophenol	50	10	50
Pentachlorophenol	20	10	50
Phenol	10	10	10
2,4,6-Trichlorophenol	10	10	10
Acenaphthene	10	10	10
Acenaphthylene	10	10	10
Anthracene	10	10	10
Benzidine	80	-	50
Benzo(a)anthracene	10	10	10
Benzo(a)pyrene	10	10	10
Benzo(b)fluoranthene	10	10	10
Benzo(ghi)perylene	10	10	10
Benzo(k)fluoranthene	10	10	10
Bis(2-chloroethoxy)methane	10	10	10
Bis(2-chloroethyl)ether	10	10	10
Bis(2-chloroisopropyl)ether	10	10	10
Bis(2-ethylhexyl)phthalate	10	10	10
4-Bromophenylphenyl ether	10	10	10
Benzylbutylphthalate	10	10	10
2-Chloronaphthalene	10	10	10
4-Chlorophenylphenyl ether	10	10	10
Chrysene	10	10	10
Dibenzo(ah)anthracene	10	10	10
1,2-Dichlorobenzene	10	10	10
1,3-Dichlorobenzene	10	10	10
1,4-Dichlorobenzene	10	10	10
3,3'-Dichlorobenzidine	20	10	20
Diethylphthalate	10	10	10
Dimethylphthalate	10	10	10
Di-n-butylphthalate	10	10	10
2,4-Dinitrotoluene	20	10	10
2,6-Dinitrotoluene	20	10	10
Di-n-octylphthalate	10	10	10
1,2-Diphenylhydrazine	10	-	10
Fluoranthene	10	10	10
Fluorene	10	10	10
Hexachlorobenzene	10	10	10
Hexachlorobutadiene	10	10	10
Hexachlorocyclopentadiene	10	10	10

Continued on next page.

---

[23] GA EPD 13 January, 1994.
[24] SC DEHC January, 1994.
[25] NC DEHNR June, 1990.

Table 1-5. Priority Pollutant lists and required reportable detection limits for monitoring, *continued*

Parameter	GA[26] DL µg/L	SC[27] DL µg/L	NC[28] DL µg/L
Hexachloroethane	2	10	10
Indeno(123-cd)pyrene	10	10	10
Isophorone	10	10	10
Naphthalene	10	10	10
Nitrobenzene	10	10	10
N-nitrosodimethylamine	10	10	10
N-nitrosodi-n-propylamine	10	10	10
N-nitrosodiphenylamine	10	10	10
Phenanthrene	10	10	10
Pyrene	10	10	10
1,2,4-Trichlorobenzene	10	10	10
Aldrin	0.1	0.05	0.05
α-BHC	0.1	0.05	0.05
β-BHC	0.1	0.05	0.05
δ-BHC	0.1	0.05	0.1
γ-BHC (Lindane)	0.1	0.05	0.05
Chlordane	0.5	0.05	0.2
4,4'-DDD	0.2	0.05	0.1
4,4'-DDE	0.2	0.05	0.1
4,4'-DDT	0.2	0.05	0.1
Dieldrin	0.1	0.05	0.02
Endosulfan I	0.5	0.05	0.1
Endosulfan II	0.5	0.05	0.1
Endosulfan sulfate	0.5	0.05	0.7
Endrin	0.2	0.05	0.06
Endrin aldehyde	0.2	0.05	0.2
Heptachlor	0.1	0.05	0.05
Heptachlor epoxide	0.1	0.05	0.8
Methoxychlor	0.3	0.05	0.5
Mirex	-	-	0.2
Toxaphene	2	0.05	2.4
PCB 1016	1	0.5	0.5
PCB 1221	1	0.5	0.5
PCB 1232	1	0.5	0.5
PCB 1242	1	0.5	0.5
PCB 1248	1	0.5	0.5
PCB 1254	1	0.5	1.0
PCB 1260	1	0.5	1.0
Demeton	-	0.1	2.5
Parathion (ethyl)	-	0.1	0.6
2,4-D	5	0.05	12
Silvex	10	0.025	2
2,4,5-T	-	0.025	2

Continued on next page.

---

[26] GA EPD 13 January, 1994.
[27] SC DEHC January, 1994.
[28] NC DEHNR June, 1990.

Table 1-5. Priority Pollutant lists and required reportable detection limits for monitoring, *continued*

Parameter	GA[29] DL µg/L	SC[30] DL µg/L	NC[31] DL µg/L
Aluminum	-	50	50
Antimony	50	50	50
Arsenic	30	5	10
Barium	-	50	500
Beryllium	10	3	25
Cadmium	10	10	2
Total Chromium	10	10	5
Hexavalent Chromium	10	-	-
Copper	20	10	2
Lead	25	50	10
Mercury	0.5	0.2	0.2
Nickel	20	20	10
Selenium	40	5	5
Silver	10	30	5
Thallium	50	500	-
Zinc	20	10	10
Chloride	-	1000	1000
Cyanide	25	10	20
Fluoride	-	100	100

Subchapter N, 40 CFR, also lists many specific types of industries that have effluent guidelines set by EPA. The list of affected industries is presented in Table 1-6 along with an indication of the class of pollutants specified.

Table 1-6. Industries with 40 CFR wastewater effluent guidelines

Part	Industry Category	Pollutant Type
405	Dairy products processing	Conventional
406	Grain mills	Conventional
407	Canned and preserved fruits and vegetables processing	Conventional
408	Canned and preserved seafood processing	Conventional
409	Sugar processing	Conventional
410	Textile mills	Conventional and toxic
411	Cement manufacturing	Conventional
412	Feedlots	Conventional
413	Electroplating	Conventional and toxic
414	Organic chemicals, plastics and synthetic fibers	Conventional and toxic
415	Inorganic chemicals manufacturing	Conventional and toxic
417	Soap and detergent manufacturing	Conventional and surfactants
418	Fertilizer manufacturing	Conventional and non-conventional
419	Petroleum refining	Conventional and non-conventional

Continued on next page.

---

[29] GA EPD 13 January, 1994.
[30] SC DEHC January, 1994.
[31] NC DEHNR June, 1990.

Table 1-6.   Industries with 40 CFR wastewater effluent guidelines, *continued*

Part	Industry Category	Pollutant Type
420	Iron and steel manufacturing	Conventional, non-conventional and toxic
421	Nonferrous metal manufacturing	Conventional and toxic
422	Phosphate manufacturing	Conventional and non-conventional
423	Steam electric power generating	Conventional and toxic
424	Ferroalloy manufacturing	Conventional and toxic
425	Leather tanning and finishing	Conventional and toxic
426	Glass manufacturing	Conventional and toxic
427	Asbestos manufacturing	Conventional and toxic
428	Rubber manufacturing	Conventional and toxic
429	Timber products processing	Conventional and toxic
430	Pulp, paper and paperboard	Conventional and toxic
431	The builder's paper and board mills	Conventional and toxic
432	Meat products	Conventional and toxic
433	Metal finishing	Conventional and toxic
434	Coal mining	Conventional and toxic
435	Oil and gas extraction	Conventional and toxic
436	Mineral mining and processing	Conventional and toxic
439	Pharmaceutical manufacturing	Conventional and toxic
440	Ore mining and dressing	Conventional and toxic
441	Industrial laundries (proposed)	Conventional and toxic
443	Paving and roof materials (tars and asphalt)	Conventional and toxic
(445)	Landfills (draft, *FR* 63(25):6425-6463, 6 Feb 98)	Conventional and toxic
446	Paint formulating	Conventional and toxic
447	Ink formulating	Conventional and toxic
454	Gum and wood chemicals manufacturing	Conventional and toxic
455	Pesticide chemicals	Conventional and toxic
457	Explosives manufacturing	Conventional and toxic
458	Carbon black manufacturing	Conventional and toxic
459	Photographic	Conventional and toxic
460	Hospitals	Conventional and toxic
461	Battery manufacturing	Conventional and toxic
463	Plastics molding and forming	Conventional and toxic
464	Metal molding and casting	Conventional and toxic
465	Coil coating	Conventional and toxic
466	Porcelain enameling	Conventional and toxic
467	Aluminum forming	Conventional and toxic
468	Copper forming	Conventional and toxic
469	Electrical and electrical components	Conventional and toxic
471	Nonferrous metals forming and metal powders	Conventional and toxic

The broad industrial categories are further broken down into Subpart groups. An example is the Organic Chemicals, Plastics and Synthetic Fibers (OCPSF) industry as indicated in Table 1-7. An example of a specific guideline is presented for the direct discharge point sources that do not use end-of-pipe biological treatment under the OCPSF category (Subpart J), Table 1-8.

Table 1-7. Subpart groups for the OCPSF industry

Subpart	Industry
B	Rayon fibers
C	Other fibers
D	Thermoplastic resins
E	Thermosetting resins
F	Commodity organic chemicals
G	Bulk organic chemicals
H	Specialty organic chemicals
I	Direct discharge point sources that use end-of-pipe biological treatment
J	Direct discharge point sources that do not use end-of-pipe biological treatment
K	Indirect discharge point source

Table 1-8. Toxic Pollutant Effluent Guideline Example, Subpart J 40 CFR 414.101, Organic Chemicals, Plastics and Synthetic Fibers[32], 9 July 1993

Effluent Characteristic	Maximum for any one day	Maximum for monthly average
Acenaphthene	47	19
Acenaphthylene	47	19
Acrylonitrile	232	94
Anthracene	47	19
Benzene	134	57
Benzo(a)anthracene	47	19
Benzo(b)fluoranthene	48	20
Benzo(k)fluoranthene	47	19
Benzo(a)pyrene	48	20
Bis(2-ethylhexyl)phthalate	258	95
Carbon tetrachloride	380	142
Chlorobenzene	380	142
Chloroethane	295	110
Chloroform	325	111
Chrysene	47	19
Di-n-butylphthalate	43	20
1,2-Dichlorobenzene	794	196
1,3-Dichlorobenzene	380	142
1,4-Dichlorobenzene	380	142
1,1-Dichloroethane	59	22
1,2-Dichloroethane	574	180
1,1-Dichloroethylene	60	22
1,2-*trans*-Dichloroethylene	66	25
1,2-Dichloropropane	794	196
1,3-Dichloropropylene	794	196
Diethylphthalate	113	46

Continued on next page.

---

[32] All units are micrograms per liter except pH.

Table 1-8.   **Toxic Pollutant Effluent Guideline Example, Subpart J 40 CFR 414.101, Organic Chemicals, Plastics and Synthetic Fibers**[33], **9 July 1993,** *continued*

Effluent Characteristic	Maximum for any one day	Maximum for monthly average
2,4-Dimethylphenol	47	19
Dimethylphthalate	47	19
4,6-Dinitro-o-cresol	277	78
2,4-Dinitrophenol	4291	1207
Ethylbenzene	380	142
Fluoranthene	54	22
Fluorene	47	19
Hexachlorobenzene	794	196
Hexachlorobutadiene	380	142
Hexachloroethane	794	196
Methyl chloride	295	110
Methylene chloride	170	36
Naphthalene	47	19
Nitrobenzene	6402	2237
2-Nitrophenol	231	65
4-Nitrophenol	576	162
Phenanthrene	47	19
Phenol	47	19
Pyrene	48	20
Tetrachloroethylene	164	52
Toluene	74	28
Total chromium	2770	1110
Total copper	3380	1450
Total cyanide	1200	420
Total lead	690	320
Total nickel	3980	1690
Total zinc	2610	1050
1,2,4-Trichlorobenzene	794	196
1,1,1-Trichloroethane	59	22
1,1,2-Tichloroethane	127	32
Trichloroethylene	69	26
Vinyl chloride	172	97

Another permitting program is the stormwater run-off. Target analytes under this program are listed in 40 CFR 122, Appendix D. EPA estimates that 30% of the pollution entering the nation's water systems comes from run-off from agriculture, large industry, and landfills (so called non-point sources).

An example of a program that falls under two sets of regulations is the Standards for the Use or Disposal of Sewage Sludge, 40 CFR 503. The regulation provides for incineration, land application, surface disposal and pathogen and vector attraction reduction, and is authorized jointly under the CWA and RCRA. The analytical requirements are for trace metals analysis on the chemistry side plus a variety of microbiological procedures.

---

33   All units are micrograms per liter except pH.

The metals are tested by SW-846 methods. The biological analyses required include fecal coliform and *Salmonella* sp. bacteria, enteric viruses, and helminth ova. Although the fecal coliform assays are simple extensions of procedures routinely performed in environmental laboratories, the other three tests are laborious and expensive. To assist laboratories and treatment facilities in coming into compliance with these regulations, EPA has published "Environmental Regulations and Technology Control of Pathogens and Vector Attraction in Sewage Sludge" (EPA/625/R-92/013, December, 1992), commonly called the "White House Manual" due to the picture on the front cover. Prior to the promulgation of the 503 regulations, EPA conducted the National Sewage Sludge Survey. The contents of the manual of analytical methods[34], which was a part of the survey, are listed in the Table. An additional relevant-methods manual is POTW *Sludge Sampling and Analysis Guidance Document*, USEPA Office of Water, August, 1989.

Table 1-9. Contents of Analytical Methods for the National Sewage Sludge Survey

Method	Title
1624C	Volatile organic compounds by isotopic dilution GCMS
1625C	Semivolatile organic compounds by isotopic dilution GCMS
1618	Organo-halide pesticides, organo-phosphorous pesticides and phenoxy-acid herbicides by wide bore capillary column gas chromatography with selective detectors
1613	Tetra- through octa- chlorinated dioxins and furans by isotope dilution HRGC/HRMS
1620	Metals by inductively coupled plasma atomic emission spectroscopy and atomic absorption spectrometry
160.3	Residue, total, gravimetric, dried at 103-105 °C
335.2	Cyanide, total titrimetric, spectrophotometric
340.2	Fluoride potentiometric, ion selective electrode
351.3	Nitrogen, Kjeldahl, total, colorimetric; titrimetric; potentiometric
353.2	Nitrogen, nitrate-nitrite, colorimetric, automated cadmium reduction
365.2	Phosphorous, all forms, colorimetric, ascorbic acid single reagent

The EPA Office of Water has established a workgroup to prepare a methods manual that is specifically applicable to biosolids as a sample matrix. Most of the methods are available as draft methods and are listed in Section 1.II.

Industries that discharge their wastewater into a sanitary sewer system that is collected for treatment at a POTW, are subject to permitting under the Industrial Pretreatment program. If it is accepted that there are variations and inconsistencies among the states in NPDES permits, then it should be expected that an even greater degree of chaos reigns in industrial pretreatment permits. EPA has published a large number of documents related to pretreatment permits, and compliance monitoring[35]. If a municipality implements a pretreatment program, complete with periodic duplicate sampling and analysis to verify industrial self-monitoring compliance, this places an extra burden on the municipal lab. On the one hand the lab is a generator of self-monitoring compliance data to the regulatory agency that issued the POTW NPDES permit,

---

[34] *Analytical Methods for the National Sewage Sludge Survey*, EPA Office of Water (WH-585), September, 1990.
[35] EPA, 1994. Industrial user inspection and sampling manual for POTW's. EPA 831-B-94-001, April, 1994

while on the other hand, the lab is also the enforcement lab for the municipality's pretreatment program. Although it might be expected that placing a municipal lab in a position of preparing legally defensible data to be used in enforcement actions would serve to increase the lab's performance and adherence to approved method protocols, this has not always been the case. The lack of legally suitable data for enforcement actions is the soft spot in most pretreatment programs.

EPA has recently published guidance for choosing a commercial laboratory to perform an industry's pretreatment monitoring. It is titled "Procuring Analytical Services: Guidance for Industrial Pretreatment Programs" and is available on the Internet (EPA 833-B-98-004).

Some states have been preparing permits based on Water Quality Criteria. These Criteria are based upon the total load of specific pollutants in the watershed and are risk- and health-based, rather than analysis-based. The Water Quality Criteria have been in development for over 20 years. From the information provided by EPA, states develop their own Water Quality Criteria. Table 1-10 is a comparison of the EPA Water Quality Criteria and the Georgia Water Quality Criteria. A recent addition to the Water Quality Criteria is a table of substances that have organoleptic (taste & odor) thresholds. In some cases these thresholds are below the risk/health-based levels and affect the aesthetic quality of the water body. These data are presented in Table 1-11.

Table 1-10. National Water Quality Criteria[36] and Georgia Water Quality Criteria[37]

Priority pollutant[38]	CAS No.	National CCC µg/L	Human consumption[39] µg/L	Georgia 7Q10 chronic µg/L
1. Antimony	7440-36-0	-	14	4308
2. Arsenic	7440-38-2			
Freshwater		150	0.018	50
Saltwater		36	-	36
3. Beryllium	7440-41-7	-	DW MCL	-
4. Cadmium	7440-43-9			
Freshwater		2.2	DW MCL	0.62
Saltwater		9.3	-	9.2
5a. Chromium III	16065-83-1			
Freshwater		74	DW MCL	100
5b. Chromium VI	18540-29-9			
Freshwater		11	DW MCL	11
Saltwater		50	-	50

---

[36] USEPA, April, 1999. National Recommended Water Quality Criteria - Correction. EPA-822-Z-99-001, available from the Office of Water webpage.

[37] Water Quality Control, Chapter 391-3-6, Rules of the Georgia Department of Natural Resources Environmental Protection Division, Proposed revisions 30 June, 1998.

[38] The values for metals often depend on hardness which are calculated from an equation. The regulation should be consulted.

[39] Water + organisms

Table 1-10. National Water Quality Criteria[40] and Georgia Water Quality Criteria[41], *continued*

Priority pollutant[42]	CAS No.	National CCC µg/L	Human consumption[43] µg/L	Georgia 7Q10 chronic µg/L
6. Copper	7440-50-8			
Freshwater		9.0	1300	6.2
Saltwater		3.1	-	2.4
7. Lead	7439-92-1			
Freshwater		2.5	DW MCL	1.2
Saltwater		8.1	-	5.3
8. Mercury	7439-97-6			
Freshwater		0.77	0.050	0.012
Saltwater		0.94	-	0.025
9. Nickel	7440-02-0			
Freshwater		52	610	88
Saltwater		8.2	-	8.2
10. Selenium	7782-49-2			
Freshwater		5.0	170	5.0
Saltwater		71	-	71
11. Silver	7440-22-4			
Freshwater		-	-	7Q10 value
Saltwater		-	-	-
12. Thallium	7440-28-0	-	1.7	6.3
13. Zinc	7440-66-6			
Freshwater		120	9100	58
Saltwater		81	-	81
14. Cyanide	57-12-5			
Freshwater		5.2	700	5.2
Saltwater		1	-	1.0
15. Asbestos	1332-21-4	-	7 million fibers/L	-
16. 2, 3, 7, 8-TCDD Dioxin	1746-01-6	-	0.000000013	-
17. Acrolein	107-02-8	-	320	780
18. Acrylonitrile	107-13-1	-	0.059	0.665
19. Benzene	71-43-2	-	1.2	71.28
20. Bromoform	75-25-2	-	4.3	360
21. Carbon tetrachloride	56-23-5	-	0.25	4.42
22. Chlorobenzene	108-90-7	-	680	21000
23. Chlorodibromomethane	124-48-1	-	0.41	34

[40] USEPA, April, 1999. National Recommended Water Quality Criteria - Correction. EPA-822-Z-99-001, available from the Office of Water webpage.

[41] Water Quality Control, Chapter 391-3-6, Rules of the Georgia Department of Natural Resources Environmental Protection Division, Proposed revisions 30 June, 1998.

[42] The values for metals often depend on hardness which are calculated from an equation. The regulation should be consulted.

[43] Water + organisms.

Table 1-10. National Water Quality Criteria[44] **and Georgia Water Quality Criteria**[45], *continued*

Priority pollutant[46]	CAS No.	National CCC µg/L	Human consumption[47] µg/L	Georgia 7Q10 chronic µg/L
24. Chloroethane	75-00-3	-	-	-
25. 2-Chloroethylvinyl ether	110-75-8	-	-	-
26. Chloroform	67-66-3	-	5.7	470.8
27. Dichlorobromomethane	75-27-4	-	0.56	22
28. 1,1-Dichloroethane	75-34-3	-	-	-
29. 1,2-Dichloroethane	107-06-2	-	0.38	98.6
30. 1,1-Dichloroethylene	75-35-4	-	0.057	3.2
31. 1,2-Dichloropropane	78-87-5	-	0.52	
32. 1,3-Dichloropropene	542-75-6	-	10	1700
33. Ethylbenzene	100-41-4	-	3100	28718
34. Methyl bromide	74-83-9	-	48	4000
35. Methyl chloride	74-87-3	-	-	-
36. Methylene chloride	75-09-2	-	4.7	1600
37. 1,1,2,2-Tetrachloroethane	79-34-5	-	0.17	10.8
38. Tetrachloroethylene	127-18-4	-	0.8	8.85
39. Toluene	108-88-3	-	6800	200000
40. 1,2- *trans*-Dichloroethylene	156-60-5	-	700	-
41. 1,1,1-Trichloroethane	71-55-6	-	DW MCL	-
42. 1,1,2-Trichloroethane	79-00-5	-	0.60	41.99
43. Trichloroethylene	79-01-6	-	2.7	80.7
44. Vinyl chloride	75-01-4	-	2.0	525
45. 2-Chlorophenol	95-57-8	-	120	-
46. 2,4-Dichlorophenol	120-83-2	-	93	790
47. 2,4-Dimethylphenol	105-67-9	-	540	-
48. 2-Methyl-4,6-dinitrophenol	534-52-1	-	13.4	765
49. 2,4-Dinitrophenol	51-28-5	-	70	14264
50. 2-Nitrophenol	88-75-5	-	-	-
51. 4-Nitrophenol	100-02-7	-	-	-
52. 3-Methyl-4-chlorophenol	59-50-7	-	-	-
53. Pentachlorophenol	87-86-5			
Freshwater		15	0.28	2.1
Saltwater		7.9	-	7.9
54. Phenol	108-95-2	-	21000	4600000
55. 2,4,6-Trichlorophenol	88-06-2	-	2.1	6.5

[44] USEPA, April, 1999. National Recommended Water Quality Criteria - Correction. EPA-822-Z-99-001, available from the Office of Water webpage.

[45] Water Quality Control, Chapter 391-3-6, Rules of the Georgia Department of Natural Resources Environmental Protection Division, Proposed revisions 30 June, 1998.

[46] The values for metals often depend on hardness which are calculated from an equation. The regulation should be consulted.

[47] Water + organisms.

Table 1-10. National Water Quality Criteria[48] and Georgia Water Quality Criteria[49], *continued*

Priority pollutant[50]	CAS No.	National CCC µg/L	Human consumption[51] µg/L	Georgia 7Q10 chronic µg/L
56. Acenaphthene	83-32-9	-	1200	-
57. Acenaphthylene	208-96-8	-	-	-
58. Anthracene	120-12-7	-	9600	110000
59. Benzidine	92-87-5	-	0.00012	0.000535
60. Benzo(a)anthracene	56-55-3	-	0.0044	0.0311
61. Benzo(a)pyrene	50-32-8	-	0.0044	0.0311
62. Benzo(b)fluoranthene	205-99-2	-	0.0044	0.0311
63. Benzo(g,h,i)perylene	191-24-2	-	-	-
64. Benzo(k)fluoranthene	207-08-9	-	0.0044	0.0311
65. Bis 2-chloroethoxymethane	111-91-1	-	-	-
66. Bis 2-chloroethylether	111-44-4	-	0.031	1.42
67. Bis 2-chloroisopropylether	39638-32-9	-	1400	170000
68. Bis 2-ethylhexylphthalate	117-81-7	-	1.8	5.92
69. 4-Bromophenyl phenyl ether	101-55-3	-	-	-
70. Butylbenzyl phthalate	85-68-7	-	3000	-
71. 2-Chloronaphthalene	91-58-7	-	1700	-
72. 4-Chlorophenyl phenyl ether	7005-72-3	-	-	-
73. Chrysene	218-01-9	-	0.0044	0.0311
74. Dibenzo(a,h)anthracene	53-70-3	-	0.0044	0.0311
75. 1,2-Dichlorobenzene	95-50-1	-	2700	17000
76. 1,3-Dichlorobenzene	541-73-1	-	400	2600
77. 1,4-Dichlorobenzene	106-46-7	-	400	2600
78. 3,3'-Dichlorobenzidine	91-94-1	-	0.04	0.077
79. Diethyl phthalate	84-66-2	-	23000	120000
80. Dimethyl phthalate	131-11-3	-	313000	2900000
81. Di-n-butyl phthalate	84-74-2	-	2700	12100
82. 2,4-Dinitrotoluene	121-14-2	-	0.11	9.1
83. 2,6-Dinitrotoluene	606-20-2	-	-	-
84. Di-n-octyl phthalate	117-84-0	-	-	-
85. 1,2-Diphenylhydrazine	122-66-7	-	0.040	0.54
86. Fluoranthene	206-44-0	-	300	370
87. Fluorene	86-73-7	-	1300	14000
88. Hexachlorobenzene	118-74-1	-	0.00075	0.00077
89. Hexachlorobutadiene	87-68-3	-	0.44	49.7

48   USEPA, April, 1999. National Recommended Water Quality Criteria - Correction. EPA-822-Z-99-001, available from the Office of Water webpage.

49   Water Quality Control, Chapter 391-3-6, Rules of the Georgia Department of Natural Resources Environmental Protection Division, Proposed revisions 30 June, 1998.

50   The values for metals often depend on hardness which are calculated from an equation. The regulation should be consulted.

51   Water + organisms.

Table 1-10. National Water Quality Criteria[52] and Georgia Water Quality Criteria[53], *continued*

Priority pollutant[54]	CAS No.	National CCC µg/L	Human consumption[55] µg/L	Georgia 7Q10 chronic µg/L
90. Hexachlorocyclopentadiene	77-47-4	-	240	17000
91. Hexachloroethane	67-72-1	-	1.9	8.85
92. Ideno 1,2,3-(c,d)pyrene	193-39-5	-	0.0044	0.0311
93. Isophorone	78-59-1	-	36	600
94. Naphthalene	91-20-3	-	-	-
95. Nitrobenzene	98-95-3	-	17	1900
96. N-nitrosodimethylamine	62-75-9	-	0.00069	8.12
97. N-nitrosodi-n-propylamine	621-64-7	-	0.005	-
98. N-nitrosodiphenylamine	86-30-6	-	5.0	16.2
99. Phenanthrene	85-01-8	-	-	-
100. Pyrene	129-00-0	-	960	11000
101. 1,2,4-Trichlorobenzene	120-82-1	-	260	-
102. Aldrin	309-00-2	-	0.00013	0.000136
103. α-BHC	319-84-6	-	0.0039	0.0131
104. β-BHC	319-85-7	-	0.014	0.046
105. γ-BHC (Lindane)	58-89-9	-	0.019	0.0625
106. δ-BHC	319-86-8	-	-	-
107. Chlordane	57-74-9			
Freshwater		0.00043	0.0021	0.0043
Saltwater		0.004		0.004
108. 4,4'-DDT	50-29-3	0.001	0.00059	0.00059
109. 4,4'-DDE	72-55-9	-	0.00059	0.00059
110. 4,4'-DDD	72-54-8	-	0.00083	0.00084
111. Dieldrin	60-57-1			
Freshwater		0.056	0.00014	0.000144
Saltwater		0.0019	-	-
112. α-Endosulfan	959-98-8			
Freshwater		0.056	110	0.056
Saltwater		0.0087		0.0087
113. β-Endosulfan	33213-65-9			
Freshwater		0.056	110	0.056
Saltwater		0.0087		0.0087
114. Endosulfan sulfate	1031-07-8	-	110	2.0

[52] USEPA, April, 1999. National Recommended Water Quality Criteria - Correction. EPA-822-Z-99-001, available from the Office of Water webpage.

[53] Water Quality Control, Chapter 391-3-6, Rules of the Georgia Department of Natural Resources Environmental Protection Division, Proposed revisions 30 June, 1998.

[54] The values for metals often depend on hardness which are calculated from an equation. The regulation should be consulted.

[55] Water + organisms.

Table 1-10. National Water Quality Criteria[56] and Georgia Water Quality Criteria[57], continued

Priority pollutant[58]	CAS No.	National CCC µg/L	Human consumption[59] µg/L	Georgia 7Q10 chronic µg/L
115. Endrin	72-20-8			
Freshwater		0.036	0.76	0.002
Saltwater		0.0023		
116. Endrin aldehyde	7421-93-4	-	0.076	0.81
117. Heptachlor	76-44-8			
Freshwater		0.0038	0.00021	0.000214
Saltwater		0.0036		0.0036
118 .Heptachlor epoxide	1024-57-3			
Freshwater		0.0038	0.00010	0.00011
Saltwater		0.0036		0.0036
119. Polychlorinated biphenyls	-			
Freshwater		0.014	0.00017	0.00045
Saltwater		0.03		-
120. Toxaphene	8001-35-2			
Freshwater		0.0002	0.00073	0.0002
Saltwater		0.0002		-
Non-Priority Pollutants				
Alkalinity				
Freshwater		20000		-
Aluminum	7429-90-5			
Freshwater		87		-
Ammonia	7664-41-7			-
Aesthetic qualities				-
Bacteria				-
Barium	7440-39-3	-	1000	-
Boron				-
Chloride	16887-00-6			
Freshwater		230000		-
Chlorine	7782-50-5			
Freshwater		11		-
Saltwater		7.5		-
2,4,5-TP	93-72-1		10	50
2,4-D	94-75-7		100	70
Chlorpyrifos	2921-88-2			-

[56]   USEPA, April, 1999. National Recommended Water Quality Criteria - Correction. EPA-822-Z-99-001, available from the Office of Water webpage.

[57]   Water Quality Control, Chapter 391-3-6, Rules of the Georgia Department of Natural Resources Environmental Protection Division, Proposed revisions 30 June, 1998.

[58]   The values for metals often depend on hardness which are calculated from an equation. The regulation should be consulted.

[59]   Water + organisms.

Table 1-10. National Water Quality Criteria[60] **and Georgia Water Quality Criteria**[61], *continued*

Priority pollutant[62]	CAS No.	National CCC µg/L	Human consumption[63] µg/L	Georgia 7Q10 chronic µg/L
Freshwater		0.041		-
Saltwater		0.0056		-
Color				-
Demeton	8065-48-3			
Freshwater		0.1		-
Saltwater		0.1		-
Bis chloromethyl ether	542-88-1		0.00013	-
Total dissolved gases				-
Guthion	86-50-0			
Freshwater		0.01		-
Saltwater		0.01		-
Hardness				-
Technical BHC	319-86-8		0.0123	-
Iron	7439-89-6		300	-
Malathion	121-75-5			
Freshwater		0.1		-
Saltwater		0.1		-
Manganese	7439-96-5		50	-
Methoxychlor	72-43-5			
Freshwater		0.03	100	0.03
Saltwater		0.03		-
Mirex	2385-85-5			
Freshwater		0.001		-
Saltwater		0.001		-
Nitrates	14797-55-8		10000	-
Nitrosamines			0.0008	-
Dinitrophenols	25550-58-7		70	-
N-nitrosodibutylamine	924-16-3		0.0064	-
N-nitrosodiethylamine	55-18-5		0.0008	-
N-nitrosopyrrolidine	930-55-2		0.016	-
Oil and grease				
Dissolved oxygen	7782-44-7			-
Parathion (freshwater)	56-38-2	0.013		-
Pentachlorobenzene	608-93-5		3.5	-

[60] USEPA, April, 1999. National Recommended Water Quality Criteria - Correction. EPA-822-Z-99-001, available from the Office of Water webpage.

[61] Water Quality Control, Chapter 391-3-6, Rules of the Georgia Department of Natural Resources Environmental Protection Division, Proposed revisions 30 June, 1998.

[62] The values for metals often depend on hardness which are calculated from an equation. The regulation should be consulted.

[63] Water + organisms

Table 1-10. National Water Quality Criteria[64] and Georgia Water Quality Criteria[65], _continued_

Priority pollutant[66]	CAS No.	National CCC µg/L	Human consumption[67] µg/L	Georgia 7Q10 chronic µg/L
pH				
Freshwater		6.5-9	5-9	5-9
Saltwater		6.5-8.5		-
Elemental phosphorus	7723-14-0			
Saltwater		0.1		-
Phosphate phosphorus				-
Dissolved solids and salinity			250000	-
Suspended solids and turbidity				-
Sulfide	7783-06-4			
Freshwater		2.0		-
Saltwater		2.0		-
Tainting substances				-
Temperature				-
1,2,4,5-Tetrachlorobenzene	95-94-3		2.3	
Tributyltin	1461-22-9			
Freshwater		0.063		-
Saltwater		0.010		-
2,4,5-Trichlorophenol	95-95-4		2600	-

Table 1-11. National Recommended Water Quality Criteria for Organoleptic Effects

Pollutant	CAS	µg/L	Georgia 7Q10 chronic µg/L
Acenaphthene	83-32-9	20	-
Chlorobenzene	108-90-7	20	21000
3-Chlorophenol	108-43-0	0.1	-
4-Chlorophenol	106-48-9	0.1	-
2,3-Dichlorophenol	576-24-9	0.04	-
2,5-Dichlorophenol	583-78-8	0.5	-
2,6-Dichlorophenol	87-65-0	0.2	-
3,4-Dichlorophenol	95-77-2	0.3	-
2,4,5-Trichlorophenol	95-95-4	1	-
2,4,6-Trichlorophenol	88-06-2	2	6.5

---

[64] USEPA, April, 1999. National Recommended Water Quality Criteria - Correction. EPA-822-Z-99-001, available from the Office of Water webpage.

[65] Water Quality Control, Chapter 391-3-6, Rules of the Georgia Department of Natural Resources Environmental Protection Division, Proposed revisions 30 June, 1998.

[66] The values for metals often depend on hardness which are calculated from an equation. The regulation should be consulted.

[67] Water + organisms.

Table 1-11. National Recommended Water Quality Criteria for Organoleptic Effects, *continued*

Pollutant	CAS	µg/L	Georgia 7Q10 chronic µg/L
2,3,4,6-Tetrachlorophenol	58-90-2	1	-
2-Methyl-4-chlorophenol	1570-64-5	1800	-
3-Methyl-4-chlorophenol	59-50-7	3000	-
3-Methyl-6-chlorophenol	615-74-7	20	-
2-Chlorophenol	95-57-8	0.1	-
Copper	7440-50-8	1000	6.2
2,4-Dichlorophenol	120-83-2	0.3	790
2,4-Dimethylphenol	105-67-9	400	-
Hexachlorocyclopentadiene	77-47-4	1	17000
Nitrobenzene	98-95-3	30	1900
Pentachlorophenol	87-86-5	30	2.1
Phenol	108-95-2	300	300
Zinc	7440-66-6	5000	58

If a body of water is found to exceed the risk/health-based Water Quality Criteria, it may be necessary for the State or EPA to issue fish consumption advisories. These advisories are based upon sampling and analysis of consumable fish and other fauna (turtles, frogs) from the water body. A testing manual has been prepared by EPA, "Guidance for Assessing Chemical Contaminant Data for Use in Fish Advisories", EPA 823-R-95-007, September, 1995. The manual is accessible on the Internet through the Office of Science and Technology, Office of Water webpage (www.epa.gov/ost).

The development of the regulatory structure enabling enforcement of the provisions of the Clean Water Act has concentrated upon a permitting and compliance monitoring system for specific contaminants known to be pollutants that have a history of degrading the environment. Whole effluent toxicity (WET) has been used with increasing frequency to monitor effluents, but it still is limited to the examination of the specific effects on one particular organism. However, the chemical cleanliness of the receiving water is but one measure of man's impact upon the environment. Within the EPA and a few of the states a move has been made toward examination of the overall biological effect of effluents on nature. These examinations have led to the concept of "biocriteria" that serve to measure the greater overall picture of biological quality. Since biological quality is a relative term, and biocriteria is formulated as a quantitative measure, the evaluation is performed on the receiving water body and a closely related environ that is minimally affected by man-derived influences. The identified variables of biological quality are:

- Water quality - Temperature, turbidity, chemical pollutants
- Habitat structure - Substrate type, water depth and velocity, physical complexity of the habitat
- Flow regime - Water volume and temporal distribution of flows
- Energy source - Type, amount and seasonal variability of food resources
- Biotic interactions - Competition, predation, disease, parasitism and mutalism of organisms.

Insofar as assessment of the biological quality of the water is concerned, four areas of analysis have been identified[68]:

- Community structure - Species richness, relative abundances and extent to which one or a few species dominates
- Taxonomic composition - Identification of the resident species
- Individual organism condition - Health evaluation of individuals of the resident species
- Biological processes - Rates of biological activities/interactions among the resident species.

Five groups of organisms are recognized as important participants in the biological system. *Periphyton* are the algae and bacterial inhabitants of the water. *Macrophytes* are the larger plants in the system. *Macroinvertebrates* consist of the visible crustaceans, mollusks, insects, nematodes and other non-vertebrate inhabitants. *Fish* and *wildlife* (mammals, birds, reptiles and amphibians) are the vertebrate groups. Sampling methods for inventory and census are fairly well established.

4. FIFRA – Federal Insecticide, Fungicide, and Rodenticide Act

Administered by EPA, this regulation requires the EPA to oversee the manufacture and use of "-icides" in the US. Most commercial environmental laboratories have little to no contact with the provisions detailed under this legislation. Various facets of the act:

- Authorize the EPA to collect risk assessment data on the manufacture, use and disposal of the substances;
- Require submission from the manufacturer of extensive health and environmental fate data resulting from the use of the compounds;
- Require analytical methodologies to be submitted for the analysis of residues in air, soil, and water, resulting from the normal use or possible misuse of the substances; and,
- Specify labeling and warning requirements for sale of the product.

The methods required to be used to generate data for FIFRA applications are found in the Office of Prevention, Pesticides, and Toxic Substances (OPPTS) Harmonized Test Guidelines (www.epa.gov/opptsfrs/home/guidelin.htm). The test methods are listed in Table 1-12.

Table 1-12. OPPTS Harmonized Test Guidelines for FIFRA Applications

	Series 810 - Product Performance Test Guidelines
	Group A - General
810.1000	Overview, definitions, and general considerations
	Group C - Invertebrate control agent product performance test guidelines
810.3000	General considerations for efficacy of invertebrate control agents
810.3100	Soil treatments for imported fire ants
810.3200	Livestock, poultry, fur- and wool-bearing animal treatments

---

68   Biological Criteria: Technical Guidance for Streams and Small Rivers, May 1996. USEPA Office of Water 822-B-96-001.

Table 1-12. OPPTS Harmonized Test Guidelines for FIFRA Applications,
continued

	Series 810 - Product Performance Test Guidelines, continued
	Group A - General
810.3300	Treatments to control pests of humans and pets
810.3400	Mosquito, black fly, and biting midge (sand fly) treatments
810.3500	Premises treatments
810.3600	Structural treatments
	Series 830 - Product Properties Test Guidelines
830.1000	Background for product properties test guidelines
	Group A - Product identity, composition, and analysis test guidelines
830.1550	Product identity and composition
830.1600	Description of materials used to produce the product
830.1620	Description of production process
830.1650	Description of formulation process
830.1670	Discussion of formation of impurities
830.1700	Preliminary analysis
830.1750	Certified limits
830.1800	Enforcement analytical method
830.1900	Submittal of samples
	Group B - Physical/chemical properties test guidelines
830.6302	Color
830.6303	Physical state
830.6304	Odor
830.6313	Stability to normal and elevated temperature, metals, and metal ions
830.6314	Oxidation/reduction: chemical incompatibility
830.6315	Flammability
830.6316	Explodability
830.6317	Storage stability
830.6319	Miscibility
830.6320	Corrosion characteristics
830.6321	Dielectric breakdown voltage
830.7000	pH
830.7050	UV/Vis absorption
830.7100	Viscosity
830.7200	Melting point/melting range
830.7220	Boiling point/boiling range
830.7300	Density/relative density/bulk density
830.7370	Dissociation constants in water
830.7520	Particle size, fiber length, and diameter distribution
830.7550	Partition coefficient (*n*-octanol/water), shake flask method
830.7560	Partition coefficient (*n*-octanol/water), generator column method
830.7570	Partition coefficient (*n*-octanol/water), estimation by liquid chromatography
830.7840	Water solubility: Column elution method; shake flask method
830.7860	Water solubility, generator column method
830.7950	Vapor pressure

Table 1-12. OPPTS Harmonized Test Guidelines for FIFRA Applications, *continued*

Series 835 - Fate, transport and transformation test guidelines	
Group A - Laboratory transport test guidelines	
835.1110	Activated sludge sorption isotherm
835.1210	Soil thin layer chromatography
835.1220	Sediment and soil adsorption/desorption isotherm
Group B - Laboratory abiotic transformation test guidelines	
835.2110	Hydrolysis as a function of pH
835.2130	Hydrolysis as a function of pH and temperature
835.2210	Direct photolysis rate in water by sunlight
835.2310	Maximum direct photolysis rate in air from UV/Vis spectroscopy
Group C - Laboratory biological transformation test guidelines	
835.3100	Aerobic aquatic biodegradation
835.3110	Ready biodegradability
835.3120	Sealed-vessel carbon dioxide production test
835.3160	Biodegradability in seawater
835.3170	Shake flask die-away test
835.3180	Sediment/water microcosm biodegradation test
835.3200	Zahn-Wellens/EMPA test
835.3210	Modified SCAS test
835.3220	Porous pot test
835.3300	Soil biodegradation
835.3400	Anaerobic biodegradability of organic chemicals
Group E - Transformation chemical-specific test guidelines	
835.5045	Modified SCAS test for insoluble and volatile chemicals
835.5154	Anaerobic biodegradation in the subsurface
835.5270	Indirect photolysis screening test: sunlight photolysis in waters containing dissolved humic substances
Series 840 - Spray drift test guidelines	
840.1000	Background for pesticide aerial drift evaluation
840.1100	Spray droplet size spectrum
840.1200	Spray drift field deposition
Series 850 - Ecological effect test guidelines	
850.1000	Special considerations for conducting aquatic laboratory studies
Group A - Aquatic fauna test guidelines	
850.1010	Aquatic invertebrate acute toxicity test, freshwater daphnids
850.1020	Gammarid acute toxicity test
850.1025	Oyster acute toxicity test (shell deposition)
850.1035	Mysid acute toxicity test
850.1045	Penaeid acute toxicity test
850.1055	Bivalve acute toxicity test (embryo larval)
850.1075	Fish acute toxicity test, freshwater and marine
850.1085	Fish acute toxicity mitigated by humic acid
850.1300	Daphnid chronic toxicity test
850.1350	Mysid chronic toxicity test

Table 1-12. **OPPTS Harmonized Test Guidelines for FIFRA Applications,** *continued*

	Series 850 - Ecological effect test guidelines, *continued*
850.1400	Fish early-life stage toxicity test
850.1500	Fish life cycle toxicity
850.1710	Oyster BCF
850.1730	Fish BCF
850.1735	Whole sediment acute toxicity invertebrates, freshwater
850.1740	Whole sediment acute toxicity invertebrates, marine
850.1790	Chironomid sediment toxicity test
850.1800	Tadpole/sediment subchronic toxicity test
850.1850	Aquatic food chain transfer
850.1900	Generic freshwater microcosm test, laboratory
850.1925	Site-specific aquatic microcosm test, laboratory
850.1950	Field testing for aquatic organisms
	Group B -Terrestrail wildlife test guidelines
850.2100	Avian acute oral toxicity test
850.2200	Avian dietary toxicity test
850.2300	Avian reproduction test
850.2400	Wild mammal acute toxicity
850.2450	Terrestrial (soil-core) microcosm test
850.2500	Field testing for terrestrial wildlife
	Group C - Beneficial insects and invertebrates test guidelines
850.3020	Honey bee acute contact toxicity
850.3030	Honey bee toxicity of residues on foliage
850.3040	Field testing for pollinators
	Group D - Nontarget plants test guidelines
850.4000	Nontarget plant testing
850.4025	Target area phytotoxicity
850.4100	Terrestrial plant toxicity, Tier I (seedling emergence)
850.4150	Terrestrial plant toxicity, Tier I (vegetative vigor)
850.4200	Seed germination/root elongation toxicity test
850.4225	Seedling emergence, Tier II
850.4230	Early seedling growth toxicity test
850.4250	Vegetative vigor, Tier II
850.4300	Terrestrial plants field study, Tier III
850.4400	Aquatic plant toxicity test using *Lemna* spp. Tiers I and II
850.4450	Aquatic plants field study, Tier III
850.4600	*Rhizobium*-legume toxicity
850.4800	Plant uptake and translocation test
	Group E - Toxicity to mircoorganisms test guidelines
850.5100	Soil microbial community toxicity test
850.5400	Algal toxicity, Tiers I and II
	Group F - Chemical-specific test guidelines
850.6200	Earthworm subchronic toxicity test

Table 1-12. OPPTS Harmonized Test Guidelines for FIFRA Applications, *continued*

	Group F - Chemical-specific test guidelines, *continued*
850.6800	Modified activated sludge respiration inhibition test for sparingly soluble chemicals
	Group G - Field test data reporting guidelines
850.7100	Data reporting for environmental chemistry methods
	Series 860 - Residue chemistry test guidelines
860.1000	Background
860.1100	Chemical identity
860.1200	Directions for use
860.1300	Nature of the residue - plants, livestock
860.1340	Residue analytical method
860.1360	Multiresidue method
860.1380	Storage stability data
860.1400	Water, fish, and irrigated crops
860.1460	Food handling
860.1480	Meat/milk/poultry/eggs
860.1500	Crop field trials
860.1520	Processed food/feed
860.1550	Proposes tolerances
860.1560	Reasonable grounds in support of the petition
860.1650	Submittal of analytical reference standards
860.1850	Confined accumulation in rotational crops
860.1900	Field accumulation in rotational crops
	Series 870 - Health effects test guidelines
	Group A - Acute toxicity test guidelines
870.1000	Acute toxicity testing - background
870.1100	Acute oral toxicity
870.1200	Acute dermal toxicity
870.1300	Acute inhalation toxicity
870.2400	Acute eye irritation
870.2500	Acute dermal irritation
870.2600	Skin sensitization
	Group B - Subchronic toxicity test guidelines
870.3100	90-Day oral toxicity in rodents
870.3150	90-Day oral toxicity in nonrodents
870.3200	21/28-Day dermal toxicity
870.3250	90-Day dermal toxicity
870.3465	90-Day inhalation toxicity
870.3700	Prenatal developmental toxicity study
870.3800	Reproduction and fertility effects
	Group C - Chronic toxicity test guidelines
870.4100	Chronic toxicity
870.4200	Carcinogenicity
870.4300	Combined chronic toxicity/carcinogenicity

Table 1-12. OPPTS Harmonized Test Guidelines for FIFRA Applications, *continued*

	Group D - Genetic toxicity test guidelines
870.5100	Bacterial reverse mutation test
870.5140	Gene mutation in *Aspergillus nidulans*
870.5195	Mouse biochemical specific locus test
870.5200	Mouse visible specific locus test
870.5250	Gene mutation in *Neurospora crassa*
870.5275	Sex-linked recessive lethal test in *Drosophila melanogaster*
870.5300	In vitro mammalian cell gene mutation test
870.5375	In vitro mammalian chromosome aberration test
870.5380	Mammalian spermatogonial chromosomal aberration test
870.5385	Mammalian bone marrow chromosomal aberration test
870.5395	Mammalian erythrocyte micronucleus test
870.5450	Rodent dominant lethal assay
870.5460	Rodent heritable translocation assays
870.5500	Bacterial DNA damage or repair tests
870.5550	Unscheduled DNA synthesis in mammalian cells in culture
870.5575	Mitotic gene conversion in *Saccharomycescerevisiae*
870.5900	In vitro sister chromatid exchange assay
870.5915	In vivo sister chromatid exchange assay
	Group E - Neurotoxicity test guidelines
870.6100	Acute and 28-day delayed neurotoxicity of organophosphorus substances
870.6200	Neurotoxicity screening battery
870.6300	Developmental neurotoxicity study
870.6500	Schedule-controlled operant behavior
870.6850	Peripheral nerve function
870.6855	Neurophysiology: sensory evoked potentials
	Group F - Special studies test guidelines
870.7200	Companion animal safety
870.7485	Metabolism and pharmacokinetics
870.7600	Dermal penetration
870.7800	Immunotoxicity
	Series 875 - Occupational and residential exposure test guidelines
	Group A - Applicator exposure monitoring test guidelines
875.1000	Background for application exposure monitoring test guidelines
875.1100	Dermal exposure - outdoor
875.1200	Dermal exposure - indoor
875.1300	Inhalation exposure - outdoor
875.1400	Inhalation exposure - indoor
875.1500	Biological monitoring
875.1600	Application exposure monitoring data reporting
	Group B - Postapplication exposure monitoring test guidelines
875.2000	Background for postapplication exposure monitoring test guidelines
875.2100	Foliar dislodgeable residue dissipation

Table 1-12. OPPTS Harmonized Test Guidelines for FIFRA Applications, *continued*

	Group B - Postapplication exposure monitoring test guidelines
875.2200	Soil residue dissipation
875.2400	Dermal exposure
875.2500	Inhalation exposure
875.2600	Biological monitoring
875.2800	Descriptions of human activity
875.2900	Data reporting and calculations
	Series 880 - Biochemical test guidelines
	Group A - Product analysis test guidelines
880.1100	Product identity and composition
880.1200	Description of starting materials, production and formulation process
880.1400	Discussion of formation of impurities
	Group B - Toxicology test guidelines
880.3550	Immunotoxicity
880.3800	Immune response
	Group C - Nontarget organisms and environmental testing test guidelines
880.4350	Nontarget insect testing
880.4425	Dispenser water leaching
	Series 885 - Microbial pesticide test guidelines
885.0001	Overview for microbial pest control agents
	Group A - Product analysis test guidelines
885.1100	Product identity
885.1200	Manufacturing process
885.1300	Discussion of formation of unintentional ingredients
885.1400	Analysis of samples
885.1500	Certification of limits
	Group B - Residue test guidelines
885.2000	Background for residue analysis of microbial pest control agents
885.2100	Chemical identity
885.2200	Nature of the residue in plants
885.2250	Nature of the residue in animals
885.2300	Analytical methods - plants
885.2350	Analytical methods - animals
885.2400	Storage stability
885.2500	Magnitude of residues in plants
885.2550	Magnitude of residues in meat, milk, poultry, eggs
885.2600	Magnitude of residues in potable water, fish, and irrigated crops
	Group C - Toxicology test guidelines
885.3000	Background - mammalian toxicity/pathogenicity/infectivity
885.3050	Acute oral toxicity/pathogenicity
885.3100	Acute dermal toxicity/pathology
885.3150	Acute pulmonary toxicity/pathogenicity
885.3200	Acute injection toxicity/pathogenicity
885.3400	Hypersensitivity incidents

Table 1-12. OPPTS Harmonized Test Guidelines for FIFRA Applications, *continued*

	Group C - Toxicology test guidelines, *continued*
885.3500	Cell culture
885.3550	Acute toxicology, Tier II
885.3600	Subchronic toxicity/pathogenicity
885.3650	Reproductive/fertility effects
	Group D - Nontarget organism and environmental expression test guidelines
885.4000	Background for nontarget organism testing of microbial pest control agents
885.4050	Avian oral, Tier I
885.4100	Avian inhalation test, Tier I
885.4150	Wild mammal testing, Tier I
885.4200	Freshwater fish testing, Tier I
885.4240	Freshwater aquatic invertebrate testing, Tier I
885.4280	Estuarine and marine animal testing, Tier I
885.4300	Nontarget plant studies, Tier I
885.4340	Nontarget insect testing, Tier I
885.4380	Honey bee testing, Tier I
885.4600	Avian chronic pathogenicity and reproduction test, Tier III
885.4650	Aquatic invertebrate range testing, Tier III
885.4700	Fish life cycle studies, Tier III
885.4750	Aquatic ecosystem test
	Group E - Environmental expression test guidelines
885.5000	Background for microbial pesticides testing
885.5200	Expression in a terrestrial environment
885.5300	Expression in a freshwater environment
885.5400	Expression in a marine or estuarine environment

Under FIFRA, EPA promulgated the Good Laboratory Practice Standards (40 CFR 160) as a means of ensuring comparable quality data on all contracted laboratory studies generating data about the biological effects on non-target organisms of proposed materials to be registered as pesticides. These standards have been defacto generalized to the whole of the environmental analysis industry and should be consulted as a guide to how the laboratory should organize and conduct business.

5. FDCA – Food, Drug, and Cosmetic Act

Administered by the Food and Drug Administration (FDA), this act governs all chemicals labeled as, or considered to be, foods, food additives, vitamins, drugs (both over-the-counter and prescription) and cosmetics. By legislative fiat these substances and mixtures are effectively removed from EPA oversight. However the wastes and by-products generated from the manufacture of these substances are controlled by EPA.

6. TSCA – Toxic Substances Control Act

Beginning in 1976 with the enactment of TSCA, the EPA was given the authority to gather basic information on the toxicity and hazardous nature of individual chemicals.

The heart of the TSCA is the list of compounds already examined by the EPA. New compounds are defined as any compound not on the list. The EPA requires chemical producers to supply information dealing with risk assessment of proposed products 90 days before proposed manufacture or import. Proposed products are defined as either new chemicals or new uses for listed chemicals. Small volume chemicals used for research and development are exempted, as are specific groups of chemicals and substances such as drugs, cosmetics, food, food additives, pesticides, tobacco products, radioactive and nuclear substances, and firearms. These latter groups are controlled under other legislation.

The information required for a new or existing compound under TSCA includes data from chemical fate testing (40 CFR 796), environmental effects testing (40 CFR 797) and health effects testing (40 CFR 798). The appropriate CFR parts have detailed directions for the testing procedures, listed in Table 1-13. As is apparent from examination of the procedures in the Table, this legislation has very little to do with the normal workload of environmental analytical laboratories. In general, very specialized laboratories provide the test results.

Laboratories performing TSCA studies are required to comply with Good Laboratory Practice Standards (40 CFR 792). These Standards are somewhat similar to those discussed under FIFRA (above), however they are applicable only to TSCA mandated studies

Table 1-13. Test Procedures in 40 CFR for data supporting TSCA submissions

Part	Title
Provisional Test Guidelines	
795.45	Inherent biogradability: Modified SCAS test for chemical substances that are water insoluble or water insoluble and volatile
795.54	Anaerobic microbiological transformation rate data for chemicals in the subsurface environment
795.70	Indirect photolysis screening test: Sunlight photolysis in waters containing dissolved humic substances
795.120	Gammarid acute toxicity test
795.223	Pharmacokinetic test
795.225	Dermal pharmocokinetics of DGBE and DGBA
795.228	Oral/dermal pharmacokinetics
795.230	Oral and inhalation pharmacokinetic test
795.231	Pharmacokinetics of isopropanal
795.232	Inhalation and dermal pharmacokinetics of commercial hexane
795.235	Toxicokinetic test
795.250	Developmental neurotoxicity screen
795.260	Subchronic oral toxicity test
795.285	Morphologic transformation of cells in culture
Chemical Fate Testing Guidelines	
796.1050	Absorption in aqueous solution: Ultraviolet/visible spectra
796.1220	Boiling point/boiling range
796.1370	Dissociation constants in water
796.1520	Particle size distribution/fiber length and diameter distributions
796.1550	Partition coefficient (n-octanol/water)

Table 1-13. Test Procedures in 40 CFR for data supporting TSCA submissions, *continued*

Part	Title
Chemical Fate Testing Guidelines, *continued*	
796.1570	Partition coefficient (n-octanol/water) - Estimation by liquid chromatography
796.1720	Octanol/water partition coefficient, generator column method
796.1840	Water solubility
796.1860	Water solubility (generator column method)
796.1950	Vapor pressure
796.2700	Soil thin layer chromatography
796.2750	Sediment and soil adsorption isotherm
796.3100	Aerobic aquatic biodegradation
796.3140	Anaerobic biodegradability of organic chemicals
796.3180	Ready biodegradability: Modified AFNOR test
796.3200	Ready biodegradability: Closed bottle test
796.3220	Ready biodegradability: Modified MITI test (I)
796.3240	Ready biodegradability: Modified OECD screening test
796.3260	Ready biodegradability: Modified Sturm test
796.3300	Simulation test - aerobic sewage treatment: Coupled units test
796.3340	Inherent biodegradability: Modified SCAS test
796.3360	Inherent biodegradability: Modified Zahn-Wellens test
796.3400	Inherent biodegradability in soil
796.3480	Complex formation ability in water
796.3500	Hydrolysis as a function of pH at 25 °C
796.3700	Photolysis in aqueous solution in sunlight
796.3780	Laboratory determination of the direct photolysis reaction quantum yield in aqueous solution and sunlight photolysis
796.3800	Gas phase absorption spectra and photolysis
Environmental Effects Testing Guidelines	
797.1050	Algal acute toxicity test
797.1060	Freshwater algae acute toxicity test
797.1075	Freshwater and marine algae acute toxicity test
797.1160	Lemna acute toxicity test
797.1300	Daphnid acute toxicity test
797.1330	Daphnid chronic toxicity test
797.1350	Daphnid chronic toxicity test
797.1400	Fish acute toxicity test
797.1440	Fish acute toxicity test
797.1520	Fish bioconcentration test
797.1560	Fish bioconcentration test
797.1600	Fish early life state toxicity test
797.1800	Oyster acute toxicity test
797.1830	Oyster bioconcentration test
797.1930	Mysid shrimp acute toxicity test
797.1950	Mysid shrimp chronic toxicity test
797.1970	Penaeid shrimp acute toxicity test
797.2050	Avian dietary toxicity test

Table 1-13. Test Procedures in 40 CFR for data supporting TSCA submissions, *continued*

Part	Title
Environmental Effects Testing Guidelines, *continued*	
797.2130	Bobwhite reproduction test
797.2150	Mallard reproduction test
797.2175	Avian acute oral toxicity test
797.2750	Seed germination/root elongation toxicity test
797.2800	Early seedling growth toxicity test
797.2850	Plant uptake and translocation test
Health Effects Testing Guidelines	
798.1100	Acute dermal toxicity
798.1150	Acute inhalation toxicity
798.1175	Acute oral toxicity
798.2250	Dermal toxicity
798.2450	Inhalation toxicity
798.2650	Oral toxicity
798.2675	Oral toxicity with satellite reproduction and fertility study
798.3260	Chronic toxicity
798.3300	Oncogenicity
798.3320	Combined chronic toxicity/oncogenicity
798.4100	Dermal sensitization
798.4350	Inhalation developmental toxicity study
798.4420	Preliminary developmental toxicity
798.4470	Primary dermal irritation
798.4500	Primary eye irritation
798.4700	Reproduction and fertility effects
798.4900	Developmental toxicity study
798.5100	Escheria coli WP2 and WP2 urvA reverse mutation assays
798.5140	Gene mutations in aspergillus nidulans
798.5195	Mouse biochemical specific locus test
798.5200	Mouse visible specific locus test
798.5250	Gene mutation in neurospora crassa
798.5265	The salmonella typhimurium reverse mutation assay
798.5275	Sex-linked recessive lethal test in drosophila melanogaster
798.5300	Detection of gene mutations in somatic cells in culture
798.5375	In vitro mammalian cytogenetics
798.5385	In vivo mammalian bone marrow cytogenetics tests: Chromosomal analysis
798.5395	In vivo mammalian bone marrow cytogenetics tests: Micronucleus assay
798.5450	Rodent dominant lethal assay
798.5460	Rodent heritable translocation assays
798.5500	Differential growth inhibition of repair proficient and repair deficient bacteria: Bacterial DNA damage or repair tests
798.5550	Unscheduled DNA synthesis in mammalian cells in culture
798.5575	Mitotic gene conversion in Saccharomyces cervisitiae
798.5900	In vitro sister chromatid exchange assay

Table 1-13. Test Procedures in 40 CFR for data supporting TSCA submissions, *continued*

Part	Title
Health Effects Testing Guidelines, *continued*	
798.5915	In vivo sister chromatid exchange assay
798.5955	Heritable translocation test in drosophila melanogaster
798.6050	Functional observational battery
798.6200	Motor activity
798.6400	Neuropathology
798.6450	NTE neurotox assay
798.6500	Schedule-controlled operant behavior
798.6540	Acute delayed neurotoxicity of organophosphorous substances
798.6560	Subchronic delayed neurotoxicity of organophosphorous substances
798.7100	Metabolism

The EPA, under the TSCA regulations, has embarked upon a program, called the Challenge Program, to collect basic health and environmental safety data for the top 2800 commercial chemicals (in terms of produced/used mass). These are termed High Production Volume (HPV) chemicals. A series of documents have been prepared and are available on the Internet (www.epa.gov/chemrtk/volchall.htm) concerning what chemicals are subject to the program, deciding how to test, and evaluation of existing/ generated data. The idea is to develop a Screening Information Data Set (SIDS) in line with the OECD protocols (see Section 2.II). The SIDS is presented in the following Table. Appropriate tests to generate the SIDS data can be either the EPA TSCA methods or the OECD test methods

Table 1-14. SIDS Endpoints

SIDS Category	Test Endpoints
Chemical and physical properties	Melting point
	Boiling point
	Vapor pressure
	Partition coefficient
	Water solubility
Environmental fate and pathways	Photodegradation
	Stability in water
	Biodegradation
	Transport/distribution
Exotoxicity tests	Acute toxicity to fish
	Acute toxicity to aquatic invertebrates
	Toxicity to aquatic plants
	Chronic aquatic invertebrate toxicity
	Terrestrial toxicity test
Human health effects	Acute toxicity
	General toxicity
	Genetic toxicity
	Reproductive toxicity
	Developmental toxicity

7. SARA – Superfund Amendments and Reauthorization Act

Passed in 1986, SARA extends the lifetime of the legislation begun in CERCLA and gives EPA the authority to remediate a site if no responsible parties can be found to pay.

8. CAA - Clean Air Act

The Clean Air Act Amendments of 1990 empowered EPA to regulate a variety of hazardous air pollutants (HAP). Under this authority EPA has established the National Emission Standards for Hazardous Air Pollutants (NESHAP). These compounds can be grouped into volatiles (vp > 0.1 mm Hg, BP <300 °C), semivolatiles (vp 10^{-1} to 10^{-7} mm Hg, BP 300-600 °C) and particulates (vp <10^{-7}, BP >600 °C). Organic materials are listed in 40 CFR 63.106, Table 2 as Hazardous Organic National Emission Standards for Hazardous Air Pollutants (HON) (Table 1-15).

Table 1-15. Hazardous organic air pollutants[69]

Compound	CAS
Acetaldehyde	75-07-0
Acetamide	60-35-5
Acetonitrile	75-05-8
Acetophenone	98-86-2
Acrolein	107-02-8
Acrylamide	79-06-1
Acrylic acid	79-10-7
Acrylonitrile	107-13-1
Allyl chloride	107-05-1
Aniline	62-53-3
o-Anisidine	90-04-0
Benzene	71-43-2
Benzotrichloride	98-07-7
Benzyl chloride	100-44-7
Biphenyl	92-52-4
Bis(chloromethyl)ether	542-88-1
Bromoform	75-25-2
1,3-Butadiene	106-99-0
Caprolactam	105-60-2
Carbon disulfide	75-15-0
Carbon tetrachloride	56-23-5
Chloroacetic acid	79-11-8
2-Chloroacetophenone	532-27-4
Chlorobenzene	108-90-7
Chloroform	67-66-3
Chloroprene	126-99-8
Cresols and cresylic acids	1319-77-3
o-Cresol and o-Cresylic acid	95-48-7

---

69   Federal Register, Vol. 57. No. 252. Thursday, December 31. 1992. p. 62690.

Table 1-15. Hazardous organic air pollutants, *continued*

Compound	CAS
m-Cresol and *m*-Cresylic acid	108-39-4
p-Cresol and *p*-Cresylic acid	106-44-5
Cumene	98-82-8
1,4-Dichlorobenzene	106-46-7
3,3'-Dichlorobenzidine	91-94-1
Dichloroethylether	111-44-4
1,3-Dichloropropene	542-75-6
Diethanolamine	11-142-2
N,N-dimethylaniline	121-69-7
Diethyl sulfate	64-67-5
3,3'-Dimethylbenzidine	119-93-7
Dimethylformamide	68-12-2
1,1-Dimethylhydrazine	57-14-7
Dimethyl phthalate	131-11-3
Dimethyl sulfate	77-78-1
2,4-Dinitrophenol	51-28-5
2,4-Dinitrotoluene	121-14-2
1,4-Dioxane	123-91-1
1,2-Diphenylhydrazine	122-66-7
Epichlorohydrin	106-89-8
Ethyl acrylate	140-88-5
Ethylbenzene	100-41-4
Ethylchloride	75-00-3
Ethylene dibromide	106-93-4
Ethylene dichloride	107-06-2
Ethylene glycol	107-21-1
Ethylene oxide	75-21-8
Ethylidene dichloride	75-34-3
Formaldehyde	50-00-0
Glycol ethers[70]	-
Hexachlorobenzene	118-74-1
Hexachlorobutadiene	87-68-3
Hexachloroethane	67-72-1
Hexane	100-54-3
Hydroquinone	123-31-9
Isophorone	78-59-1
Maleic anhydride	108-31-6
Methanol	67-56-1
Methyl bromide	74-83-9
Methyl chloride	74-87-3
Methyl chloroform	71-55-6
Methyl ethyl ketone	78-93-3

Continued on next page.

[70] Includes mono- and di-ethers of ethylene glycol, diethylene glycol, and triethylene glycol R-$(OCH_2CH_2)_n$-OR', where n=1,2, or 3, R = alkyl or aryl groups and R'=R, H or groups, which, when removed, yield glycol ethers with the structure R-$(OCH_2CH_2)_n$-OH. Polymers are excluded from the glycol ether category.

Table 1-15. Hazardous organic air pollutants, *continued*

Compound	CAS
Methyl hydrazine	60-34-4
Methyl isobutyl ketone	108-10-1
Methyl isocyanate	624-83-9
Methyl methacrylate	80-62-6
Methyl tert-butyl ether	1634-04-4
Methylene chloride	75-09-2
Methylene diphenyl diisocyanate	101-68-8
4,4'-Methylene dianiline	101-77-9
Naphthalene	91-20-3
Nitrobenzene	98-95-3
4-Nitrophenol	100-02-7
2-Nitropropane	79-46-9
Phenol	108-95-2
p-Phenylenediamine	106-50-3
Phosgene	75-44-5
Phthalic anhydride	85-44-9
Polycyclic organic matter[71]	-
Propiolactone	57-57-8
Propionaldehyde	123-38-6
Propylene dichloride	78-87-5
Propylene oxide	75-56-9
Quinone	106-51-4
Styrene	100-42-5
1,1,2,2-Tetrachloroethane	79-34-5
Tetrachloroethylene	127-18-4
Toluene	108-88-3
2,4-Toluene diamine	95-80-7
2,4-Toluene disocyanate	584-84-9
o-Toluidine	95-53-4
1,2,4-Trichlorobenzene	120-82-1
1,1,2-Trichloroethane	79-00-5
Trichloroethene	79-01-6
2,4,5-Trichlorophenol	95-95-4
Triethylamine	121-44-8
2,2,4-Trimethylpentane	540-84-1
Vinyl acetate	108-05-4
Vinyl chloride	75-01-4
Vinylidene chloride	75-35-4
Xylenes	1330-20-7
o-Xylene	95-47-6
m-Xylene	108-38-3
p-Xylene	106-42-3

[71] Includes organic compounds with more than one benzene ring, and that have a boiling point greater than or equal to 100 °C.

Table 1-16. Hazardous Air Pollutants under Title III CAAA

Compound	CAS
Acetaldehyde	75-07-0
Acetamide	60-35-5
Acetonitrile	75-05-8
Acetophenone	98-86-2
2-Acetylaminofluorene	53-96-3
Acrolein	107-02-8
Acrylamide	79-06-1
Acrylic acid	79-10-7
Acrylonitrile	107-13-1
Allyl chloride	107-05-1
4-Aminobiphenyl	92-67-1
Aniline	62-53-3
o-Anisidine	90-04-0
Asbestos	1332-21-4
Benzene	71-43-2
Benzidine	92-87-5
Benzotrichloride	98-07-7
Benzyl chloride	100-44-7
Biphenyl	92-52-4
Bis(2-ethylhexyl) phthalate	117-81-7
Bis(chloromethyl)ether	542-88-1
Bromoform	75-25-2
1,3-Butadiene	106-99-0
Calcium cyanamide	156-62-7
Caprolactam	105-60-2
Captan	133-06-2
Carbaryl	63-25-2
Carbon disulfide	75-15-0
Carbon tetrachloride	56-23-5
Carbonyl sulfide	463-58-1
Catechol	120-80-9
Chloramben	133-90-4
Chlordane	57-74-9
Chlorine	7782-50-5
Chloroacetic acid	79-11-8
2-Chloroacetophenone	532-27-4
Chlorobenzene	108-90-7
Chlorobenzilate	510-15-6
Chloroform	67-66-3
Chloromethyl methyl ether	107-30-2
Chloroprene	126-99-8
Cresols/cresylic acids	1319-77-3
o-Cresol	95-48-7
m-Cresol	108-39-4
p-Cresol	106-44-5
Cumene	98-82-8
2,4-D, salts and esters	94-75-7
DDE	3547-04-4
Diazomethane	334-88-3
Dibenzofurans	132-64-9
1,2-Dibromo-3-chloropropane	96-12-8

Continued on next page.

Table 1-16. Hazardous Air Pollutants under Title III CAAA, *continued*

Compound	CAS
Dibutylphthalate	84-74-2
1,4-Dichlorobenzene	106-46-7
3,3'-Dichlorobenzidine	91-94-1
Dichloroethylether	111-44-4
1,3-Dichloropropene	542-75-6
Dichlorvos	62-73-7
Diethanolamine	111-42-2
N,N-dimethylaniline	121-69-7
Diethyl sulfate	64-67-5
3,3'-Dimethoxybenzidine	119-90-4
Dimethyl aminoazobenzene	60-11-7
3,3'-Dimethyl benzidine	119-93-7
Dimethyl carbamoyl chloride	79-44-7
Dimethylformamide	68-12-2
1,1-Dimethylhydrazine	57-14-7
Dimethyl phthalate	131-11-3
Dimethyl sulfate	77-78-1
4,6-Dinitrophenol and salts	534-52-1
2,4-Dinitrophenol	51-28-5
2,4-Dinitrotoluene	121-14-2
1,4-Dioxane	123-91-1
1,2-Diphenylhydrazine	122-66-7
Epichlorohydrin	106-89-8
1,2-Epoxybutane	106-88-7
Ethyl acrylate	140-88-5
Ethylbenzene	100-41-4
Ethyl carbamate	51-79-6
Ethylchloride	75-00-3
Ethylene dibromide	106-93-4
Ethylene dichloride	107-06-2
Ethylene glycol	107-21-1
Ethylene imine	151-56-4
Ethylene oxide	75-21-8
Ethylene thiourea	96-45-7
Ethylidene dichloride	75-34-3
Formaldehyde	50-00-0
Heptachlor	76-44-8
Hexachlorobenzene	118-74-1
Hexachlorobutadiene	87-68-3
Hexachlorocyclopentadiene	77-47-4
Hexachloroethane	67-72-1
Hexamethylene-1,6-diisocyanate	822-06-0
Hexamethylphosphoramide	680-31-9
Hexane	100-54-3
Hydrazine	302-01-2
Hydrochloric acid	7647-01-0
Hydrofluoric acid	7664-39-3
Hydroquinone	123-31-9
Isophorone	78-59-1
Lindane	58-89-9

Continued on next page.

Table 1-16. Hazardous Air Pollutants under Title III CAAA, *continued*

Compound	CAS
Maleic anhydride	108-31-6
Methanol	67-56-1
Methoxychlor	72-43-5
Methyl bromide	74-83-9
Methyl chloride	74-87-3
Methyl chloroform	71-55-6
Methyl ethyl ketone	78-93-3
Methyl hydrazine	60-34-4
Methyl iodide	74-88-4
Methyl isobutyl ketone (hexone)	108-10-1
Methyl isocyanate	624-83-9
Methyl methacrylate	80-62-6
Methyl tert-butyl ether	1634-04-4
4,4'-Methylene bis(2-chloroaniline)	101-14-4
Methylene chloride	75-09-2
Methylene diphenyl diisocyanate	101-68-8
4,4'-Methylene dianiline	101-77-9
Naphthalene	91-20-3
Nitrobenzene	98-95-3
4-Nitrobiphenyl	92-93-3
4-Nitrophenol	100-02-7
2-Nitropropane	79-46-9
N-Nitroso-N-methylurea	684-93-5
N-Nitrosodimethylamine	62-75-9
N-Nitrosomorpholine	59-89-2
Parathion	56-38-2
Pentachloronitrobenzene	82-68-8
Pentachlorophenol	87-86-5
Phenol	108-95-2
p-Phenylenediamine	106-50-3
Phosgene	75-44-5
Phosphine	7803-51-2
Phosphorous	7723-14-0
Phthalic anhydride	85-44-9
PCB	1336-36-3
1,3-Propane sultone	1120-71-4
Propiolactone	57-57-8
Propionaldehyde	123-38-6
Propoxur	114-26-1
Propylene dichloride	78-87-5
Propylene oxide	75-56-9
1,2-Propylenimine	75-55-8
Quinoline	91-22-5
Quinone	106-51-4
Styrene	100-42-5
Styrene oxide	96-09-3
2,3,7,8-Tetrachlorodibenzo-p-dioxin	1746-01-6
1,1,2,2-Tetrachloroethane	79-34-5
Tetrachloroethylene	127-18-4

Continued on next page

Table 1-16. Hazardous Air Pollutants under Title III CAAA, *continued*

Compound	CAS
Titanium tetrachloride	7550-45-0
Toluene	108-88-3
2,4-Toluene diamine	95-80-7
2,4-Toluene diisocyanate	584-84-9
o-Toluidine	95-53-4
Toxaphene	8001-35-2
1,2,4-Trichlorobenzene	120-82-1
1,1,2-Trichloroethane	79-00-5
Trichloroethene	79-01-6
2,4,5-Trichlorophenol	95-95-4
2,4,6-Trichlorophenol	88-06-2
Triethylamine	121-44-8
Trifluralin	1582-09-8
2,2,4-Trimethylpentane	540-84-1
Vinyl acetate	108-05-4
Vinyl bromide	593-60-2
Vinyl chloride	75-01-4
Vinylidene chloride	75-35-4
Xylenes	1330-20-7
o-Xylene	95-47-6
m-Xylene	108-38-3
p-Xylene	106-42-3
Antimony compounds	-
Arsenic compounds	-
Beryllium compounds	-
Cadmium compounds	-
Chromium compounds	-
Cobalt compounds	-
Coke oven emissions	-
Cyanide compounds	-
Glycol ethers[72]	-
Lead compounds	-
Manganese compounds	-
Mercury compounds	-
Fine mineral fibers	-
Nickel compounds	-
Polycyclic organic matter[73]	-
Radionuclides	-
Selenium compounds	-

A number of different techniques have been developed by EPA for analysis of the compounds and substances on the HAP list. These have been reviewed by Winberry in

---

[72] Includes mono- and di-ethers of ethylene glycol, diethylene glycol, and triethylene glycol R-$(OCH_2CH_2)_n$-OR', where n=1,2, or 3, R = alkyl or aryl groups and R'=R, H or groups, which, when removed, yield glycol ethers with the structure R-$(OCH_2CH_2)_n$-OH. Polymers are excluded from the glycol ether category.

[73] Includes organic compounds with more than one benzene ring, and which have a boiling point greater than or equal to 100 °C.

two articles[74]. These are also presented in a publication, *Instant EPA's Air Toxics*, from Instant Reference Sources, Inc., Austin, Texas. The applicable methods encompass sampling and analysis in the 00xx series methods in SW-846, the draft Air CLP-SOW, 40 CFR parts 60 and 61 and the TO-1 to -14 manual. Although a number of analytical procedures are available, as far as the list of HAP target compounds is concerned the analysis technology lags behind the regulations. With respect to the HAP list, 19% of the target analytes have validated methods, 24% have partially validated methods, 32% have possibly applicable methods and a full 25% of the compounds have no reliable analytical technique. Multi-analyte methods are the preferred techniques, and for the majority of the HAP, Method 29 for the metals, Method 18 for the volatile organics, and Method 0010/8270 (SW-846) are the most efficient techniques.

The CAA also requires EPA to establish permits for maximum amounts of emissions by industries, similar to the NPDES program for wastewater effluent. For many specific type industries, the EPA has defined air emission standards. These are listed in 40 CFR 60 and consist, in general, of an applicability statement, definitions, required standards, monitoring requirements, approved test methods and procedures, and reporting and recordkeeping requirements. Most of the approved methods of analysis are found in 40 CFR 60, Appendix A. Table 1-17 lists industries for which air emission standards exist.

Table 1-17. Standards of performance for new stationary sources listed in 40 CFR 60, 1 July, 1993

Subpart	Title
Ca	Emissions guidelines and compliance times for municipal waste combustors
Cb	Emissions guidelines and compliance times for sulfuric acid production units
D	Standards of performance for fossil-fuel fired steam generators for which construction is commenced after August 17, 1971
Da	Standards of performance for electric utility steam generating units for which construction is commenced after September 18, 1978
Db	Standards of performance for industrial-commercial-institutional steam generating units
Dc	Standards of performance for small industrial-commercial-institutional steam generating units
E	Standards of performance for incinerators
Ea	Standards of performance for municipal waste combustors
F	Standards of performance for Portland cement plants
G	Standards of performance for nitric acid plants
H	Standards of performance for sulfuric acid plants
I	Standards of performance for asphalt concrete plants
J	Standards of performance for petroleum refineries
K	Standards of performance for storage vessels for petroleum liquids for which construction, reconstruction, or modification commenced after June 11, 1973 and prior to May 18, 1978
Ka	Standards of performance for storage vessels for petroleum liquids for which construction, reconstruction, or modification commenced after May 18, 1978 and prior to July 23, 1984

Continued on next page.

---

[74] Winberry, W.T. Jr. *Sampling and Analysis Under Title III. Part I.* "Environmental Lab," June/July 1993. pp. 46-58; *Part II: Source Test Methodology.* "Environmental Lab," August/September, 1993. pp. 52-67.

Table 1-17. Standards of performance for new stationary sources listed in 40 CFR 60, 1 July, 1993, *continued*

Subpart	Title
Kb	Standards of performance for volatile organic liquid storage vessels (including petroleum liquid storage vessels) for which construction, reconstruction or modification commenced after July 23, 1984
L	Standards of performance for secondary lead smelters
M	Standards of performance for secondary brass and bronze production plants
N	Standards of performance for primary emissions from basic oxygen process furnaces for which construction is commenced after June 11, 1973
Na	Standards of performance for secondary emissions from basic oxygen process steelmaking facilities for which construction is commenced after January 20, 1983
O	Standards of performance for sewage treatment plants
P	Standards of performance for primary copper smelters
Q	Standards of performance for primary zinc smelters
R	Standards of performance for primary lead smelters
S	Standards of performance for primary aluminum reduction plants
T	Standards of performance for the phosphate fertilizer industry: wet-process phosphoric acid plants
U	Standards of performance for the phosphate fertilizer industry: superphosphoric acid plants
V	Standards of performance for the phosphate fertilizer industry: diammonium phosphate plants
W	Standards of performance for the phosphate fertilizer industry: triple superphosphate plants
X	Standards of performance for the phosphate fertilizer industry: granular triple superphosphate storage facilities
Y	Standards of performance for coal preparation plants
Z	Standards of performance for ferroalloy production facilities
AA	Standards of performance for steel plants: electric arc furnaces constructed after October 21, 1974 and on or before August 17, 1983
AAa	Standards of performance for steel plants: electric arc furnaces and argon-oxygen decarburization vessels constructed after August 7, 1983
BB	Standards of performance for kraft pulp mills
CC	Standards of performance for glass manufacturing plants
DD	Standards of performance for grain elevators
EE	Standards of performance for surface coating of metal furniture
GG	Standards of performance for stationary gas turbines
HH	Standards of performance for lime manufacturing plants
KK	Standards of performance for lead-acid battery manufacturing plants
LL	Standards of performance for metallic mineral processing plants
MM	Standards of performance for automobile and light-duty truck surface coating operations
NN	Standards of performance for phosphate rock plants
PP	Standards of performance for ammonium sulfate manufacture
QQ	Standards of performance for the graphic arts industry: publication rotogravure printing
RR	Standards of performance for pressure sensitive tape and label surface coating operations
SS	Standards of performance for industrial surface coating: large applications
TT	Standards of performance for metal coil surface coating

Continued on next page.

Table 1-17. Standards of performance for new stationary sources listed in 40 CFR 60, 1 July, 1993, *continued*

Subpart	Title
UU	Standards of performance for asphalt processing and asphalt roofing manufacture
VV	Standards of performance for equipment leaks of VOC in the synthetic organic chemicals manufacturing industry
WW	Standards of performance for the beverage can surface coating industry
XX	Standards of performance for bulk gasoline terminals
AAA	Standards of performance for new residential wood heaters
BBB	Standards of performance for the rubber tire manufacturing industry
DDD	Standards of performance for volatile organic compound (VOC) emissions from the polymer manufacturing industry
FFF	Standards of performance for flexible vinyl and urethane coating and printing
GGG	Standards of performance for equipment leaks of VOC in petroleum refineries
HHH	Standards of performance for synthetic fiber production facilities
III	Standards of performance for volatile organic compound (VOC) emissions from the synthetic organic chemical manufacturing industry (SOCMI) air oxidation unit processes
JJJ	Standards of performance for petroleum dry cleaners
KKK	Standards of performance for equipment leaks of VOC from on-shore natural gas processing plants
LLL	Standards of performance for onshore natural gas processing: SO_2 emissions
NNN	Standards of performance for volatile organic compound (VOC) emissions from synthetic organic chemical manufacturing industry (SOCMI) distillation operations
OOO	Standards of performance for nonmetallic mineral processing plants
PPP	Standards of performance for wool fiberglass insulation manufacturing plants
QQQ	Standards of performance for VOC emissions from petroleum refinery wastewater systems
SSS	Standards of performance for magnetic tape coating facilities
TTT	Standards of performance for industrial surface coating: surface coating of plastic parts for business machines
UUU	Standards of performance for calciners and dryers in mineral industries
VVV	Standards of performance for polymeric coating of supporting substrates facilities

The number of industries with standards is growing rapidly and the most recent edition of 40 CFR Part 60 should be consulted. The EPA Air Website at www.epa.gov/ttn contains a listing of all the promulgated and proposed industry standards.

For example, Subpart V, Standards of performance for the phosphate fertilizer industry: diammonium phosphate plants, specifies that fluoride emissions to the air will not exceed 30 g/metric ton of equivalent phosphorus pentoxide feed. The Standard then specifies that this shall be verified by installation and use of a continuous monitoring device for mass flow of phosphorus bearing feed material to the system, installation and use of a monitoring device that constantly records the pressure drop across the scrubbing system, and, finally, use of either methods 13A or 13B to measure fluoride concentration and flow rate of effluent gas from each emission point. An equation is presented that uses these measurements to arrive at the g/metric ton Standard.

II. ANALYTICAL METHODOLOGIES

There are many different analytical methods circulating through the environmental industry. Many are published by the EPA. The offices within EPA that are responsible for generating or requiring the use of specific analytical methods are shown in Figure 1-1.

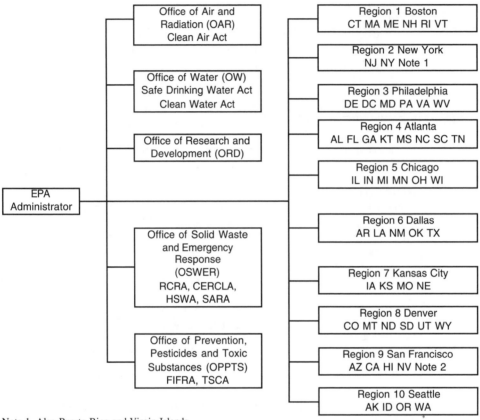

Note 1. Also Puerto Rico and Virgin Islands
Note 2. Also American Samoa, Guam and Trust territories of the Pacific

Figure 1-1. Offices within EPA that generate and specify methods.

There are also officially recognized compilations of methods that are published by the commercial side of the industry. The regulations discussed above often specify approved methods of analysis as a part of the regulation. Following is a list of published methods that are available and should be present in an environmental lab.

Federal Methods

Methods Series 1-29
Air monitoring methods 40 CFR 60 Appendix A (see Table 5-4 at end of Section 5)

Methods 101-115
Air monitoring methods 40 CFR 61 Appendix B (see Table 5-4 at end of Section 5)

Methods Series 110.0-430.2

Methods for Chemical Analysis of Water and Wastes 1983 (EPA-600/4-79/020 PB84-128677) and *Methods for the determination of inorganic substances in environmental samples* 1993 (EPA 600/R-93/100), *Methods for the determination of chemical substances in marine and estuarine environmental samples* (EPA/600/R-92/121), November 1992, *Methods for the Determination of Metals in Environmental Samples*, 1991 (EPA 600/4-91/010), and *Methods for the Determination of Metals in Environmental Samples* Supplement I, 1994 (EPA-600/R-94/111)

100's	Physical Properties
200's	Metals
300's	Inorganic, Non-metallics
400's	Aggregate Organics

Table 1-18. EPA 100-400 series methods

Method[75]	Title/Description
100.1 (f)	Asbestos fibers by TEM
100.2 (g)	Asbestos fiber size by TEM
110.1 (a)	ADMI colorimetric color
110.2 (a)	Platinum-cobalt colorimetric color
110.3 (a)	Spectrophotometric color
120.1 (a)	Specific conductance
130.1 (a)	EDTA automated hardness
130.2 (a)	EDTA titration hardness
140.1 (a)	Odor
150.1 (a)	pH, electometric
150.2 (a)	pH electrometric continuous monitoring
160.1 (a)	Filterable residue (TDS)
160.2 (a)	Non-filterable residue (TSS)
160.3 (a)	Total residue (TS)
160.4 (a)	Volatile residue (VS)
160.5 (a)	Settleable matter
170.1 (a)	Temperature
180.1 (b)	Nephelometric turbidity
200.1 (d)	Determination of acid-soluble metals
200.2 (e)	Sample preparation procedure for spectrochemical determination of total recoverable elements
200.3 (d)	Sample preparation procedure for spectrochemical determination of total recoverable elements in biological tissues

Continued on next page.

---

[75] (a) *Methods for Chemical Analysis of Water and Wastes* 1983 (EPA-600/4-79/020 PB84-128677); (b) *Methods for the determination of inorganic substances in environmental samples* 1993 (EPA 600/R-93/100); (c) *Methods for the determination of chemical substances in marine and estuarine environmental samples* (EPA/600/R-92/121), November 1992; (d) *Methods for the Determination of Metals in Environmental Samples*, 1991 (EPA 600/4-91/010); (e) *Methods for the Determination of Metals in Environmental Samples* Supplement I, 1994 (EPA-600/R-94/111); (f) *Analytical method for the determination of asbestos fibers in water*, September, 1983 NTIS PB83-260471; (g) *Determination of asbestos structure over 10 μm in length in drinking water*, June 1994, EPA 600/R-94-134, NTIS PB94-201902.

Table 1-18. EPA 100-400 series methods, *continued*

Method[76]	Title/Description
200.7 (e)	Determination of metals and trace elements in water and wastes by ICP-AES
200.8 (e)	Determination of trace elements in water and wastes ICP-MS
200.9 (e)	Determination of trace elements by stabilized temperature GFAA
200.10 (c)(d)	Determination of trace elements in marine waters by on-line chelation preconcentration and ICP-MS
200.11 (d)	Determination of metals in fish tissue by ICP-AES
200.12 (c)	Determination of trace elements in marine waters by STGFAA
200.13 (c)	Determination of trace elements in marine waters by off-line chelation pre-concentration with GFAA
200.15 (e)	Determination of metals and trace elements in water by ultrasonic nebulization ICP-AES
202.1 (a)	Aluminum FLAA
202.2 (a)	Aluminum GFAA
204.1 (a)	Antimony FLAA
204.2 (a)	Antimony GFAA
206.2 (a)	Arsenic GFAA
206.3 (a)	Arsenic hydride AA
206.4 (a)	Arsenic SDDC Spectrophotometric
206.5 (a)	Arsenic digestion method for hydride and SDDC
208.1 (a)	Barium FLAA
208.2 (a)	Barium GFAA
210.1 (a)	Beryllium FLA
210.2 (a)	Beryllium GFAA
212.3 (a)	Boron, Curcumin colorimetric
213.1 (a)	Cadmium FLAA
213.2 (a)	Cadmium GFAA
215.1 (a)	Calcium FLAA
215.2 (a)	Calcium EDTA titrimetric
218.1 (a)	Chromium FLAA
218.2 (a)	Chromium GFAA
218.3 (a)	Chromium chelation-extraction
218.4 (a)	Hexavalent chromium chelation-extraction
218.5 (a)	Hexavalent chromium dissolved
218.6 (e)	Determination of dissolved hexavalent chromium in drinking water, groundwater, and industrial wastewater effluents by ion chromatography
219.1 (a)	Cobalt FLAA
219.2 (a)	Cobalt GFAA

Continued on next page.

---

[76] (a) *Methods for Chemical Analysis of Water and Wastes* 1983 (EPA-600/4-79/020 PB84-128677); (b) *Methods for the determination of inorganic substances in environmental samples* 1993 (EPA 600/R-93/100); (c) *Methods for the determination of chemical substances in marine and estuarine environmental samples* (EPA/600/R-92/121), November 1992, and Second Edition EPA/600-R-97/072; (d) *Methods for the Determination of Metals in Environmental Samples*, 1991 (EPA 600/4-91/010); (e) *Methods for the Determination of Metals in Environmental Samples* Supplement I, 1994 (EPA-600/R-94/111); (f) *Analytical method for the determination of asbestos fibers in water*, September, 1983 NTIS PB83-260471; (g) *Determination of asbestos structure over 10 μm in length in drinking water*, June 1994, EPA 600/R-94-134, NTIS PB94-201902.

Table 1-18. EPA 100-400 series methods, *continued*

Method[77]	Title/Description
220.1 (a)	Copper FLAA
220.2 (a)	Copper GFAA
231.1 (a)	Gold FLAA
231.2 (a)	Gold GFAA
235.1 (a)	Iridium FLAA
235.2 (a)	Iridium GFAA
236.1 (a)	Iron FLAA
236.2 (a)	Iron GFAA
239.1 (a)	Lead FLAA
239.2 (a)	Lead GFAA
242.1 (a)	Magnesium FLAA
243.1 (a)	Manganese FLAA
243.2 (a)	Manganese GFAA
245.1 (e)	Determination of mercury in water by manual CVAA
245.2 (a)	Mercury by automated CVAA
245.3 (d)	Determination of inorganic mercury (II) and selected organomercurials in drinking and ground water by HPLC with electrochemical detection
245.5 (d)	Determination of mercury in sediment by CVAA
245.6 (d)	Determination of mercury in tissues by CVAA
245.7 (draft)	Mercury in water by cold vapor atomic fluorescence spectrometry
246.1 (a)	Molybdenum FLAA
246.2 (a)	Molybdenum GFAA
249.1 (a)	Nickel FLAA
249.2 (a)	Nickel GFAA
252.1 (a)	Osmium FLAA
252.2 (a)	Osmium GFAA
253.1 (a)	Palladium FLAA
253.2 (a)	Palladium GFAA
255.1 (a)	Platinum FLAA
255.2 (a)	Platinum GFAA
258.1 (a)	Potassium FLAA
264.1 (a)	Rhenium FLAA
264.2 (a)	Rhenium GFAA
265.1 (a)	Rhodium FLAA
265.2 (a)	Rhodium GFAA
267.1 (a)	Ruthenium FLAA
267.2 (a)	Ruthenium GFAA

Continued on next page.

[77] (a) *Methods for Chemical Analysis of Water and Wastes* 1983 (EPA-600/4-79/020 PB84-128677); (b) *Methods for the determination of inorganic substances in environmental samples* 1993 (EPA 600/R-93/100); (c) *Methods for the determination of chemical substances in marine and estuarine environmental samples* (EPA/600/R-92/121), November 1992; (d) *Methods for the Determination of Metals in Environmental Samples*, 1991 (EPA 600/4-91/010); (e) *Methods for the Determination of Metals in Environmental Samples* Supplement I, 1994 (EPA-600/R-94/111); (f) *Analytical method for the determination of asbestos fibers in water*, September, 1983 NTIS PB83-260471; (g) *Determination of asbestos structure over 10 μm in length in drinking water*, June 1994, EPA 600/R-94-134, NTIS PB94-201902.

Table 1-18. EPA 100-400 series methods, *continued*

Method[78]	Title/Description
270.2 (a)	Selenium GFAA
270.3 (a)	Selenium hydride
272.1 (a)	Silver FLAA
272.2 (a)	Silver GFAA
273.1 (a)	Sodium FLAA
273.2 (a)	Sodium GFAA
279.1 (a)	Thallium FLAA
279.2 (a)	Thallium GFAA
282.1 (a)	Tin FLAA
282.2 (a)	Tin GFAA
283.1 (a)	Titanium FLAA
283.2 (a)	Titanium GFAA
286.1 (a)	Vanadium FLAA
286.2 (a)	Vanadium GFAA
289.1 (a)	Zinc FLAA
289.2 (a)	Zinc GFAA
300.0 (b)	Ion chromatography of anions
300.1 (h)	Determination of inorganic anions in drinking water by ion chromatography
305.1 (a)	Acidity
310.1 (a)	Alkalinity titrimetric
310.2 (a)	Alkalinity automated colorimetric
320.1 (a)	Bromide titrimetric
321.8	Determination of bromate in drinking water by ion chromatography-ICP-MS (www.epa.gov/ogwdw)
325.1 (a)	Chloride automated ferricyanide I
325.2 (a)	Chloride automated ferrocyanide II
325.3 (a)	Chloride mercuric nitrate titration
330.1 (a)	Chlorine amperometric titration
330.2 (a)	Chlorine back-iodometric titration
330.3 (a)	Chlorine iodometric titration
330.4 (a)	Chlorine DPD-FAS titration
330.5 (a)	Chlorine DPD colorimetric
335.1 (a)	Cyanide amenable to chlorination
335.2 (a)	Total cyanide, titrimetric spectrophotometric
335.3 (a)	Total cyanide automated UV colorimetric
335.4 (b)	Total cyanide semi-automated colorimetry
340.1 (a)	Fluoride SPADNS

Continued on next page.

---

[78]   (a) *Methods for Chemical Analysis of Water and Wastes* 1983 (EPA-600/4-79/020 PB84-128677); (b) *Methods for the determination of inorganic substances in environmental samples* 1993 (EPA 600/R-93/100); (c) *Methods for the determination of chemical substances in marine and estuarine environmental samples* (EPA/600/R-92/121), November 1992; (d) *Methods for the Determination of Metals in Environmental Samples*, 1991 (EPA 600/4-91/010); (e) *Methods for the Determination of Metals in Environmental Samples* Supplement I, 1994 (EPA-600/R-94/111); (f) *Analytical method for the determination of asbestos fibers in water*, September, 1983 NTIS PB83-260471; (g) *Determination of asbestos structure over 10 μm in length in drinking water*, June 1994, EPA 600/R-94-134, NTIS PB94-201902; (h) www.epa.gov\ogwdw.

Table 1-18. EPA 100-400 series methods, *continued*

Method[79]	Title/Description
340.2 (a)	Fluoride ion selective electrode
340.3 (a)	Fluoride automated complexone
345.1 (a)	Iodine titration
349.0 (c)	Ammonia in estuarine and coastal waters by gas segmented continuous flow colorimetric analysis
350.1 (b)	Ammonia semi-automated colorimetry
350.2 (a)	Ammonia distillation with titration, colorimetric or electrode
350.3 (a)	Ammonia electrode
351.1 (b)	TKN semi-automated phenate
351.2 (a)	TKN Block digester AAII colorimetric
351.3 (a)	TKN colorimetric, titrimetric, potentiometric
351.4 (a)	TKN ion selective electrode
352.1 (a)	Nitrate brucine sulfate
353.1 (a)	Nitrate-nitrite automated hydrazine reduction
353.2 (b)	Nitrate-nitrite automated cadmium reduction colorimetry
353.3 (a)	Nitrate-nitrite manual cadmium reduction colorimetry
353.4 (c)	Nitrate-nitrite in estuarine and coastal waters by automated colorimetric analysis
354.1 (a)	Nitrite colorimetric
360.1 (a)	Oxygen membrane electrode
360.2 (a)	Oxygen modified Winkler titration
365.1 (b)	Phosphorus automated ascorbic acid
365.2 (a)	Phosphorus ascorbic acid single reagent
365.3 (a)	Phosphorus ascorbic acid two reagent
365.4 (a)	Phosphorus automated block digester AAII colorimetric
365.5 (c)	Orthophosphate in estuarine and coastal waters by automated colorimetry
366.0 (c)	Dissolved silicate in estuarine and coastal waters by automated colorimetry
370.1 (a)	Silica colorimetric
375.1 (a)	Sulfate automated chloranilate colorimetric
375.2 (b)	Sulfate automated methyl thymol blue
374.3 (a)	Sulfate gravimetric
375.4 (a)	Sulfate turbidimetric
376.1 (a)	Sulfide iodine titrimetric
376.2 (a)	Sulfide methylene blue colorimetric
377.1 (a)	Sulfite titrimetric
405.1 (a)	Biochemical oxygen demand (BOD)
410.1 (a)	Chemical oxygen demand (COD) mid-level titrimetric
410.2 (a)	COD low level titrimetric

Continued on next page.

[79] (a) *Methods for Chemical Analysis of Water and Wastes* 1983 (EPA-600/4-79/020 PB84-128677); (b) *Methods for the determination of inorganic substances in environmental samples* 1993 (EPA 600/R-93/100); (c) *Methods for the determination of chemical substances in marine and estuarine environmental samples* (EPA/600/R-92/121), November 1992, and Second Edition EPA/600-R-97/072; (d) *Methods for the Determination of Metals in Environmental Samples,* 1991 (EPA 600/4-91/010); (e) *Methods for the Determination of Metals in Environmental Samples* Supplement I, 1994 (EPA-600/R-94/111); (f) *Analytical method for the determination of asbestos fibers in water,* September, 1983 NTIS PB83-260471; (g) *Determination of asbestos structure over 10 μm in length in drinking water,* June 1994, EPA 600/R-94-134, NTIS PB94-201902.

Table 1-18. EPA 100-400 series methods, *continued*

Method[80]	Title/Description
410.3 (a)	COD high level titrimetric
410.4 (a)	COD automated or manual colorimetry
413.1 (a)	Oil and grease gravimetric
413.2 (a)	Oil and grease infrared
415.1 (a)	Total organic carbon (TOC) combustion or oxidation
415.2 (a)	TOC UV-persulfate oxidation
418.1 (a)	Total petroleum hydrocarbons extraction infrared
420.1 (a)	Total phenolics manual 4-AAP
420.2 (a)	Total phenolics automated 4-AAP
420.3 (a)	Total phenolics MBTH colorimetric
420.4 (b)	Total phenolics semi-automated colorimetry
425.1 (a)	MBAS surfactants
430.1 (a)	NTA manual zinc-zincon
430.2 (a)	NTA automated zinc-zincon
440.0 (c)	Carbon and nitrogen in estuarine/coastal sediments using elemental analysis
445.0 (c)	Chlorophyll ∂ and Pheophytin ∂ in marine and freshwater phytoplankton by fluorescence
446.0 (c)	Chlorophylls and pheopigments in algae by visible spectrometry
447.0 (c)	Chlorophylls and other pigments in algae using HPLC with visible wavelength detection

Methods Series 500-555

Methods for the Determination of Organic Compounds in Drinking Water (EPA-600/4-88/039) 1988, Supplement I (EPA 600/4-90/020) 1990, Supplement II (EPA 600/R-92/129) 1992, and Supplement III (EPA 600/R-95/131) 1995.

Table 1-19. EPA 500 series methods

Method[81]	Revision	Title
502.1 (a)	2.0	Volatile organic compounds in water by purge and trap GC
502.2 (d)	2.1	Volatile organic compounds in water by purge and trap capillary column gas chromatography with photoionization and electrolytic conductivity detectors in series
503.1 (a)	2.0	Volatile aromatic and unsaturated organic compounds in water by purge and trap GC

Continued on next page.

---

[80] (a) *Methods for Chemical Analysis of Water and Wastes* 1983 (EPA-600/4-79/020 PB84-128677); (b) *Methods for the determination of inorganic substances in environmental samples* 1993 (EPA 600/R-93/100); (c) *Methods for the determination of chemical substances in marine and estuarine environmental samples* (EPA/600/R-92/121), November 1992, and Second Edition EPA/600-R-97/072; (d) *Methods for the Determination of Metals in Environmental Samples*, 1991 (EPA 600/4-91/010); (e) *Methods for the Determination of Metals in Environmental Samples* Supplement I, 1994 (EPA-600/R-94/111); (f) *Analytical method for the determination of asbestos fibers in water*, September, 1983 NTIS PB83-260471; (g) *Determination of asbestos structure over 10 μm in length in drinking water*, June 1994, EPA 600/R-94-134, NTIS PB94-201902.

[81] (a) *Methods for the Determination of Organic Compounds in Drinking Water* (EPA-600/4-88/039) 1988; (b) Supplement I (EPA 600/4-90/020) 1990; (c) Supplement II (EPA 600/R-92/129) 1992; and (d) Supplement III (EPA 600/R-95/131) 1995.

Table 1-19. EPA 500 series methods, *continued*

Method[82]	Revision	Title
504 (a)	2.0	1,2-dibromoethane (EDB) and 1,2-dibromo-3-chloropropane (DBCP) in water by microextraction and GC
504.1 (d)	1.1	1,2-dibromoethane (EDB), 1,2-dibromo-3-chloropropane (DBCP) and 1,2,3-trichloropropane (123TCP) in water by microextraction and gas chromatography
505 (d)	2.1	Analysis of organohalide pesticides and commercial polychlorinated biphenyl (PCB) products in water by microextraction and gas chromatography
506 (d)	1.1	Determination of phthalate and adipate esters in drinking water by liquid-liquid extraction or liquid-solid extraction and gas chromatography with photoionization detection
507 (d)	2.1	Determination of nitrogen- and phosphorus-containing pesticides in water by gas chromatography with a nitrogen-phosphorus detector
508 (d)	3.1	Determination of chlorinated pesticides in water by gas chromatography with an electron capture detector
508.1 (d)	2.0	Determination of chlorinated pesticides, herbicides, and organohalides by liquid-solid extraction and electron capture gas chromatography
508A (a)	1.0	Screening for polychlorinated biphenyls by perchlorination and GC
509 (d)	1.1	Determination of ethylene thiourea (ETU) in water using gas chromatography with a nitrogen-phosphorus detector
513 (b)	1	Determination of 2,3,7,8-tetrachloro-dibenzo-p-dioxin in drinking water by liquid-liquid extraction and GC with high resolution MS
515.1 (d)	4.1	Determination of chlorinated acids in water by gas chromatography with an electron capture detector
515.2 (d)	1.1	Determination of chlorinated acids in water using liquid-solid extraction and gas chromatography with an electron capture detector
515.3 (e)	1.0	Determination of chlorinated acids in drinking water by liquid-liquid extraction, derivatization and GC with ECD
524.2 (d)	4.1	Measurement of purgeable organic compounds in water by capillary column gas chromatography/mass spectrometry
525.2 (d)	2.0	Determination of organic compounds in drinking water by liquid-solid extraction and capillary column gas chromatography/mass spectrometry
531.1 (d)	3.1	Measurement of N-methylcarbamoyloximes and N-methylcarbamates in water by direct aqueous injection HPLC with post column derivatization
547 (b)	1	Determination of glyphosate in drinking water by direct aqueous injection HPLC, post-column derivatization and fluorescence detection
548 (b)	1	Determination of endothall in drinking water by aqueous derivatization, liquid-solid extraction and GC with ECD
548.1 (c)	1.0	Determination of endothall in drinking water by ion exchange extraction, acidic methanol methylation and GC/MS
549 (b)	1	Determination of diquat and paraquat in drinking water by liquid-solid extraction and HPLC with ultraviolet detection
549.1 (c)	1.0	Determination of diquat and paraquat in drinking water by liquid-solid extraction and HPLC with ultraviolet detector
550 (b)	1	Determination of polycyclic aromatic hydrocarbons in drinking water by liquid-liquid extraction and HPLC with coupled ultraviolet and fluorescence detection

Continued on next page.

[82]   (a) *Methods for the Determination of Organic Compounds in Drinking Water* (EPA-600/4-88/039) 1988; (b) Supplement I (EPA 600/4-90/020) 1990; (c) Supplement II (EPA 600/R-92/129) 1992; and (d) Supplement III (EPA 600/R-95/131) 1995; (e) www.epa.gov/ogwdw.

Table 1-19. EPA 500 series methods, *continued*

Method[83]	Revision	Title
550.1 (b)	1	Determination of polycyclic aromatic hydrocarbons in drinking water by liquid-liquid extraction and HPLC with coupled ultraviolet and fluorescence detection
551 (b)	1	Determination of chlorination disinfection byproducts and chlorinated solvents in drinking water by liquid-liquid extraction and GC with ECD
551.1 (d)	1.0	Determination of chlorination disinfection byproducts, chlorinated solvents and halogenated pesticides/herbicides in drinking water by liquid-liquid extraction and GC with ECD
552 (b)	1	Determination of haloacetic acids in drinking water by liquid-liquid extraction, derivatization and GC with ECD
552.2 (d)	1.0	Determination of haloacetic acids and dalapon in drinking water by liquid-liquid extraction and GC with ECD
553 (c)	1.1	Determination of benzidines and nitrogen-containing pesticides in water by liquid-liquid extraction or liquid-solid extraction and reversed phase high performance liquid chromatography/particle beam/mass specrometry
554 (c)	1.0	Determination of carbonyl compounds in drinking water by DNPH derivatization and high performance liquid chromatography
555 (c)	1.0	Determination of chlorinated acids in water by high performance liquid chromatography with a photodiode array ultraviolet detector
556	1.0[84]	Determination of carbonyl compounds in drinking water by pentafluorobenzylhydroxylamine derivation and capillary gas chromatography with ECD

Methods Series 600's (developed by EMSL Cincinnati) and 1600's (developed by ORD/OST)

Guidelines Establishing Test Procedures for the Analysis of Pollutants (in Water) (40 CFR - Part 136, Appendix A), *Methods for the Determination of Nonconventional Pesticides in Municipal and Industrial Wastewater* (EPA 821 RR-92-002) 1992, *Analytical Methods for the Determination of Pollutants in Pulp and Paper Industry Wastewater*, EPA 821-R-93-017 (PB94-107059), October 1993; *Analytical Methods for the Determination of Pollutants in Pharmaceutical Manufacturing Industry Wastewater* (EPA-821-94-001) February, 1995.

Table 1-20. EPA 600 series methods

Method[85]	Title/Description
601 (a)	Purgeable halocarbons by purge and trap GC-ELCD
602 (a)	Purgeable aromatics by purge and trap GC-PID
603 (a)	Acrolein and Acrylonitrile by purge and trap GC-FID
604 (a)	Phenold by GC-FID

Continued on next page.

---

[83] (a) *Methods for the Determination of Organic Compounds in Drinking Water* (EPA-600/4-88/039) 1988; (b) Supplement I (EPA 600/4-90/020) 1990; (c) Supplement II (EPA 600/R-92/129) 1992; and (d) Supplement III (EPA 600/R-95/131) 1995; (e) www.epa.gov/ogwdw.

[84] Available at www.epa.gov/ogwdw/met556.html

[85] (a) 40 CFR 136, Appendix A; (b) *Methods for the Determination of Nonconventional Pesticides in Municipal and Industrial Wastewater* (EPA 821 RR-92-002) 1992; (c) *Analytical Methods for the Determination of Pollutants in Pulp and Paper Industry Wastewater*, EPA 821-R-93-017 (PB94-107059), October, 1993; (d) *Analytical Methods for the Determination of Pollutants in Pharmaceutical Manufacturing Industry Wastewater* (EPA-821-94-001) February, 1995.

Table 1-20. EPA 600 series methods, *continued*

Method[86]	Title/Description
604.1 (b)	Hexachlorophene and dichlorophen by HPLC
605 (a)	Benzidines by HPLC
606 (a)	Phthalate esters by GC-ECD
607 (a)	Nitrosamines by GC-NPD
608 (a)	Organochlorine pesticides by GC-ECD
608.1 (b)	Organochlorine pesticides by GC
608.2 (b)	Certain organochlorine pesticides and PCBs by GC
609 (a)	Nitroaromatics and isophorone by GC-FID and GC-ECD
610 (a)	Polynuclear aromatic hydrocarbons by GC or HPLC
611 (a)	Haloethers by GC-ECD or ELCD
612 (a)	Chlorinated hydrocarbons by GC-ECD
613 (b)	2,3,7,8-TCDD by HRGC-HRMS Revision B, 1994 EPA 821-B-94-005
614 (b)	Organophosphorus pesticides by GC-NPD or FPD
614.1 (b)	Organophosphorus pesticides by GC-NPD
615 (b)	Chlorinated herbicides by GC-ECD
616 (b)	Certain carbon-, hydrogen- and oxygen containing pesticides by GC-FID
617 (b)	Organochlorine pesticides and PCBs by GC-ECD
618 (b)	Volatile pesticides by GC-ECD
619 (b)	Triazine pesticides by GC-NPD
620 (b)	Diphenylamine by GC-AFD (Alkali flame detector)
622 (b)	Organophosphorus pesticides by GC-NPD or FPD
622.1 (b)	Thiophosphate pesticides by GC-AFD
624 (a)	Purgeables by purge and trap GC/MS
625 (a)	Base/neutrals and acids by GC/MS
627 (b)	Dinitroaniline pesticides by GC-ECD
629 (b)	Cyanazine by HPLC
630 (b)	Dithiocarbamate pesticides by carbon disulfide colorimetry
630.1 (b)	Dithiocarbamate pesticides by detection of carbon disulfide by GC-sulfur mode ELCD
631 (b)	Benomyl and Carbendazim by HPLC
632 (b)	Carbamate and urea pesticides by HPLC-UV
632.1 (b)	Carbamate and amide pesticides by HPLC-UV
633 (b)	Organonitrogen pesticides by GC-NPD
633.1 (b)	Neutral nitrogen-containing pesticides by GC-AFD
634 (b)	Thiocarbate pesticides by GC-AFD
635 (b)	Rotenone by HPLC
636 (b)	Bensulfide by HPLC
637 (b)	MBTS and TCMTB by HPLC
638 (b)	Oryzalin by HPLC
639 (b)	Bendiocarb by HPLC

Continued on next page.

---

[86] (a) 40 CFR 136, Appendix A; (b) *Methods for the Determination of Nonconventional Pesticides in Municipal and Industrial Wastewater* (EPA 821 RR-92-002) 1992; (c) *Analytical Methods for the Determination of Pollutants in Pulp and Paper Industry Wastewater*, EPA 821-R-93-017 (PB94-107059), October, 1993; (d) *Analytical Methods for the Determination of Pollutants in Pharmaceutical Manufacturing Industry Wastewater* (EPA-821-94-001) February, 1995.

Table 1-20. EPA 600 series methods, *continued*

Method[87]	Title/Description
640 (b)	Mercaptobenzothiazole by HPLC
641 (b)	Thiabendazole by HPLC-fluorescence detection
642 (b)	Biphenyl and *o*-phenylphenol by HPLC-UV
643 (b)	Bentazon by HPLC
644 (b)	Pichloram by HPLC
645 (b)	Certain amine pesticides and lethane by GC-NPD
646 (b)	Dinitro aromatic pesticides by GC-ECD
EV-024/EV-025 (b)	Total tin and organotin in wastewater

Table 1-21. EPA 1600 series methods

Method[88]	Title/Description
1600[89]	Membrane filter test method for Enterococci in water
1613 rev. B	Tetra- through octa-chlorinated dioxins and furans by isotope dilution HRGC/HRMS, EPA 821-B-94-005, October 1994, see also 1622
1618 (e)	Organohalide pesticides, organophosphorus pesticides and phenoxyacid herbicides by wide bore capillary GC with selective detectors
1620 (e)	Metals by ICP-AES and AA spectrometry
1622[90]	Cryptosporidium in water by filtration/IMS/FA
1624 (a)	Volatile organic compounds by isotope dilution GC/MS
1624C (e)	Volatile organic compounds by isotope dilution GC/MS
1625 (a)	Semivolatile organic compounds by isotope dilution GC/MS
1625C (e)	Semivolatile organic compounds by isotope dilution GC/MS
1631	Mercury in water by oxidation, purge and trap, and cold vapor atomic fluorescence spectrometry EPA 821-R-95-027, April 1995
1632	Determination of inorganic arsenic in water by hydride generation flame atomic absorption EPA 821-R-95-028 April 1995
1636	Determination of hexavalent chromium by ion chromatography EPA 821-R-95-029 April 1995

Continued on next page.

---

[87] (a) 40 CFR 136, Appendix A; (b) *Methods for the Determination of Nonconventional Pesticides in Municipal and Industrial Wastewater* (EPA 821 RR-92-002) 1992; (c) *Analytical Methods for the Determination of Pollutants in Pulp and Paper Industry Wastewater*, EPA 821-R-93-017 (PB94-107059), October, 1993; (d) *Analytical Methods for the Determination of Pollutants in Pharmaceutical Manufacturing Industry Wastewater* (EPA-821-94-001) February, 1995.

[88] (a) 40 CFR 136, Appendix A; (b) *Methods for the Determination of Nonconventional Pesticides in Municipal and Industrial Wastewater* (EPA 821 RR-92-002) 1992; (c) *Analytical Methods for the Determination of Pollutants in Pulp and Paper Industry Wastewater*, EPA 821-R-93-017 (PB94-107059), October, 1993; (d) *Analytical Methods for the Determination of Pollutants in Pharmaceutical Manufacturing Industry Wastewater* (EPA-821-94-001) February, 1995; (e) *Analytical Methods for the National Sewage Sludge Survey*, Office of Water WH-585, September, 1990; (f) *Methods for the determination of diesel, mineral, and crude oils in offshore oil and gas industry discharges*, December, 1992, EPA 821-R-92-008, PB 93-166932; (g) *Compendium of Chemical and Biological Biosolid Methods*, EPA 1998 draft.

[89] Available at www.epa.gov/ost/methods

[90] Available at www.epa.gov/ost/methods

Table 1-21. EPA 1600 series methods, *continued*

Method[91]	Title/Description
1637	Determination of trace elements in ambient waters by chelation preconcentration with graphite furnace atomic absorption EPA 821-R-95-030, April 1995
1638	Determination of trace elements in ambient waters by inductively coupled plasma-mass spectrometry EPA 821-R-95-031, April 1995
1639	Determination of trace elements in ambient waters by stabilized temperature graphite furnace atomic absorption EPA 821-R-95-032 April 1995
1640	Determination of trace elements in ambient waters by on-line chelation preconcentration and inductively coupled plasma-mass spectrometry EPA 821-R-95-033, April 1995
1650 (c)	Absorbable organic halides by adsorption and coulometric titration
1651 rev A (f)	Total oil and diesel oil in drilling muds and drill cuttings by retort, gavimetry, and GC/FID
1653 (c)	Chlorinated phenolics in wastewater by *in situ* acetylation and GC-MS
1654 rev A (f)	PAH content of oil by HPLC/UV
1656 (b)	Organohalide pesticides by GC
1657 (b)	Organophosphorus pesticides by GC-FPD
1658 (b)	Phenoxy-acid herbicides by GC-ECD
1659 (b)	Dazomet by GC-NPD
1660 (b)	Pyrethrins and pyrethroids by HPLC-UV
1661 (b)	Bromoxynil by HPLC-UV
1662 (f)	Total extractable material in drilling mud by SDS extraction and gravimetry
1663 (f)	Differentiation of diesel and crude oil by GC/FID
1664	*N*-hexane extractable material (HEM) and silica gel treated *n*-hexane extractable material (SGT-HEM) by extraction and gravimetry (oil and grease and total petroleum hydrocarbons) EPA-821-B-94-004b, April 1995
1665 (d)	Semi-volatile organic compounds specific to the pharmaceutical manufacturing industry by isotope dilution GC/MS
1666 (d)	Volatile organic compounds specific to the pharmaceutical manufacturing industry by isotope dilution GC/MS
1667 (d)	Formaldehyde, isobutyraldehyde, and furfural by derivatization and high-pressure liquid chromatography
1668 (g)	Toxic PCDs in sludge (draft)
1669	Sampling ambient water for determination of trace metals at EPA water quality criteria levels and Quality Control Supplement for Determination of Trace Metals at EPA Water Quality Criteria Levels using EPA Metals Methods. EPA 821-R-95-034, April 1995
1671 (d)	Volatile organic compounds specific to the pharmaceutical manufacturing industry by GC/FID
1673 (d)	Poly(ethylene glycol)-600 by derivatization and high-pressure liquid chromatography

Continued on next page.

[91] (a) 40 CFR 136, Appendix A; (b) *Methods for the Determination of Nonconventional Pesticides in Municipal and Industrial Wastewater* (EPA 821 RR-92-002) 1992; (c) *Analytical Methods for the Determination of Pollutants in Pulp and Paper Industry Wastewater*, EPA 821-R-93-017 (PB94-107059), October, 1993; (d) *Analytical Methods for the Determination of Pollutants in Pharmaceutical Manufacturing Industry Wastewater* (EPA-821-94-001) February, 1995; (e) *Analytical Methods for the National Sewage Sludge Survey*, Office of Water WH-585, September, 1990; (f) *Methods for the determination of diesel, mineral, and crude oils in offshore oil and gas industry discharges*, December, 1992, EPA 821-R-92-008, PB 93-166932; (g) *Compendium of Chemical and Biological Biosolid Methods*, EPA 1998 draft.

Table 1-21. EPA 1600 series methods, *continued*

Method[92]	Title/Description
1677[93]	Available cyanide by flow injection with ligand exchange
1679 (g)	Enteric viruses in sludge (draft)
1680 (g)	Fecal coliform in sludge (draft)
1681 (g)	Helminth ova in sludge (draft)
1682 (g)	Salmonella in sludge (draft)
1683 (g)	SOUR on sludge (draft)
1684 (g)	Total, fixed, and volatile solids on sludge (draft)
1685 (g)	Nitrate/nitrite-N in sludge by automated photometry (draft)
1686 (g)	Nitrate/nitrite-N in sludge by manual colorimetry (draft)
1687 (g)	Total Kjeldahl nitrogen in sludge by automated colorimetry with preliminary distillation/digestion (draft)
1688 (g)	Total Kjeldahl nitrogen in sludge by block digestion and automated analysis (draft)
1689 (g)	Ammonia-N in sludge by ion-selective electrode potentiometry with preliminary distillation (draft)
1690 (g)	Ammonia-N in sludge by automated colorimetry with preliminary distillation (draft)
1691 (g)	Sampling guidance for sludge (draft)

Methods Series 900's

Prescribed Procedures for Measurement of Radioactivity in Drinking Water (EPA-600/4-80-032) 1980.

Table 1-22. EPA 900 series methods

Method	Title/Description
900.0	Gross alpha and gross beta radioactivity
900.1	Gross radium alpha screening procedure
901.0	Radioactive cesium
901.1	Gamma emitting radionuclides
902.0	Radioactive iodine
903.0	Alpha-emitting radium isotopes
903.1	Radium-226 Radon emanation technique
904.0	Radium-228
905.0	Radioactive strontium
906.0	Tritium
907.0	Actinide elements
908.0	Uranium - Radiochemical method
908.1	Uranium - Fluorometric method

---

[92] (a) 40 CFR 136, Appendix A; (b) *Methods for the Determination of Nonconventional Pesticides in Municipal and Industrial Wastewater* (EPA 821 RR-92-002) 1992; (c) *Analytical Methods for the Determination of Pollutants in Pulp and Paper Industry Wastewater*, EPA 821-R-93-017 (PB94-107059), October, 1993; (d) *Analytical Methods for the Determination of Pollutants in Pharmaceutical Manufacturing Industry Wastewater* (EPA-821-94-001) February, 1995; (e) *Analytical Methods for the National Sewage Sludge Survey*, Office of Water WH-585, September, 1990; (f) *Methods for the determination of diesel, mineral, and crude oils in offshore oil and gas industry discharges*, December, 1992, EPA 821-R-92-008, PB 93-166932; (g) *Compendium of Chemical and Biological Biosolid Methods*, EPA 1998 draft.

[93] Available at www.epa.gov/ost/methods

Methods Series 1000's

A set of microbiological and toxicity procedures used for compliance monitoring under the Clean Water Act. Reference documents include those listed in the footnotes to Table 1-23.

Table 1-23. EPA 1000 series methods for WET compliance monitoring

Method[94]	Title
1000.0 (a)	Fathead minnow, *Pimephales promelas*, larval survival and growth test method
1001.0 (a)	Fathead minnow, *Pimephales promelas,* embryo-larval survival and teratogenicity test method
1002.0 (a)	Daphnid, *Ceriodaphnia dubia*, survival and reproduction test method
1003.0 (a)	Green alga, *Selenastrum Capricornutum*, growth test method
1004.0 (b)	Sheepshead minnow, *Cyprinodon variegatus*, larval survival and growth test method
1005.0 (b)	Sheepshead minnow, *Cyprinodon variegatus*, embryo-larval survival and teratogenicity test method
1006.0 (b)	Inland silverside, *Menidia beryllina*, larval survival and growth method
1007.0 (b)	Mysid, *Mysidopsis bahia*, survival, growth and fecundity test method
1008.0 (b)	Sea urchin, *Arbacia punctulata*, fertilization test method
1009.0 (b)	Red macroalga, *Champia parvula*, reproduction test method
1103.1 (c)	Test method for *Escherichia coli* in water by the membrane filter procedure
1106.1 (c)	Test method for *Enterococci* in water by the membrane filter procedure

Methods Series 0000-9999

Test Methods for Evaluating Solid Wastes Physical/Chemical Methods, or as it is commonly called, SW-846, is the testing manual for RCRA. The third edition was proposed in 1986, with draft updates published in 1987 and 1990. These draft updates oriented SW-846 toward the prescriptive analysis and stringent reporting formats of the Contract Laboratory Program Statement of Work (CLP-SOW), which was during this time the darling of the environmental industry and the EPA. Chapter 1, Quality Control, even went so far as to reproduce the CLP reporting forms as the standard for reporting RCRA data. A guidance manual was prepared and distributed that presented the legal formalisms in the CLP requirements as the desired model for the RCRA program[95], and participating laboratories.

In 1990-1991 a major philosophical change occurred in the Analytical Methods Section of the Solid Waste Program. The decision was made to present SW-846 as analytical guidance rather than prescriptive methods of analysis. This meant that the draft updates of 1987 and 1990 had to be abandoned and new updates written. Promulgation of the third edition, which incorporated this shift in emphasis, did not occur until July, 1993. In the same final notice, the 1987 and 1990 draft updates were officially scrapped by the Office of Solid Waste in favor of promulgating a completely new Update 1, dated

---

[94] (a) *Short-term Methods for Estimating the Chronic Toxicity of Effluents and Receiving Water to Freshwater Organisms*, Third Edition, July, 1994. EPA-600-4-91-002; (b) *Short-term Methods for Estimating the Chronic Toxicity of Effluents and Receiving Water to Marine and Estuarine Organisms*, Second Edition, July, 1994 EPA-600-4-91-003; (c) *Test methods for Eschericia coli and Enterococci in Water by the Membrane Filter Procedure*, EPA 600/4-85-076 1985, NTIS PB86-158052.

[95] *RCRA Laboratory Audit Inspection Guidance Document*, USEPA September, 1988

July 1992. On 13 February, 1995, EPA announced in the *Federal Register* the promulgation of Updates II and IIa, with the date of September, 1994 on the pages. On 13 June, 1997, Update III to SW-846 was promulgated, with a date of December, 1996 on the pages of the update.

Update III presents a watershed change in analysis conducted under the Solid Waste program. For the first time methods are deleted from SW-846. For the most part the deleted methods are out-dated technology that most practitioners had abandoned years ago, such as the use of packed-columns in GC determinations. Thus Methods 8010B, 8020A, 8030A, 8040A, 8060, 8080A, 8090, 8110, 8120A, 8140, 8150B, 8240B, and 8250A were deleted. Existing versions of these methods that specify the use of capillary columns, for example. 8021B, 8141A, 8151A, 8260B, and 8270C, were updated and promulgated. More was in store for Method 8080, Determination of Chlorinated Pesticides and PCB, than a simple change of separation column. It was split into a Method for chlorinated pesticides by GC (Method 8081A) and a separate Method for PCB (Method 8082). The deletions were not limited to outdated organic methods. Method 9200 (nitrate by brucine sulfate colorimetry) and 9252A (chloride by mercuric nitrate titration) were dropped. The cyanide and sulfide methods, 9010 and 9030, were split into sample preparation (distillation) procedures, 9010B and 9030B, and determinative methods, 9014 and 9034. Update III introduced a major new method into SW-846 for the preparation of solid samples for volatile organic analysis (5035), in addition to many other new procedures.

Draft update IVA was distributed to subscribers during the latter part of Summer, 1998. Analytically the major change is consolidation of the myriad direct aspiration atomic absorption (FLAA) and graphite furnace atomic absorption (GFAA) methods into generic FLAA (7000B) and GFAA (7010) procedures, with simultaneous deletions of the individual FLAA and GFAA methods. For example the FLAA method for aluminum, 7020, and the GFAA method for lead, 7421, are gone. The Analytical Methods Sections is also proposing to not promulgate Update IV and future updates to SW-846. To support this move, the Solid Waste regulations are being revised to delete any regulatory requirement to specifically use methods in SW-846. This revision is called the Dereg-reg, as it deregulates existing regulations requiring mandatory use of SW-846.

The layout of SW-846 is by Chapters, such as Chapter 3 for metals, Chapter 4 for organics, etc. With few exceptions the methods are modular, with one method relating to the sample preparation, another method relating to sample clean-up, and a final method describing the determinative (instrument) operating procedures. In addition there are general methods that describe in broad strokes techniques to be used in all methods. For example Method 3500B is a complete description of organic surrogates, and Method 8000B discusses the calibration options and variations for organic determinative methods. Table 1-24 presents the general numbering scheme of SW-846, while Table 1-25 presents a detailed list of the contents by Method number.

Table 1-24. General numbering scheme of *Test Methods for Evaluating Solid Wastes Physical/Chemical Methods* **(SW-846, 3rd Edition, Revisions I through IV)**

Method	Title
0000's	Air Sampling Methods
1000's	Determination of Hazardous Characteristics
2000's	(Unused)
3000's	Sample Preparation Methods
30xx's	Sample Preparation for Metals Analysis
35xx's	Sample Extraction for Organic Analysis
36xx's	Sample Cleanup for Organic Analysis
38xx's	Volatile Organic Screening Methods
4000's	Field Screening Methods
5000's	Volatile and Miscellaneous Sample Preparation Methods
6000's	Multi-metal Instrumental Determinations
7000's	Single-metal Instrumental Determinations
8000's	Determination of Organic Analytes
80xx-81xx's	GC
82xx's	GC-MS
83xx's	HPLC
8400's	GC-FTIR
9000's	Miscellaneous Test Methods
90xx-92xx's	Miscellaneous Analytes
93xx's	Radioisotopes

Table 1-25. Contents of SW-846 including the proposed Update IV to the Third Edition

0010	Modified method 5 sampling train
0011	Sampling for formaldehyde emissions from stationary sources
0020	Source assessment sampling system (SASS)
0023A	Sampling method for dioxins and furans from stationary sources
0030	Volatile organic sampling train (VOST)
0031	Sampling method for volatile organic compounds (SMVOC)
0040	Sampling of principal organic hazardous constituents from combustion sources using Tedlar bags
0050	Isokenetic HCl/Cl$_2$ emission sampling train
0051	Midget impinger HCl/Cl$_2$ emission sampling train
0060	Determination of metals in stack emissions
0061	Determination of hexavalent chromium emissions from stationary sources
0100	Sampling for formaldehyde and other carbonyl compounds in indoor air
1010	Pensky-Martins closed cup method for determining ignitability
1020A	Setaflash closed cup method for determining ignitability
1030	Ignitability of solids
1110	Corrosivity toward steel
1120	Dermal corrosion

Continued on next page.

Table 1-25. Contents of SW-846 including the proposed Update IV to the Third Edition, *continued*

1310A	Extraction procedure (EP) toxicity test method and structural integrity test
1311	Toxic characteristic leaching procedure
1312	Synthetic precipitation leaching procedure
1320	Multiple extraction procedure
1330A	Extraction procedure for oily wastes
3005A	Acid digestion of waters for total recoverable or dissolved metals by FLAA or ICP
3010A	Acid digestion of aqueous samples and extracts for total metals for analysis by FLAA or ICP
3015	Microwave assisted acid digestion of aqueous samples and extracts (3015A in IVA)
3020A	Acid digestion of aqueous samples and extracts for total metals for analysis by GFAA
3031	Acid digestion of oils for metals analysis by FLAA or ICP
3040A	Dissolution procedure for oils, greases or waxes
3050B	Acid digestion of sediments, sludges, or soils
3051	Microwave assisted acid digestion of sediments, sludges, soils and oils (3051A in IVA)
3052	Microwave assisted acid digestion of siliceous and organically based matrices
3060A	Alkaline digestion for hexavalent chromium
3500B	Organic extraction and sample preparation
3510C	Separatory funnel liquid-liquid extraction
3520C	Continuous liquid-liquid extraction
3535	Solid phase extraction (SPE) (3535A in IVB)
3540C	Soxhlet extraction
3541	Automated soxhlet extraction
3542	Extraction of semivolatile analytes collected using modified method 5 (Method 0010) sampling train
3545	Accelerated solvent extraction (ASE) (3545A in IVB)
3550B	Ultrasonic extraction
3560	Supercritical fluid extraction of total recoverable petroleum hydrocarbons (TRPH)
3561	Supercritical fluid extraction of polynuclear aromatic hydrocarbons
3562	Supercritical fluid extraction of PCB and organochlorine pesticides (IVB)
3580A	Waste dilution
3585	Waste dilution for volatile organics
3600C	Cleanup
3610B	Alumina cleanup
3611B	Alumina column cleanup and separation of petroleum wastes
3620B	Florisil cleanup
3630C	Silica gel cleanup
3640A	Gel-permeation cleanup
3650B	Acid-base partition cleanup
3660B	Sulfur cleanup
3665A	Sulfuric acid/permanganate cleanup
3810	Headspace
3820	Hexadecane extraction and screening of purgeable organics
4000	Immunoassay
4010A	Screening for pentachlorophenol by immunoassay
4015	Screening for 2,4-D by immunoassay
4020	Screening for PCBs by immunoassay

Continued on next page.

Table 1-25. Contents of SW-846 including the proposed Update IV to the Third Edition, *continued*

4030	Soil screening for petroleum hydrocarbons by immunoassay
4035	Soil screening for PAH by immunoassay
4040	Soil screening for toxaphene by immunoassay
4041	Soil screening for chlordane by immunoassay
4042	Soil screening for DDT by immunoassay
4050	TNT explosives in water and soils by immunoassay
4051	RDX in soil and water by immunoassay
4500	Mercury in soil by immunoassay (Update IVA)
4670	Triazine herbicides by quantitative immunoassay (Update IVA)
5000	Sample preparation for volatile organic compounds
5021	Volatile organic compounds in soils and other solid matrices using equilibrium headspace
5030B	Purge and trap for aqueous samples
5031	Volatile, nonpurgeable, water-soluble compounds by azeotropic distillation
5032	Volatile organic compounds by vacuum distillation
5035	Closed system purge and trap and extraction for volatile organics in soil and waste samples
5041A	Analysis for desorption of sorbent cartridges from volatile organic sampling train (VOST): capillary GC/MS technique
5050	Bomb preparation method for solid waste
6010B	ICP-AES
6020	ICP-MS (6020A in Update IVA)
6200	Field portable X-ray fluorescence spectrometry (Update IVA)
6500	Inorganic anions by capillary ion electrophoresis (Update IVA)
6800	Elemental and speciated isotope dilution mass spectrometry (Update IVA)
7000A	AA Methods
7000B	FLAA Generic method (Update IVA)
7010	GFAA Generic method (Update IVA)
7020	Aluminum FLAA (deleted in draft Update IVA)
7040	Antimony FLAA (deleted in draft Update IVA)
7041	Antimony GFAA (deleted in draft Update IVA)
7060A	Arsenic GFAA (deleted in draft Update IVA)
7061A	Arsenic Hydride AA
7062	Antimony and Arsenic (Borohydride reduction AA)
7063	Arsenic by anodic stripping voltammetry (ASV)
7080A	Barium FLAA (deleted in draft Update IVA)
7081	Barium GFAA (deleted in draft Update IVA)
7090	Beryllium FLAA (deleted in draft Update IVA)
7091	Beryllium GFAA (deleted in draft Update IVA)
7130	Cadmium FLAA (deleted in draft Update IVA)
7131A	Cadmium GFAA (deleted in draft Update IVA)
7140	Calcium FLAA (deleted in draft Update IVA)
7190	Chromium FLAA (deleted in draft Update IVA)
7191	Chromium GFAA (deleted in draft Update IVA)
7195	Chromium, hexavalent (Coprecipitation)
7196A	Chromium, hexavalent (Colorimetric)
7197	Chromium, hexavalent (Chelation/extraction)

Continued on next page.

Table 1-25. Contents of SW-846 including the proposed Update IV to the Third Edition, *continued*

7198	Chromium, hexavalent (Differential pulse polarography)
7199	Determination of hexavalent chromium in drinking water, groundwater and industrial wastewater effluents by ion chromatography
7200	Cobalt FLAA (deleted in draft Update IVA)
7201	Cobalt GFAA (deleted in draft Update IVA)
7210	Copper FLAA (deleted in draft Update IVA)
7211	Copper GFAA (deleted in draft Update IVA)
7380	Iron FLAA (deleted in draft Update IVA)
7381	Iron GFAA (deleted in draft Update IVA)
7420	Lead FLAA (deleted in draft Update IVA)
7421	Lead GFAA (deleted in draft Update IVA)
7430	Lithium FLAA (deleted in draft Update IVA)
7450	Magnesium FLAA (deleted in draft Update IVA)
7460	Manganese FLAA (deleted in draft Update IVA)
7461	Manganese GFAA (deleted in draft Update IVA)
7470A	Mercury in liquid waste CVAA
7471A	Mercury in solid or semi-solid waste CVAA (7471B in Update IVA)
7472	Mercury in aqueous samples and extracts by anodic stripping voltammetry (ASV)
7473	Mercury by thermal decomposition, amalgamation and CVAA (Update IVA)
7474	Mercury by atomic fluorescence spectrometry (Update IVA)
7480	Molybdenum FLAA (deleted in draft Update IVA)
7481	Molybdenum GFAA (deleted in draft Update IVA)
7520	Nickel FLAA (deleted in draft Update IVA)
7521	Nickel GFAA (deleted in draft Update IVA)
7550	Osmium FLAA (deleted in draft Update IVA)
7580	White phosphorus by solvent extraction and gas chromatography
7610	Potassium FLAA (deleted in draft Update IVA)
7740	Selenium GFAA (deleted in draft Update IVA)
7741A	Selenium Hydride AA
7742	Selenium Borohydride reduction AA
7760A	Silver FLAA (deleted in draft Update IVA)
7761	Silver GFAA (deleted in draft Update IVA)
7770	Sodium FLAA (deleted in draft Update IVA)
7780	Strontium FLAA (deleted in draft Update IVA)
7840	Thallium FLAA (deleted in draft Update IVA)
7841	Thallium GFAA (deleted in draft Update IVA)
7870	Tin FLAA (deleted in draft Update IVA)
7910	Vanadium FLAA (deleted in draft Update IVA)
7911	Vanadium GFAA (deleted in draft Update IVA)
7950	Zinc FLAA (deleted in draft Update IVA)
7951	Zinc GFAA (deleted in draft Update IVA)
8000B	Determinative chromatographic separations
8011	EDB and DBCP by microextraction and GC
8015B	Nonhalogenated organics using GC/FID
8021B	Halogenated volatiles by GC using PID and ECD in series; capillary column technique

Continued on next page.

Table 1-25. Contents of SW-846 including the proposed Update IV to the Third Edition, *continued*

8031	Acrylonitrile by GC
8032A	Acrylamide by GC
8033	Acetonitrile by GC-NPD
8041	Phenols by GC: capillary column technique
8061A	Phthalate esters by capillary GC-ECD
8070A	Nitrosamines by GC
8081A	Organochlorine pesticides by capillary column GC (8081B in Update IVB)
8082	PCB by capillary GC (8082A in Update IVB)
8085	Pesticides by GC-AED (draft)
8091	Nitroaromatics and cyclic ketones: capillary column technique
8095	Explosives by GC (draft)
8100	Polynuclear aromatic hydrocarbons
8111	Haloethers: capillary column technique
8121	Chlorinated hydrocarbons by GC: capillary column technique
8131	Aniline and selected derivatives by GC: capillary column technique
8141A	Organophosphorus compounds by GC: capillary column technique (8141B in IVB)
8151A	Chlorinated herbicides by GC using methylation or pentafluorobenzylation derivatization
8260B	Volatile organic compounds by GC/MS
8261	Volatiles by vacuum distillation with GC-MS (draft)
8270C	Semivolatile organic compounds by GC/MS (8270D in Update IVB)
8275A	Semivolatile organic compounds (PAH and PCB) in soils/sludges and solid wastes using TE/GC/MS
8280A	Dioxins and furans by HRGC/LRMS (8280B in Update IVB)
8290	Dioxins and furans by HRGC/HRMS (8290A in Update IVB)
8310	Polynuclear aromatic hydrocarbons
8315A	Determination of carbonyl compounds by HPLC
8316	Acrylamide, acrylonitrile and acrolein by HPLC
8318	N-Methylcarbamates by HPLC
8321A	Solvent extractable non-volatile compounds by HPLC/TS/MS or UV (8321B in Update IVB)
8325	Solvent extractable non-volatile compounds by HPLC/PB/MS
8330	Nitroaromatics and nitramines by HPLC (8330A in Update IVB)
8331	Tetrazene by HPLC
8332	Nitroglycerine by HPLC
8410	GC/FTIR for semivolatile organics
8430	Analysis of bis(2-chloroethyl)ether hydrolysis products by direct aqueous injection GC/FTIR
8440	TRPH by IR
8515	Colorimetric screening method for TNT in soil
8520	Continuous measurement of formaldehyde in ambient air
9000	Water by Karl Fischer titration (Update IVA)
9001	Water by calcium hydride reaction (Update IVA)
9010B	Distillation of total and amenable cyanide
9012A	Total and amenable cyanide by automated colorimetry with off-line distillation
9013	Cyanide extraction procedure for solids and oils
9014	Total and amenable cyanide (titration and colorimetric manual determination)

Continued on next page.

Table 1-25. Contents of SW-846 including the proposed Update IV to the Third Edition, *continued*

9020B	Total organic halides (TOX)
9021	Purgeable organic halides
9022	TOX by neutron activation analysis
9023	Extractable organic halides (EOX) in solids
9030B	Distillation of acid-soluble and acid-insoluble sulfides
9031	Extractable sulfides
9034	Titrimetric determinative procedure for sulfide
9035	Sulfate (colorimetric, automated chloranilate)
9036	Sulfate (colorimetric, automated methylthymol blue)
9038	Sulfate (turbidimetric)
9040B	pH electrometric measurement
9041A	pH paper method
9045C	Soil and waste pH
9050A	Specific conductance
9056	Determination of inorganic anions by ion chromatography
9057	Determination of chloride from HCl/Cl$_2$ emissions sampling train (Methods 0050 and 0051) by anion chromatography
9060	Total organic carbon (TOC)
9065	Phenolics (spectrophotometric 4AAP manual)
9066	Phenolics (colorimetric, automated 4AAP)
9067	Phenolics (spectrophotometric, MBTH)
9070	Total recoverable oil & grease
9071A	Oil & grease extraction method for sludge and sediment samples
9074	Turbidimetric screening for TRPH (Update IVA)
9075	Test method for total chlorine in new and used petroleum products by XRF
9076	Test method for total chlorine in new and used petroleum products by oxidative combustion and microcoulometry
9077	Test methods for total chlorine in new and used petroleum products (field test kit methods)
9078	Screening test method for PCB in soil
9079	Screening test method for PCB in transformer oil
9080	Cation exchange capacity of soils (ammonium acetate)
9081	Cation exchange capacity of soils (sodium acetate)
9090A	Compatibility test for wastes and membrane liners
9095A	Paint filter liquids test
9096	Liquid release test
9100	Saturated hydraulic conductivity, saturated leachate conductivity and intrinsic permeability
9131	Total coliform MPN
9132	Total coliform MF
9210	Nitrate ISE
9211	Bromide ISE
9212	Chloride ISE
9213	Cyanide ISE
9214	Fluoride ISE
9215	Sulfide ISE

Continued on next page.

Table 1-25. Contents of SW-846 including the proposed Update IV to the Third Edition, *continued*

9216	Nitrite by ISE (Update IVA)
9250	Chloride (automated ferricyanide AAI)
9251	Chloride (automated ferricyanide AAII)
9253	Chloride (titrimetric, silver nitrate)
9310	Gross alpha and gross beta
9315	Alpha-emitting radium isotopes
9320	Radium-228

Methods TO1-TO14
  Compendium of Methods for the Determination of Toxic Organic Compounds in Ambient Air (PB90-127374) (see Table at end of Section 5)

Methods IP1A-IP10B
  Compendium of Methods for the Determination of Air Pollutants in Indoor Air (PB90-200288) (see Table at end of Section 5)

DOE Methods for Evaluating Environmental and Waste Management Samples, 1997 edition. Initially prepared under contract to DOE (DOE/EM-0089T, from NTIS) by employees of Battelle Northwest, now a private effort and available through Battelle Press, 1-800-451-3543. A listing of the methods is included in Section 4

NIOSH Manual of Analytical Methods, 3rd Edition, 1988 and 4th Edition, 1995. Volumes 1-2 cover air analysis. The 4th Edition is available as a disk for operation in *Windows* on a PC. The method numbers are assigned in the NIOSH methods by sampling technique. The general categories are listed in Table 1-26. The following Table lists the contents of the 4th Edition.

Table 1-26. General method numbering of NIOSH Manual of Analytical Methods, 4th Edition

Method	Sampling Technique
0001-0899	General air samples
0900-0999	Bioaerosols
1000-1999	Organic gases on charcoal
2000-3499	Organic gases on other solid supports
3500-3999	Organic gases on other samplers
4000-4999	Organic gases on diffusive samplers
5000-5999	Organic aerosols
6000-6999	Inorganic gases
7000-7999	Inorganic aerosols
8000-8999	Biological samples
9000-9999	Bulk samples

Table 1-27. Method contents of NIOSH Manual of Analytical Methods, 4th Edition

Method	Title/Description
2538	Acetaldehyde by GC
3507	Acetaldehyde by HPLC
1603	Acetic acid
3506	Acetic anhydride
2506	Acetone cyanohydrin
1606	Acetonitrile
7903	Acids, inorganic
2501	Acrolein
1604	Acrylonitrile
1400	Alcohols I (tert-butyl, isopropyl and ethyl alcohols)
1401	Alcohols II (*n*-butyl, *s*-butyl, isobutyl and *n*-propyl alcohols)
1402	Alcohols III (allyl, isoamyl, cyclohexyl, and diacetone alcohols, methyl isobutyl carbinaol)
1403	Alcohols IV (2-butoxyethyl, 2-ethoxyethyl and 2-methoxyethyl alcohols)
2539	Aldehydes, screening
5502	Aldrin and lindane
7401	Alkaline dusts
1000	Allyl chloride
2545	Allyl glycidyl ether
7013	Aluminum
2010	Aliphatic amines
2002	Aromatic amines
2007	Aminoethanol compounds I
3509	Aminoethanol compounds II
6015	Ammonia
2514	Anisidine
7900	Arsenic (hydride AA)
5022	Arsenic, organo-
7901	Arsenic trioxide
6001	Arsine
9002	Asbestos
9000	Asbestos, chrysotile by XRD
7400	Asbestos and other fibers
7402	Asbestos fibers by TEM
5031	Aspartame
5019	Azelaic acid
7056	Barium, soluble compounds
3700	Benzene
5509	Benzidine and 3,3'-dichlorobenzidine
8306	Benzidine in urine
5009	Benzoyl peroxide
7102	Beryllium

Continued on next page.

Table 1-27. Method contents of NIOSH Manual of Analytical Methods, 4th Edition, *continued*

Method	Title/Description
7506	Boron carbide
5010	Bromoxynil and bromoxynil octanoate
1024	1,3-Butadiene
2012	*n*-Butylamine
1616	*n*-Butyl glycidyl ether
7048	Cadmium
7020	Calcium
5006	Carbaryl
5000	Carbon black
6603	Carbon dioxide
1600	Carbon disulfide
5510	Chlordane
5039	Chlorinated camphene (toxaphene)
5025	Chlorinated diphenyl oxide
5014	Chlorinated terphenyl
6011	Chlorine and bromine
2015	Chloroacetaldehyde
2008	Chloroacetic acid
2014	*p*-Chlorophenol
1002	*b*-Chloroprene
7024	Chromium by FAAS
7600	Chromium, hexavalent by Vis
7604	Chromium, hexavalent by IC
7027	Cobalt
7029	Copper dust and fume
2546	Cresols and phenol
3516	Crotonaldehyde
7904	Cyanides by ISE
5030	Cyanuric acid
2523	1,3-Cyclopentadiene
5001	2,4-D and 2,4,5-T
5514	Demeton
2515	Diazomethane
6006	Diborane
5017	Dibutylphosphate
5020	Dibutyl and Bis(2-ethylhexyl) phthalates
1018	Freons
1004	Dichloroethylether
2516	Dichlorofluoromethane
1601	1,1-Dichloro-1-nitroethane
1012	Difluorodibromomethane

Continued on next page.

Table 1-27. Method contents of NIOSH Manual of Analytical Methods, 4th Edition, *continued*

Method	Title/Description
2004	Dimethylacetamide and dimethylformamide
3515	1,1-Dimethylhydrazine
2524	Dimethyl sulfate
1602	Dioxane
2530	Diphenyl
5013	Dyes
8005	Elements (metals) in blood or tissue
7300	Elements (metals) by ICP
5519	Endrin
1010	Epichlorohydrin
5012	EPN
1450	Esters I
1457	Ethyl acetate
1011	Ethyl bromide
2519	Ethyl chloride
1610	Ethyl ether
1452	Ethyl formate
2513	Ethylene chlorohydrin
2540	Ethylene diamine, diethylene triamine and triethylene tetraamine
1008	Ethylene dibromide
1614	Ethylene oxide
3702	Ethylene oxide (portable GC)
5011	Ethylene thiourea
3514	Ethylenimine
8308	Fluorides in urine
7906	Fluorides by IC
7902	Fluorides by ISE
1006	Fluorotrichloromethane
2541	Formaldehyde (2-hydroxymethyl-piperidine) by GC
3500	Formaldehyde (chromotropic acid)
5700	Formaldehyde on dust
2011	Formic acid by IC
2529	Furfural
2505	Furfuryl alcohol
2532	Glutaraldehyde by HPLC
1608	Glycidol
2543	Hexachlorobutadiene
2518	Hexachloro-1,3-cyclopentadiene
8300	Hippuric acid in urine (Vis)
8301	Hippuric and methyl hippuric acid in urine (HPLC)
3503	Hydrazine

Continued on next page.

Table 1-27. Method contents of NIOSH Manual of Analytical Methods, 4th Edition, *continued*

Method	Title/Description
1500	Hydrocarbons BP 36-126 °C
1501	Hydrocarbons, aromatic
1003	Hydrocarbons, halogenated
6010	Hydrogen cyanide
6013	Hydrogen sulfide by IC
5004	Hydroquinone
6005	Iodine
5521	Isocyanates
2508	Isophorone
1454	Isopropyl acetate
1618	Isopropyl ether
1620	Isopropyl glycidyl ether
5508	Kepone
1300	Ketones I
1301	Ketones II
8003	Lead in blood and urine
9100	Lead in surface wipe samples
7082	Lead by FAAS
7105	Lead by HGAAS
7505	Lead sulfide
3512	Maleic anhydride
8302	MBOCA in urine
2542	Mercaptans
6009	Mercury
8310	Metals in urine (ICP)
2000	Methanol
1458	Methyl acetate
1459	Methyl acrylate
1611	Methylal
1451	Methyl cellosolve acetate
1001	Methyl chloride
1404	Methylcyclohexanol
2521	Methylcyclohexanone
1005	Methylene chloride
5029	4,4'-Methylenedianiline (MDA)
2500	Methyl ethyl ketone
8002	Methyl ethyl ketone, ethanol and toluene in blood
3508	Methyl ethyl ketone peroxide
1014	Methyl iodide
2537	Methyl methacrylate
1615	Methyl *t*-butyl ether
3511	Monomethylaniline

Continued on next page.

Table 1-27. Method contents of NIOSH Manual of Analytical Methods, 4th Edition, *continued*

Method	Title/Description
3510	Monomethylhydrazine
1550	Naphthas
5518	Naphthylamines
6007	Nickel carbonyl
2544	Nicotine
6014	Nitric oxide and nitrogen dioxide
5033	*p*-Nitroaniline
2005	Nitrobenzenes
2526	Nitroethane
2507	Nitroglycerin/EGDN
2527	Nitromethane
2528	2-Nitropropane
2522	Nitrosamines
6600	Nitrous oxide
2510	1-Octanethiol
5026	Oil mist - mineral
5600	Organophosphorus pesticides
5504	Organotin compounds
6601	Oxygen
5003	Paraquat
0600	Particulates, respirable
0500	Particulates, total
2517	Pentachloroethane
5512	Pentachlorophenol
8001	Pentachlorophenol in blood
8303	Pentachlorophenol in urine
5032	Pentamidine isothionate
8305	Phenol and *p*-cresol in urine
1617	Phenyl ether
2013	Phenyl ether-diphenyl mix
1619	Phenyl glycidyl ether
3518	Phenylhydrazine
6002	Phosphine
7905	Phosphorus
6402	Phosphorus trichloride
5517	Polychlorobenzenes
5503	Polychlorobiphenyls
8004	Polychlorobiphenyls in serum
5506	Polynuclear aromatic hydrocarbons (HPLC)
5515	Polynuclear aromatic hydrocarbons (GC)
1013	Propylene dichloride

Continued on next page.

Table 1-27. Method contents of NIOSH Manual of Analytical Methods, 4th Edition, *continued*

Method	Title/Description
1612	Propylene oxide
5008	Pyrethrum
1613	Pyridine
5027	Ribavirin
5007	Rotenone
7501	Silica, amorphous
7603	Silica in coal mine dust by IR
7500	Silica, crystalline respirable by XRD
7601	Silica, crystalline by Vis
7602	Silica, crystalline by IR
6008	Stilbine
5016	Strychnine
6004	Sulfur dioxide
6602	Sulfur hexafluoride
6012	Sulfuryl fluoride
5035	Super absorbent polymer
5021	o-Terphenyl
2003	1,1,2,2-Tetrabromoethane
1016	Tetrachlorodifluoroethane
1019	1,1,2,2-Tetrachloroethane
2533	Tetraethyl lead
2504	Tetraethyl pyrophosphate (TEPP)
1609	Tetrahydrofuran
2534	Tetramethyl lead
3505	Tetramethyl thiourea
3513	Tetranitromethane
5005	Thiram
4000	Toluene
5516	2,4- and 2,6-Toluenediamine
2535	Toluene, 2,4-diisocyanate
5034	Tributylphosphate
1022	Trichloroethylene
3701	Trichloroethylene (portable GC)
1020	1,1,2-Trichlorotrifluoroethane
1017	Trifluorobromomethane
5036	Trimellitic anhydride
5018	2,4,7-Trinitrofluoren-9-one
5037	Triorthocresol phosphate
5038	Triphenyl phosphate
7074	Tungsten
1551	Turpentine

Continued on next page.

Table 1-27. Method contents of NIOSH Manual of Analytical Methods, 4th Edition, *continued*

Method	Title/Description
2536	Valeraldehyde
7504	Vanadium oxides
1453	Vinyl acetate
1009	Vinyl bromide
1007	Vinyl chloride
1015	Vinylidene chloride
5002	Warfarin
7030	Zinc
7502	Zinc oxide

40 CFR Part 50, Appendix A-J and 40 CFR 52 Appendix D,
 Air Methods for Lead, Ozone, particulates, NO_x, etc. (see Table at end of Section 5)

40 CFR 80, Appendix A and B
 Phosphorous and lead in gasoline (see Table at end of Section 5)

EPA Contract Laboratory Protocol Statement of Work for Organics, Dioxins and Inorganics. Updated for every contract period. A SOW for air analysis exists.

Table 1-28. EPA CLP methods and documents. PB numbers are NTIS document identifiers

SOW	Title/Description
7/88	Laboratory Data Validation Functional Guidelines for Evaluating Inorganics Analyses 7/88 PB95-963525
7/88	USEPA CLP SOW for Inorganics Analysis, multi-media, multi-concentration PB95-963516
2/88	Laboratory Data Validation Functional Guidelines for Evaluating Organics Analyses 2/88 PB95-963526
2/88	USEPA CLP SOW for Organics Analysis, multi-media, multi-concentration 2/88 PB95-963512
1989	USEPA CLP SOW for Organics Analysis, multi-media, high-concentration PB95-963507
IHC01.3	USEPA CLP SOW for Inorganic Analysis, multi-media high-concentration PB95-963504
ILM01.0	USEPA CLP SOW for Inorganics Analysis, multi-media, multi-concentration PB95-963515
10/91	Superfund Analytical Methods for Low Concentration Water for Inorganics Analysis 10/91 PB95-963517
OLM01.1	USEPA CLP SOW for Organics Analysis, multi-media, multi-concentration and revisions 8/91 PB95-963508
OLC01.0	Superfund Analytical Methods for Low Concentration Water for Organics Analysis 6/91 PB95-963505
	USEPA CLP National Functional Guidelines for Organic Data Review, multi-media, multi-concentration (OLM01.0) and Low concentration water (OLC01.0) 6/91 PB95-963519
ILM02.1	USEPA CLP SOW for Inorganics Analysis, multi-media, multi-concentration 9/91 PB95963514

Continued on next page.

Table 1-28. EPA CLP methods and documents. PB numbers are NTIS document identifiers, *continued*

SOW	Title/Description
ILM03.0	USEPA CLP SOW for Inorganics Analysis, multi-media, multi-concentration 12/94 PB95-963506
	USEPA CLP National Functional Guidelines for Inorganic Data Review 2/94 PB94-963502
ILMO4.0	USEPA CLP SOW for Inorganics Analysis, multi-media 7/95 PB95-963545
OLM03.1	USEPA CLP SOW for Organic Analysis 8/94 PB95-963503
	USEPA CLP National Functional Guidelines for Organic Data Review 2/94 PB94-963501
ILC03.1	Superfund Analytical Methods for Low Concentration Water for Inorganics Analysis, March, 1996 PB96-963504
VCAAO 1.0	USEPA Volatile Organics of Ambient Air in Canisters 12/91 PB95-963524
DFLM01.0	USEPA CLP SOW for Analysis of Polychlorinated Dibenzo-P-Dioxins (PCDD) and Polychlorinated Dibenzofurans (PCDF), multi-media, multi-concentration 9/91 PB95-963520
	USEPA CLP SOW for Rapid Turnaround Dioxin Analysis, multi-media 11/92 PB95-963518
	USEPA CLP draft SOW for Quick Turnaround Analysis 8/94 PB95-963523
	USEPA CLP National Functional Guidelines for Quick Turnaround Method Data Review 7/94 PB95-963535
IAIR01.2	USEPA CLP SOW for Analysis of Ambient Air 7/91 PB95-963537

EPA has also incorporated by reference into Title 40 CFR many methods from ASTM (American Society for Testing and Materials), ASME (American Society of Mechanical Engineers) and other groups.

USGS Methods

The United States Geological Survey (USGS) has published a large number of methods in the *Techniques of Water Resource Investigations* (TWI). Book 5 of TWI addresses laboratory analysis. Book 5 is actually divided into 7 separately bound chapters. Many of these methods are approved for use in analysis of wastewater compliance monitoring samples.

1) TWI 5-A1 Methods for the determination of inorganic substances in water and fluvial sediments (3rd edition 1989)

2) TWI 5-A2 Determination of minor elements in water by emission spectroscopy (1971)

3) TWI 5-A3 Methods for the determination of organic substances in water and fluvial sediments (revised 1987)

4) TWI 5-A4 Methods for the collection and analysis of aquatic biological and microbiological samples (revised 1989)

5) TWI 5-A5 Determination of radioactive substances in water and fluvial sediments (1977)

6) TWI 5-A6 Quality assurance practices for the chemical and biological analysis of water and fluvial sediments (1982)

7) TWI 5-C1 Laboratory theory and practice for sediment analysis (1969)

The USGS methods are identified by a letter followed by a four-digit number and then a year designator to indicate the revision date. The letters are (P) physical characteristic, (I) inorganic substance, (O) organic substance, (B) biological method, (R) radioactive determination, (S) sediment characteristic, and (E) emission spectrographic method. The first digit of the four-digit code for the organic and inorganic methods indicates the type of determination:

0   Sample preparation

1   Manual method for dissolved parameters

2   Automated method for dissolved parameters

3   Manual method for analyzing water-suspended sediment mixtures

4   Automated method for analyzing water-suspended sediment mixtures

5   Manual method for analyzing bottom material

6   Automated method for analyzing bottom material

7   Method for determining suspended parameters

9   Method for fish and other materials.

The last three digits of the four-digit code identify the parameter. For instance barium by direct atomic absorption spectrometry (FLAA) has the parameter code 084. A method identified as I-7084-85 is a FLAA barium method performed on suspended material, last updated in 1985.

Table 1-29. USGS Methods

Method code	Title/Description
Inorganic (I)	
020	Acidity by electrometric titration
030	Alkalinity by electrometric titration
051	Aluminum by FLAA
052	Aluminum by chelation-extraction FLAA
054	Aluminum by d-c plasma AES
055	Antimony by hydride FLAA
057	Anions by ion chromatography
058	Anions by ion-exchange chromatography
060	Arsenic by silver diethyldithiocarbamate colorimetric
062	Arsenic by hydride FLAA
084	Barium by FLAA
095	Beryllium by FLAA
110	Boron colorimetric dianthrimide
112	Boron colorimetric curcumin
114	Boron by d-c plasma AES
115	Boron colorimetric azomethine H
125	Bromide titrimetric hypochlorite oxidation
128	Bromide ion-chromatography electrochemical detection

Continued on next page.

Table 1-29. USGS Methods, *continued*

Method code	Title/Description
	Inorganic (I), *continued*
129	Bromide by fluorescein colorimetric
135	Cadmium by FLAA
136	Cadmium by chelation-extraction FLAA
137	Cadmium by GFAA
152	Calcium by FLAA
153	Calcium by EPA FLAA
160	Carbon dioxide calculation
183	Chloride, Mohr titration
184	Chloride titrimetric mercurimetric
187	Chloride ferric thiocyanate colorimetric
230	Hexavalent chromium diphenylcarbazide colorimetric
232	Hexavalent chromium chelation-extraction FLAA
235	Chromium GFAA
236	Chromium FLAA
238	Chromium chelation-extraction FLAA
239	Cobalt FLAA
240	Cobalt chelation-extraction FLAA
241	Cobalt GFAA
250	Color, visual comparison Pt-Co
270	Copper FLAA
271	Copper chelation-extraction FLAA
272	Copper GFAA
300	Cyanide pyridine-pyrazolone colorimetric
302	Cyanide barbituric acid colorimetric
312	Density, gravimetric
325	Fluoride zirconium-eriochrome cyanine R colorimetric
327	Fluoride ISE
338	Hardness complexometric titration
340	Hardness calculation
344	Hardness, non-carbonate calculation
370	Iodide bromine oxidation titration
371	Iodide ceric-arsenious oxidation colorimetric
381	Iron FLAA
399	Lead FLAA
400	Lead chelation-extraction FLAA
401	Lead GFAA
425	Lithium FLAA
447	Magnesium FLAA
448	Magnesium EPA FLAA
454	Manganese FLAA

Continued on next page.

Table 1-29. USGS Methods, *continued*

Method code	Title/Description
Inorganic (I), *continued*	
455	Manganese GFAA
456	Manganese chelation-extraction FLAA
462	Mercury CVAA
472	Metals by ICP-AES
473	Metals total-in-sediment by lithium fusion and FLAA
474	Metals total-in-sediment by acid digestion FLAA
475	Metals total-in-sediment by hydride FLAA
490	Molybdenum chelation-extraction FLAA
499	Nickel FLAA
500	Nickel chelation-extraction FLAA
501	Nickel GFAA
520	Ammonia distillation nesslerization
521	Ammonia salicylate-hypochlorite colorimetric (automated discrete)
522	Ammonia salicylate-hypochlorite colorimetric (separated flow)
523	Ammonia indophenol colorimetric
524	Ammonia ISE
539	Nitrite colorimetric automated
540	Nitrite colorimetric
543	Nitrate + Nitrite hydrazine reduction
545	Nitrate + Nitrite cadmium reduction-diazotization
550	Ammonia + organic nitrogen nesslerization
552	Ammonia + organic nitrogen salicylate-hypochlorite colorimetric
553	Ammonia + organic nitrogen titration
554	Total nitrogen digestion distillation
558	Ammonia + organic nitrogen salicylate-hypochlorite colorimetric
561	COD colorimetric
562	COD titration
586	pH electrode
598	Orthophosphate colorimetric automated
599	Phosphorus phosphomolybdate automated colorimetric
600	Phosphorus phosphomolybdate colorimetric
601	Orthophosphate colorimetric
602	Phosphate digestion colorimetric
630	Potassium FLAA
631	Potassium EPA FLAA
667	Selenium hydride AA
700	Silica molybdate colorimetric
702	Silica FLAA
720	Silver chelation-extraction FLAA
735	Sodium FLAA

Continued on next page.

Table 1-29. USGS Methods, *continued*

Method code	Title/Description
Inorganic (I), *continued*	
736	Sodium EPA FLAA
738	Sodium adsorption ratio calculation
740	Sodium percent calculation
749	Solids at 105 °C
750	Solids at 180 °C
751	Solids, calculation
752	Solids non-volatile at ignition
753	Solids volatile at ignition
765	Solids suspended at 105 °C
766	Solids non-volatile suspended at ignition
767	Solids volatile suspended at ignition
780	Specific conductance electrometric
800	Strontium FLAA
820	Sulfate thorin titration
822	Sulfate methylthymol blue colorimetric
823	Sulfate turbidometric
840	Sulfide iodometric titration
851	Tin hydride AA
860	Turbidity
866	Thallium GFAA
880	Vanadium catalytic oxidation colorimetric
900	Zinc FLAA
901	Zinc GFAA
Organics (O)	
100	Organic carbon wet oxidation
101	Total carbon dry weight induction furnace
102	Inorganic carbon modified Van Slyke
103	Organic carbon fractionation
104	Organochlorine and organophosphorus pesticides GC
105	Chlorophenoxy acids GC
106	Triazines GC
107	Carbamate pesticides HPLC
108	Oil & Grease extraction-gravimetric
109	Light fuel oils GC
110	Phenols colorimetric
111	MBAS surfactants
112	TNT, RDX and picric acid HPLC
113	PAH HPLC
114	Ethylene and propane GC
115	Purgeable organic compounds GC/MS

Continued on next page.

Table 1-29. USGS Methods, *continued*

Method code	Title/Description
	Organics (O), *continued*
117	Acid extractable compounds GC/MS
118	Base/neutral extractable compounds GC/MS
	Biological (B)
0001	Standard plate count membrane filter
0025	Total coliform MF immediate incubation
0030	Total coliform MF delayed incubation
0035	Total coliform MPN
0040	Total coliform MPN presumptive on-site
0045	Total coliform MPN confirmation
0050	Fecal coliform MF immediate incubation
0051	Fecal coliform MPN presumptive
0055	Fecal streptococcal MF immediate incubation
0060	Fecal streptococcal MF confirmation
0065	Fecal streptococcal MPN presumptive and confirmation
0420	Nitrifying bacteria MPN
0430	Denitrifying and nitrate-reducing bacteria MPN
0400	Sulfate-reducing bacteria MPN
0005	Total bacteria epifluorescence
0100	Salmonella and shigella
0105	Pseudomonas aeruginosa
1505	Phytoplankton counting cell
1520	Phytoplankton inverted microscope
1580	Planktonic diatoms permanent slide
2501	Zooplankton counting cell
2520	Zooplankton gravimetric biomass
3401	Seston glass-fiber filter
3501	Periphyton Sedgwick-Rafter
3520	Periphyton gravimetric biomass
3540	Periphytic diatoms permanent slide
3545	Periphytic diatoms inverted microscope
4501	Macrophytes Floral survey
4520	Macrophytes distribution and abundance
5001	Benthic invertebrates faunal survey
5020	Benthic invertebrates numerical assessment
5040	Benthic invertebrate distribution and abundance
5050	Benthic invertebrate drift
5200	Chironomidae larvae permanent slide
5220	Identification of immature simuliidae
5240	Aquatic acari slide
6001	Aquatic vertebrates faunal survey

Continued on next page.

Table 1-29. USGS Methods, *continued*

Method code	Title/Description
	Biological (B), *continued*
6020	Aquatic vertebrates life history
6040	Investigation of aquatic vertebrate kills
6501	Phytoplankton chlorophyll spectroscopy
6520	Phytoplankton chlorophyll TLC
6530	Phytoplankton chlorophyll HPLC
6540	Phytoplankton chlorophyll TLC fluorometry
6560	Phytoplankton biomass/chlorophyll ratio
6601	Periphyton chlorophyll spectroscopy
6620	Periphyton chlorophyll TLC spectrometry
6630	Periphyton chlorophyll HPLC
6640	Periphyton chlorophyll TLC fluorometry
6660	Periphyton biomass/chlorophyll ratio
6700	Adenosine triphosphate
8001	Phytoplankton productivity oxygen light- and dark-bottle
8020	Phytoplankton productivity carbon-14 light- and dark-bottle
8040	Periphyton productivity oxygen light- and dark-bottle
8120	Stream productivity and community metabolism Diel oxygen-curve
8100	Stratified water productivity and community metabolism Diel oxygen-curve
8502	Algal growth potential

State Methods

Many states have methods that are approved for use in that state under a variety of monitoring programs. An example of this involves the petroleum LUST program. Total Petroleum Hydrocarbons (TPH) are tested by either gas chromatography (the California method or EPA Method 8015B), IR spectroscopy (EPA method 9073 or 418.1), or gravimetry (EPA method 413.1 modified or EPA Method 1664). Other variations exist such as the Wisconsin methods for Gasoline Range Organics (GRO) and Diesel Range Organics (DRO). See the petroleum hydrocarbon discussion in Section 3 and Section 4.

Commercial Private Sources of Methods

Standard Methods for the Examination of Water and Wastewater (APHA, AWWA, WEF, 18th Edition, 1992, 19th Edition, 1995, and 20th Edition, 1998) (abbreviated in this book as SM_{18}, SM_{19}, or SM_{20}).

Table 1-30. Method contents of Standard Methods, 20th Edition

Method	Title/Description
	Physical and Aggregate Properties
2110	Appearance
2120	Color
B	Visual comparison method

Continued on next page.

Table 1-30. Method contents of Standard Methods, 20th Edition, *continued*

Method	Title/Description
	**Physical and Aggregate Properties,** *continued*
C	Spectrophotometric method
D	Tristimulus filter method
E	ADMI method
2130	Turbidity
2150	Odor
2160	Taste
2170	Flavor profile analysis
2310	Acidity
2320	Alkalinity
2330	Calcium carbonate saturation
2340	Hardness
B	Calculation
C	Titration
2350	Oxidant demand/requirement
B	Chlorine demand
C	Chlorine dioxide demand
D	Ozone demand - batch
E	Ozone demand - semibatch
2510	Conductivity
2520	Salinity
B	Electrical conductivity method
C	Density method
2530	Floatables
B	Particulate floatables
C	Floatable oil and grease
2540	Solids
B	Total solids (TS)
C	Total dissolved solids (TDS)
D	Total suspended solids (TSS)
E	Fixed and volatile solids
F	Settleable solids
G	Total, fixed and volatile solids in solid and semisolid samples
2550	Temperature
2560	Particulate counting and size
B	Electrical sensing zone method
C	Light-blockage methods
D	Light-scattering methods
2570	Asbestos
2580	Oxidation-reduction potential
2710	Tests on sludges

Continued on next page.

Table 1-30. Method contents of Standard Methods, 20th Edition, *continued*

Method	Title/Description
Physical and Aggregate Properties, *continued*	
B	Oxygen consumption rate
C	Settled sludge volume
D	Sludge volume index
E	Zone settling rate
F	Specific gravity
G	Capillary-suction factor
H	Time-to-filter
2720	Anaerobic sludge digester gas analysis
B	Volumetric method
C	Gas chromatographic method
2810	Dissolved gas supersaturation
Metals	
3030	Preliminary treatment
B	Filtration for dissolved and suspended metals
C	Treatment for acid extractable metals
D	Digestion for metals
E	Nitric acid digestion
F	Nitric acid-Hydrochloric acid digestion
G	Nitric acid-Sulfuric acid digestion
H	Nitric acid-Perchloric acid digestion
I	Nitric acid-Perchloric acid-Hydrofluoric acid digestion
J	Dry ashing
K	Microwave-assisted digestion
3110	Metals by atomic absorption spectrometry
3111	Metals by flame atomic absorption
B	Direct air-acetylene flame
C	Extraction/air-acetylene flame
D	Direct nitrous oxide-acetylene flame
E	Extraction/nitrous oxide-acetylene flame
3112	Metals by cold vapor atomic absorption spectrometry
3113	Metals by electrothermal atomic absorption spectrometry
3114	Arsenic and selenium by hydride generation atomic absorption spectrometry
B	Manual hydride generation
C	Continuous hydride generation
3120	Metals by plasma emission spectrometry
3125	Metals by inductively coupled plasma/mass spectrometry
3130	Metals by anodic stripping voltammetry
Inorganic Nonmetallic Constituents	
4110	Determination of anions by ion chromatography
4120	Segmented continuous flow analysis
4130	Inorganic nonmetals by flow injection analysis

Continued on next page.

Genium Publishing Corporation

Table 1-30. Method contents of Standard Methods, 20th Edition, *continued*

Method	Title/Description
	Inorganic Nonmetallic Constituents, *continued*
4140	Inorganic anions by capillary ion electrophoresis
4500-B	Boron
B	Curcumin method
C	Carmine method
D	ICP
4500-Br⁻	Bromine
B	Phenol red colorimetric
C	Ion Chromatography
D	Flow injection analysis
4500-CO_2	Carbon dioxide
B	Nomographic determination
C	Titration for free carbon dioxide
D	Carbon dioxide by calculation
4500-CN⁻	Cyanide
B	Preliminary treatment
C	Total cyanide after distillation
D	Titrimetric method
E	Colorimetric method
F	Cyanide-selective electrode
G	Cyanides amenable to chlorination with distillation
H	Cyanides amenable to chlorination without distillation
I	Weak acid dissociable cyanide
J	Cyanogen chloride
K	Spot test for sample screening
L	Cyanates
M	Thiocyanate
N	Total cyanide by FIA
O	Total and WAD cyanide by FIA
4500-Cl	Chlorine (Residual)
B	Iodometric I
C	Iodometric II
D	Amperometric titration
E	Low-level amperometric titration
F	DPD Ferrous titrimetric
G	DPD colorimetric
H	Syringaldazine (FACTS) method
I	Iodometric Electrode technique
4500-Cl⁻	Chloride
B	Argentometric method
C	Mercuric nitrate method

Continued on next page.

Table 1-30. Method contents of Standard Methods, 20th Edition, *continued*

Method	Title/Description
Inorganic Nonmetallic Constituents, *continued*	
D	Potentiometric method
E	Automated ferrocyanide method
F	Ion chromatography
G	Mercury thiocyanate FIA
4500-ClO$_2$	Chlorine dioxide
B	Iodometric method
C	Amperometric method I
D	DPD method
E	Amperometric method II
4500-F$^-$	Fluoride
B	Preliminary distillation
C	Ion selective electrode
D	SPADNS
E	Complexone method
F	Ion chromatography
G	Ion-selective electrode FIA
4500-H$^+$	pH
4500-I	Iodine
B	Leuco crystal violet
C	Amperometric titration
4500-I$^-$	Iodide
B	Leuco crystal violet
C	Catalytic reduction
D	Voltammetric
4500-IO$_3^-$	Iodate
B	Polarographic
4500-N	Nitrogen
B	In-line UV/persulfate digestion with FIA
C	Persulfate method
4500-NH$_3$	Nitrogen (ammonia)
B	Preliminary distillation
C	Titrimetric method
D	Ammonia selective electrode
E	Ammonia selective electrode with known addition
F	Phenate method
G	Automated phenate
H	FIA
4500-NO$_2^-$	Nitrogen (nitrite)
B	Colorimetric method

Continued on next page.

Table 1-30. Method contents of Standard Methods, 20th Edition, *continued*

Method	Title/Description
	Inorganic Nonmetallic Constituents, *continued*
$4500\text{-}NO_3^-$	Nitrogen (nitrate)
B	UV spectrophotometric screening
C	Ion chromatography
D	Nitrate electrode
E	Cadmium reduction
F	Automated cadmium reduction
G	Titanous chloride reduction
H	Automated hydrazine reduction
I	Cadmium reduction FIA
$4500\text{-}N_{org}$	Nitrogen (organic)
B	Macro-Kjeldahl
C	Semimicro-Kjeldahl
D	Block digestion and FIA
4500-O	Oxygen (dissolved)
B	Iodometric method
C	Azide modification
D	Permanganate modification
E	Alum flocculation modification
F	Copper sulfate-sulfamic acid flocculation modification
G	Membrane electrode
$4500\text{-}O_3$	Ozone (residual)
B	Indigo colorimetric
4500-P	Phosphorus
B	Sample preparation
C	Vanadomolybdophosphoric acid colorimetric method
D	Stannous chloride method
E	Ascorbic acid method
F	Automated ascorbic acid reduction method
G	FIA for orthophosphate
H	Manual digestion and FIA
I	In-line UV/persulfate digestion with FIA
$4500\text{-}KMnO_4$	Permanganate
B	Spectrophotometric
$4500\text{-}SiO_2$	Silica
C	Molybdosilicate method
D	Heteropoly blue method
E	Automated method for molybdate reactive silica
F	FIA for molybdate-reactive silica
$4500\text{-}S^{2-}$	Sulfide

Continued on next page.

Table 1-30. Method contents of Standard Methods, 20th Edition, *continued*

Method	Title/Description
Inorganic Nonmetallic Constituents, *continued*	
B	Separation of soluble and insoluble sulfides
C	Sample pretreatment to remove interferences
D	Methylene blue method
E	Gas dialysis automated methylene blue
F	Iodometric method
G	Ion selective electrode method
H	Calculation of un-ionized hydrogen sulfide
I	Distillation, methylene blue FIA
$4500\text{-}SO_3^{2-}$	Sulfite
B	Iodometric method
C	Phenanthroline method
$4500\text{-}SO_4^{2-}$	Sulfate
C	Gravimetric method with ignition
D	Gravimetric method with drying
E	Turbidimetric method
F	Automated methylthymol blue
G	Methylthymol blue FIA
Aggregate Organic Constituents	
5210	Biochemical oxygen demand (BOD)
B	5-day BOD
C	Ultimate BOD
D	Respirometric method
5220	Chemical oxygen demand (COD)
B	Open reflux method
C	Closed reflux, titrimetric
D	Closed reflux, colorimetric
5310	Total organic carbon (TOC)
B	Combustion-Infrared
C	Persulfate-Ultraviolet oxidation
D	Wet oxidation
5320	Dissolved organic halogen
B	Adsorption-pyrolysis titrimetric method
5510	Aquatic humic substances
B	Diethylaminoethyl (DEAE) method
C	XAD method
5520	Oil and grease
B	Partition-gravimetric method
C	Partition-infrared method
D	Soxhlet extraction method

Continued on next page.

Table 1-30. Method contents of Standard Methods, 20th Edition, *continued*

Method	Title/Description
\multicolumn{2}{c}{**Aggregate Organic Constituents,** *continued*}	
E	Extraction method for sludge samples
F	Hydrocarbons
5530	Phenols
B	Cleanup procedures
C	Chloroform extraction method
D	Direct photometric method
5540	Surfactants
B	Surfactant separation by sublation
C	Anionic surfactants as MBAS
D	Nonionic surfactants as CTAS
5550	Tannin and lignin
5560	Organic and volatile acids
B	Chromatographic separation method for organic acids
C	Distillation method
5710	Formation of trihalomethanes and other disinfection by-products
B	Trihalomethane formation potential
C	Simulated distribution system trihalomethanes (SDS-THM)
D	Formation of other disinfection by-products (DBPs)
5910	UV-absorbing organic constituents
\multicolumn{2}{c}{**Individual Organic Compounds**}	
6040	Constituent concentration by gas extraction
B	Closed loop stripping, GC/MS analysis
C	Purge and trap technique
6200	Volatile organic compounds
B	Purge and trap capillary column GC/MS
C	Purge and trap capillary column GC
6211	Methane
B	Combustible gas indicator method
C	Volumetric method
6231	1,2-Dibromoethane (EB) and 1,2-dibromo-3-chloropropane (DBCP)
B	Liquid-liquid extraction GC method
C	Purge and trap GC/MS method
D	Purge and trap GC method
6232	Trihalomethanes and chlorinated organic solvents
B	Liquid-liquid extraction GC method
C	Purge and trap GC/MS method
D	Purge and trap GC method
6251	Disinfection by-products: haloacetic acids and trichlorophenol
B	Micro liquid-liquid extraction GC method
6252	Disinfection by-products: aldehydes

Continued on next page.

Table 1-30. Method contents of Standard Methods, 20th Edition, *continued*

Method	Title/Description
	**Individual Organic Compounds,** *continued*
B	PFBHA liquid-liquid extraction GC method
6410	Extractable base/neutrals and acids
B	Liquid-liquid extraction GC/MS method
6420	Phenols
B	Liquid-liquid extraction GC method
C	Liquid-liquid extraction GC/MS method
6431	Polychlorinated biphenyls (PCBs)
B	Liquid-liquid extraction GC method
C	Liquid-liquid extraction GC/MS method
6440	Polynuclear aromatic hydrocarbons
B	Liquid-liquid extraction chromatographic method
C	Liquid-liquid extraction GC/MS method
6610	Carbamate pesticides
B	HPLC method
6630	Organochlorine pesticides
B	Liquid-liquid extraction GC method I
Appendix	Lauric acid standardization of magnesia-silica gel columns
C	Liquid-liquid extraction GC method II
D	Liquid-liquid extraction GC/MS method
6640	Acidic herbicide compounds
B	Micro liquid-liquid extraction GC method
6651	Glyphosate herbicide
	**Radioactivity**
7110	Gross alpha and gross beta radioactivity
B	Evaporation method for gross alpha
C	Coprecipitation method for gross alpha radioactivity in drinking water
7120	Gamma-emitting radionuclides
7500-Cs	Cesium
B	Precipitation method
7500-I	Radioactive iodine
B	Precipitation method
C	Ion-exchange method
D	Distillation method
7500-Ra	Radium
B	Precipitation method
C	Emanation method
D	Sequential precipitation method
7500-Rn	Radon
B	Liquid scintillation
7500-Sr	Strontium

Continued on next page.

Table 1-30. Method contents of Standard Methods, 20th Edition, *continued*

Method	Title/Description
Radioactivity, *continued*	
B	Precipitation method
7500-^{3}H	Tritium
B	Liquid scintillation spectrometric method
7500-U	Uranium
B	Radiochemical method
C	Isotopic method
Toxicity	
8030	Mutagenesis
8050	Bacterial bioluminescence
8070	P450 Reporter gene response to dioxin-like organic compounds
8080	Sediment pore water testing
8110	Algae
8111	Biostimulation
8112	Phytoplankton
8211	Duckweed
8220	Aquatic rooted plants
8310	Ciliated protozoa
8420	Rotifers
8510	Annelids
8610	Mollusks
8710	Microcrustaceans
8711	Daphnia
8712	Ceriodaphnia
8714	Mysids
8740	Decapods
8750	Aquatic insects
8810	Echinoderm fertilization and development
8910	Fish
8921	Fathead minnow
Microbiological Examination	
9211	Rapid detection methods
B	Seven hour fecal coliform
D	Coliphage detection
9212	Stressed organisms
9215	Heterotrophic plate count
B	Pour plate method
C	Spread plate method
D	Membrane filter method
9216	Direct total microbial count
9217	Assimilable organic carbon

Continued on next page.

Table 1-30. Method contents of Standard Methods, 20th Edition, *continued*

Method	Title/Description
Microbiological Examination, *continued*	
9221	Multiple tube fermentation technique for members of the coliform group
9222	Membrane filter technique for members of the coliform group
9223	Enzyme substrate coliform test
9225	Differentiation of the coliform bacteria
9230	Fecal streptococcus and enterococcus groups
9240	Iron and sulfur bacteria
B	Iron bacteria
C	Sulfur bacteria
9250	Detection of actinomycetes
9260	Detection of pathogenic bacteria
9510	Detection of enteric viruses
9610	Detection of fungi
9711	Pathogenic protozoa
Biological Examination	
10200	Plankton
10300	Periphyton
10400	Macrophyton
10500	Benthic macroinvertebrates
10550	Nematological examination
10600	Fish
10900	Identification of aquatic organisms

ASTM Standards: *Water and Environmental Technology* (Updated yearly)

Volumes 11.01 and 11.02, Water

Volume 11.03, Atmospheric Analysis, Occupational Health and Safety

Volume 11.04, Pesticides, Resource Recovery, Hazardous Substances, Waste Disposal and Biological Effects.

Methods of soil characterization and analysis: *Methods of Soil Analysis*, Part 1: Physical and Mineralogical Methods Second Edition, 1986, and *Methods of Soil Analysis*, Part 2: Chemical and Microbiological Properties Second Edition, 1982, both from American Society of Agronomy, Inc., Soil Science Society of America, Inc., 677 South Segoe Rd, Madison, WI 53711; *Soil Sampling and Methods of Analysis*, 1993, Canadian Society of Soil Science, 907-151 Slater St., Ottawa, Ontario K1P5H4 Canada, Lewis Publishers, Boca Raton FL. See Table at the end of Section 2.

Methods of Air Sampling and Analysis (3rd Edition, 1990, Lodge, MASA), Lewis Publishers, Boca Raton, FL.

Table 1-31. Method contents of Air Sampling, 3rd Edition

Method	Title/Description
Ambient Air Methods	
101	Determination of C1 through C5 atmospheric hydrocarbons
102	Separation and determination of PAH and benzo(a)pyrene
102A	Extraction and cleanup procedures for PAH in atmospheric particulate matter
102B	Separation and microanalysis of airborne particulate matter for benzo(a)pyrene using TLC and spectrofluorimetry
102C	Measurement of benzo(a)pyrene and benzo(k)fluoranthene by spectrofluorimetry
102D	Measurement of PAH using HPLC with fluorescence detection
108	Continuous determination of total hydrocarbons (FID)
109	Flame ionization detector
114	Determination of acrolein (colorimetric)
116	Determination of formaldehyde (colorimetric)
117	Determination of formaldehyde (MBTH colorimetric)
118	Determination of mercaptans
121	Determination of phenols (GC)
122	Determination of C1-C5 aldehydes by HPLC
128	Continuous determination of CO (Nondispersive infrared)
133	Determination of O_2, N_2, CO, CO_2, and CH_4 (GC)
134	Constant pressure volumetric analysis for O_2, N_2, CO and CO_2
135	Determination of volatile organic compounds in surface coatings
201	Chloride content
202	Free chlorine (Methyl orange)
203	Fluoride in atmosphere and plant tissues (manual)
204	Fluoride in atmosphere and plant tissues (semi-automated)
205	Fluoride in plant tissues (potentiometric)
206	Particulate and gaseous fluorides (Sodium bicarbonate coated glass tube and filter)
207	Particulate and gaseous fluorides (double paper tape)
301	Antimony
302	Arsenic
303A	Preparation of environmental samples for trace metal analysis
317	Mercury by collection on Ag wool and AAS
319	Molybdenum by AAS

Continued on next page.

Table 1-31. Method contents of Air Sampling, 3rd Edition, *continued*

Method	Title/Description
	Ambient Air Methods, *continued*
401	Ammonia (indophenol method)
404	Nitrate (brucine method)
405	Nitric oxide
406	Nitrogen dioxide (Greiss-Saltzman reaction)
407	Total nitrogen oxides as nitrate (phenoldisulfonic acid method)
408	Nitrogen dioxide (24H average)
411	Oxidizing substances
413	Ozone by gas phase chemiluminescence
415	Nitric acid
416	Continuous monitoring of nitric oxide and nitrogen dioxide
417	Continuous monitoring of ozone
501	High volume measurement of size classified particulates
502	Measurement of dustfall
503	Continuous tape sampling of coefficient of haze
507	Nephelometer measurement of scattering coefficient and fine particles
601	Gross alpha
602	Gross beta
603	Iodine-131
606	Radon-222
609A	Tritium in water vapor
609B	Total tritium
701	Hydrogen sulfide
704A	Sulfur dioxide (tetrachloromercurate/pararosaniline)
704B	Sulfur dioxide (formaldehyde/pararosaniline)
704C	Sulfur dioxide (hydrogen peroxide method)
707	Continuous sulfur dioxide measurement (amperometric)
708	Mercaptans
709	Sulfur containing gases (continuous with FPD)
709A	Sulfur containing gases (GC-FPD)
709B	Sulfur containing gases (total with FPD)
711	Gaseous sulfuric acid and sulfur dioxide in stack gases
713	Semi-continuous particulate sulfur, sulfuric acid and ammonium sulfates
714	Sulfur dioxide emissions in stack gases by pulsed fluorescence
720A	Suppressed anion chromatography
720B	Nonsuppressed anion chromatography
720C	Flow injection determination of aqueous sulfate (MTB method)
720D	Barium sulfate turbidimetry
720E	Barium perchlorate microtitration

Continued on next page.

Table 1-31. Method contents of Air Sampling, 3rd Edition, *continued*

Method	Title/Description
Ambient Air Methods, *continued*	
720F	Barium chloranilate spectrophotometry
730	Particulate sulfur by X-ray fluorescence
Workplace Air and Biological Samples	
801	Ammonia in air
804	As, Se, and Sb in urine and air by hydride generation AAS
805	Chloride in air
806	Free chlorine in air
807	Chromic acid mist in air
808	Cyanide in air
809	Flouride and hydrogen fluoride in air
810	Particulate and gaseous fluorides in air
811	Fluoride in urine
812	Hydrogen sulfide in air
815	Mercury in urine
818	Nitrogen dioxide in air
819	Ozone in air
821	Phosgene in air
822	AAS method for trace metals in air
822A	Preparation of tissue samples for analysis of trace metals
822B	X-ray fluorescence for multi-element analysis of particulate and biological materials
824	Sulfates in air
825	Acrolein in air
826	Acrolein in air
827	Aromatic amines in air
828	Bis-2-chloromethyl ether
829	Chloromethyl methyl ether and bis-2-chloromethyl ether in air
830	3,3'-Dichloro-4,4'-diaminodiphenylmethane in air
831	p,p'-Diphenylmethane diisocyanate
832	Nitroglycerine and ethylene glycol dinitrate in air
833	N-Nitrosodimethylamine in air
834	Organic solvent vapors
835	EPN, malathion and parathion in air
836	Total particulate PAH (ultrasonic extraction method)
837	2,4-Toluenediisocyanate in air

III. SAMPLING PROCEDURES

It is a commonly held belief that over 50% of all errors in environmental analysis result from incorrect sampling. I personally do not ascribe to this belief, as most of these "sampling" problems can be traced back to a lack of communication between the sampler and the laboratory. Most of these problems can be avoided if provisions are made ahead of time for the five factors that control sampling. They are:

1) The safety of the person performing the sampling,
2) Obtaining a representative sample of whatever is being tested,
3) Preventing contamination of the sample,
4) Providing legal documentation of the sampling event, and finally,
5) Protecting the sample from chemical, physical or biological change prior to analysis.

All these factors are discussed in detail in the EPA Region IV *Standard Operating Procedure and Quality Assurance Manual* (March, 1996), available on the internet at www.epa.gov/region04/sesd. Other good sources for information about sampling are *Standard Operating Procedures for Laboratory Operations and Sample Collection Activities* by the Florida Department of Environmental Regulation Quality Assurance Section, 2600 Blair Stone Road, Tallahassee, FL 32399-2400 (publication DER QA-001/92) and two books by Larry Keith *Environmental Sampling and Analysis, A Practical Guide* (1991, Lewis Publishers) and *Principles of Environmental Sampling* (1988, American Chemical Society, a second edition has been published). Also helpful is a database from Instant Reference Resources, 7605 Rockpoint Dr., Austin, TX, 78731, *Instant Gloves + CPC Database*. ASTM has published in book form a collection of 81 ASTM procedures related to sampling, *ASTM Standards on Environmental Sampling* (1995, ASTM, 1916 Race St., Philadelphia PA 19103). EPA published a two volume desk reference guide, *Subsurface Characterization and Monitoring Techniques*, (EPA 625/R-93/003 a and b) that includes a substantial amount of information of sampling soil and groundwater sources.

A. Safety of Collector

Environmental samples must always be considered to be hazardous to the health of the person performing the sampling. The samples can have toxic, corrosive, explosive, and flammable properties. The minimum protection consists of eye protection, latex or other types of gloves, steel-capped workboots, and normal clothing. Other specialized protection could include respirators and oxygen breathing apparatus for sampling from manholes, enclosed areas, and chemical waste drums. Special protective clothing such as overalls and Tyvek® (Trade mark of Dupont U.K. Ltd.) polyethylene suits may be required. Mixed waste (radioactive) samples present their own particular hazards, and the appropriate DOE (Department of Energy) guidelines should be consulted.

B. Record Keeping

Environmental sampling always has the potential of leading to legal court challenges. As a result, each sampling event must be legally defensible. Adequate documentation and records must be obtained prior to, during, and after the field operations. Satisfactory site description could be augmented with field pictures by the sampling technicians. A field log book that is bound with waterproof resin-coated pages must be maintained and must fully document everything performed by the field technicians during the sampling event. Other information in the log book includes time and date of the sampling event, names of persons performing the sampling, lot numbers of the pre-cleaned sample containers used, duration and flow rates of sampling equipment, results of field tests performed, lists of samples obtained, preservatives used, QC measures or samples obtained, weather and site conditions, etc. All entries are made in waterproof ink. Corrections are lined through with a single line, and the person making the correction dates and initials it. Some sort of laboratory analysis request form should be used for sampling and invoicing records.

The most important part of the required legal documentation is the chain of custody record. It is a form that lists a description of the sample, who collected it in what container, and where and when the sample was collected. The form has room for the signatures and times/dates when the sample was passed from person to person as it made its way to the laboratory. Other information on the chain of custody record could include the requested test parameters, preservatives used, comments on the condition of the sample when it arrived in the laboratory, verification of correct preservation by the lab, contact persons for information about the sample and possibly notes about particular characteristics of the sample that may be of interest to the laboratory.

Sample labeling is very important. Since many samples are sent to the laboratory in ice chests containing a slurry of ice and water, each sample container must be properly labeled. This may consist of a tag or waterproof gummed label, written in waterproof ink and containing the name of the collector, date, time, exact location of sampling, preservatives added, analysis desired, sample number, and other information such as weather, temperature, water level, flow rate, pump rate, and downdraw (wells). Each sample container in the ice chest must have a corresponding entry in the chain of custody record, and the information on the sample label must agree with the chain of custody record entry.

A record of the sample receipt in the laboratory is maintained in the laboratory log book. The entries may be very detailed, particularly in the situations where the receipts book is maintained in a central computerized Laboratory Information Management System (LIMS), however the minimum information contained must consist of time and date of sampling, time and date of receipt, field and laboratory sample number, client information and desired analysis.

Detailed records must be maintained of the work performed upon the sample in the laboratory. A discussion of appropriate records supporting these procedures is included in the next section. One record that must be generated and maintained in the laboratory that directly affects field operations is the performance of blank analysis upon sample container lots. A laboratory will purchase many cases of pre-cleaned sample containers from the same vendor's lot number. A random selection of the containers is filled with analyte-free water, then the water is analyzed for the parameters for which the sample containers are intended. The blank tests must give BDL results for all the intended parameters, or the lot is not suitable for sampling. These records must be maintained by the lab to verify the suitablility of the sample containers.

The final report of analysis should contain a summary of the field operations that collected the sample. Problems with the sample resulting from the sampling procedures that result in unacceptable deviations from the required procedure must be indicated on the final report as qualified data. A flag is placed by the parameter result, and a footnote is attached to that page of the final result, beginning with the statement that the data is unsuitable for regulatory reporting due to a reason. Figure 1-2 has an example.

ANALYTICAL SERVICES, INC.

ENVIRONMENTAL MONITORING & LABORATORY ANALYSIS
110 TECHNOLOGY PARKWAY • NORCROSS, GEORGIA 30092
(770) 743-4200 • FAX (770) 734-4201

LABORATORY REPORT

Springfield Power Plant   December 12, 1992
PO Box 1234
1st St.
Springfield, Ohio

Attention: Mr. Homer Simpson   Report No. <u>9999-1</u>

Sample: Water, grab, 435Z, 10-18-92, Time, received 10-25-92

RESULTS

	Result	Detection Limit
Total Lead (Pb) (mg/L) (EPA 239.2)	1.41*	0.005
Total Copper (Cu) (mg/L) (EPA 220.2)	0.12*	0.002

Respectfully submitted,

By:

* Result Not Suitable for Regulatory Reporting: Sample Received Incorrectly Preserved,
   Not Acidified.

Figure 1–2. Example of a final analytical report.

C. Sample Security

Another aspect of producing legally defensible data is establishing and documenting sample security. Most people would not consider tampering with samples to be a serious problem in real life, and it probably is not. However, within the legal system, sample tampering must always be considered a possibility, and active steps must be taken to eliminate it. The chain of custody record is the primary document of sample security, and it records the length of time that each person who came in contact with the sample was responsible for the sample's security. The security is defined as either the sample being in the physical possession of the person, in the unimpeded eyesight of the person, or in a locked container that provided restricted access to the sample by the responsible person.

Sample security can be further verified by placing a sample seal across the opening of the sample container. A sample seal is a strip of adhesive plastic or waterproofed paper that contains many small cuts so that after application to the sample container, the seal will tear upon attempted removal. The seal is labeled with the initials of the person applying it and the time and date. The condition of the sample seals are noted in writing by each person receiving custody of the sample on the chain of custody record.

Sample security also involves restricted storage, which can consist of locked refrigerators or storage cabinets with limited access, locked sample rooms with limited access, locked buildings with controlled access, or in the most extreme case, locked sample access that is controlled by a dedicated clerk or guard. An internal chain of custody is maintained in any of these cases. A recent innovation to the written internal chain of custody record is to let the LIMS maintain the records and to inform the LIMS of sample movement through use of bar code readers, where each sample container has a unique bar code, and each analyst has a unique password to activate the reading function. Restricted storage includes not only the sample itself but any digestates or extracts made from the sample.

D. Obtaining a Representative Sample

The best sample is the whole item, either a lake, stream, landfill, hazardous waste dump, field, or whatever. Due to laboratory size and transportation restraints, analyzing a whole lake is not feasible, thus a small portion of the water from the lake is taken for analysis and the result extrapolated back to represent the whole of the lake. From this point of view, no sample is truly representative of the system as a whole. Over time a number of sampling schemes have been developed that attempt to represent the whole.

A single sampling event is called a grab sample. Many analytes such as oil & grease, petroleum hydrocarbons, dissolved oxygen, total coliform, fecal coliform, and volatile organics can only be sampled as grabs. A grab sample is limited to the single time (less than a period of 15 minutes) and location of the sample. Representation of the whole sampling area requires the obtaining of many grab samples over a period of time, analysis of each sample and then averaging the results.

The concept of multiple sampling as a means of obtaining an overall picture of a test site has been formalized into a series of variables. These variables of multiple sampling are based upon obtaining a standard size sample per unit time, per unit flow, or per unit distance from one sampling point to the next. The time domain is where a sample is obtained at regular time intervals, generally at one sampling location. The flow domain is when a sample is obtained from a stationary sampling location after every set amount of flow, such as every 1000 gallons. The areal domain can be either vertical or horizontal, but both are based upon obtaining a sample at a set distance frequency through a sampling site. Sequential samples are samples obtained under a particular domain that are maintained and analyzed as separate samples. Composite samples are samples obtained under a variety of domains that are mixed together to form an average sample, then subsamples of the well-mixed composite are analyzed for the parameters of interest. The most common situation is under either time- or flow- domain. Both sequential and composite samples are assisted in the flow- or time- domain through the use of automated samplers designed to refrigerate the samples as they are obtained. An areal composite sample is obtained from samples taken over an area under the same conditions, then mixed to form a composite. An example is taking grab samples from a number of points around the shore of a lake, then compositing the samples to obtain an average of the lake. A vertical composite sample is obtained from samples taken from a variety of depths at one or several sampling points. The most complete sampling scheme is the integrated sample, which uses a variety of different methods of sampling together to form an overall picture of the site.

E. Sample Containers

Sample containers are normally borosilicate glass or high density polyethylene (HDPE). Sample containers must be clean and proven free of target analytes. Some directions for cleaning containers are given in Appendix E. Similar instructions are provided in guidance[96] published under the Superfund program. Containers can also be purchased as pre-cleaned and then checked by the laboratory to insure that the container is not adding or subtracting analytes to the sample. The idea is to avoid situations such as a sample taken in a metal solvent can with requested parameter tests for iron, chromium, zinc and tin. Containers must be of an appropriate size to obtain enough sample for performing the analysis and the associated QC procedures such as duplicates and matrix spikes.

- Some samples must be collected in several containers as only one analysis is performed per container.
- Samples for volatile organic analysis must be obtained in duplicate (or better triplicate) in glass with a Teflon® (Trademark of Dupont) faced silicone cap liner and no headspace.
- Non-volatile organics are normally obtained in glass with a Teflon-lined cap.
- Microbiological samples must be obtained in sterile containers.
- Metals are normally collected in HDPE containers as glass can exchange out metal ions. Mercury in elemental form will pass through the walls of an HDPE container and should be collected in glass.

F. Preservatives

Preservatives are used to maintain the chemical integrity of the sample. Most solid samples have only cooling as a preservative. Water samples are subject to a variety of specific preservation techniques, depending on the target analytes. Preservatives can consist of chemical additives such as acids or bases added to control pH, ascorbic acid or thiosulfate added to reduce the effect of residual chlorine and other oxidizers, etc. A common preservative is storage temperature, normally 4 °C, however, metals may

---

[96] *Specifications and Guidance for Contaminant-free Sample Containers.* USEPA Office of Solid Waste and Emergency Response. December, 1992. (EPA 540/R-93/051, PB93-963316).

precipitate out of solution on cooling, such solutions should be kept at room temperature. The cool temperature of 4 °C is obtained by storing the samples in an ice chest of either metal or polyethylene construction with a slurry of ice and water used to maintain the proper temperature. The use of reusable cold packs is not currently accepted. Preservation may also include the storing of the samples in the dark or in amber bottles. See Tables 1-32 through 1-41.

Preservation always has a quantitative measure of success associated with it. For example, when the indicated preservation technique is to cool the sample, a desired temperature is included, such as, "Cool 4 °C". The existence of the quantitative aspect of preservation means that the pH, removal of residual chlorine, or temperature of the sample should be checked in the field and definitely in the laboratory. At the same time concern over possible contamination of the sample resulting from dipping a probe or a test strip into the sample suggests that a slight modification in how samples are obtained may be in order. The suggested modification is to take at least two identical samples for each analytical parameter, then use one of the samples to determine the preservation requirements. If it is found that say 1.2 mL of nitric acid are required to lower the sample pH to <2, then addition of the same amount of acid to the other container of sample will achieve the correct preservation, without contaminating the sample to be sent to the laboratory.

Preservation techniques in conjunction with holding times have come under scrutiny, particularly the preservation of volatiles. References to these research efforts are in the following holding time discussion.

G. Holding Times

The holding time before analysis is of critical practical and regulatory importance. Analytes will degrade and be lost from the sample over time, even when correctly preserved and stored. All analytes have required holding times, from immediate analysis for dissolved oxygen, to 6 hours for coliform determination, and up to 6 months for heavy metals. The holding time clock starts with the moment of sampling and ends with the beginning of the analysis procedure. Holding times are not (except in the CLP) measured as the lapsed time from receipt of the sample in the laboratory to the beginning of the analysis. Holding times are often required parts of submitted QA reports on data submitted in support of regulatory requirements. The assorted regulations commonly conflict in terms of sample containers, holding times and preservation, thus it is necessary to consult the appropriate regulation reference to discover the compliance requirements. The most frequently used charts are reproduced in Tables 1-32 through 1-41.

Holding times were the subject of a symposium during a July 1994 EPA conference in Washington, D.C. Holding times were originally conceived with the idea of providing guidelines for performing analyses within a sensible timeframe to minimize sample degradation. Now holding times have taken on a legal life of their own, often with no connection to scientific reality. The inconsistency of the regulatory interpretation of holding times was most succinctly made by John Gumper from DataChem in Utah. He described the phenomenon of how a sample with a holding time of 7 days prior to extraction, is acceptable if extraction is begun 6 days, 23 hours, 59 minutes and 59 seconds after the moment of sampling, but magically turns to garbage one second later if not in a separatory funnel. Not particularly obvious at the moment of occurrence in the laboratory, this transition is most easily observed 5 years later in a courtroom.

A number of studies of suitable preservation and holding times have recently been performed and reported for mercury[97], volatile organic compounds[98] and explosives residues[99]. As to be expected the instructions included in many regulatory methods are found in some cases appropriate while in others they are simply wrong.

Table 1-32. Drinking water holding time, preservation and sample container requirements from Manual for the Certification of Laboratories Analyzing Drinking Water - Criteria and Procedures Quality Assurance, Fourth Edition, March, 1997

Parameter	Sample Volume & Container[100]	Preservation	Max. Holding Time
Bacterial Tests			
Coliform, Fecal and Total	100 ml, Sterile P	Cool 4 °C, 0.1 mL of 10% $Na_2S_2O_3$	30 hours from time of collection
Inorganic Tests			
Alkalinity	200 ml, P, G	Cool, 4 °C	14 days
Antimony	500 ml, P, G	Conc HNO_3 to pH <2	6 months
Arsenic	500 ml, P, G	Conc HNO_3 to pH <2	6 months
Asbestos	1000 ml, P, G	Cool, 4 °C	-
Barium	500 ml, P, G	Conc HNO_3 to pH <2	6 months
Beryllium	500 ml, P, G	Conc HNO_3 to pH <2	6 months
Cadmium	500 ml, P, G	Conc HNO_3 to pH <2	6 months
Calcium	500 ml, P, G	Conc HNO_3 to pH <2	6 months
Chloride	200 ml, P, G	None	28 days
Chromium	500 ml, P, G	Conc HNO_3 to pH <2	6 months
Copper	500 ml, P, G	Conc HNO_3 to pH <2	6 months
Cyanide	500 ml, P, G	NaOH to pH >12, cool 4° C, 0.6 g ascorbic acid	14 days
Fluoride	500 ml, P, G	None	1 month
Free Chlorine Residual	100 ml, P, G	None	Analyze immediately
Lead	500 ml, P, G	Conc HNO_3 to pH <2	6 months
Mercury	500 ml, P, G	Conc HNO_3 to pH <2	28 days
Nickel	500 ml, P, G	Conc HNO_3 to pH <2	6 months

Continued on next page.

97 Hamlin, S.N. Preservation of Samples for Dissolved Mercury, 1989. *Water Resources Bulletin*, 25(2):255-262.
98 Turriff, D., C. Reitmeyer, L. Jacobs and N. Melberg. *Comparison of Alternatives for Sampling & Storage of VOCs in Soil*; Hewitt, A. *Determining Volatile Organic Compound Concentration Stability in Soil*. Eleventh Annual Waste Testing and Quality Assurance Symposium, July 22-26, 1995. Washington, D.C.; Liikala, T.L., K.B. Olsen, S.S. Teel, and D.C. Lanigan. 1996. "Volatile Organic compounds: Comparison of Two Sample Collection and Preservation Methods." *Environ. Sci. Technol.* 30(12). pp. 3441-3447; Hewett, A. D. 1997. "Chemical Preservation of Volatile Organic Compounds in Soil." *Environ. Sci. Technol.* 31(1). pp. 67-70.
99 Jenkins, T., and P.G. Thorne, *Evaluation of the New Clean Solid Phases for Extraction of Nitroaromatics and Nitramines from Water*. Eleventh Annual Waste Testing and Quality Assurance Symposium. July 22-26, 1995. Washington, D.C.
100 Polyethylene (P) or Glass (G).

Table 1-32. Drinking water holding time, preservation and sample container requirements from Manual for the Certification of Laboratories Analyzing Drinking Water - Criteria and Procedures Quality Assurance, Fourth Edition, March, 1997, *continued*

Parameter	Sample Volume & Container[101]	Preservation	Max. Holding Time
Inorganic Tests, *continued*			
Nitrate N	500 ml, P, G	Cool, 4 °C	28 days
Total Nitrate/Nitrite	500 ml, P, G	Cool, 4 °C, H_2SO_4 to pH <2	28 days
Nitrite N	500 ml, P, G	Cool 4 °C	48 hours
o-Phosphate	500 ml, P, G	Filter immediately, Cool 4 °C	48 hours
pH	500 ml, P, G	None	Analyze immediately
Selenium	500 ml, P, G	Conc HNO_3 to pH <2	6 months
Silica	500 ml, P	Cool 4 °C	28 days
Sodium	500 ml, P, G	Conc HNO_3 to pH <2	6 months
Temperature	500 ml, P, G	None	Analyze immediately
Thallium	500 ml, P, G	Conc HNO_3 to pH <2	6 months
Total Filterable Residue (TDS)	500 ml, P, G	Cool 4 °C	7 days
Turbidity	500 ml, P, G	Cool 4 °C	48 hours
Organic Tests (method)			
EDB & DBPC (504)	40 mL glass with Teflon cap liner	3 mg sodium thiosulfate, HCl to pH <2, Cool 4 °C	28 days to extraction, analyze immediately
Chlorinated pesticides (505)	40 mL glass with Teflon cap liner	3 mg sodium thiosulfate, Cool 4 °C	14 days to extraction, analyze immediately
Phthalates and Adipates (506)	1 L amber glass with Teflon cap liner	60 mg/L sodium thiosulfate, Cool 4 °C	14 days to extraction, 14 days to analysis
NP pesticides (507)	1 L amber glass with Teflon cap liner	10 mg/L mercuric chloride, 80 mg/L sodium thiosulfate, Cool 4 °C	7 days to extraction, 14 days to analysis
Chlorinated pesticides (508)	1 L glass with Teflon cap liner	10 mg/L mercuric chloride, 80 mg/L sodium thiosulfate, Cool 4 °C	7 days to extraction, 14 days to analysis
PCB (508A)	1 L glass with Teflon cap liner	Cool 4 °C	14 days to extraction, 30 days to analysis
Herbicides (515.1)	1 L amber glass with Teflon cap liner	10 mg/L mercuric chloride, 80 mg/L sodium thiosulfate, Cool 4 °C	14 days to extraction, 28 days to analysis
BNA (525.1)	1 L glass with Teflon cap liner	40-50 mg/L sodium sulfite, HCl to pH <2, Cool 4 °C	7 days to extraction, 30 days to analysis
Carbamates (531.1)	1 L glass with Teflon cap liner	Monochloroacetic acid to pH 3, 80 mg/L sodium thiosulfate, Cool 4 °C until storage at -10 °C	28 days with storage at -10 °C
Glyphosate (547)	1 L amber glass with Teflon cap liner	100 mg/L sodium thiosulfate, Cool 4 °C	14 days

Continued on next page.

---

[101] Polyethylene (P) or Glass (G).

Table 1-32. Drinking water holding time, preservation and sample container requirements from Manual for the Certification of Laboratories Analyzing Drinking Water - Criteria and Procedures Quality Assurance, Fourth Edition, March, 1997, *continued*

Parameter	Sample Volume & Container	Preservation	Max. Holding Time
Organic Tests, *continued*			
Endothall (548 and 548.1)	1 L glass with Teflon cap liner	Cool 4 °C	7 days to extraction, 1 day to analysis
Diquat & Paraquat (549)	1 L amber high density PVC or silanized amber glass	100 mg/L sodium thiosulfate, sulfuric acid to pH <2, Cool 4 °C	7 days to extraction, 21 days to analysis
PAH (550 or 550.1)	1 L amber glass with Teflon cap liner	100 mg/L sodium thiosulfate, 6N HCl to pH <2, Cool 4 °C	7 days to extraction, 40 days to analysis
Dioxins (1613)	1 L amber glass with Teflon cap liner	80 mg/L sodium thiosulfate, Cool 4 °C	40 days
TTHM (501.1 or 501.2)	40 mL glass with Teflon lined septa	3 mg sodium thiosulfate or sodium sulfite	14 days
VOC (502.1, 502.1, or 503.1)	40 mL glass with Teflon lined silicon septa	25 mg ascorbic acid or 3 mg sodium thiosulfate, 1:1 HCl to pH <2, Cool 4 °C	14 days
VOC (524.1 or 524.2)	40 mL glass with Teflon lined silicon septa	25 mg ascorbic acid, 1:1 HCl to pH <2, Cool 4 °C	14 days
Radiological Tests[102]			
Gross alpha	1 L, P, G	Conc. HCl or HNO_3 to pH <2	-
Gross beta	1 L, P, G	Conc. HCl or HNO_3 to pH <2	-
Strontium-89	1 L, P, G	Conc. HCl or HNO_3 to pH <2	-
Strontium-90	1 L, P, G	Conc. HCl or HNO_3 to pH <2	-
Radium-226	1 L, P, G	Conc. HCl or HNO_3 to pH <2	-
Radium-228	1 L, P, G	Conc. HCl or HNO_3 to pH <2	-
Cesium-134	1 L, P, G	Conc. HCl to pH <2	-
Iodine-131	2 L, P, G	None	-
Tritium	1 L, P, G	None	-
Uranium	1 L, P, G	Conc. HCl or HNO_3 to pH <2	-
Photon emitters	P, G	Conc. HCl or HNO_3 to pH <2	-

---

[102] *Prescribed Procedures for Measurement of Radioactivity in Drinking Water*, EPA-600/4-80-032 1980.

Table 1-33. Holding times, containers and preservatives for wastewater samples. From 40 CFR 136, Table II, 1 July, 1998

Parameter	Sample volume & Container[103]	Preservation[104,105]	Max. Holding Time[106]
Biological Tests			
Coliform, Fecal and Total	100 ml, Sterile P or G	Cool 4 °C, 0.008% $Na_2S_2O_3$[107]	6 hours from time of collection
Fecal streptococci	100 ml, Sterile P or G	Cool 4 °C, 0.008% $Na_2S_2O_3$[68]	6 hours from time of collection
Acute or chronic WET	1000 mL P or G	Cool 4°C	36 hours
Inorganic Tests			
Acidity	500 ml, P, G	Cool 4 °C	14 days
Alkalinity	500 ml, P, G	Cool 4 °C	14 days
Ammonia	500 ml, P, G	Cool 4 °C, H_2SO_4 to pH <2	28 days
BOD	1000 ml, P, G	Cool, 4 °C	48 hours
Bromide	500 ml, P, G	None required	28 days
CBOD	1000 ml, P, G	Cool, 4 °C	48 hours
COD	500 ml, P, G	Cool 4 °C, H_2SO_4 to pH <2	28 days
Chloride	500 ml, P, G	None required	28 days
Chlorine, total residual	500 ml, P, G	None required	Analyze immediately
Color	500 ml, P, G	Cool 4 °C	48 hours

Continued on next page.

[103] Polyethylene (P) or Glass (G).

[104] Sample preservation should be performed immediately upon sample collection. For composite chemical samples each aliquot should be preserved at the time of collection. When use of an automated sampler makes it impossible to preserve each aliquot, then chemical samples may be preserved by maintaining at 4 °C until compositing and sample splitting is completed.

[105] When any sample is to be shipped by common carrier or sent through the US Postal System, it must comply with the Department of Transportation Hazardous Materials Regulations (49 CFR 172). The person offering such material for transportation is responsible for ensuring such compliance. For the preservation requirements of the Table, the Office of Hazardous Materials, Materials Transportation Bureau, Department of Transportation has determined that the Hazardous Materials Regulations do not apply to the following materials: Hydrochloric acid (HCl) in water solutions at concentrations of 0.04% by weight or less (pH about 1.96 or greater); Nitric acid in water solutions of 0.15% by weight or less (pH about 1.62 or greater); Sulfuric acid (H_2SO_4) in water solutions at concentrations of 0.35% by weight or less (pH about 1.15 or greater); and Sodium Hydroxide (NaOH) in water solutions at concentrations of 0.080% by weight or less (pH about 12.30 or less).

[106] Samples should be analyzed as soon as possible after collection. The times listed are the maximum times that samples may be held before analysis and still be considered valid. Samples may be held for longer periods only if the permittee, or monitoring laboratory, has data on file to show that the specific types of samples under study are stable for longer time, and has received a variance from the Regional Administrator under 40 CFR 136.3(e). Some samples may not be stable for the maximum time period given in the Table. A permittee, or monitoring laboratory, is obligated to hold the sample for a shorter time if knowledge exists to show that this is necessary to maintain sample stability. See 40 CFR 136.3(e) for details.

[107] Should only be used in the presence of residual chlorine.

Table 1-33. Holding times, containers and preservatives for wastewater samples. From 40 CFR 136, Table II, 1 July, 1998, *continued*

Parameter	Sample volume & Container[108]	Preservation[109,110]	Max. Holding Time[111]
Inorganic Tests, *continued*			
Cyanide, total and amenable to chlorination	P, G	Cool 4 °C, NaOH to pH >12, 0.6 g ascorbic acid[112]	14 days[113]
Fluoride	P	None required	28 days
Hardness	P, G	HNO_3 to pH <2, H_2SO_4 to pH < 2	6 months
Hydrogen ion (pH)	P, G	None required	Analyze immediately
Kjeldahl and organic nitrogen	P, G	Cool 4 °C, H_2SO_4 to pH <2	28 days
Metals[114]			
Boron	P(PTFE) or quartz	HNO_3 to pH <2,	6 months
Chromium VI	P, G	Cool 4 °C	24 hours
Mercury	P, G	HNO_3 to pH <2,	28 days
Metals, other	P, G	HNO_3 to pH <2,	6 months
Nitrate	P, G	Cool 4 °C	48 hours
Nitrate-nitrite	P, G	Cool 4 °C, H_2SO_4 to pH <2	28 days
Nitrite	P, G	Cool 4 °C	48 hours
Oil and grease	G	Cool 4 °C, HCl or H_2SO_4 to pH <2	28 days
Organic carbon	G	Cool 4 °C, HCl, H_2SO_4 or H_3PO_4 to pH <2	28 days
Orthophosphate	P, G	Filter immediately, Cool 4 °C	48 hours
Oxygen, dissolved probe	500 ml, Glass bottle and top	None required	Analyze immediately
Oxygen, dissolved Winkler	300 ml, Glass bottle and top	Fix on site and store in dark	8 hours
Phenols, total	500 ml, G only	Cool 4 °C, H_2SO_4 to pH <2	28 days

Continued on next page.

---

[108] See footnote 103.
[109] See footnote 104.
[110] See footnote 105.
[111] See footnote 106.
[112] Should only be used in the presence of residual chlorine.
[113] Maximum holding time is 24 hours when sulfide is present. Optionally, all samples may be tested with lead acetate paper before pH adjustments in order to determine if sulfide is present. If sulfide is present, it can be removed by the addition of cadmium nitrate powder until a negative spot test is obtained. The sample is filtered, and then NaOH is added to pH 12.
[114] Samples should be filtered immediately on-site before adding preservative for dissolved metals.

Table 1-33. Holding times, containers and preservatives for wastewater samples. From 40 CFR 136, Table II, 1 July, 1998, *continued*

Parameter	Sample volume & Container[115]	Preservation[116,117]	Max. Holding Time[118]
Metals, *continued*			
Phosphorous (elemental)	500 ml, G	Cool 4 °C	48 hours
Phosphorous, total	500 ml, P, G	Cool 4 °C, H_2SO_4 to pH <2	28 days
Residue, total (TS)	500 ml, P, G	Cool 4 °C	7 days
Residue, Filterable (TDS)	500 ml, P, G	Cool 4 °C	7 days
Residue, Nonfilterable (TSS)	500 ml, P, G	Cool 4 °C	7 days
Residue, settleable	1000 ml, P, G	Cool 4 °C	48 hours
Residue, volatile	500 ml, P, G	Cool 4 °C	7 days
Silica	500 ml, PTFE or quartz	Cool 4 °C	28 days
Specific conductance	500 ml, P, G	Cool 4 °C	28 days
Sulfate	P, G	Cool 4 °C	28 days
Sulfide	P, G	Cool 4 °C, add zinc acetate and NaOH to pH >9	7 days
Sulfite	P, G	None required	Analyze immediately
Surfactants	P, G	Cool 4 °C	48 hours
Temperature	P, G	None required	Analyze immediately
Turbidity	P, G	Cool 4 °C	48 hours
Organic Tests (method)			
Purgeable halocarbons (601, 624, or 1624)	40 mL glass, Teflon lined silicon septum	Cool 4 °C, 0.008% $Na_2S_2O_3$[119]	14 days
Purgeable aromatic hydrocarbons (602, 624, or 1624)	40 mL glass, Teflon lined silicon septum	Cool 4 °C, 0.008% $Na_2S_2O_3$[80], HCl to pH 2 [120]	14 days
Acrolein and acrylonitrile (603, 624, or 1624)	40 mL glass, Teflon lined silicon septum	Cool 4 °C, 0.008% $Na_2S_2O_3$[80], adjust pH to 4-5 [121]	14 days

Continued on next page.

---

[115] See footnote 103.
[116] See footnote 104.
[117] See footnote 105.
[118] See footnote 106.
[119] Should only be used in the presence of residual chlorine.
[120] Sample receiving no pH adjustment must be analyzed within 7 days of sampling.
[121] The pH adjustment is not required if acrolein will not be measured. Samples for acrolein receiving no pH adjustment must be analyzed within 3 days of sampling.

Table 1-33. Holding times, containers and preservatives for wastewater samples. From 40 CFR 136, Table II, 1 July, 1998, *continued*

Parameter	Sample volume & Container[122]	Preservation[123],[124]	Max. Holding Time[125]
Organic Tests, *continued*			
Phenols[126] (604, 625, or 1625)	1L glass with Teflon lined cap	Cool 4 °C, 0.008% $Na_2S_2O_3$[127]	7 days until extraction, 40 days after extraction
Benzidine[128] (605, 625, or 1625)	1 L, glass with Teflon lined cap	Cool 4 °C, 0.008% $Na_2S_2O_3$[88]	7 days until extraction[129]
Phthalates (606, 625, or 1625)	1 L, glass with Teflon lined cap	Cool 4 °C	7 days until extraction, 40 days after extraction
Nitrosamines[130] (607, 625, or 1625)	1 L, glass with Teflon lined cap	Cool 4 °C, 0.008% $Na_2S_2O_3$[88], store in dark	7 days until extraction, 40 days after extraction
PCB (608 or 625)	1 L, glass with Teflon lined cap	Cool 4 °C	7 days until extraction, 40 days after extraction
Nitroaromatics and isophorone (609, 625 or 1625)	1 L, glass with Teflon lined cap	Cool 4 °C, 0.008% $Na_2S_2O_3$[88], store in dark	7 days until extraction, 40 days after extraction
PAH (610, 625 or 1625)	1 L, glass with Teflon lined cap	Cool 4 °C, 0.008% $Na_2S_2O_3$[88], store in dark	7 days until extraction, 40 days after extraction
Haloethers (611, 625 or 1625)	1 L, glass with Teflon lined cap	Cool 4 °C, 0.008% $Na_2S_2O_3$[88]	7 days until extraction, 40 days after extraction

Continued on next page.

[122] See footnote 103.

[123] See footnote 104.

[124] See footnote 105.

[125] See footnote 106.

[126] When the extractable analytes of concern fall within a single chemical category, the specified preservative and maximum holding time should be observed for optimum safeguard of sample integrity. When the analytes of concern fall within two or more chemical categories, the sample may be preserved by cooling to 4 °C, reducing residual chlorine with 0.008% sodium thiosulfate, storing in the dark, and adjusting the pH to 6-9; samples preserved in this manner may be held for 7 days before extraction and for 40 days after extraction. Exceptions to this optional preservation and holding time procedure are noted in footnote 107 (re: the requirement for thiosulfate reduction of residual chlorine) and footnotes 127 and 128 (re the analysis of benzidine).

[127] Should only be used in the presence of residual chlorine.

[128] If 1,2-diphenylhydrazine is likely to be present, adjust the pH of the sample to 4.0 ± 0.2 to prevent rearrangement to benzidine.

[129] Extracts may be stored for up to 7 days if storage is conducted under an inert (oxidant-free) atmosphere.

[130] For the analysis of diphenylnitrosamine, add 0.008% sodium thiosulfate and adjust pH to 7-10 with sodium hydroxide within 24 hours of sampling.

Table 1-33. Holding times, containers and preservatives for wastewater samples. From 40 CFR 136, Table II, 1 July, 1998, *continued*

Parameter	Sample volume & Container[131]	Preservation[132,133]	Max. Holding Time[134]
Organic Tests, *continued*			
Chlorinated hydrocarbons (612, 625 or 1625)	1 L, glass with Teflon lined cap	Cool 4 °C	7 days until extraction, 40 days after extraction
TCDD (613)	1 L, glass with Teflon lined cap	Cool 4 °C, 0.008% $Na_2S_2O_3$[135]	1 year
Chlorinated pesticides[136] (608 or 625)	1 L, glass with Teflon lined cap	Cool 4 °C, pH 6-9	7 days until extraction, 40 days after extraction
Radiological Tests			
Alpha, beta and radium[137]	1L P or G	HNO_3 to pH <2	6 months

---

[131] See footnote 103.

[132] See footnote 104.

[133] See footnote 105.

[134] See footnote 106.

[135] Should only be used in the presence of residual chlorine.

[136] The pH adjustment may be performed upon receipt at the laboratory and may be omitted if samples are extracted within 72 hours of collection. For the analysis of aldrin, add 0.008% sodium thiosulfate.

[137] *Prescribed Procedures for Measurement of Radioactivity in Drinking Water*, EPA-600/4-80-032 1980.

Table 1-34 Preservation, holding times and sample containers for aqueous matrices, Table 2-21 from Chapter 2, SW-846, Third Edition, Revision 1, July, 1992

Parameter	Container[138]	Preservation	Max. Holding Time
Bacterial Tests			
Coliform, total	P, G	Cool 4 °C, 0.008% $Na_2S_2O_3$	6 hours
Inorganic Tests			
Chloride	P, G	None required	28 days
Cyanide, total and amenable to chlorination	P, G	If oxidizing agents are present add 0.6 g ascorbic acid per liter; adjust pH >12 with 10N NaOH, Cool 4°C	14 days
Hydrogen ion (pH)	P, G	None required	Analyze immediately
Nitrate	P, G	Cool 4 °C	48 hours
Sulfate	P, G	Cool 4 °C	28 days
Sulfide	P, G	Cool 4 °C, add zinc acetate	7 days
Metals			
Chromium VI	P, G	Cool 4 °C	28 hours
Mercury	P, G	HNO_3 to pH <2	38 days glass 13 days plastic
Other metals	P, G	HNO_3 to pH <2	6 months
Organic Tests			
Oil & Grease	G	Cool 4 °C; adjust pH to <2 with HCl, H_2SO_4 or solid $NaHSO_4$	28 days
TOC	P, G	Cool 4 °C; adjust pH to <2 with HCl, H_2SO_4 or solid $NaHSO_4$	28 days
Purgeable halocarbons	Glass with Teflon lined septum	Cool 4 °C [139]	14 days
Purgeable aromatic hydrocarbons	Glass with Teflon lined septum	Cool 4 °C; adjust pH to <2 with HCl, H_2SO_4 or solid $NaHSO_4$[140]	14 days
Acrolein and acrylonitrile	Glass with Teflon lined septum	Cool 4 °C, 0.008% $Na_2S_2O_3$, adjust pH to 4-5	14 days
Phenols	Glass with Teflon lined cap	Cool 4 °C, 0.008% $Na_2S_2O_3$	7 days until extraction, 40 days after extraction
Benzidines	Glass with Teflon lined cap	Cool 4 °C, 0.008% $Na_2S_2O_3$	7 days until extraction, 40 days after extraction

Continued on next page.

---

[138] Polyethylene (P) or Glass (G).
[139] Free chlorine must be removed by appropriate addition of sodium thiosulfate.
[140] Free chlorine must be removed by appropriate addition of sodium thiosulfate, prior to acidification.

Table 1-34 Preservation, holding times and sample containers for aqueous matrices, Table 2-21 from Chapter 2, SW-846, Third Edition, Revision 1, July, 1992, *continued*

Parameter	Container[141]	Preservation	Max. Holding Time
Organic Tests, *continued*			
Phthalate esters	Glass with Teflon lined cap	Cool 4°C	7 days until extraction, 40 days after extraction
Nitrosamines	Glass with Teflon lined cap	Store in dark, Cool 4 °C, 0.008% $Na_2S_2O_3$	7 days until extraction, 40 days after extraction
PCBs	Glass with Teflon lined cap	Cool 4°C	7 days until extraction, 40 days after extraction
Nitroaromatics and cylic ketones	Glass with Teflon lined cap	Store in dark, Cool 4 °C, 0.008% $Na_2S_2O_3$	7 days until extraction, 40 days after extraction
PAH	Glass with Teflon lined cap	Store in dark, Cool 4 °C, 0.008% $Na_2S_2O_3$	7 days until extraction, 40 days after extraction
Haloethers	Glass with Teflon lined cap	Cool 4 °C, 0.008% $Na_2S_2O_3$	7 days until extraction, 40 days after extraction
Chlorinated hydrocarbons	Glass with Teflon lined cap	Cool 4 °C, 0.008% $Na_2S_2O_3$	7 days until extraction, 40 days after extraction
Dioxins and furans	Glass with Teflon lined cap	Cool 4 °C, 0.008% $Na_2S_2O_3$	7 days until extraction, 40 days after extraction
TOX	Glass with Teflon lined cap	Cool 4 °C; adjust pH to <2 with HCl, H_2SO_4 or solid $NaHSO_4$	28 days
Pesticides	Glass with Teflon lined cap	Cool 4 °C, pH 5-9	7 days until extraction, 40 days after extraction
Radiological Tests			
Alpha, beta and radium	P, G	HNO_3 to pH <2	6 months

Table 1-35. Sample containers, preservatives and holding times for hazardous waste samples analyzed by SW-846 methods

Parameter	Container[142]	Preservation	Max. Holding Time
Metals[143]			
Aqueous, Total	600 mL, P, G	Cool 4 °C, HNO_3 to pH < 2	6 months
Aqueous, Dissolved	600 mL, P, G	Filter on site, Cool 4 °C, HNO_3 to pH <2	6 months
Aqueous, Suspended	600 mL, P, G	Filter on site, Cool 4 °C	6 months
Solid, Total	200 g, P, G	Cool 4 °C	6 months
Chromium VI, aqueous	400 mL, P, G	Cool 4 °C	24 hours
Chromium VI, Solid	200 g, P, G	Cool 4 °C	As soon as possible

Continued on next page.

---

[141] Polyethylene (P) or Glass (G).
[142] Polyethylene (P) or Glass (G).
[143] Table 3-1, Chapter 3, page 3, SW-846, Revision 1, July, 1992 and proposed Revision 2, November, 1992.

Table 1-35. Sample containers, preservatives and holding times for hazardous waste samples analyzed by SW-846 methods, *continued*

Parameter	Container[144]	Preservation	Max. Holding Time
Metals, *continued*[145]			
Mercury, aqueous, total	400 mL, P, G	Cool 4 °C, HNO_3 to pH < 2	38 days G 13 days P
Mercury, aqueous, dissolved	400 mL, P, G	Filter, Cool 4 °C, HNO_3 to pH <2	38 days G 13 days P
Mercury, solid	200 g, P, G	Cool 4 °C	28 days
Organic Tests[146]			
VOA, concentrated waste samples	8 oz (125 mL) wide mouth glass with Teflon cap liner	None	14 days
VOA, liquid sample	2 x 40 mL glass with Teflon lined septum cap	Adjust to pH <2 with H_2SO_4, HCl or solid $NaHSO_4$, Cool 4 °C	14 days
VOA, liquid sample, chlorine residual present	2 x 40 mL glass with Teflon lined septum cap	Collect sample in 4 oz container with 4 dps 10% $Na_2S_2O_3$, dispense into 40 mL vials, Adjust to pH <2 with H_2SO_4, HCl or solid $NaHSO_4$, Cool 4 °C	14 days
VOA, soil, sediment or sludge	4 oz (125 mL) wide mouth glass with Teflon cap liner	Cool 4 °C	14 days
Acrolein and acrylonitrile, liquid sample	2 x 40 mL glass with Teflon lined septum cap	Adjust to pH 4-5, Cool 4 °C	14 days
Semivolatile, concentrated waste	8 oz (125 mL) wide mouth glass with Teflon cap liner	None	14 days before extraction, analyzed within 40 days after extraction
Semivolatile, water sample	1 gal or 2 x 0.5 gal amber glass with Teflon cap liner	Cool 4 °C	7 days before extraction, analyzed within 40 days after extraction
Semivolatile, water sample, chlorine residual present	1 gal or 2 x 0.5 gal amber glass with Teflon cap liner	3 mL 10% $Na_2S_2O_3$ per gal, Cool 4 °C	7 days before extraction, analyzed within 40 days after extraction
Semivolatile, soil, sediment or sludge sample	8 oz (125 mL) wide mouth glass with Teflon cap liner	Cool 4 °C	14 days before extraction, analyzed within 40 days after extraction

Continued on next page.

---

[144] Polyethylene (P) or Glass (G).
[145] Table 3-1, Chapter 3, page 3, SW-846, Revision 1, July, 1992 and proposed Revision 2, November, 1992.
[146] Table 4-1, Chapter 4, page 6-7, SW-846, Revison 1, July, 1992.

Table 1-35. Sample containers, preservatives and holding times for hazardous waste samples analyzed by SW-846 methods, *continued*

Parameter	Sample volume & Container[147]	Preservation	Max. Holding Time
TCLP, Method 1311[148]			
Volatiles	Glass with Teflon lined septum	Cool 4 °C and minimal headspace before and after TCLP	14 days to TCLP, 14 days after TCLP to analysis
Semi-volatiles	Glass with Teflon lined cap	Cool 4 °C before and after TCLP	14 days to TCLP, 7 days after TCLP to extraction, 40 days after extraction to analysis
Mercury	P, G	Preserve with HNO_3 to pH <2 after TCLP	28 days to TCLP, 28 days after TCLP to analysis
Other metals	P, G	Preserve with HNO_3 to pH <2 after TCLP	180 days to TCLP, 180 days after TCLP to analysis

Table 1-36. Sampling and preservation procedures for groundwater detection monitoring, Table 11-1, Chapter 11, page 7, SW-846, Third Edition, Revision 0, September, 1986

Parameter	Sample Volume & Container[149]	Preservation	Max. Holding Time
pH	25 mL, T, P, G	None	Analyze immediately
Specific Conductance	100 mL, T, P, G	None	Analyze immediately
TOC	4 x 15 mL, Glass, Teflon lined cap	Cool 4 °C, HCl to pH < 2	28 days
TOX	4 x 15 mL, Amber glass, Teflon lined cap	Cool 4 °C, 1 mL of 1.1 M sodium sulfite	7 days
Chloride	50 mL, T, P, G	Cool 4 °C	28 days
Metals, Total[150]	1000 mL, T, P[151]	Field acidified to pH < 2 with HNO_3	6 months
Metals, Dissolved[152]	1000 mL, T, P[153]	Field filtration (0.45 mm) then acidify to pH < 2 with HNO_3	6 months
Phenols	500 mL, G	Cool 4 °C, H_2SO_4 to pH < 2	28 days
Sulfate	50 mL, T, P, G	Cool 4 °C	28 days

Continued on next page.

---

[147] Polyethylene (P) or Glass (G).
[148] Method 1311, SW-846, Third Edition, Revision 0, July, 1992.
[149] Teflon (T), Polyethylene (P), Polypropylene (PP) or Glass (G).
[150] Includes iron, manganese, arsenic, barium, cadmium, chromium, lead, mercury, selenium, sodium and silver.
[151] Silver sample is collected in a dark bottle.
[152] Includes iron, manganese, arsenic, barium, cadmium, chromium, lead, mercury, selenium, sodium and silver.
[153] Silver sample is collected in a dark bottle.

Table 1-36. Sampling and preservation procedures for groundwater detection monitoring, Table 11-1, Chapter 11, page 7, SW-846, Third Edition, Revision 0, September, 1986, *continued*

Parameter	Sample Volume & Container[154]	Preservation	Max. Holding Time
Fluoride	300 mL, T, P	Field acidified to pH < 2 with HNO_3	28 days
Nitrate	1000 mL, T, P, G	Cool 4 °C, H_2SO_4 to pH < 2	14 days
Chlorinated pesticides and herbicides	2000 mL, T, G	Cool 4 °C	7 days
Radium, Gross alpha, and Gross beta	1 gal, P, G	Field acidified to pH < 2 with HNO_3	6 months
Coliform bacteria	200 mL, Sterilized PP or G	Cool 4 °C	6 hours
Cyanide	500 mL, P, G	NaOH to pH >12, Cool 4 °C	14 days
Oil & Grease	100 mL, G	H_2SO_4 to pH < 2, Cool 4 °C	28 days
Semivolatile, volatile organics	1000 mL, T, G	Cool 4 °C	7 days

Table 1-37. Sample container, preservation and holding time requirements in CLP-SOW

Parameter	Container[155]	Preservative[156]	Max. Holding Time
Inorganic Tests[157]			
Metals, other than mercury, aqueous samples	P, G	HNO_3 to pH < 2	180 days
Metals, other than mercury, soil/sediment samples	P, G	Cool 4 °C	180 days
Mercury, aqueous samples	P, G	HNO_3 to pH < 2	26 days
Mercury, soil/sediment samples	P, G	Cool 4 °C	26 days
Cyanide, total and amenable to chlorination, aqueous samples	P, G	0.6 g ascorbic acid[158], NaOH to pH >12, Cool 4 °C	12 days
Cyanide, total and amenable to chlorination, soil/sediment samples	P, G	Cool 4 °C	12 days

Continued on next page.

---

[154] Teflon (T), Polyethylene (P), Polypropylene (PP) or Glass (G).
[155] Polyethylene (P), or Glass (G).
[156] Sample preservation is performed by the sampler immediately upon sample collection.
[157] USEPA CLP-SOW for inorganic analysis, multi-media, multi-concentration, Document Number ILM03.0.
[158] Only used in the presence of residual chlorine.

Table 1-37. Sample container, preservation and holding time requirements in CLP-SOW, *continued*

Parameter	Container[159]	Preservative[160]	Max. Holding Time
Organic Tests[161]			
VOA, all samples	Glass	Protected from light and cool 4 °C	10 days of sample receipt
SV, water samples	Glass	Protected from light and cool 4 °C	Extraction begun within 5 days of receipt, analysis within 40 days from extraction
SV, soil/sediment samples	Glass	Protected from light and cool 4 °C	Sonication complete within 10 days of receipt, analysis within 40 days from extraction
Pesticides, water samples	Glass	Protected from light and cool 4 °C	Extraction started within 5 days of receipt, analysis completed within 40 days of extraction
Pesticide, soil/sediment samples	Glass	Protected from light and Cool 4 °C	Sonication complete within 10 days of receipt, analysis complete within 40 days of extraction.

Table 1-38. USACE Sample Containers, Preservatives and Holding Times, Low Concentration Samples[162]

Parameter	Container[163]	Preservative[164, 165]	Max. Holding Time
Water Matrix			
Volatiles	2 x 40 mLG, Septa vial	Ice to 4 °C, 4 drops conc, HCl or $NaHSO_4$ to pH < 2	14 days
BNA	2 x 1 L[166] amber G	Ice to 4 °C	7 days to extraction, 40 days after extraction to analysis
PCBs, Pesticides	2 x 1 L amber G	Ice to 4 °C	7 days to extraction, 40 days after extraction to analysis

Continued on next page.

---

[159] Polyethylene (P), or Glass (G).

[160] Sample preservation is performed by the sampler immediately upon sample collection.

[161] USEPA CLP-SOW for organics analysis, multi-media, multi-concentration, Document Number OLM02.1, November, 1993.

[162] Table F-1, USACE Chemical Data Quality Management for Hazardous Waste Remediation Activities, ER 1110-1-263, 1 October, 1990, pg F-9.

[163] All containers must have Teflon-lined seals (Teflon-lined septa for VOA vials). G = Glass; P = High density polyethylene.

[164] Samples with residual chlorine present will be dechlorinated with sodium thiosulfate as specified in SW-846 (Third Edition).

[165] Samples with residual chlorine present will be dechlorinated with sodium thiosulfate as specified in SW-846 (Third Edition).

[166] Three bottles are required on at least 5-10% (but at least one) sample so that the laboratory can perform all method QC checks for SW-846 method.

Table 1-38. USACE Sample Containers, Preservatives and Holding Times, Low Concentration Samples[167], *continued*

Parameter	Container[168]	Preservative[169, 170]	Max. Holding Time
Water Matrix, *continued*			
Metals[171]	1 x 1 L P	HNO_3 to pH < 2	6 months
Total Recoverable Petroleum Hydrocarbons (TRPH)	2 x 1 L G	Ice to 4 °C, HCl to pH < 2	28 days
Common anions[172]	1 x 1 L G	Ice to 4 °C	28 days
Explosives	2 x 1 L G (amber)	Ice to 4 °C	7 days to extraction, 40 days after extraction to analysis
Cyanide	1 x 1 L P	NaOH to pH >12, Ice to 4 °C	14 days
Soil/Sediment Matrix			
Volatiles	2 x 40 mL G or 2 x 125 mL G Septa vial	Ice to 4 °C	14 days
BNA, PCB, Pesticides	1 x 8 oz G	Ice to 4 °C	14 days to extraction, 40 days after extraction to analysis
Metals, Cyanide, TRPH	1 x 8 oz G	Ice to 4 °C (Cyanide & TRPH)	6 months (TRPH: 28 days)
Explosives	1 x 4 oz G	Ice to 4 °C	14 days to extraction, 40 days after extraction to analysis

---

[167] Table F-1, USACE Chemical Data Quality Management for Hazardous Waste Remediation Activities, ER 1110-1-263, 1 October, 1990, pg F-9.

[168] All containers must have Teflon-lined seals (Teflon-lined septa for VOA vials). G = Glass; P = High density polyethylene.

[169] Samples with residual chlorine present will be dechlorinated with sodium thiosulfate as specified in SW-846 (Third Edition).

[170] Samples with residual chlorine present will be dechlorinated with sodium thiosulfate as specified in SW-846 (Third Edition).

[171] Total Recoverable Metals for water samples. Holding time for mercury is 28 days in glass; for hexavalent chromium is 24 hours.

[172] Cl^-, Br^-, F^-, NO_3^-, NO_2^-, PO_4^{3-}, SO_4^{2-}; 1 L for each method; orthophosphate requires filtration. Holding time for extraction is 48 hrs for NO_2^-, NO_3^-, and PO_4^{3-} if not preserved with H_2SO_4 to pH < 2.

Table 1-39. USACE Sample Containers, Preservatives and Holding Times, Medium and High Concentration Samples[173]

Parameter	Container[174]	Preservative[175, 176]	Max. Holding Time
Medium Concentration - Water Matrix			
Volatiles	2 x 40 mL G, Septa vial	Ice to 4 °C	14 days
BNA	2 x 32 oz wide mouth jars[177] G	Ice to 4 °C	7 days to extraction, 40 days after extraction to analysis
PCBs, Pesticides	2 x 32 oz wide mouth jars G	Ice to 4 °C	7 days to extraction, 40 days after extraction to analysis
Metals[178]	1 x 16 oz wide mouth jar, G	HNO_3 to pH < 2	6 months
Explosives	2 x 1 L G (amber)	Ice to 4 °C	7 days to extraction, 40 days after extraction to analysis
Cyanide	1 x 16 oz wide mouth jar, G	Ice to 4 °C	14 days
Medium Concentration - Soil/Sediment Matrix			
Volatiles	2 x 40 mL G or 2 x 125 mL G	Ice to 4 °C	14 days
BNA, PCB, Pesticides	1 x 8 oz G	–	14 days to extraction, 40 days after extraction to analysis
Metals, Cyanide, TRPH	1 x 8 oz G	Ice to 4 °C (Cyanide & TRPH)	6 months (TRPH: 28 days)
Explosives	1 x 4 oz G	Ice to 4 °C	14 days to extraction, 40 days after extraction to analysis
High Concentration Samples			
Liquid - all organic and inorganic analyses	1 x 8 oz wide mouth jar, G	–	Same as above for individual analytes
Solid - all organic and inorganic analyses	1 x 8 oz wide mouth jar, G	–	Same as above for individual analytes

---

[173] Table F-2, USACE Chemical Data Quality Management for Hazardous Waste Remediation Activities, ER 1110-1-263, 1 October, 1990, pg F-9.

[174] All containers must have Teflon-lined seals (Teflon-lined septa for VOA vials). G = Glass; P = High density polyethylene.

[175] Samples with residual chlorine present will be dechlorinated with sodium thiosulfate as specified in SW-846 (Third Edition).

[176] Samples with residual chlorine present will be dechlorinated with sodium thiosulfate as specified in SW-846 (Third Edition).

[177] Three bottles are required on at least 5-10% (but at least one) sample so that the laboratory can perform all method QC checks for SW-846 method.

[178] Total Recoverable Metals for water samples. Holding time for mercury is 28 days in glass; for hexavalent chromium is 24 hours.

Table 1-40. AFCEE requirements for containers, preservation techniques, sample volumes and holding times[179]

Parameter	Method	Container[180]	Preservation[181,182]	Minimum sample volume/ weight	Maximum holding time
Alkalinity (field test)	A2320	P,G	None required	50 mL	Analyze immediately
Alkalinity (lab test)	A2320	P,G	4 °C	50 mL	14 days
Common anions	SW9056	P,G	None	50 mL	28 days for Br, F, Cl, SO_4 48 hrs for NO_3, NO_2, PO_4
Cyanide, total and amenable	SW9010	P,G,T	4 °C, NaOH to pH >12, 0.6 g ascorbic acid	500 mL or 4 oz	14 days (water and soil)
Filterable residue	E160.1	P,G	4 °C	100 mL	7 days
Non-filterable residue	E160.2	P,G	4 °C	100 mL	7 days
pH (field test)	SW9040, SW9045	P,G	None	N/A	Analyze immediately
Nitrate + nitrite	E353.1	P,G	4 °C, H_2SO_4 to pH < 2	500 mL	28 days
Specific conductance (field test)	SW9050	P,G	None	N/A	Analyze immediately
Temperature	E170.1	P,G	None	N/A	Analyze immediately
Total organic carbon	SW9060	P,G,T	4 °C, HCl or H_2SO_4 to pH < 2	500 mL or 4 oz	28 days (water and soil)
Chromium^{+6}	SW7196	P,G,T	4 °C	500 mL or 8 oz	24 hrs[183]
Mercury	SW7470, 7471	P,G,T	HNO_3 to pH < 2, 4 °C	500 mL or 8 oz	28 days
Metals	SW6010, SW-AA	P,G,T	HNO_3 to pH < 2, 4 °C	500 mL or 8 oz	180 days
Petroleum hydrocarbons	E418.1[184]	G,T	H_2SO_4 to pH < 2, 4 °C	1 L or 8 oz	28 days

Continued on next page.

---

[179] *AFCEE Handbook for the Installation Restoration Program (IRP) Remedial Investigations and Feasibility Studies* (RI/FS), September, 1993.

[180] Polyethylene (P); Glass (G); Brass sleeves in the sample barrel, sometimes called California Brass (T).

[181] No pH adjustment for soil.

[182] Preservation with 0.008% sodium thiosulfate is only required when residual chlorine is present.

[183] Holding time for hexavalent chromium in soils has not been established. The recommended holding time for extracting into water is 48 hrs. The sample must be analyzed within 24 hrs of extraction.

[184] The use of method E418.1 requires specific AFCEE approval because of the use of ozone depleting reagents.

Table 1-40. AFCEE requirements for containers, preservation techniques, sample volumes and holding times[185], *continued*

Parameter	Method	Container[186]	Preservation[187, 188]	Minimum sample volume/ weight	Maximum holding time
Volatile fuel hydrocarbons	SW8015 modified	G, Teflon lined septum, T	4 °C, HCl to pH <2	2x40 mL or 4 oz	14 days; 7 days if not preserved
Extractable fuel hydrocarbons	SW 8015 modified	G, amber, T	4 °C	1 L or 8 oz	water 7 days to extraction, 40 days after extraction; soil 14 days to extraction, 40 days after extraction
Aromatic volatile organics	SW8020	G, Teflon lined septum, T	4 °C, HCl to pH < 2, 0.008% $Na_2S_2O_3$	2x40 mL or 4 oz	14 days; 7 days if not preserved
Chlorinated herbicides	SW8150	G, Teflon lined cap, T	4 °C, pH 5-9	1 L or 8 oz	water 7 days to extraction, 40 days after extraction; soil 14 days to extraction, 40 days after extraction
Pesticides and PCBs	SW8080, 8140	G, Teflon lined cap, T	4 °C, pH 5-9	1 L or 8 oz	water 7 days to extraction, 40 days after extraction; soil 14 days to extraction, 40 days after extraction
Phenols	SW8040	G, Teflon lined cap, T	4 °C, 0.008% $Na_2S_2O_3$	1 L or 8 oz	water 7 days to extraction, 40 days after extraction; soil 14 days to extraction, 40 days after extraction
Semivolatile organics	SW8270	G, Teflon lined cap, T	4 °C, 0.008% $Na_2S_2O_3$	1 L or 8 oz	water 7 days to extraction, 40 days after extraction; soil 14 days to extraction, 40 days after extraction

Continued on next page.

---

[185] See footnote 178.
[186] See footnote 179.
[187] See footnote 180.
[188] See footnote 181.

Table 1-40. AFCEE requirements for containers, preservation techniques, sample volumes and holding times[189], *continued*

Parameter	Method	Container[190]	Preservation[191,192]	Minimum sample volume/ weight	Maximum holding time
Volatile organics	SW8240, 8015 modified, 8010, 8260	G, Teflon lined septum, T	4 °C, HCl to pH < 2 for aromatic volatiles by 8240 or 8260, 0.008% $Na_2S_2O_3$	2x40 mL or 4 oz	14 days; 7 days if not preserved
PAH	SW8310	G, Teflon lined cap, T	4 °C, 0.008% $Na_2S_2O_3$, store in dark	1 L or 8 oz	water 7 days to extraction, 40 days after extraction; soil 14 days to extraction, 40 days after extraction
Carbamate pesticides	SW8314	G, Teflon lined cap, T	4 °C, 0.008% $Na_2S_2O_3$	1 L or 8 oz	water 7 days to extraction, 40 days after extraction; soil 14 days to extraction, 40 days after extraction
Dioxins	SW8280, 8290	G, Teflon lined cap, T	4 °C, 0.008% $Na_2S_2O_3$	1 L or 8 oz	30 days until extraction, 45 days after extraction
1,2-dibromoethane	E504	G, Teflon lined septum, T	4 °C, 0.008% $Na_2S_2O_3$	2x40 mL	28 days
alpha, beta and radium	SW9310, 9315, 9320	G,P,T	HNO_3 to pH < 2	2 L or 16 oz	180 days
TCLP	SW1311	G, Teflon lined cap, T	4 °C	1 L or 8 oz	See footnote[193]
Explosive residues	SW8330	P,G,T	4 °C	1 L or 8 oz	Water - 7 days to extraction; Soils - 14 days to extraction; Analysis within 40 days after extraction

---

[189] See footnote 178.
[190] See footnote 179.
[191] See footnote 180.
[192] See footnote 181.
[193] Volatiles - 14 days to TCLP extraction, 14 days after extraction; Semivolatiles - 14 days to TCLP extraction, 40 days after prep. extraction; Mercury - 28 days to TCLP extraction, 28 days after extraction; Metals - 180 days to TCLP extraction, 180 days after extraction.

Table 1-41. Holding times, preservatives, containers and minimum sample size for HAZWRAP[194]

Parameter	Matrix	Holding time	Container	Preservative	Min. sample size[195]
CLP methods					
Volatile organics	water	14 days	2 x 40 mL with Teflon lined cap	4 drops conc. HCl	40 mL
	soil	14 days	Brass or Teflon core tube sealed on both ends	4 °C	10 g
Extractable organics	water	7 days extraction, 40 days to analysis	1 L glass with Teflon liner	4 °C	1000 mL
	soil	14 days extraction, 40 days to analysis	Glass jar with Teflon liner or core tube	4 °C	50 g
Metals, except Hg	water	180 days	polyethylene or glass	HNO_3 to pH <2	100 mL
	soil	180 days	ditto	4 °C	10 g
Mercury	water	28 days	polyethylene or glass	HNO_3 to pH <2	100 mL
	soil	28 days	ditto	4 °C	10 g
Cyanide	water	14 days	polyethylene or glass	0.6 g ascorbic acid, NaOH to pH >12, 4 °C	100 mL
	soil	14 days	ditto	4 °C	10 g
Other methods					
Volatile organics[196]	water, no res. chlorine	14 days	2 x 40 mL vials with Teflon lined septum caps	4 drops conc. HCl, 4 °C	40 mL
	water, res. chlorine pres.	14 days	2 x 40 mL vials with Teflon lined septum caps	4 drops 10% $Na_2S_2O_3$, 4 dps conc. HCl, 4°C	40 mL
	soil/ sediments and sludges	14 days	Brass or Teflon core tube sealed on both ends	4 °C	10 g
Acrolein and acrylonitrile[197]	water	14 days	2 x 40 mL vials with Teflon lined septum caps	Adjust to pH 4-5, 4 °C	40 mL

Continued on next page.

---

[194] HAZWRAP requirements for quality control of analytical data, Document DOE/HWP-65/R1, July, 1990, Tables 6.1-6.5.

[195] Additional samples must be collected for matrix spike/matrix spike duplicate samples or matrix spike/duplicate.

[196] Methods 601, 602, 8010, 8015 or 8020.

[197] Methods 603 or 8030.

Table 1-41. Holding times, preservatives, containers and minimum sample size for HAZWRAP[198], *continued*

Parameter	Matrix	Holding time	Container	Preservative	Min. sample size[199]
Extractable organics[200]	water, no res. chlorine	7 days to extraction, 40 days to analysis	1 L glass with Teflon liner	4 °C	1 L
	water, res. chlorine present	7 days to extraction, 40 days to analysis	1 L glass with Teflon liner	1 mL 10% $Na_2S_2O_3$ per liter, 4 °C	1 L
	soil/ sediments and sludges	14 days to extraction, 40 days to analysis	Glass jar with Teflon liner or core tube	4 °C	50 g
Dioxins/ furans[201]	water	30 days to extraction, 45 days to analysis	1 L glass	4 °C	1000 mL
	soil/waste	30 days to extraction, 45 days to analysis	core tube	4 °C	50 g
Petroleum hydrocarbons as gasoline[202]	water	14 days	2 x 40 mL vials with Teflon liners	4 °C, HCl to pH < 2	40 mL
	soil/waste	14 days	core tube	4 °C	50 g
Petroleum hydrocarbons as gasoline[203]	water	14 days to extraction, 40 days to analysis	1 L glass	4 °C, HCl to pH < 2	500 mL
	soil/waste	ditto	core tube	4 °C	50 g
Petroleum hydrocarbons as diesel[204]	water	14 days to extraction, 40 days to analysis	1 L glass	4 °C	500 mL
	soil/waste	14 days to extraction, 40 days to analysis	core tube	4 °C	50 g
Petroleum hydrocarbons (TPH)[205]	water	28 days	1 L glass	4 °C, HCl to pH <2	1000 mL
	soil	28 days	glass jar with Teflon liner or core tube	4 °C	50 g

Continued on next page.

---

[198] See footnote 179.
[199] See footnote 180.
[200] Methods 604, 606, 608, 610, 614, 615, 632, 8040, 8060, 8080, 8140, 8150, or 8310.
[201] Method 8280.
[202] TPH-gasoline by purge and trap, Leaking Underground Fuel Tank Manual (LUFT).
[203] TPH-gasoline extractable (LUFT).
[204] TPH-diesel extractable (LUFT).
[205] TPH-IR method 418.1.

Table 1-41. Holding times, preservatives, containers and minimum sample size for HAZWRAP[206], *continued*

Parameter	Matrix	Holding time	Container	Preservative	Min. sample size[207]
ICP metals[208]	water	6 mo	polyethylene	HNO_3 to pH < 2	100 mL
	soil/waste	6 mo	core tube/glass jar	4 °C	10 g
Arsenic[209]	water	6 mo	polyethylene	HNO_3 to pH < 2	100 mL
	soil/waste	6 mo	core tube/glass jar	4 °C	10 g
Mercury[210]	water	28 days	polyethylene	HNO_3 to pH < 2	100 mL
	soil/waste	28 days	core tube/glass jar	4 °C	10 g
Selenium[211]	water	6 mo	polyethylene	HNO_3 to pH < 2	100 mL
	soil/waste	6 mo	core tube/glass jar	4 °C	10 g
Thallium[212]	water	6 mo	polyethylene	HNO_3 to pH < 2	100 mL
	soil/waste	6 mo	core tube/glass jar	4 °C	10 g
Lead[213]	water	6 mo	polyethylene	HNO_3 to pH < 2	100 mL
	soil/waste	6 mo	core tube/glass jar	4 °C	10 g
Chromium VI[214]	water	24 hrs	polyethylene	4 °C	100 mL
	soil/waste	24 hrs	core tube/glass jar	4 °C	10 g

---

[206] See footnote 179.
[207] See footnote 180.
[208] Methods 200.7 or 6010.
[209] GFAA methods 206.2 or 7060.
[210] Cold vapor methods 245.1, 7470 or 7471.
[211] GFAA methods 270.2 or 7740.
[212] GFAA methods 279.2 or 7841.
[213] GFAA methods 239.2 or 7421.
[214] Methods 218.4, 218.5, 7196 or 7197.

IV. QUALITY ASSURANCE AND QUALITY CONTROL

Quality assurance and quality control (QA/QC) are often spoken of as if they are synonymous terms. In the environmental industry, however, they are quite distinct. Quality control is defined as a single step or procedure that is performed to evaluate a single aspect of the analysis or test. Examples of quality controls are PE samples, matrix spikes and analysis of blanks. Quality assurance is defined as the sum of all the quality controls performed in the laboratory plus everything else that is done with respect to producing reliable data. The quality assurance program used in an environmental laboratory attempts to satisfy two general criteria for acceptance of results. The first criteria assesses the ability of the laboratory and the analytical method to perform an analysis within set tolerances. This is described as data that are analytically valid. The second criteria assesses the legality of the reported results, i.e., are the results defensible in United States court of law? This legal criteria is met through the chain of documents that accompany the sample and verify the actual analysis. This criteria is generally termed the legally defensible aspect of the data.

The intent of the quality program in the laboratory from the analytical validity viewpoint is to recognize, quantitate, and minimize errors. Errors are classified as either random or systematic. Random errors are inherent parts of any analysis, although steps are taken to minimize their magnitude. Random errors are associated with an even distribution of results around the mean of the results. On the molecular level the Heisenburg uncertainty principle is a recognition of random error in the measurement of an electron's simultaneous position (x) and momentum (p):

$$\Delta x \Delta p > \frac{h}{4\pi}$$

where h is Planck's constant 6.63×10^{-34} Js. Random errors are composed of two parts. The first part of random error is associated with the background or instrument noise from the test. The second part of random error results from the spread of results around the true value of the sample. Random errors affect the reproducibility of an analysis. Systemic errors arise from a bias in the method of analysis or the instrument. They always tend to cluster on one side or another of the actual value for the test. Systemic errors can also be caused by the particular matrix of a sample.

The laboratory's quality assurance program is documented in the Quality Assurance Manual. The QA Manual is a legal document of the laboratory and is commonly the first point of examination of the lab by regulators, state and federal certification/validation officers and attorneys. The QA Manual is also the single most useful sales tool of the laboratory. Legally defensible QA Manuals are not produced in an afternoon's worth of work, but are the result of close examination of the lab by the QA Manager or consultant, documentation of the findings and then periodic review to insure that the QA Manual in fact reflects and accurately describes the activities of the lab. Although there is no universally applicable standard format for QA Manuals, most of the required formats, for example those of the State of Florida, the Contract Laboratory Program, and the U.S. Army Environmental Center, are minor variations on a general theme. For those individuals or organizations receiving EPA grants, 40 CFR 30.503 has specific requirements for the contents of a QA project plan as presented in Table 1-42. The generalized contents of a more comprehensive QA Manual, are presented in Table 1-43.

Table 1-42. Contents for a Quality Assurance Project Plan in compliance with 40 CFR 30.503

Section	Contents
1	Title of project and name of principal investigators
2	Table of Contents
3	Project description
4	Project organization and responsibilities
5	Quality assurance objectives and criteria for determining precision, accuracy, completeness, representativeness, and comparability of data
6	Sampling procedures
7	Sample custody
8	Calibration procedures and frequency and traceability of standards
9	Analytical procedures
10	Data reduction, validation and reporting
11	Internal quality control checks
12	Performance and system audits
13	Preventative maintenance
14	Specific standard operating procedures used to assess data precision, accuracy, representativeness, and comparability
15	Corrective action for out-of-control situations
16	Quality assurance reporting procedures

Table 1-43. Generalized contents for a Quality Assurance Manual

Section	Title and Description
1	Title Page with authorization signatures and dates
2	Table of Contents
3	Statement of QA Policy
4	Organizational tables and job descriptions for supervisory positions
5	Data quality objectives for accuracy, precision, and method detection limits for each test, target analyte and sample matrix
6	Sampling procedures, field equipment lists, field decontamination protocols and documentation
7	Sample custody procedures and documentation
8	Analytical methods variances, glassware washing protocols, etc.
9	Equipment and instrument lists and calibration procedures along with documentation descriptions and acceptance criteria
10	Preventative maintenance schedules and documentation description for each analytical instrument
11	Quality control procedures and frequency for each test for determination of laboratory contamination, accuracy, precision and method detection limits along with acceptance criteria
12	Data reduction, validation, reviews and reporting procedures
13	Standard corrective action procedures for QC failures in Sections 9 and 11
14	Performance and system audit procedures and example documentation
15	Frequency and content of QA reports
16	Resumes of key personnel
Appendices	References, glossary of terms and miscellaneous information

A frequently encountered requirement for QA Manuals and for Standard Operating Procedures (SOP) is document control. This labels each page of each section as part of a known number of pages of a specified revision and date. This information is commonly supplied in a page header such as that illustrated in Figure 1-3.

Analytical Services Inc.	Section No. 2
Quality Assurance Manual	Revision No. 2
	Date 15 December, 1993
	Page 2 of 3

Figure 1-3.   Example of a page header to establish document control.

A. Calibration

Calibration is the process where an initial analytical response is related to an amount of analyte present in the sample. Examples of analytical responses include volume of titrant, millivolts/potential, picoamps/current, peak area, peak height, absorbance of light, emission of light, generation of heat, and mass of residue. Although several EPA procedures, in particular analyses using titration, allow a single point calibration, for the majority of the methods multi-point calibrations are required.

All multi-point calibrations in EPA methods have common characteristics, which are illustrated in Figure 1-4, a calibration generated from the data in Table 1-44. The first characteristic is lower and upper ends to the calibration curve (no calibration curves are open ended), which defines the calibrated range. The second characteristic is saturation at both the lower and upper ends of the calibration curve. Saturation is defined for two different cases. The first is no change in response with decreasing amounts of analyte, and the second is no change in response with increasing amounts of analyte. These cases cover situations with either positive or negative slopes to the calibration and the background noise from the instrument not allowing calibration at lower levels. The calibration presented in Figure 1-4 has a positive slope and exhibits saturation at the upper levels of the curve.

Table 1-44. General calibration example

Response	Amount
.100	.100
.200	.200
.300	.300
.400	.400
.500	.500
.580	.600
.640	.700
.650	.800
.650	.900

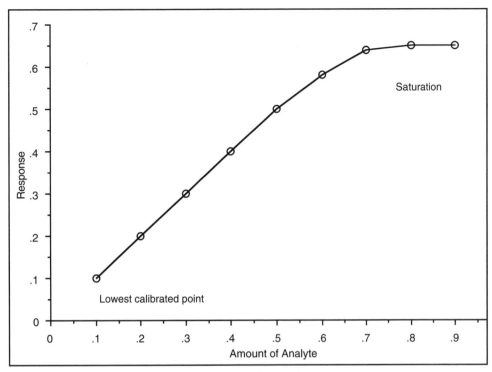

Figure 1-4. Generalized point-to-point calibration curve.

For any calibration there are highest and lowest calibrated points that define the range of the calibration. It is legally non-defensible and poor analytical practice to report concentrations of target analytes that are either below or above the range of the calibration unless steps have been taken to either concentrate or dilute the solution of the target analyte, and a re-analysis result has been obtained within the calibration range. The re-analysis result is then adjusted for the concentration or dilution factor, and the fact of the concentration or dilution reported on the laboratory worksheet. This requires that if the laboratory is reporting below detection limit (BDL) results for target analytes, then a calibrated point at the concentration of the detection limit must be included on each calibration curve.

1. Calibration Curves by Point-to-Point Curve Fitting

Point-to-point calibration curves are quite common and are very useful. They are plotted on graph paper and read by finding the appropriate response level, moving horizontally until the curve is intersected, then moving down vertically until the concentration axis is intersected. Graphing programs on personal computers make the technique even easier.

Table 1-45. Calibration of sulfate analysis by EPA method 375.4 using spectrophotometric analysis at 420 nm

Sulfate mg/L	ABS
0.1	.004
0.5	.024
1.0	.079
1.5	.138
2.0	.202
2.5	.272
3.0	.367
4.0	.513
5.0	.642

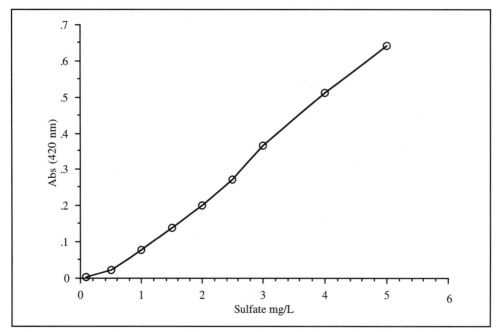

Figure 1-5. Non-linear point-to-point calibration curve for sulfate analysis in Table 1-45.

2. Calibration Curves by Linear Regression

Linear regression is a more rigorous approach to generating a calibration that employs statistical techniques to smooth the random error from the analysis. The most commonly used regression procedure is least squares, however other regression techniques are available in various computer statistics packages[167]. A general diagram of the method is illustrated in Figure 1-6. The major value of the technique is the generation of a

---

[167] Birkes, D. and Y. Dodge, *Alternative Methods of Regression.* 1993. Wiley Interscience, New York, NY. ISBN 0-471-56881-3.

calibration equation that can be used in computerized instruments to result in a direct read-out of concentration data by the instrument. A second benefit is a quantitative measure of the "goodness-of-fit" of the calibration.

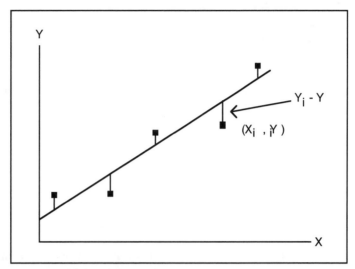

Figure 1-6.   Linear regression calculation.

The idea is to construct the best straight line through the points, which minimizes the separation of the points from the line. The equation of the line for a linear regression takes the form:

$$Y = a + bX$$

If

$$x_i = X_i - X_{ave} ;$$

where x_i is the separation of the observed value X_i from the mean value X_{ave}; and

$$y_i = Y_i - Y_{ave} ;$$

with similar meaning, then the appropriate values for a and b become:

$$b = \frac{\sum\limits_{i=1}^{n} x_i y_i}{\sum\limits_{i=1}^{n} x_i^2} \quad ; \text{ and } a = Y_{ave} - bX_{ave}$$

The goodness of fit of the regression line to the observed data points is expressed by the correlation coefficient, r, where:

$$r = \frac{\sum\limits_{i=1}^{n} x_i y_i}{\sqrt{\sum\limits_{i=1}^{n} x_i^2 \sum\limits_{i=1}^{n} y_i^2}}$$

r is related to the coefficient of determination, r^2, by squaring r. r^2 is also directly accessible through the following:

$$r^2 = \frac{b \sum\limits_{i=1}^{n} x_i y_i}{\sum\limits_{i=1}^{n} y_i^2}$$

The absolute values of r lie between 0 and 1, with the higher values indicating a greater correlation. A negative value for r indicates a line with a negative slope, rather than the more common positive slope.

The following machine formulas are used by computers in performing the calculations:

$$\sum\limits_{i=1}^{n} x_i^2 = \sum\limits_{i=1}^{n} X_i^2 - \frac{\sum\limits_{i=1}^{n} X_i \sum\limits_{i=1}^{n} X_i}{n}$$

$$\sum\limits_{i=1}^{n} y_i^2 = \sum\limits_{i=1}^{n} Y_i^2 - \frac{\sum\limits_{i=1}^{n} Y_i \sum\limits_{i=1}^{n} Y_i}{n}$$

$$\sum\limits_{i=1}^{n} x_i y_i = \sum\limits_{i=1}^{n} X_i Y_i - \frac{\sum\limits_{i=1}^{n} X_i \sum\limits_{i=1}^{n} Y_i}{n}$$

Application of the linear regression technique to the data in Table 1-45 generates the calibration in Figure 1-7.

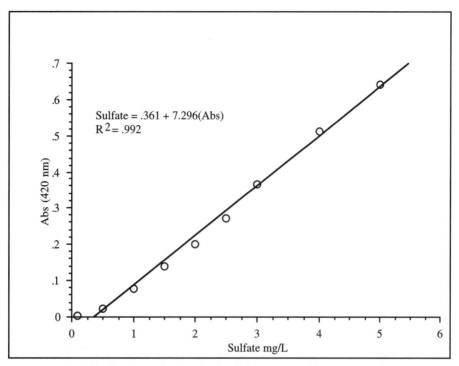

Sulfate = .361 + 7.296(Abs)
$R^2 = .992$

Figure 1-7. Linear regression calibration curve for sulfate analysis in Table 1-45.

3. Calibration Curves by Polynomial Regression

Just as a linear regression results in an equation of the form y = a + bx, a polynomial regression of the second degree results in an equation of the form:

$$y = a + bx + cx^2$$

allowing an actual curve in the calibration. Some methods, particularly in the 500 and 600 series allow these type calibrations if the RF fit is not linear. However, one must be cautious in the polynomial regression application. The major reason is that any three points can be fit with a polynomial curve with a correlation coefficient of r = 1.00. As a rule of thumb, five different concentration standards should be analyzed before attempting to calibrate with a second degree polynomial regression. Application of second and third degree polynomial regressions to the sulfate data (Table 1-45) are illustrated (Figures 1-8 and 1-9, respectively). In most situations a higher than second degree regression fit is probably unwarranted for applications in environmental analysis. However in this example the third degree polynomial gives a very accurate description of the calibration curve and further suggests that the upper levels of the calibration are possibly approaching saturation.

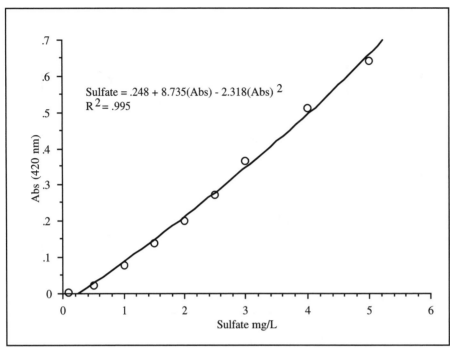

Figure 1-8. **Sulfate second degree polynomial regression calibration.**

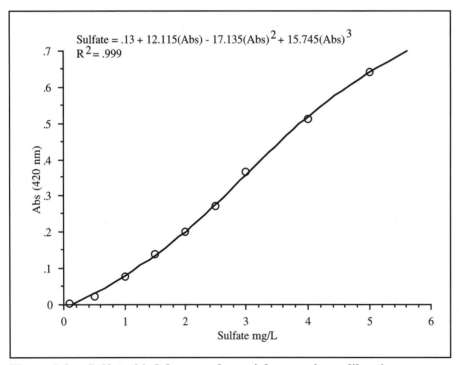

Figure 1-9. **Sulfate third degree polynomial regression calibration.**

4. Calibration Factor Calibrations

A calibration factor (CF) is a derived number used to multiply the raw response and give the analytical concentration as follows:

Result = CF x response

This type of calibration is found in many different types of tests such as titration analyses and other wet chemistry procedures and some organic analyses by GC. The calibration factor may be based on a combination of theoretical considerations of the involved chemistry and experimental standardizations, such as occurs in titrations, or it may be derived as an average of testing calibration standards at a series of concentrations. Regardless of the derivation, use of the calibration factor requires the explicit assumption that the relation between the concentration of the target analyte and the analytical response is exactly linear, and the line passes through the origin. For most applications in wet chemistry, these assumptions are probably valid over the calibrated range. However, when applied to organic instrumental determinations by GC, these assumptions are often not valid.

The use of calibration factors in GC analysis arises from the external standard calibration procedure. In this technique a known volume of a known concentration of the target analyte is injected into the GC, and the resulting peak area tabulated and related to the amount of analyte. The procedure is repeated for the set of calibrations standards (3 to 5 or more), then the mean of the individual CF's is determined and the %RSD. The %RSD is evaluated against the acceptance criteria of the method, with examples from chlorinated hydrocarbon pesticide analysis procedures by GC-ECD: 508 CF %RSD <20%; 608 CF %RSD <10%; 8081 CF %RSD <20%; and CLP-SOW OLM03.0 CF %RSD <20% (except α-BHC, δ-BHC and surrogates). If the acceptance criteria are met the calibration factor is considered constant over the calibrated range, however see Response Factor Calibrations below for some of the consequences of this assumption.

$$CF = \frac{Area_{analyte}}{Amount_{analyte}}$$

5. Response Factor Calibrations

Response factors (RF) are commonly used in organic analysis by gas chromatography (GC) or gas chromatography-mass spectrometry (GC-MS). They often are calculated in conjunction with the use of internal standards. Internal standards are known amounts of compounds that are added to each sample immediately before instrumental analysis. The response of the internal standard is used to establish a standard response for the instrument. Each analyte is calibrated against the internal standard(s), generating the response factors.

$$RF = \frac{Area_{analyte} \times Amount_{internal\ standard}}{Area_{internal\ standard} \times Amount_{analyte}}$$

The idea behind the use of average RF is that the relative response of internal standard and target analytes remains constant across the calibrated range. Although this may be a valid assumption for detectors such as the flame ionization detector, when applied to the mass spectrometer the justification is simply not present. Reduced analyte response in mass spectrometers at increasing concentration is a fact of life and can be attributed to the initial inefficiency of the ionization, reduced mean free path, reduced relative ion throughput in the mass analyzer, and counting rate limitations in the ion detector and the associated software. If the internal standard is very similar to the calibrated analyte, such as chrysene-d_{12} and chrysene, the above effects are essentially constant for the two compounds, whereas when the internal standard and analyte are very different chemically, these effects become pronounced.

The acceptance of the average RF is assessed quantitatively by calculating the percent relative standard deviation (%RSD) for the set of RF's generated from the calibrated concentrations and then applying an acceptance criteria to the %RSD. The acceptance criteria vary from method to method: 525 %RSD <30; 625 %RSD <35; 8270 %RSD <15 except for CCC where %RSD <30. The data for the example are presented in Table 1-46.

$$\%RSD = 100 \text{ x } \frac{S_{RF}}{RF_{ave}}$$

where: %RSD is the percent relative standard deviation,
S_{RF} is the standard deviation of the RFs, and
RF_{ave} is the average RF of the calibration standards.

Using the criteria for acceptance of the RF calibration from method 625, all three of the example compounds would be treated as exhibiting a linear calibration. The plot in Figure 1-10 illustrates that the RF calibration for chrysene (%RSD = 5.5) is linear across the concentrations, however, the other two examples exhibit a pronounced downward slope. This becomes of greater concern with the issue of continuing calibration acceptance. Method 625 allows continuing calibration RF's to vary up to ±20% from the initial calibration. Some data systems calculate the daily continuing calibration RF and, if it is acceptable, replace the initial calibration RF with the daily value. What this in effect does is replace a three to five point calibration curve with a one point calibration, and is another example of poor analytical practice. The possible allowed day-to-day variation on RF is illustrated in Figure 1-11 for bis(2-chloroisopropyl) ether.

Table 1-46. Raw areas and RFs of compounds and associated internal standards vs. concentration (ng/μL)

Compound	Concentration (ng/μL)					Ave RF	% RSD
	20	50	80	120	160		
1,4-Dichlorobenzene D_4	67626	46894	56641	59557	58943		
bis(2-chloroisopropyl) ether	89307	150720	235334	324271	318733		
As/Ais	1.321	3.214	4.155	5.445	5.407		
RF	2.641	2.571	2.077	1.815	1.352	2.091	25.7
Acenaphthene D_{10}	98841	79437	90211	93294	90856		
Diethyl phthalate	89892	171722	275156	384749	393958		
As/Ais	0.909	2.162	3.050	4.124	4.336		
RF	1.819	1.729	1.525	1.375	1.084	1.506	19.5
Chrysene D_{12}	80918	71426	73597	75327	75816		
Chrysene	40668	80933	127936	213813	277181		
As/Ais	0.503	1.133	1.738	2.838	3.656		
RF	1.005	0.906	0.869	0.914	0.928	0.928	5.5

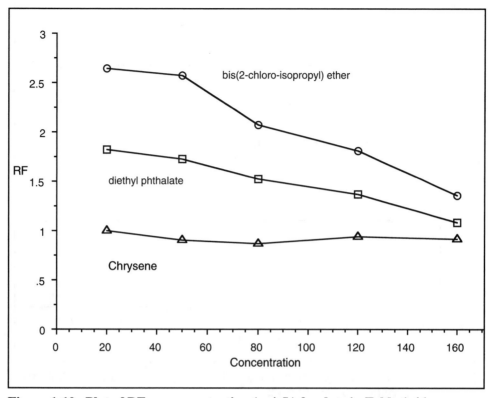

Figure 1-10. Plot of RF *vs*. concentration (ng/μL) for data in Table 1-46.

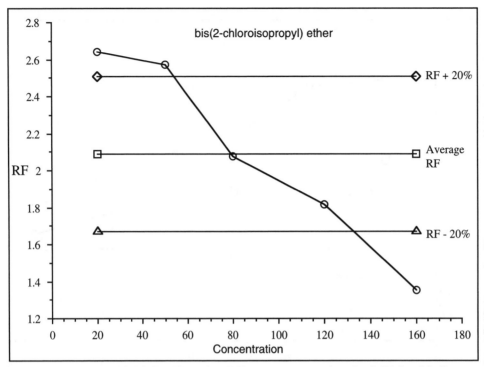

Figure 1-11. Plot of initial calibration RF *vs*. concentration (ng/μL) for bis(2-chloroisopropyl) ether along with average RF and allowed daily RF variations by method 625.

Allowed variations to the average RF calibration are manual or computer plotting of RF or concentration *vs.* the area ratio of the target analyte to the internal standard (As/Ais). This is illustrated in Figure 1-12.

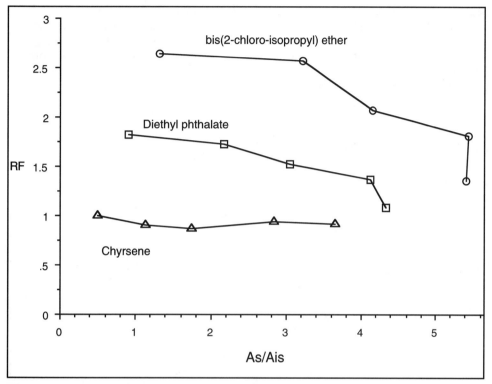

Figure 1-12. Plot of RF *vs.* As/Ais for manual calibration.

More accurate calibrations can be obtained by performing regression analyses on the RF *vs.* As/Ais data. Figure 1-13 illustrates the results of a linear regression analysis applied to the first two compounds in Table 1-46. Figure 1-14 shows a second degree polynomial regression of the same data, while Figures 1-15 and 1-16 illustrate third degree polynomial regressions. The latter plot demonstrates the necessity for a visual checking of the calibration plot, because the result in this instance is clearly nonsense, even though it exhibits a desirable correlation coefficient. Considering the large amount of analytical error associated with GC and GC-MS determinations of semivolatile organics after extractive sample preparation, it is probably not warranted to use regression calibrations of greater than linear degree.

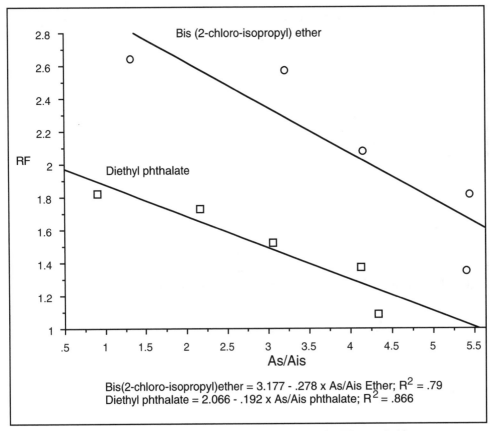

Figure 1-13. Linear regression performed on the data in Figure 1-12.

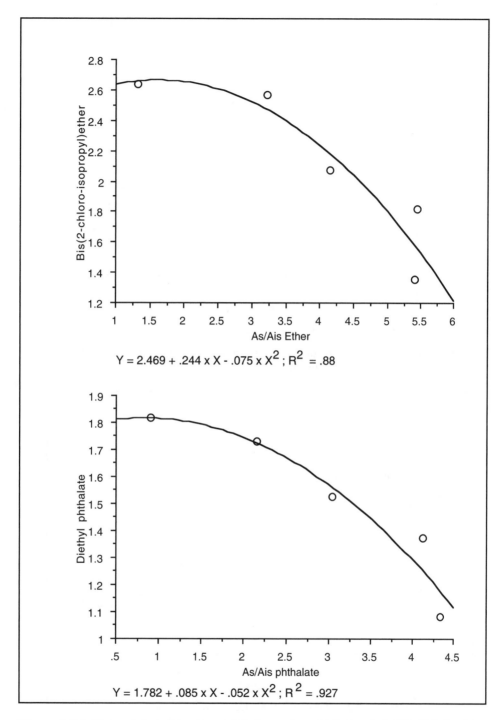

Figure 1-14. Second degree polynomial regression performed on the data in Figure 1-12.

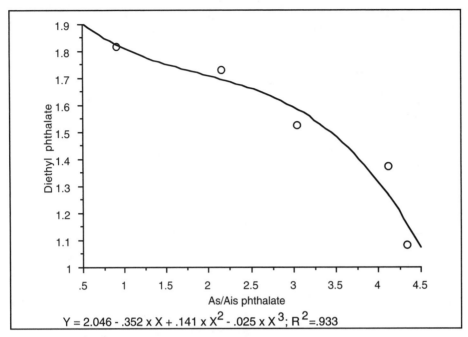

Figure 1-15. Third degree polynomial regression performed on the diethyl phthalate data from Table 1-46.

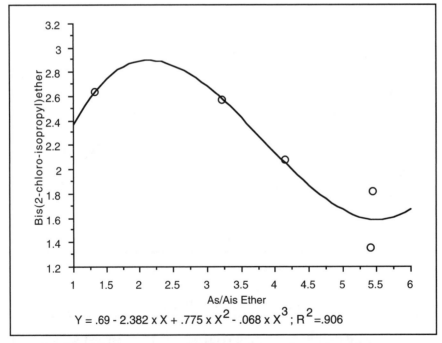

Figure 1-16. Third degree polynomial regression performed on the bis(2-chloroisopropyl) ether data from Table 1-46.

6. Multi-peak Target Analytes.

A number of the pesticide target analytes of methods 508, 608, 8081, and 8082 and the petroleum fuels of method 8015B are composed of a variety of compounds. Examples are chlordane, toxaphene, and the PCBs and PCTs. Several techniques can be used to identify these analytes[168], the most common being a visual pattern recognition although computerized algorithms are available. Quantitation can be performed either by selected indicator peaks (area or peak height) or by total area under the analyte envelope. The latter method suffers when more than one multi-peak analyte is present, the envelopes overlap and the same peaks show up in two or more target analytes, or the target analyte is subject to selective losses of some of the lighter or more reactive components (weathering).

A simplified approach for dealing with overlapping target analytes is to calibrate each of the indicator peaks as an independent measure of the target analyte. For example, considering PCB 1242, six peaks may be calibrated in a single calibration table for PCB 1242. The sample chromatogram is quantitated against the calibration table, and if the target analyte is uncontaminated, all six indicator peaks should give very similar values as PCB 1242. If another PCB, for example 1248, is also present, the six peaks will give a range of substantially different values as PCB 1242. The sample chromatogram is then quantitated against the 1248 calibration table.

However a word of caution about chlordane. The most common indicator peaks used for chlordane quantitation are alpha-chlordane and gamma-chlordane, and particularly gamma-chlordane is available as a pure compound. If gamma-chlordane is the only compound present in the sample and the analyst has calibrated it as representing technical chlordane, it should be obvious that falsely high values are going to be obtained. The calibration needs to be re-worked in terms of only gamma-chlordane to allow correct quantitation.

---

[168] Erickson, M.D. *Analytical Chemistry of PCBs*. 2nd Edition, 1997. CRC Press, Boca Raton, FL.

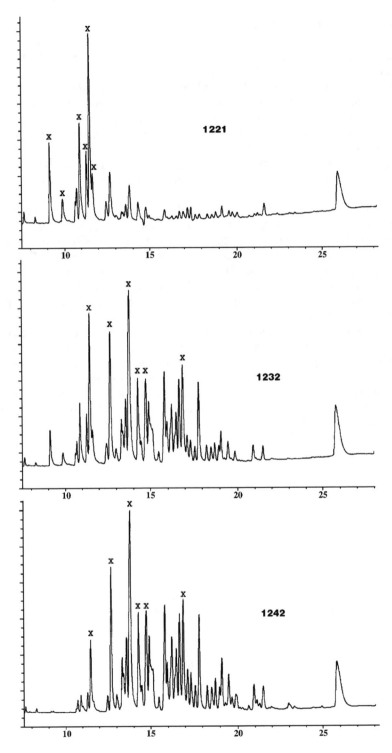

Figure 1-17. Multi-component target analytes (PCBs)

On the other hand target analytes such as the petroleum hydrocarbon fuels are difficult to quantitate based on indicator peaks, as these vary greatly in abundance from one
manufacturer to the next. Once the sample is identified, the most practical method of
quantitation is total area above the baseline from the beginning to the end of the analyte's
elution pattern. See Section 3 for a more detailed discussion.

7. Multiple Standard Addition

Multiple standard addition is a calibration technique used most commonly in metals
analysis by AA, however it can be applied in many areas of the laboratory. It serves to
correct for matrix effects in the sample. Aliquots of a digested or extracted sample are
spiked with at least three different concentrations of a standard. The solutions are
analyzed, and the responses recorded and plotted on graph paper. A linear regression is
performed on the responses, and the line extended down to the zero response intercept.
The concentration of the sample is then read off as the absolute value at the intercept or
by setting the response equal to zero in the regression equation. For the example shown,
the sample concentration would be 1.50.

The technique works best when the response of the instrument is known to be linear,
and the standard additions are chosen to bracket the expected unknown sample concentration. In the CLP (ILM03.0) the linearity requirement is determined by having a
correlation coefficient of at least 0.995. In cases where the IDL of the analysis is known,
the IDL value on the response axis would be chosen for the intercept rather than zero.

Table 1-47. Example of MSA data

Response	Amount
0.246	1.00
0.461	3.00
0.644	5.00

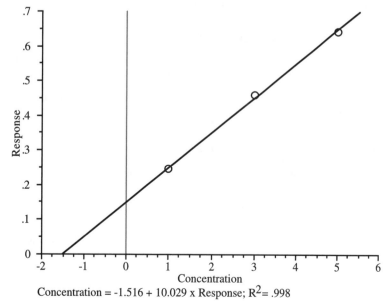

Concentration = -1.516 + 10.029 x Response; R^2 = .998

Figure 1-18. Graph of MSA example.

B. Measurement Quality Objectives

Measurement quality objectives (MQO) can be defined as what the analyst expects to obtain from the analysis. Or maybe a more realistic definition is what the data reviewer expects to obtain as a result of the technician's work. Measurement quality objectives are the laboratory's sub-set of Data Quality Objectives (DQO). The definition is, "Data Quality Objectives are qualitative and quantitative statements which specify the quality of the data required to support Agency decisions during remedial response activities." The DQO are the result of a formalized process of examining a project and determining what has to be done to allow what decisions to be made. Measurement quality objectives are composed of written expectations for accuracy, precision, and detection limits for each analyte for each test and for each different analytical matrix that will be needed to make the decisions that arise from the DQO process. EPA also adds written expectations for completeness, comparability and representativeness. Completeness is defined as the percentage of samples that meet or exceed all the MQOs for accuracy, precision, and detection limits. Representativeness is the degree to which the results of the analysis reflect the target analyte concentrations in the site sampled. Comparability is the degree of confidence with which results from two or more data sets, or two or more laboratories may be compared. Comparability, completeness and representativeness are difficult to quantitate, and most numbers quoted for them are strictly guesses, although comparability may be performed with the relative percent difference (RPD) metric and completeness can be expressed as a fraction:

$$\text{completeness} = \frac{\text{number of completely acceptable results}}{\text{number of results needed to make a decision}} \times 100$$

Measurement Quality Objectives for a specific project will depend on what information is required and how it will be used. Five levels of measurement quality are generally recognized as defined in Table 1-48.

Table 1-48. Measurement Quality Levels

Level I	Field based analytical screening procedures using organic vapor analyzers, and other essentially non-calibrated instruments. Reportable data includes method, detection limit, result, date, time, and person conducting analysis.
Level II	Field based analyses using instruments that are calibrated and blanks are performed to ascertain contamination. May include data from field GCs and other advanced screening methods. Reportable data include method, detection limit, results, date, time, and person conducting analysis, and may include information on blanks.
Level III	Laboratory based batch analyses that use calibration and continuing calibration, blanks, QC procedures to determine accuracy and precision, MDL studies are documented, and the data is of sufficient quality to satisfy most regulatory reporting requirements. Report includes method, detection limit, results, and external chain-of-custody. Summaries of QC data, such as date, time and person conducting analysis and batch blanks, surrogate recoveries, accuracy, and precision may be supplied with Final Analytical Reports.

Continued on next page.

Table 1-48. Measurement Quality Levels, *continued*

Level IV	Laboratory based analyses that comply with all requirements and provide full documentation as stated in the appropriate CLP-SOW. Data package is capable of surviving the most rigorous legal examination. Final report includes a case narrative and method, detection limit, and results for each sample along with a data package. Reported data in the package includes chain-of-custody copy, initial and continuing calibration data, blank results, system monitoring compound results, accuracy and precision results, surrogate recoveries, daily tuning results, extraction and sample preparation log copies, internal standard area and RT summaries, run log copies, TIC results and mass spectra copies, raw data, and quantitation reports in both hardcopy and electronic media.
Level V	Laboratory analyses that utilize or seek to validate non-standard methods. Detailed descriptions of all analytical procedures used are provided along with data that indicate single laboratory precision, accuracy, and MDL obtained from multiple determinations of the target analytes. May include comparison data to a promulgated method.

1. Accuracy and Precision

Accuracy and precision are two measures of the reliability of an analytical result. Accuracy is the degree with which the obtained result agrees with the actual result, often expressed as recovery. In mathematical terms accuracy is the average of the results from repeated analysis of the same sample, compared to the actual amount of analyte in the sample. Precision is the ability to generate the same result in repeated tests of the same sample. In mathematical terms precision is the percent difference of the results from re-analysis of a sample. Graphic representations of accuracy and precision are shown in Figure 1-19. The desire of all analysts is to obtain results that are both highly accurate and highly precise. However in the cases where one or the other is not present, the preferred situation is a highly precise analysis. If the analysis is precise then the "sights" can be adjusted to give the desired accuracy. The other situations are useless.

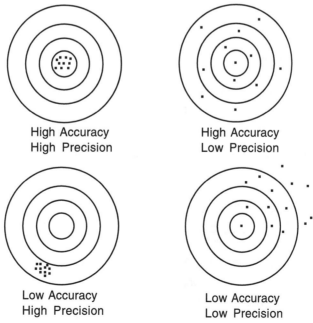

High Accuracy
High Precision

High Accuracy
Low Precision

Low Accuracy
High Precision

Low Accuracy
Low Precision

Figure 1-19. Accuracy and precision.

Accuracy is calculated as follows for spikes into laboratory water:

$$\%R = 100 \times \frac{\text{Observed value}}{\text{Known value}}$$

where: %R is the percentage recovery
Observed value is the analytical result, and
Known value is the concentration of the spike.

For calculation of accuracy of spikes into natural matrices:

$$\%R = 100 \times \frac{\text{Observed value - Background value}}{\text{Known value}}$$

where: %R is the percentage recovery.
Observed value is the analytical result after spiking.
Background value is the analytical result of the matrix before spiking, and
Known value is the concentration of the spike.

The following calculations for the average percent recovery and the standard deviation of the recovery are used in generation of MQOs. The standard deviation can be calculated by one of two procedures, the machine formula and the manual formula. The manual formula requires first calculation of the average from the data set, then on a second pass going back through the data and determining the difference between the average and each datum. The machine formula gives the exact same result for the standard deviation; however, it requires only one pass through the data set and is much faster when dealing with large data sets. The manual formula can be derived from the machine formula by expanding and collecting the terms.

$$\%R_{ave} = \frac{\sum\limits_{i=1}^{n} \%R_i}{n}$$

where: $\%R_{ave}$ is the average percent recovery,
$\%R_i$ is the percent recovery of observation i, and
n is the number of observations.

The machine formula used in computers for calculating standard deviation is:

$$S_{\%R} = \sqrt{\frac{\sum\limits_{i=1}^{n} \%R_i^2 - [\sum\limits_{i=1}^{n} \%R_i]^2 / n}{n-1}}$$

where: $S_{\%R}$ is the standard deviation of percent recovery,
$\%R_i$ is the percent recovery of observation i, and
n is the number of observations.

The manual formula for calculating standard deviation is:

$$S_{\%R} = \sqrt{\dfrac{\displaystyle\sum_{i=1}^{n}[\%R_{ave} - \%R_i]^2}{n-1}}$$

Precision is assessed through the following calculation:

$$RPD = \frac{2\,[A-B]}{A+B} \times 100$$

where: RPD is the relative percent difference between duplicate determinations,
A and B are the analytical results for the duplicate determinations, and
[A - B] is the absolute difference between the determinations.

The concepts of percent difference and standard deviation are somewhat similar and many times confused. The distinction between the two concepts is that percent difference (RPD) is limited to an actual comparison of two and only two values, while standard deviation is a statistical concept that attempts to relate the spread of values in a small subset of data to the width of the distribution of values in an entire population of data. The RSD for two points is not the same as the RPD as can be seen as follows.

$$RSD = \frac{\sqrt{2}\,[A-B]}{A+B} \times 100$$

where: RSD is the relative standard deviation calculated from duplicate determinations,
A and B are the analytical results for the duplicate determinations, and
[A - B] is the absolute difference between the determinations.

2. Calculation of Measurement Quality Objectives for Accuracy and Precision

Measurement quality objectives for both accuracy and precision for a laboratory test represent a statistically derived 95% confidence level. Mathematically this is a range of plus and minus 2 standard deviations from the mean.

Table 1-49. Oil and grease batch data for MQO calculation

DATE	MS	MSD	True Value	%R1	%R2	%R ave	Precision
5-11-92	42.0	37.6	51.0	82.3	74.0	78.0	10.3
5-12-92	39.2	40.0	51.0	77.0	78.0	77.5	1.3
5-14-92	39.6	39.8	51.0	77.6	78.0	77.8	0.5
5-18-92a	41.4	42.0	51.0	81.0	82.2	81.6	1.5
5-18-92b	42.0	36.4	51.0	82.0	71.0	76.5	14.4
5-20-92	40.0	40.6	51.0	78.4	79.6	79.0	1.5
5-21-92	40.4	34.4	51.0	79.0	67.5	73.0	15.8
5-26-92	42.8	43.0	51.0	84.0	84.3	84.2	0.4
5-28-92	44.2	43.0	51.0	86.7	84.3	85.5	2.8
5-29-92	39.6	46.2	51.0	77.6	90.6	84.1	15.5

Continued on next page.

Table 1-49. Oil and grease batch data for MQO calculation, *continued*

DATE	MS	MSD	True Value	%R1	%R2	%R ave	Precision
6-02-92	43.0	43.8	51.0	84.3	85.9	85.1	1.9
6-04-92	40.8	39.2	51.0	80.0	76.9	78.5	3.9
6-08-92	39.6	36.8	51.0	77.6	72.4	74.9	7.2
6-09-92	48.4	42.4	51.0	94.9	83.0	89.0	13.4
6-11-92	41.4	42.0	51.0	81.2	82.4	81.8	1.5
					Mean	80.43	6.12
					SD	4.32	5.82

For example, repeat duplicate analysis of a mid-range standard for Oil & Grease gives $\%R_{ave}$ of 80.43 with $S_{\%R}$ of 4.32 (Table 1-49). The measurement quality objective for accuracy is:

$\%R_{ave} - 2S_{\%R}$ to $\%R_{ave} + 2S_{\%R}$, or

80.43 - 2(4.32) to 80.43 + 2(4.32), or

71.8 - 89.1, rounded to 72-89.

Precision for the Oil & Grease example generates RPD_{ave} 6.12 and S_{RPD} 5.82. The measurement quality objective for precision is:

$RPD_{ave} - 2S_{RPD}$ to $RPD_{ave} + 2S_{RPD}$, or

6.12 - 2(5.82) to 6.12 + 2(5.82), or

0 - 17.8, rounded to 0-18

A negative value for precision is nonsense, and so zero is always the lower value for the range. Although it is possible for the lower value to be some other positive value than zero, in general zero is used because the analyst never wants to eliminate the possibility that he can get exactly the same answer twice in a row as an acceptable result. It is important to realize that MQO are statistical ranges and that under normal operating conditions around 5% of test results will fall outside these ranges. Data quality objectives should be updated at least on an annual basis if not more frequently. Within the laboratory, it is possible to calculate MQO for each analyst for each test, however when providing MQO to end users of the data, it is probably more representative of the laboratory's capabilities to report a composite value from all the technicians performing a test.

3. Instrument Detection Limits

In Figure 1-20 the question arises as to whether the signal at point A indicates the presence of an analyte or is just instrument noise. Instrument detection limit (IDL) is a measure of the normal instrument noise. It provides a guide to what is noise and what is a real signal and is an evaluation of the maximum sensitivity of an analytical instrument to perform an analysis. It is set at three times the standard deviation of the instrument noise level. IDL is determined by the following procedure (EPA 40 CFR Part 136, Appendix B, July 1993):

1. Prepare a calibration curve for the test with standards.
2. Analyze seven (7) laboratory water blanks.
3. Record the response of the test for the blanks.
4. Prepare the mean ($\%R_{ave}$) and standard deviation ($S_{\%R}$) of the results from the blanks as above.
5. The IDL is three times the $S_{\%R}$ on the calibration curve (Figure 1-21).

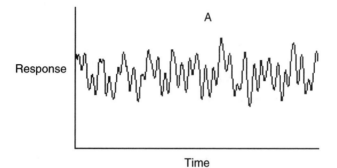

Figure 1-20. Instrument detection limit problem.

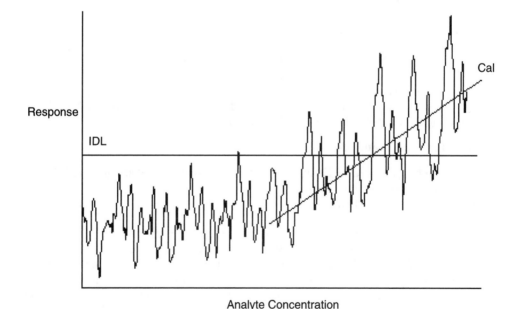

Figure 1-21. Intersection of IDL with calibration curve.

The major function of the IDL is to separate noise from analyte responses. The presence of a signal above the IDL is most often real and serves to eliminate the false positive (Type I) error at the 99% confidence level. See Figure 1-22.

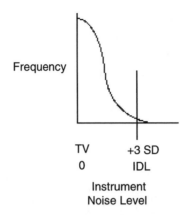

Figure 1-22. Distribution of instrument noise levels.

4. Method Detection Limits

There are many different manners in which laboratories report results for low concentrations of target analytes. Some are as follows[169]:

1. Trace
2. ND (not detected)
3. Numerical value of MDL
4. A "less than" the numerical value of the MDL (BDL)
5. Zero
6. Some value between zero and the MDL, for example, half the MDL
7. Actual measured value, even if below the MDL
8. Actual measured value, followed by MDL in parentheses
9. Actual measured value with an estimate of precision, for example $2 \pm 4 \ \mu g/L$, where the estimate of error can be the MDL.

Additional reporting forms are:

10. A number followed by Estimated Maximum Possible Concentration (EMPC)
11. Detected, but less than MDL
12. Detected, but less than PQL

The plethora of reporting techniques results in a real problem for some of the end users of the data. Those who wish to know whether their effluent is above or below a regulatory limit do not really care about the exact value of a parameter when it's on the safe side; however other users, especially those who input the results into mathematical models for site assessments, are very exacting in their data requirements. For these latter applications "Not Detected" is quite different from a "Detected, but less than the MDL" or "Below Detection Limits." It is somewhat imperative for the laboratory to develop a dialog with the end user to determine the exact requirements of the data.

Method detection limits (MDL) are the minimum level of an analyte that can be determined with 99% confidence. Once an IDL has been determined, it is readily apparent that for samples that have target analyte present at the IDL, at least half the analyses

[169] Berthouex, P.M. 1993. "A Study of the Precision of Lead Measurements at Concentrations Near the Method Limit of Detection." *Water Environment Research.* 65(5). pp. 620-629.

of the sample will result in responses below the IDL (Figure 1-21). The objective of the analyst becomes a determination of how high on the calibration curve one must go so that all signals will be above the IDL, in other words, no false negatives will be reported. The MDL attempts to answer this question. The procedure that follows is again drawn from EPA 40 CFR Part 136, Appendix B. The analyst should consult the 40 CFR reference, as there are a number of specific conditions and choices that must be made during the MDL procedure. In brief the method is as follows:

1. Prepare a spike of the analyte into laboratory water that is very close (2 to 5 times) to the IDL obtained above or the expected MDL.

2. Take seven aliquots of this spiked solution and process each through the sample clean-up and preparation procedure.

3. Analyze each of the prepared aliquots in the exact same manner as prescribed in the Method used.

4. Calculate the standard deviation ($S_{\%R}$) of the aliquot results as described above.

5. The MDL is equal to the one-tailed t-statistic at a 99% confidence level for the performed number of samples times the standard deviation:

$$MDL = t_{0.99,n} \times S_{\%R} \text{ or in this case } MDL = 3.143 \, S_{\%R}$$

For other numbers of repetitions in the MDL study, the appropriate value of $t_{0.99}$ can be found in Table 1-50.

Table 1-50. One-tailed t-statistic at 99% confidence level for a variety of repetitions

Repetitions	$t_{0.99}$	Repetitions	$t_{0.99}$
3	6.965	15	2.624
4	4.541	16	2.602
5	3.747	17	2.583
6	3.365	18	2.567
7	3.143	19	2.552
8	2.998	20	2.539
9	2.896	21	2.528
10	2.821	22	2.518
11	2.764	23	2.508
12	2.718	24	2.500
13	2.681	25	2.492
14	2.650	26	2.485

In practice, determination of MDLs is quite challenging. If the spike level is too high, the resulting standard deviation will be so small, that the calculated MDL can actually be below the instrument detection level. On the other hand, if the spike level is too low, the standard deviation can be so high that the calculated MDL is useless for most regulatory purposes. Due to the considerable time that can be spent on these procedures, most analysts seek only to verify the MDLs listed in most of the published regulatory methods. This practice in itself causes problems for end users who have exacting data requirements.

The determination of the MDL for total suspended solids is illustrated in Table 1-51. In the first trial, the spike level was 12 mg/L while for the second trial the spike was increased to 16 mg/L. The EPA expected MDL for this test is 5 mg/L. Trial 1 gives an MDL that is not usable for the most part, while the second trial verifies the EPA MDL, yet there is only a slight difference in the spike level.

Table 1-51. MDL example for Total Suspended Solids in mg/L

	Trial 1	Trial 2
	12.5	14.5
	17	16
	15.5	18.5
	13	17
	8	15.5
	16	16
	13.5	16
	17	15
	16	16
Mean	14.28	16.06
SD	2.89	1.16
MDL	8.37	3.36

In all analyses there is a spread of results around the true value (TV). The MDL eliminates the false positive by having the reporting level generally several standard deviations above the IDL, thus any signal seen is real. However for analyte spikes at the MDL itself, 50% of the obtained results are going to be less than the MDL (the shaded area in the graph), and not reporting them constitutes a Type II error, a false negative[170]. To avoid the problem many labs use Practical Quantitation Levels (PQL), which are set at a variety of amounts, the most common being 12 times the standard deviation resulting from the MDL procedure. Three different types of result now can be given by the laboratory: a numerical value above the PQL, a detect but less than the PQL, or a non-detect. See Figures 1-23 and 1-24.

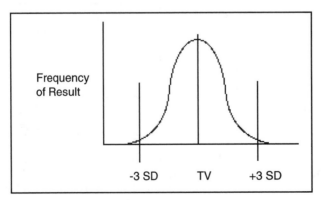

Figure 1-23. Distribution of results around a true value.

---

[170] L. Keith, *Environmental Laboratory*, June/July 1992. pp. 58-61.

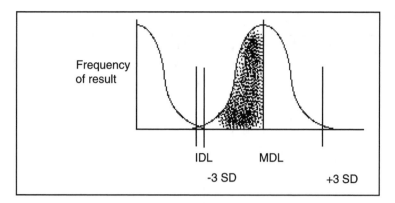

Figure 1-24. False negative determinations at the MDL.

MDLs are always linked to a standard sample size such as 200.0 mL of sample titrated for alkalinity (310.1), 1.00 L of sample extracted and concentrated to 1.00 mL for semivolatile organics analysis (8270), or 5.00 mL sparged for GC-MS analysis (8260). Attempts to lower MDLs through increasing the processed sample size are generally not productive due to the simultaneous increase in background interferences.

The reduction of standard sample size is commonly done as a measure to reduce interference and permit a determination in the presence of severe backgrounds. This effectively serves to increase the MDL by the same degree in which the sample size is reduced. Thus decreasing the sample size by one half, doubles the MDL. Reducing the sample size by 10, multiplies the MDL by 10.

The physical characterization of solids in samples as total solids (TS), total dissolved solids (TDS) and total suspended solids (TSS) have an absolute requirement of a minimum of 2.5 mg of residue detected. For 50 mL of sample processed the MDL will be 50 mg/L, while for 500 mL sample the MDL is 5 mg/L. As samples are quite variable in filtering ability, in a sample batch there will often be a wide range of MDLs.

A final problem with the use of MDL as currently defined, concerns those analyses in which there is not 100% recovery of target analyte. By its very definition the MDL is a measure of the precision of an analysis and no account is taken of accuracy[171]. Quite erratic results and misinterpretations of results are possible by data reviewers if this aspect of the MDL is not recognized. Remember that the MDL is determined using reagent water, so it is not surprising that MDL levels usually cannot be achieved when complex samples of wastewater, soils, fish, etc., are analyzed by a lab.

C. Reporting Units and Common Conversions

Scientific results are almost always reported in metric units such as grams, kilograms, liters, etc. SI prefixes are used to indicate variations on the basic units of grams, liters, moles and others, as indicated in the table.

---

[171] Kimbrough, D.E., and J. Wakakuwa. "Method Detection Limits in Solid Waste Analysis." *Environ. Sci. Technol.* 1993. 27(13). pp. 2692-2699.

Table 1-52. SI prefixes

Prefix	Abbv	Multiplier		Prefix	Abbv	Multiplier
zepto-	z	10^{-21}		zetta-	Z	10^{21}
atto-	a	10^{-18}		exa-	E	10^{18}
femto-	f	10^{-15}		peta-	P	10^{15}
pico-	p	10^{-12}		tera-	T	10^{12}
nano-	n	10^{-9}		giga-	G	10^{9}
micro-	u (μ)	10^{-6}		mega-	M	10^{6}
milli-	m	10^{-3}		kilo-	k	10^{3}
centi-	c	10^{-2}		hecta-	h	10^{2}
deci-	d	10^{-1}		deca-	da	10

Environmental results are often expressed in the units of parts per million (ppm), parts per billion (ppb), and parts per trillion (ppt). These have different meanings depending on the sample matrix. With liquids and solids the units are in terms of mass/volume and mass/mass respectively, and are often interchanged based on the assumption that the density of water is 1.000 g/mL (1.000 kg/L), although this is strictly true only at 4 °C. For massively contaminated samples, the concentrations are expressed as parts per hundred or percents (%) with 1000 ppm being equal to 0.10%.

Table 1-53. Common environmental reporting units

Unit	Liquids			Solids	
%	–	g/100 mL	–	–	g/100 g
ppm	mg/L	μg/mL	ng/μL	mg/kg	μg/g
ppb	μg/L	ng/mL	pg/μL	μg/kg	ng/g
ppt	ng/L	pg/mL	fg/μL	ng/kg	pg/g

A number of common conversions from the English system of weights and measures to the Metric system are encountered in the environmental business as indicated in the Table 1-54.

Table 1-54. Commonly encountered conversions and definitions

Unit	Definition
1.000 mL	volume of 1.000 g of water at 4 °C
1.000 calorie	amount of heat necessary to raise the temperature of 1.000 g of water 1 °C
1.000 BTU	amount of energy necessary to raise the temperature of 1.000 lb of water 1 °F
1.000 calorie	equal to 4.184 joules
1.000 BTU	equal to 1055 joules or 252 calories
1.000 atmosphere of pressure	equal to 14.7 psi
ppm	equal to gallons/million gallons
ppm x 8.34	equal to pounds/million gallons

D. Volumetric Measurements

Most analytical procedures in the lab require accurate measurement of amounts of samples, reagents, and standards. The most frequently used methods of measurement commonly depend on the materials being in a solution of known concentration and then dispensing the solution. Burets, volumetric pipets, and volumetric flasks are the tools of precise volume measurements. They are produced by a number of manufacturers in a variety of grades. The only grade present in an analytical laboratory should be Class A. Class A standards for volumetric measuring devices are set by ASTM. ASTM E287 covers standards for burets; E969-83 covers volumetric pipets; E288, E542 and E694 cover volumetric flasks; and E694 and E542 are for graduated cylinders. Graduated cylinders are not precise volumetric measuring devices, although commonly used for this purpose, especially for aliquoting samples. Table 1-55 lists the allowed tolerances under the Class A designation for volumetric devices and compares these with the most accurate graduated cylinders commercially available. Note that Erlenmeyer flasks, beakers and other miscellaneous laboratory glassware are not measuring devices. The volume markings on the sides of these containers are approximate with a tolerance of from ± 5 to 10%.

Table 1-55. Class A tolerances for volumetric measuring devices

Capacity mL	Buret	Graduated Cylinder	Volumetric Flask	Volumetric Pipet
0.5	-	-	-	±0.006
1	-	-	±0.01	±0.006
2	±0.01	-	±0.015	±0.006
3	-	-	-	±0.01
4	-	-	-	±0.01
5	±0.01	-	±0.02	±0.01
6	-	-	-	±0.02
7	-	-	-	±0.02
8	-	-	-	±0.02
9	-	-	-	±0.02
10	±0.02	±0.08	±0.02	±0.02
15	-	-	-	±0.03
20	-	-	-	±0.03
25	±0.03	±0.14	±0.03	±0.03
50	±0.05	±0.2	±0.05	±0.05
100	±0.10	±0.35	±0.08	±0.08
200	-	-	±0.10	-
250	-	±0.65	±0.12	-
500	-	±1.1	±0.20	-
1000	-	±2.0	±0.30	-
2000	-	±4.0	±0.50	-

Also missing from the list of Class A volumetric measuring devices are syringes and automatic disposable tip pipettors, although these are used throughout the laboratory industry. To be used in a legally defensible manner these must be calibrated and the calibration documented. The most common method of calibration is to dispense a volume of reagent grade water from the syringe or pipettor onto an analytical balance. The density of water is affected by the temperature and the atmospheric pressure, however the second effect is quite small and normally ignored. The density of water at various temperatures is listed in Table 1-56. Intermediate values can be obtained through extrapolation.

Table 1-56. Density of reagent water at different temperatures

Temp °C	Density g/mL	Temp °C	Density g/mL
10	0.99970	24	0.99730
12	0.99950	26	0.99678
14	0.99924	28	0.99623
16	0.99894	30	0.99565
18	0.99860	32	0.99503
20	0.99820	34	0.99437
22	0.99777	36	0.99369

E. Significant Figures

Significant figures are an important concept in analytical chemistry as they give an implicit indication of the degree of confidence of the results. This becomes of greater impact in these closing years of the twentieth century due to the prominent use of electronic calculators and computers in the laboratory to perform data conversions while at the same time many older model measuring devices are still being used to obtain the data. Suppose that the analyst needs to multiply 2.13 times 4.67 and uses a calculator to obtain 9.9471. Does the precision implied by the last number reflect the precision of the numbers used to derive it?

In analytical chemistry the uncertainty implied in a number is a variation of ± 1 in the final decimal place, unless otherwise explicitly stated. When the number 2.13 is reported, the analyst means that the value 2.13 is the best estimate of a result that exists somewhere in the range 2.12 to 2.14. Compare the ranges of the following numbers and how increasing numbers of significant figures imply greater degrees of measurement precision.

Reported number	Implied precision
2	1 to 3
2.0	1.9 to 2.1
2.00	1.99 to 2.01
2.000	1.999 to 2.001

The consequence of this definition and use of significant figures is that when the notation of 5 mL is seen on a benchsheet when referring to a sample aliquot, the immediate interpretation is a dispensing of 4 to 6 mL by the technician and an implied initial error in the analysis of 20%. On the other hand if a Class A volumetric pipet was used to dispense that sample the number should be recorded as 5.00 mL with a significant decrease in initial analytical error (0.2%).

The number of significant figures allowed in a final result is limited by the maximum inaccuracy in the measuring tools used. For example suppose we want to multiply 1.7 times 2.4 and we are limited to an old instrument called a slide rule. The calculation is illustrated in Figure 1-25, where the positions of 1.7, 2.4 and the result 4.1 are estimated and to the limits of our measurement, 4.1 is a pretty good estimate of the range 4.0 to 4.2. On the other hand, use of a calculator gives the exact answer of 4.08 with the implied estimate range 4.07 to 4.09, which is a misrepresentation of the accuracy possible from the slide rule.

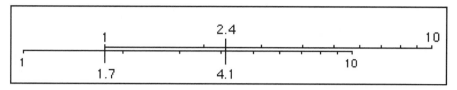

Figure 1-25. Multiplication of two numbers using an old fashioned slide rule.

Most environmental laboratories use Class A glassware for volume measurements, and this places a limitation on the number of significant figures reportable. For example preparation of a standard by dilution of a 5.00 mL aliquot of a 21.00 mg/L standard solution to 100.0 mL limits the concentration of the working standard to three significant figures, 1.05 mg/L not 1.050 mg/L. This in turn limits any final results reported from this analysis to three significant figures. In general three significant figures is the maximum number that can be reported from any environmental analytical procedure.

There was a metals section in a laboratory that always reported recovery data with four significant figures (93.12%). An audit of the procedure was performed and Class A glassware was found to be used in all parts of the analysis except one. This one excepted use was in adding matrix spike solutions to the samples where a 20 μL disposable tip pipettor was employed. These type devices in the hands of an experienced technician are accurate to ± 1 μL which translates to a ± 5% variation in the amount of matrix spike added to the sample. Following this error through the procedure and into the recovery calculations suggests that the recovery data reported had a built in variation of ± 5% or allowable reporting values of 90% or 95%, not the figure provided. When questioned about this, the technician was aware of the problem, however the computer that processed the QC data was programmed to report all numbers with 2 decimal places, regardless of the input data.

F. Record Keeping and File Management

Many records are required to be kept to support the legally defensible aspect of the data reported from the lab. Possible records that need to be maintained include, but are not limited to, the following list. Most of these records do not have a set format, however, they should all supply the answers to the questions, who did what to which sample, how was it done and when? Some of the forms have formats specified in the most recent CLP SOWs. In laboratories with LIMS, the forms are computer generated, and the laboratory establishes a format that is the most compatible with the computers in use.

ASI ANALYTICAL SERVICES, INC.
ENVIRONMENTAL MONITORING & LABORATORY ANALYSIS
110 TECHNOLOGY PARKWAY • NORCROSS GEORGIA 30092
(770) 734-4200 • FAX (770) 734-4201

CHAIN OF CUSTODY RECORD

CLIENT NAME | # OF CONTAINERS | PROJECT NAME | PROJECT NUMBER | LAB ID | PURCHACE ORDER NO.
CLIENT ADDRESS AND PHONE NUMBER | ANALYSES REQUESTED
PROJECT MANAGER | COPY TO (if applicable)
REQUESTED COMP. DATE | SAMPLING REQUIREMENTS: SDWA ☐ NPDES ☐ RCRA ☐ OTHER ____

FOR LAB USE ONLY: LAB# | PROJECT NO. | ACK | VERIFIED | QUOTE# | BS | NO. OF SAMP | PG | OF

SAMPLE ID	DATE	TIME	COMP	GRAB	SOIL	SAMPLE DESCRIPTIONS	# OF CONTAINERS	ANALYSES REQUESTED									LAB ID	REMARKS/ADDITIONAL INFORMATION

SAMPLED BY AND TITLE | DATE/TIME | RELINQUISHED BY: | DATE/TIME | HAZWRAP/NEESA Y N
RECEIVED BY: | DATE/TIME | RELINQUISHED BY: | DATE/TIME | QC LEVEL 1 2 3
RECEIVED BY: | DATE/TIME | RELINQUISHED BY: | DATE/TIME | COC | ICE | ANA REQ | TEMP | CUST SEAL | PH
RECEIVED BY LAB: | DATE/TIME | SAMPLE SHIPPED VIA UPS BUS FED-EX HAND OTHER ____ | AIR BILL # | SAMPLE COND.
REMARKS | ENTERED INTO LIMS____ | COC REVIEWD____

Figure 1-26. Chain of custody form.

Chain of Custody forms - These are used to document the custody of a sample as it travels from the person collecting the sample through the transportation process until its receipt in the laboratory. It has spaces for signatures and times of persons having custody. See Figure 1-26.

Field monitoring reports and worksheets - These are all of the items of documentation that verify the field operations and field analysis.

Sample receipt logbooks - These document the arrival and condition of the sample at the laboratory. They also serve as the primary documentation of what field sample number corresponds to what laboratory sample number.

Work assignments - Most commonly produced from LIMS, these list the samples and their location for a test parameter to be performed by the technician.

WORK ASSIGNMENT

Analyst: LMB	Date: 10-29-96	Test: TSS (mg/L)(EPA 160.2)	
Sample #	**Location**	**Due Date**	**Client**
43012-1	C7	11-07-96	Springfield Power Plant
43012-2	C7	11-07-96	Springfield Power Plant
43012-3	C7	11-07-96	Springfield Power Plant
43012-4	C7	11-07-96	Springfield Power Plant
43012-5	C7	11-07-96	Springfield Power Plant
43013	H1	11-06-96	Springfield Dairy
43014-3	R2	11-11-96	Springfield Fire Department

Figure 1-27. Work assignment for TSS.

Bench worksheets - These are often bound into books or spiral bound and serve to record the preparation and analysis of the samples. Each benchsheet is generally limited to a single analytical batch and documents the QC measures such as blanks, sample duplicates, calibration checks, matrix spikes, etc. that were performed with the batch. Operational information of the test such as times, temperatures, and amounts and sources of reagents and standards can also be listed on the benchsheet. A sample benchsheet is shown in Figure 1-28.

GRAVIMETRIC ANALYSIS BENCHSHEET

ANALYST_____ DATE/TIME_____

METHOD NUMBER_____ TEST_____

INITIAL OVEN TEMPERATURE _____ FINAL OVEN TEMPERATURE_____

Thermometer Certification Number:

SAMPLE	CLIENT	TARE	TOTAL	NET	DRY 1 TOTAL	NET	DRY 2 TOTAL	NET	NOTES
BLANK									
Check Sample									
	MS								
	MSD								
	Duplicate								

Figure 1-28. Example of a bench worksheet.

Sample preparation logbooks - These are particular to procedures that involve separate sample preparation and instrument analysis. The most common forms are extraction logs in the organics area and digestion logs in metals analysis.

Instrument maintenance and run logs - The instrument maintenance logs serve to document that the instrument is operating per manufacturer's specifications. They document both preventative maintenance performed by the instrument operator and service calls by factory technicians. The run log documents every sample that has been tested on the instrument and what data file the information is stored under. Instruments often maintain an internal run log in the computer memory that should duplicate the manual run log kept by the technician.

Raw data from the analysis (chromatograms, strip charts, absorbances, etc.) - Often kept as computer records, hardcopy should be maintained and filed in such a fashion as to be readily available for a period of at least 5 years.

Sample result calculation worksheets - These records may be part of the raw data from the analysis, with the transformation of the raw data to the final result included as part of the document. Often a single detailed calculation is illustrated on the worksheet. The assumption is made that all the calculations were performed in the same manner. A laboratory may chose to attach detailed calculations for each result to the analysis benchsheet.

Calibration curves and the raw data - Instruments and procedures must be calibrated and documentation kept supporting the calibration. Many instruments maintain this data as computer memory on tape or disk. Manual procedures may require hand-plotting of the calibration curve, however, a better solution is to use a statistics package on a PC and have the computer draw the calibration curve and at the same time calculate the correlation coefficient (r). Some procedures require a coefficient of at least 0.995 for acceptance of the calibration. If several technicians are performing the same test, each must prepare and maintain his/her calibrations. Most test methods specify the frequency of recalibration, ranging from each use to once a year. "Calibrations" should indicate who performed it, when, the specific test or instrument, and the correlation coefficient. All instruments must be calibrated. There are several commercial instruments on the market for spectrophotometric analysis of water pollutants that have a built-in factory-set calibration. None of these instruments are known to be approved for regulatory reporting. The calibration curve must be checked immediately prior to beginning analysis of a batch, and the check documented.

Analytical balance daily calibration check logbook - The analytical balance is the most important instrument in the laboratory. It is used for weighing samples and standards, and in gravimetric analysis, it is the determinative instrument. The calibration of the balance should be adjusted by a service technician at least twice a year and the service call documented. The calibration should be checked on a daily basis by weighing a set of Class S weights and recording the results (Figure 1-29). There are a variety of calibration masses available commercially. ASTM (standard E617) and NIST have established tolerances for different class weights as in Table 1-57.

ANALYTICAL BALANCE DAILY CALIBRATION CHECK

Balance Serial Number: _____   Date: _____

Analytst: _____   Page: _____

Class S Weight Serial Number: _____

Nominal Class S Weight	Acceptance Range	Result
10 mg	0.0099-0.0101	
20 mg	0.0199-0.0201	
50 mg	0.0495-0.0505	
100 mg	0.0990-0.1010	
200 mg	0.1990-0.2010	
500 mg	0.4900-0.5050	
1 g	0.9990-1.0010	
5 g	4.9990-5.0010	
10 g	9.9990-10.0010	
100 g	99.9900-100.0100	

Figure 1-29. Analytical balance daily calibration logbook.

Internal chain of custody - The internal chain of custody is most commonly maintained as a computer record in the LIMS. It may rely on manual entry of the sample numbers, time, date and the name of the technician acquiring or relinquishing custody or it may be driven with a bar code reader.

Sample result worksheets - These forms are the working draft of the final analytical report. They may be computer generated as a result of the sample receipt process, or they may be hand typed. They serve as a summary of information about the sample, the test parameters required, methods required, and have space for the technicians to enter the result, their MDL for the test, and their initials. The forms may be color coded according to a priority of testing scheme, such as orange for 24-hour turn-around, or blue for regular turn-around. When the technicians have entered all the sample results onto these forms, they are reviewed and initialed by the supervisors and laboratory managers before being sent on for final report generation. See Figure 1-30.

Table 1-57. Tolerances (in mg) of various ASTM and NIST Classes of Standard Weights

Mass	ASTM Class 1	NIST Class S	NIST Class S-1[172]	NIST Class P[173]	NIST Class C	NIST Class F
1 mg	0.010	0.014	0.025	0.050	0.04	0.10
2 mg	0.010	0.014	0.025	0.050	0.05	0.12
5 mg	0.010	0.014	0.028	0.055	0.10	0.17
10 mg	0.010	0.014	0.030	0.060	0.15	0.21
20 mg	0.010	0.014	0.035	0.070	0.20	0.26
50 mg	0.010	0.014	0.042	0.085	0.35	0.35
100 mg	0.010	0.025	0.050	0.10	0.5	0.43
200 mg	0.010	0.025	0.060	0.12	0.7	0.54
500 mg	0.010	0.025	0.080	0.16	1.5	0.72
1 g	0.034	0.054	0.10	0.20	2	0.90
2 g	0.034	0.054	0.13	0.26	3	1.1
5 g	0.034	0.054	0.18	0.36	5	1.5
10 g	0.050	0.074	0.25	0.50	7	2.0
20 g	0.074	0.074	0.35	0.70	10	4.0
50 g	0.12	0.12	0.60	1.2	20	10
100 g	0.25	0.25	1.0	2.0	30	20

[172] Equivalent to ASTM Class 3.
[173] Equivalent to ASTM Class 4.

Final analytical reports - These are the written reports sent to the client that convey the results of the analysis. Information that should be included is a description of the sample, where it came from, the time and date of sampling, the client's name and address, the parameters reported, test method, test results, detection limits of the test, and any data qualifiers. The report must be signed by an official of the laboratory. A modern innovation is to submit final reports on computer readable media such as tapes or disk, or over data transmission lines. However, each final report submitted on computer media should also be duplicated and sent as hardcopy to the client. See Figure 1-2 for an example.

Sample container logs - These records take the form of a bound logbook that, for manual cleaning, contains a written description of the cleaning process along with the date, time and initials of the person performing the cleaning. The page number of the log accompanies the sample container through the sampling process and should appear in the field notebook, the chain of custody and the sample receipt logbook. For precleaned sample containers the logbook has pasted into it the manufacturer's certificate of analysis, the lot number and references the in-house container blank QA results. Either the lot number or logbook page should appear in the field notebook, chain of custody, and the sample receipt logbook.

Standard receipt logs - These are logbooks that document the receipt of analytical standards in the laboratory. They take many forms but should include the time and date of receipt, the source of the standard and lot number, and the storage location. These records may be maintained in the purchasing office rather than in the laboratory.

Standard preparation logs - These records document the preparation of standards used for instrument calibrations. They must be linked by reference to the calibration and the manufacturer's certificate of analysis. They include the time and date of preparation, the vendor, manufacturer, and lot number of the standard, the volume or weight of standard used, the calculation of final concentration of the standard, the storage container and location, and the expiration date of the standard. The log must be countersigned and dated by the section supervisor. See Figure 1-31.

Sample disposition logs - Most samples have a required 30-day holding time after analysis and before disposal. As samples are logged out from the laboratory, they are removed from the sample storage locations and transferred to a holding location. A LIMS can handle the paperwork documenting this function very easily by generating a purge list each morning for all samples completed on the previous day. The receipt technicians go find all the samples (and extracts and digestates), marking off on the list all that they find and moving the purge samples to the holding area with the purge list attached to the shelf. The list is dated, and 30 days from its issuance the technicians remove the samples from the holding area and either safely dispose of the benign samples or return the hazardous samples to the client. The LIMS can facilitate this process by placing an asterisk next to each sample that tested hazardous and needs to be returned to the client. The hazardous determination is normally made during the report review process.

Priority **3** Due 12/12/96 Sample # 9999-1,2

Notes: Metals not Preserved

Phone: 619-555-0386 ext 4439

Springfield Power Plant   Date Received: 10-25-96
PO Box 1234   PO #
1st St.
Springfield, Ohio   # Samples = 2 # Containers = 6

ATTN: Mr. Homer Simpson

Location: **C 3**

Description:
Water, grab, 435Z, 10-18-96, Time, received 10-25-96

TEST	Result	Detection	By
Sample 1			
Total Lead (Pb)(mg/L)(EPA 239.2)	_____	0.005	_____
Total Copper (Cu)(mg/L)(EPA 220.2)	_____	0.002	_____
Sample 2			
Chemical Oxygen Demand (COD)(mg/L)(EPA 410.1)	_____	5	_____
Total Phosphorous (P)(mg/L)(EPA 365.1)	_____	0.02	_____
Total Kjeldahl Nitrogen (N)(mg/L)(EPA 351.3)	_____	0.1	_____
Total Suspended Solids (mg/L)(EPA 160.2)	_____	40	_____
Total Zinc (Zn)(mg/L)(EPA 200.7)	_____	0.02	_____

DATES: Completed: Typed: Mailed:

         Review: Review:

         Review:

Figure 1-30. Sample report worksheet.

BNA STANDARD PREPARATION LOG

Date:	Time:
Analyst:	Page Number:

BASE/NEUTRAL STANDARD

Vendor:	Manufacturer:
Catalog Number:	Lot Number:
Receipt Date:	Expiration Date:
Dilution Solvent:	Dilution Solvent Lot Number:
Volume used:	Final Volume:
Final Concentration:	Storage location and expiration date:

ACID STANDARD

Vendor:	Manufacturer:
Catalog Number:	Lot Number:
Receipt Date:	Expiration Date:
Dilution Solvent:	Dilution Solvent Lot Number:
Volume used:	Final Volume:
Final Concentration:	Storage location and expiration date:

CALCULATIONS

B/N	Acid

Supervisor verification: Date:

Figure 1-31. Standard preparation log.

G. Quality Control Procedures for Sampling

Container blanks - Analyte free water placed in random samples from a vendor's lot number of containers, then analyzed for the target parameters. BDL results for the target analytes indicate the lot is appropriate for use in sampling.

Blank samples - Analyte free water placed in a container in the field, preservatives added and the sample submitted with the rest of the samples from that field operation. Serves to check on the preservatives and laboratory water used in the field, along with incidental contamination that may be present at the sampling site.

Blank preservatives - Similar to the container blank, it concentrates upon the purity of the preservatives. May be performed in the laboratory if preservatives are purchased in single-use sealed ampules by vendor's lot number.

Equipment blanks - Equipment is rinsed with laboratory water immediately prior to use in sampling, and the rinsings submitted to the laboratory as a sample for analysis. This is especially pertinent if equipment is cleaned between uses in the field.

Trip blanks (VOA only) - VOA vials are filled with laboratory water at the lab and sealed. These go to the field and return where they are analyzed as a regular sample. They check for permeation of volatile contaminants through the container septum. A recent example that detected hydrocarbon contamination in the trip blank was traced to the technician storing the VOC samples in a box over a running truck's exhaust tailpipe for several hours.

Field duplicate samples - The sample is split into two or more containers, which are then analyzed as regular samples. Checks for consistency in sampling and analysis.

H. Quality Control Procedures for Sample Preparation

Spikes and recovery (matrix spikes) - A matrix spike is the addition of a known amount of a target analyte to a sample. Analysis of the sample and the matrix-spiked sample generate recovery numbers. These recovery numbers give an indication of the accuracy of the analytical procedure for the particular sample. Matrix spike results are normally reported on a batchwise basis. In test procedures where the target analyte is infrequently found in samples, realistic evaluations of precision are best obtained through performance of a matrix spike and matrix spike duplicate.

SEMIVOLATILE BNA SPIKE RESULTS
AQUEOUS SAMPLES

Data Quality Objectives	%Recovery	RPD
Phenol	12-89	0-42
2-Chlorophenol	27-123	0-40
1,4-Dichlorobenzene	36-97	0-28
N-Nitrosodipropylamine	41-116	0-38
1,2,4-Trichlorobenzene	44-142	0-28
4-Chloro-3-methylphenol	23-97	0-42
Acenaphthene	46-118	0-31
2,4-Dinitrotoluene	24-96	0-38
4-Nitrophenol	10-80	0-50
Pentachlorophenol	9-103	0-50
Pyrene	26-127	0-31

Compound	%R1	%R2	%R$_{ave}$	RPD	Notes
Phenol					
2-Chlorophenol					
1,4-Dichlorobenzene					
N-Nitrosodipropylamine					
1,2,4-Trichlorobenzene					
4-Chloro-3-methylphenol					
Acenaphthene					
2,4-Dinitrotoluene					
4-Nitrophenol					
Pentachlorophenol					
Pyrene					

Batch Number:

File Name (MS):   File Name (MSD):

Analyst: Date:

Figure 1-32. Batch matrix spike results for BNA analysis.

Surrogates - Surrogates are compounds added to every single QC, blank, and analytical sample. They are calibrated just like target analytes. The surrogates are present to evaluate the success or lack of success of the sample preparation. Surrogates are chosen to expose sample preparation problems, thus they must be very similar chemically to the target analytes. Since they are added to every sample, they must never be found naturally in a sample. For this reason surrogates are often isotope-labeled target analytes such as toluene-D_8, where all the hydrogens have been replaced with deuterium.

VOA BATCH SURROGATE RECOVERY SUMMARY

WATER SAMPLES

% Recovery Objectives

S1	1,2-Dichloroethane-D4	76-114
S2	Toluene-D8	88-110
S3	4-Bromofluorobenzene	86-115

Sample	File	S1	S2	S3	Notes
Blank					
MS					
MSD					
Duplicate					
QC Check					

Analyst: Batch: Date:

Figure 1-33. Batch surrogate recovery form.

Sample duplicates - Sample duplicate analysis must be performed at a rate varying from 1 every 10 samples to 1 every 20 samples, depending on the regulatory agency. When performing tests for target analytes that are often found in the sample, such as nutrients, duplicates should be used for the determination of precision results and MQO. In cases where the target analytes are seldom present, the duplicate analysis is still performed; however, precision is calculated from matrix spike duplicate analysis.

Reagent blanks - Reagent blanks are the first test performed in any batch to determine the level of laboratory contamination in reagents, solvents, glassware, etc. The blank must give BDL results for each target analyte before continued sample analysis is allowed.

In an analysis[174] of results reported from groundwater samples obtained from over 500 RCRA and CERCLA sites distributed over all 10 EPA Regions, out of 425 total contaminants detected, the most frequently reported volatile organic contaminant found was dichloromethane, and the most frequently reported semi-volatile organic compound was bis (2-ethylhexyl) phthalate. Ranking the results by individual sites or by individual analyses did not change this observation. The list[175] of the top 50 chemicals in production contains methyl-*tert*-butyl ether, vinyl chloride, benzene, ethyl benzene, styrene, xylene, toluene, cumene, phenol, vinyl acetate, acrylonitrile, acetone, and *n*-butyl alcohol, which are also prominent on various target compound lists as environmental contaminants. Although methylene chloride and bis(2-ethylhexyl) phthalate are important industrially, they are not that overwhelmingly prevalent in the environment, with the above list of compounds probably present in greater frequency, simply based on the amounts in existence. Instead these analytical results must be viewed as an indication of the pervasiveness of laboratory contamination as a problem to environmental laboratories.

Virtually every solvent used in the organics laboratory, except methanol, is a listed target analyte of one or more EPA methods. Examples of listed solvents include acetone, hexane, methylene chloride, toluene, ethyl ether, methyl ethyl ketone and methyl isobutyl ketone. Other common lab contaminants found in the volatiles lab are naphthalene (old fashioned mothballs) and para-dichlorobenzene (new formulation mothballs). Limonene and citral can be present from floor waxes and cleaning formulations. Acrylonitrile and other compounds are found in carpet glue and backing. Methyl and ethylmethacrylate are common in fingernail polishes.

These can normally be minimized in the volatiles lab by situating the lab up-wind and in an independent building from the semi-volatiles extraction laboratory. However we have seen the wind shift 180° from the prevailing direction and at a distance of 100 yards, the VOA GC-MS background starts to register increased levels of methylene chloride within an hour. Housing the volatiles lab under the same roof as the rest of the laboratory creates the need for either a completely separate ventilation system effectively isolating the VOA area, or arranging the HVAC ducting so that all the exchange air in the building enters through the volatiles lab, creating a positive air pressure in the room.

The situation is different in the semi-volatiles extraction laboratory where the biggest contaminants are a variety of phthalates found in almost all products manufactured in the USA. The most common culprits are di-*n*-butyl phthalate and bis(2-ethylhexyl) phthalate although benzylbutyl-, di-*n*- octyl- and diethylphthalate can be a problem at times. The list of products that contribute these contaminants in the lab are impressive, ranging from plastic bags used to hold 25 kg lots of anhydrous sodium sulfate to the gloves the technicians wear to protect their hands. A survey was conducted in a laboratory to determine sources of phthalate contamination. The results are in Table 1-58.

174 Plumb, R. H. Jr., "The Importance of Volatile Organic Compounds as a Disposal Site Monitoring Parameter." in *Groundwater Contamination and Analysis at Hazardous Waste Sites*. S. Lesage and R.E. Jackson (Eds), Marcel Dekker, Inc, 270 Madison Ave, New York, NY 10016. 1992. pp. 173-197.

175 *Chemical and Engineering News*. April 11, 1994. p. 13.

Other contaminants seen in the semi-volatiles lab arise from the solvents[176] that are used in the extraction process. Methylene chloride and other chlorinated solvents are subject to free-radical degradation initiated by ultraviolet light. Degradation products include hydrochloric acid, phosgene, and a variety of hydrocarbons and chlorinated hydrocarbons of increasing chain-length. Free-radical scavengers used to stabilize chlorinated solvents include amylene and ethanol (up to 1%). Phosgene is of particular interest, not only because it is toxic (it was employed as one of the first chemical warfare agents during World War I) but also because it is extremely reactive toward alcohols, phenols and amines that originally may be in the sample. Reaction with phosgene can transform target analytes into unrecognizable by-products.

Ether solvents are prone to formation of hydroperoxides, initiated by exposure of the solvent to air and ultraviolet light. Not only are hydroperoxides famous for their instability, old opened bottles of ether and tetrahydrofuran have been known to spontaneously explode, but the peroxides are effective oxidizing agents of target analytes. Ether solvents are stabilized by addition of either BHT or ethanol, and by packaging the solvent in a light-proof container under a nitrogen atmosphere. Bottles or cans of ether solvents should be purchased in the minimum size needed for weekly analysis use. Any excess should be disposed of properly. Containers that have been opened and stored more than 30 days should be suspected as having peroxides present. The presence of peroxides can be checked by shaking a 5 mL portion of the solvent with 1 mL of a 10% potassium iodide solution. Any formation of a yellow to brown or purple color in the solvent layer is interpreted as indicating that peroxides are present.

Ketone solvents such as acetone or methylethyl ketone (MEK) can form peroxides; however, the more frequently noted mode of degradation is condensation of two or more molecules of the solvent in the aldol reaction. 4-Hydroxy-4-methyl-2-pentanone (diacetone alcohol) is found as a contaminant in almost every instance when acetone has been used in the glassware washing process. Acetone and MEK can also condense with anilines and other aromatic amines to form very stable imines ($Ph-N=C[CH_3]_2$) that change the retention time and mass spectum of the target analyte.

Table 1-58. Phthalates and other contaminants found in common laboratory items. Amounts are in ng/μL injected into the GC-MS from 1.0 mL final volume of extract

Item and number	Contaminant found	Amount
sodium sulfate	di-*n*-butyl phthalate	5-100
1 g glass wool	di-*n*-octylphthalate	2
1 sheet of paper towel roll	di-*n*-butyl phthalate	36.5
	N,N-dimethyl-9-octadecenamide	-
	4,4'-butylidenebis[2-(1,1-dimethylethyl)-5-methyl] phenol	-
	pentatriacontane	-
#4 filter paper	di-*n*-butyl phthalate	139
	butylbenzyl phthalate	0.8
	Bis(2-ethylhexyl) phthalate	1.1
	di-*n*-octyl phthalate	0.2
	decamethylcyclopentasiloxane	-

Continued on next page.

---

[176] Seaver, C., J. Przybytek, and N. Roelofs, 1995. "Solvent Selection, Part III - Solvent Life and Degradation." *LC-GC*, 13(11). pp. 860-864. November, 1995.

Table 1-58. Phthalates and other contaminants found in common laboratory items. Amounts are in ng/μL injected into the GC-MS from 1.0 mL final volume of extract, *continued*

Item and number	Contaminant found	Amount
Acrodisk PTFE 0.45 mm filter disk (15)	di-*n*-butyl phthalate	3.8
Safeskin glove	di-*n*-butyl phthalate	1.1
	Bis(2-ethylhexyl) phthalate	12.2
	butylbenzyl phthalate	2.4
	N,N-bis(2-hydroxyethoxy)-dodecamide	-
	octadecadienal	-
	octadecene	-
	hydrocarbon oils	-
Triclean glove	Bis(2-ethylhexyl) phthalate	4.3
	butylbenzyl phthalate	11.4
	4-chloro-3-methyl phenol	6.5
	N,N-bis(2-hydroxyethoxy)-dodecamide	-
	Hexadecanoic acid	-
	4,4'-butylidene bis[2-(1,1-dimethylethyl)-5-methyl]phenol	-
	octadecadienal	-
N-Dex nitrile glove	di-*n*-butyl phthalate	6.3
	benzyl alcohol	56.8
	Bis-(2-ethylhexyl) phthalate	4.6
	3,3'-imino bis propanenitrile	-
	2-mercaptobenzothiazole	-
	hydrocarbon oils	-
	4,4'-butylidene bis[2-(1,1-dimethylethyl)-5-methyl]phenol	-
Chemsolve (1 g)	hexamethylcyclotrisiloxane	-
	pentamethyldisiloxane	-
	octamethylcyclotetrasiloxane	-
	2-[2-[4-(1,1,3,3-tetramethylbutyl)phenoxy]ethoxy]ethanol	-
	di-*n*-octylphthalate	1.4
HDPE container (500 mL)	2,5,8,11,14-pentaoxahexadecan-16-ol and other alcohols	-
Rubber suction bulb (large)	large amounts of hydrocarbon oils	-
Latex suction bulb (3)	4 unknown compounds	-
1 Alumina PrepSep column	(none detected)	
Tygon R-3603 tubing (41 inches)	Bis(2-ethylhexyl)phthalate	44,000
Fisher disposable Pasteur pipets (12)	(none detected)	
Soxhlet extraction thimble	di-*n*-butyl phthalate	9.3
	unidentified phthalate	-
	unidentified adipate	-
Silastic tubing (27")	diethyl phthalate	6.0
	phenanthrene	2
	anthracene	1.9
	di-*n*-butyl phthalate	5.1
	Bis(2-ethylhexyl) phthalate	15.5
	ethanol, 2-(2-butoxyethoxy)-acetate	-
	unidentified siloxane polymer series	-
Aluminum foil	(none detected)	
Baker C18 SPE	Bis(2-ethylhexyl) phthalate	2.7
	unidentified siloxane polymer series	-
McDonald's fingers	C_{12}-C_{18} Fatty acid series	varies

Reagent blanks normally substitute reagent or laboratory water for the sample volume. In the case of marine (seawater) samples, a more representative blank can be prepared using a preparation in either 40 CFR 796.1860 for synthetic seawater, EPA method 350.1 for substitute ocean water, or *Standard Methods* 19th Edition 4500-NH₃ G and 8010 E, summarized in Table 1-59. The 796.1860 preparation results in a solution of 34 ± 0.5 g/kg salinity and pH 8.0 ± 0.2. These solutions are also suitable for matrix spike, laboratory control samples or standard preparation.

Table 1-59. Preparation of 1 L of synthetic seawater

Reference Method	350.1[177]	4500-NH₃ G	SM 8010E	796.1860
Chemical	Amounts			
NaF	3 mg	3 mg	3 mg	3 mg
SrCl₂•6H₂O	30 mg (anh)	30 mg (anh)	20 mg	20 mg
H₃BO₃	30 mg	30 mg	30 mg	30 mg
KBr	100 mg	100 mg	100 mg	100 mg
KCl	700 mg	700 mg	700 mg	700 mg
CaCl₂•2H₂O	1.16 g (anh)	1.16 g (anh)	1.470 g	1.47 g
Na₂SO₄	4.09 g	4.09 (anh)	4.00 g	4.00 g
MgCl₂•6H₂O	5.20 (anh)	5.20 (anh)	10.780 g	10.78 g
NaCl	24.53 g	24.53 g	23.500 g	23.50 g
Na₂SiO₃•9H₂O	-	-	20 mg	20 mg
NaHCO₃	200 mg	200 mg	200 mg	200 mg
Na₄EDTA	-	-	1 mg	-

Freshwater blank matrices can be generated from laboratory purified water using a recipe in *Standard Methods* 19th Edition 8080E for synthetic freshwater. ASTM has generated a standard specification for substitute wastewater, ASTM D5905, that is useful for determination of the ruggedness of proposed test procedures.

Table 1-60. Synthetic freshwater recipe amounts in mg/L

Water type	NaHCO₃	CaSO₄•2H₂O	MgSO₄	KCl
Very Soft	12	7.5	7.5	0.5
Soft	48	30	30	2.0
Mod. Hard	96	60	60	4.0
Hard	192	120	120	8.0
Very Hard	384	240	240	16.0

QC check standards (lab control standards or samples) - These QC measures are used to determine if the sample preparation for the batch is successful on an ideal sample. The ideal sample can consist of a matrix spike into analyte-free water, in which case it is called a laboratory control sample. It could also be one of a variety of commercially available check samples where the level of target analytes are known and provided with the sample, in which case it is called a QC check sample. The recovery of the target analytes must be within the laboratory's MQO for the test. Specific MQO for the

---

[177] Anhydrous (anh) weight of salt.

lab control samples may be established, and many methods have a standard requirement of 70-130 for %R.

I. Quality Control Procedures during Analysis

Operator Certification - The certification may be general for laboratory operations, such as a wastewater laboratory analyst certificate, or specific for each test, for example, passing a PE sample. The certificate may be for attending a formal training course at an instrument manufacturer's facility. Many methods have a one-time demonstration of ability the analyst must pass before being allowed to test samples. All of these must be documented and copies of the documentation placed in the employee's training file. Having an SOP for employee training is a required part of the QA program under a number of laboratory certification programs.

Calibration curves - These are required for each analyst performing the test and are updated on a regular basis. Calibration curves must be immediately verified with testing of a mid-level calibration standard that comes from a different manufacturer than that of the standards used for the calibration. This procedure is called an initial calibration verification (ICV).

Calibration checks - The calibration curve must be checked on a batchwise basis to verify if it is still valid. The normal check is testing of one of the original mid-level calibration standards and verifying that the RPD is within the acceptance range of the method. The procedure is called a continuing calibration verification (CCV).

QC check standards - These are often repeat analysis of the ICV standard on a batchwise basis or at least 5% of the samples in the batch.

Post digestion spikes (PDS) - These procedures are used to specifically separate sample preparation problems from sample matrix problems during the digestion of samples for metals analysis. The PDS consists of adding matrix spike to the final analytical volume of the digested sample.

Duplicate analysis - Sample duplicate analysis must be performed at a rate varying from 1 every 10 samples to 1 every 20 samples, depending on the regulatory agency. When performing tests for target analytes that are often found in the sample, such as nutrients, duplicates should be used for the determination of precision results and MQO. In cases where the target analytes are seldom present, the duplicate analysis is still performed, however, precision is calculated from matrix spike duplicate analysis.

Blind check samples - These are samples inserted into the normal laboratory workload by the lab manager or QC manager. The samples have known target analyte concentrations and serve as an evaluation tool of the laboratory.

Laboratory certification samples - These blind samples, also known as Performance Evaluation or PE samples, are sent to the laboratory by another party. Analyte concentrations in the samples are known by the sender but not by the laboratory, and the laboratory's results are compared to the true value or acceptance range.

Internal performance and system audits - These audits are performed by either the QA Manager or the Laboratory Director and are an intense examination of a particular function or test procedure in the lab. The audits may be strictly observational, or they may include detailed examination of paperwork or even the use of blind laboratory check samples. The results of these audits are written and included in the QA record. Most regulatory agencies require at least an annual audit of each functioning area in the lab.

EPA, OSHA, state, third party, and client audits - Formal announced or surprise visits by a variety of interested parties are the norm for most environmental labs. They range from cursory visits to exhaustive investigations of analytical procedures, facilities, personnel, and especially documentation. These visits are almost always followed by a written report to which the laboratory is given a set amount of time to respond, again in writing.

Sample splits - Sample splits are performed by outside parties where a single well-mixed sample is divided into two samples, and the samples sent to different laboratories for analysis. The results from the laboratories are compared.

Florida DEP minimum QC procedures - In the absence of specified quality control procedures, the Florida Department of Environmental Protection (DEP) recommends the following minimum QC procedures:

1. Method reagent blanks analyzed at a rate of one every set of samples.
2. Matrix spikes analyzed at a rate of at least one or 5% of the samples with the same matrix in a sample set. Each different type of matrix in a sample set should be spiked.
3. Reagent water or reagent matrix spikes analyzed at a rate of 5% of the samples analyzed.
4. Quality control check samples analyzed in duplicate as blind samples at least twice a year.
5. Quality control check standards analyzed at a rate of 5% of the samples in a set.
6. Duplicate samples or matrix spike duplicates analyzed at a rate of at least one or 5% of the samples of differing matrix types in a sample set.
7. Continuing calibration standards analyzed at a rate of 5% of the samples in a sample set. (Item 5 may substitute for this procedure.)

J. Control Charts

Control charts were developed in the 1920's by Dr. Walter A. Shewhart of Bell Labs. Originally designed to monitor manufacturing processes with set tolerance limits, they have been generalized to many process control situations. In analytical chemistry, control charts are used to monitor accuracy and precision of analytical methods.

A control chart can be maintained for any individual repetitive quality control checks such as analysis of a constant concentration matrix spike and a matrix spike duplicate at a rate of 5% of the analytical samples. Charts for accuracy and precision can be maintained for these QC measures. After 10 repeats of the QC check, the mean and standard deviation of the %R and RPD are calculated and the control charts established. The ±Warning Level is set at the Mean ±2 standard deviations and the Control level at the Mean ±3 standard deviations. Daily plotting of new points on the control chart gives the type figures shown in Figures 1-34 and 1-35, which are termed "I" charts for the individual plotted observations.

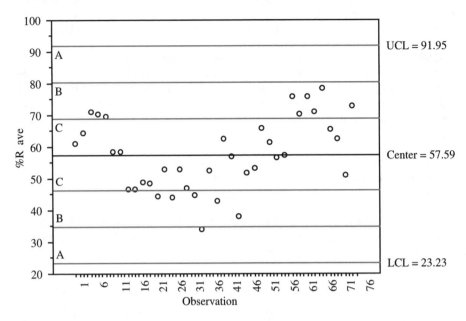

Figure 1-34. I chart of average recovery for trichlorobenzene.

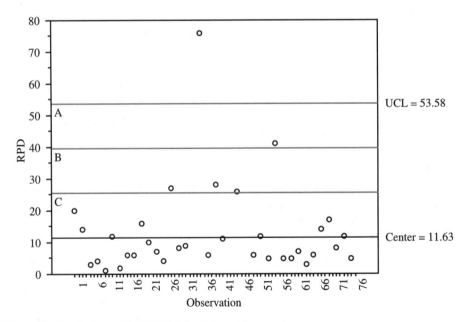

Figure 1-35. I chart for RPD for trichlorobenzene.

The control chart assumes that the distribution of values around the mean is binomial, thus the following distribution should be obtained:

Mean ±1 sd = 68% of observations

Mean ±2 sd = 95% of observations (Warning Level)

Mean ±3 sd = 99.7% of observations (Control Level)

It is expected that 5% of the QC results will fall between the Warning and Control Levels, however two points in a row outside the Warning Level should be investigated. Three out of 1000 observations are expected to fall outside the Control level. Two points outside control within a short period of time are definite signs for concern. The 600 series EPA methods call for updating control charts every 5 to 10 additional QC results.

Another control chart method generates X-bar and R charts. Instead of treating each quality control in a batch as an independent observation, these charts group the quality controls in a batch as a single observation, or what is termed a subgroup. The X-bar chart plots and calculates the $\%R_{ave}$ on a batch basis, then determines control limits based on the average range. The range is defined as the absolute difference between the two observations in the batch and is used instead of RPD as an indicator of precision. Examples of the X-bar and R charts are presented in Figures 1-36 and 1-37 for the same data plotted in Figures 1-34 and 1-35.

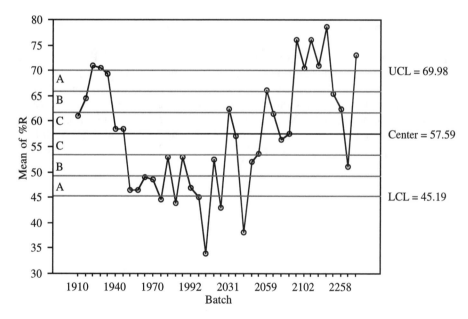

Figure 1-36. X-bar chart for recovery of trichlorobenzene.

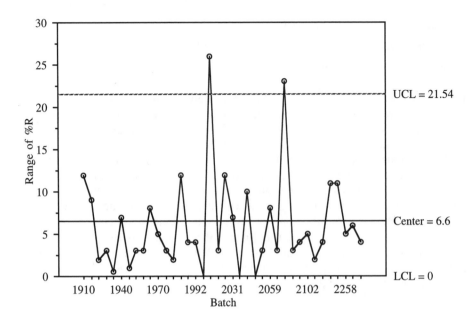

Figure 1-37. R chart for recovery of trichlorobenzene.

The U.S. Army Environmental Center (USAEC, formerly USATHAMA) requires control charts to be maintained and copies submitted with each sample result[178]. These control charts have control limits that are updated for every day of operation and extend back through the last 39 batches. Control limits are established based on the average range. An example of a USAEC X-bar control chart with moving limits using the above data for trichlorobenzene is presented in Figure 1-38. The USAEC also allows for control chart preparation that uses control limits based on 3-day moving averages.

---

[178] *U.S. Army Environmental Center Guidelines for Implementation of ER1110-1-263 for USAEC Projects.* May 1993.

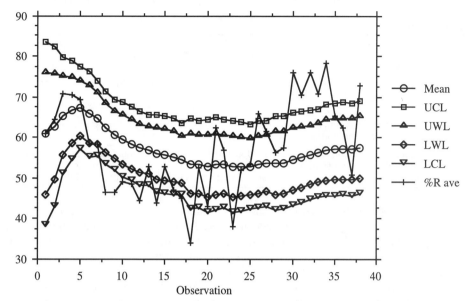

Figure 1-38. X-bar chart for recovery of trichlorobenzene with daily moving limits.

There is a list of eight standard tests[179] that have been used to evaluate control charts, Table 1-61. The applicability of all eight to analytical processes in the laboratory is uncertain as there are oftentimes short-term shifts in the mean or standard deviation of the procedure that are inconsequential in the longer term for analytical validity. BOD tests are famous for these small, short-lived trends, as are other tests with high degrees of variability such as instrumental organic procedures. Statistical packages for personnel computers are increasingly used for generation of control charts, and several have automatic flagging of the data based on the Western Electric Rules. The USAEC has established a simplified set of rules for evaluation of control charts. Out-of-control situations are indicated by a point outside the control limit, 7 consecutive points on the same side of the mean, 5 consecutive points in the same direction, a cyclical pattern of control values, or two points between the UCL and UWL or LCL and LWL.

Table 1-61. Western Electric rules for evaluating control charts

Test	Analysis
1	1 point beyond 3 SD - detects a shift in the process mean, an increase in the estimated standard deviation or a single aberration.
2	9 consecutive points above or below the centerline - detects a shift in the process mean.
3	6 consecutive increasing or decreasing points - detects a trend or drift in the process mean.
4	14 consecutive alternating points - detects systematic alternating effects, such as alternating use of different machines, operators or materials.

Continued on next page.

---

[179] Western Electric Co., Inc. 1956. *Statistical Quality Control Handbook.* Western Electric Co. Inc., Newark, NJ.

Table 1-61. Western Electric rules for evaluating control charts, *continued*

Test	Analysis
5	2 of 3 consecutive points beyond 2 SD - detects a shift in the process mean, or an increase in the standard deviation. The two points must be on the same side of the centerline.
6	4 of 5 points beyond 1 SD - detects a shift in the process mean. The 4 points must be on the same side of the centerline.
7	15 consecutive points within 1 SD - detects stratification within subgroups when the observations in a single subgroup come from various sources with different means. The points must be on both sides of the centerline.
8	8 consecutive points beyond 1 SD - detects stratification of subgroups when the observations in one subgroup come from a single source, but subgroups come from different sources with different means. The points must lie on both sides of the centerline.

Control charts can also be established for preventative maintenance purposes. Examples are the plotting of internal standard areas for GC-MS batches and the plotting of weekly calibrations of automatic dispensing pipets. Although it is possible to develop control and warning limits for these purposes, the value of the time spent in the calculation will probably not be recovered in the use of the chart, as all the analyst is looking for is a significant change as a sign for needed cleaning or repair. Further the act of maintenance often creates a new norm of operations that can be quite different from the previous norm, and the first set of points collected may be out-of-control as compared to the previous limits, although in actuality the system may be in perfect working order.

When the analyst or QA personnel are updating control limits on the charts, the question of data censoring must be answered. This boils down to whether all collected data points are used in the update, or only those points obtained under complete control operations. An example is RPD calculated from 1 and 3 %R results as compared to a 95 and 105 %R batch. Intuitively, both sets of points are in control as far as reproducibility is concerned but the RPDs are 100 and 10 respectively. An RPD of 100 may be fine for a recovery of 2%, but totally unacceptable for a 100% average recovery. What is being seen is a severe matrix effect on the recovery, which may be a very common occurrence in the lab. The problem lies in the decision as to whether the control limits are to reflect all data from the lab and give a realistic insight on the performance or if only perfect conditions are to be allowed.

K. Performance Evaluation (PE) samples

Performance evaluation (PE) samples measure the ability of the lab to correctly identify and quantitate unknown target analytes in samples. PE samples are also called quality control check samples or validation samples. Under the National Environmental Laboratory Accreditation Program (NELAP) these are termed Performance Testing (PT) samples. They are an essential "final exam" on the laboratory. PE samples used to be available from the EPA (WP, WS and DMR series) at no charge, however the program was terminated as of 1 January, 1999 (with the exception of the Toxicity DMR QA Studies). Some state laboratories (New York, North Carolina, and Wisconsin, for example), will provide the samples as part of the state's certification program. Government agencies other than the EPA (USACE, etc.) still provide PE samples. However as a replacement for the EPA samples, commercial vendors (ASI, APG, and ERA, see Appendix E for a more complete list and addresses) under the oversight of EPA and the National Institute for Standards and Technology (NIST) are selling the PE studies and providing result evaluation.

PE sample analysis is an essential part of laboratory certification and accreditation by most regulatory agencies. While ability to pass PE samples may not be a completely accurate measure of the lab's competence, failure to pass PE samples is a distinctly bad sign that will doom a laboratory to a very short life as a profitable company.

Most often PE samples are obtained as concentrates in sealed glass ampules, or as powders in sealed serum vials. Directions accompany the PE samples detailing how to prepare the sample by dilution for analysis. PE samples occasionally come as ready-prepared solutions. An example of the ready-prepared PE samples are those provided by the U.S. Army Corps of Engineers (USACE). PE samples should always be prepared and analyzed at least in duplicate.

The regularly scheduled EPA PE samples consisted of twice-annual drinking water (WS or Water Supply) and wastewater (WP or Water Pollution) sets. Holders of Federal- or State- issued NPDES permits are required to participate annually in the analysis of Discharge Monitoring Report (DMR) QA Study samples. Facilities permitted by cities or other POTWs do not receive DMR PE samples nor do they submit monthly reports on EPA Form 3320. Each PE analyte in the WS and WP studies was provided to the participant in a low and high concentration form. The DMR studies were also available in two concentrations, which were identical to the WP study samples being conducted concurrently. However the DMR participants received only one of the concentrations. Participants with odd NPDES permit numbers received one set, while those with even permit numbers received the other.

These program characteristics have been adopted into State certification requirements in some interesting ways. North Carolina certifies laboratories for high and low concentrations for each analyte, and requires that the lab annually pass at least one PE sample for each concentration level. Since not all parameters covered in NPDES permits are present in the WP samples, North Carolina also developed its own PE sample preparation capabilities to provide labs with PE samples for Method 625, BN/A analysis, MBAS, color, etc. Arkansas has regulations requiring the lab to pass over 50% of annual PE samples for each certified parameter that is included in the WP set. This requires that the lab analyze successfully 1 of 1 try, 2 of 2 tries, 2 of 3 tries, 3 of 4 tries. If the lab analyzes one sample but misses it, they then have to analyze two more samples successfully to pass the requirement. South Carolina requires participation in at least two studies of each type each year, with at least one successful result for each analyte. On the other hand Tennessee in the drinking water program only requires a single successful attempt for each certified parameter each year.

During 1996 EPA combined the WP and the DMR QA studies samples. For each study, the number of concentrations was reduced from two to one. Prior to 1996, DMR QA Study participants were completely segregated from the WP participants, even though they received identical samples. The program structure was changed so that if a laboratory participated in the WP studies, all the DMR participant has to do is inform the EPA Study Coordinator which lab is doing the work. The idea behind the change was to reduce the large number of duplicate PE samples that each commercial laboratory was receiving (the WP ampules and one set of DMR QA Study ampules from each of the lab's clients).

Table 1-62. Analytes in WP studies

Ampule(s)	Analytes
Trace Metals	Aluminum, Arsenic, Beryllium, Cadmium, Cobalt, Chromium, Copper, Iron, Mercury, Manganese, Nickel, Lead, Selenium, Vanadium, Zinc, Antimony, Silver, Thallium, Molybdenum, Strontium, Titanium
Minerals	pH, Specific Conductivity, TDS, Hardness, Calcium, Magnesium, Potassium, Sodium, Alkalinity, Chloride, Fluoride, Sulfate
Nutrients	Ammonia, Nitrate, Orthophosphate, Kjeldahl nitrogen, Total phosphorus
Demand	COD, 5 day BOD, TOC, 5 day carbonaceous BOD
PCBs in Water	1016/1242, 1232, 1248, 1254, 1260
PCBs in Transformer Oil	1016/1242, 1254, 1260
Pesticides	Chlordane, Aldrin, Dieldrin, DDD, DDE, DDT, Heptachlor, Heptachlor epoxide
Volatile Halocarbons	1,2-Dichloroethane, Chloroform, 1,1,1-Trichloroethane, Trichloroethene, Carbon tetrachloride, Tetrachloroethene, Bromodichloromethane, Dibromochloromethane, Bromoform, Methylene chloride, Chlorobenzene
Volatile Aromatics	Benzene, Ethylbenzene, Toluene, 1,2-Dichlorobenzene, 1,3-Dichlorobenzene, 1,4-Dichlorobenzene
Cyanide	Total cyanide
Residue	TSS
Phenolics	Total phenolics (4-AAP)
Oil & Grease	Oil & Grease
Chlorine	Total Residual Chlorine

Figure 1-39 is an example of the reporting form. The blocks labeled MC are for entering the Method Code of the analysis.

CHEMISTRY DATA							Page 2 of 8

Study Number	EPA Lab I.D.			Results			
W S 0 3 8							
Analyte Number & Name	Sample #	MC	< / >	Quantity			
TRACE METALS							
140 Antimony	2						µg/L
001 Arsenic	1						µg/L
002 Barium	2						µg/L
141 Beryllium	1						µg/L
226 Boron	2						µg/L
003 Cadmium	1						µg/L
004 Chromium	1						µg/L
091 Copper	1						µg/L
005 Lead	1						µg/L
236 Manganese	1						µg/L
006 Mercury	1						µg/L
237 Molybdenum	2						µg/L
142 Nickel	1						µg/L
007 Selenium	1						µg/L
143 Thallium	2						µg/L
239 Zinc	1						µg/L
NITRATE & NITRITE & FLUORIDE & ORTHOPHOSPHATE							
009 Nitrate as N	1						mg/L
092 Nitrite as N	1						mg/L
010 Fluoride	1						mg/L
261 Orthophosphate as P	1						mg/L

EPA-359 (Cin) Rev. 8-96. Previous editions are obsolete. (Note: The Data Report Form is continued on the next page.)

Figure 1-39. Example of WP sample reporting form.

The WS PE samples test the laboratory's ability to perform the tests required for monitoring of the primary and secondary drinking water parameters. Similar to the WP samples, beginning in 1996, only a single concentration level was provided.

Table 1-63. Analytes in WS studies

Ampule(s)	Analytes
Trace Metals	Antimony, Arsenic, Barium, Beryllium, Boron, Cadmium, Chromium, Copper, Lead, Manganese, Mercury, Molybdenum, Nickel, Selenium, Thallium, Zinc
Nitrate/Nitrite/Fluoride	Nitrate, Nitrite, Fluoride. Orthophosphate
Insecticides	Alachlor, Atrazine, Chlordane, Endrin, Heptachlor, Heptachlor epoxide, Hexachlorobenzene, Hexachlorocyclopentadiene, Lindane, Methoxychlor, Metolachlor, Metribuzin, Prometon, Simazine, Toxaphene, Trifluralin, Aldrin, Butachlor, Dieldrin, Propachlor
Carbamates and Vydate	Aldicarb, Aldicarb sulfone, Aldicarb sulfoxide, Carbofuran, Methomyl, Oxamyl (Vydate)
Herbicides	2,4-D, 2,4,5-TP, Dalapon, Dicamba, Dinoseb, DCPA, Pentachlorophenol, Picloram, Acifluorifen
PCBs	Decachlorobiphenyl
PAHs	Benzo(*a*)pyrene
Adipates/Phthalates	Di(2-ethylhexl)phthalate, Di(2-ethylhexyl)adipate,
Miscellaneous SOCs	Diquat, Endothall, Glyphosate
Trihalomethanes	Bromodichloromethane, Dibromochloromethane, Bromoform, Chloroform, Total Trihalomethane
Regulated VOCs	Benzene, Carbon tetrachloride, Chlorobenzene, 1,2-Dichlorobenzene, 1,4-Dichlorobenzene, 1,2-Dichloroethane, 1,1-Dichloroethene, *cis*-1,2-Dichloroethene, *trans*-1,2-Dichloroethene, 1,2-Dichloropropane, Ethylbenzene, Styrene, Tetrachloroethene, Toluene, 1,1,1-Trichloroethane, Trichloroethene, Vinyl chloride, Xylenes
Unregulated VOCs	Bromobenzene, Bromochloromethane, Bromodichloromethane, Bromoform, Bromomethane, *n*-Butylbenzene, *sec*-Butylbenzene, *tert*-Butylbenzene, Chlorodibromomethane, Chloroethane, Chloroform, Chloromethane, 2-Chlorotoluene, 4-Chlorotoluene, DBCP, Dibromomethane, 1,3-Dichlorobenzene, Dichlorodifluoromethane, 1,1-Dichloroethane, Dichloromethane, 1,3-Dichloropropane, 2,2-Dichloropropane, 1,1-Dichloropropene, *cis*-1,3-Dichloropropene, *trans*-1,3-Dichloropropene, EDB, Fluorotrichloromethane, Hexachlorobutadiene, Isopropylbenzene, 4-Isopropyltoluene, Naphthalene, *n*-Propylbenzene, 1,1,1,2-Tetrachloroethane, 1,1,2,2-Tetrachloroethane, 1,2,3-Trichlorobenzene, 1,2,4-Trichlorobenzene, 1,1,2-Trichloroethane, 1,2,3-Trichloropropane, 1,2,4-Trimethylbenzene, 1,3,5-Trimethylbenzene
Organic Disinfection By-products	Chloral hydrate, Dibromoacetic acid, Dichloroacetic acid, Monobromoacetic acid, Monochloroacetic acid, Trichloroacetic acid, Bromochloroacetic acid
Inorganic Disinfection By-products	Bromate, Chlorate, Chlorite, Bromide
Miscellaneous Analytes	Residual Free Chlorine, Turbidity, Total cyanide, Sulfate, pH, Alkalinity, Sodium, Total Dissolved Solids, Calcium Hardness, Ethylene thiourea, Dioxin, Asbestos, TOC

The reporting forms for the WS samples were virtually identical to those for the WP samples.

The DMR QA studies included all the WP analytes and in addition to the chemical target analytes, the DMRs add acute and/or chronic toxicity testing samples. Organisms calibrated against the samples include fathead minnow, *Ceriodaphnia*, *Mysidopsis bahia*, *Menidia beryllina*, sheepshead minnow, *Daphnia magna*, *Daphnia pulex*, and rainbow trout. Figure 1-40 is an example of the reporting form (covered in more detail in Section 2.II). In the Toxicity part of the studies the samples were sent directly to the toxicity lab, which then provided copies of the results to their clients and EPA. The EPA in return provided result evaluations to both the clients and the lab. This is different than the administration of the chemistry side of the DMR QA studies, where only the client received the result evaluation.

Interpretation of the DMR, WS, and WP results when the programs were initiated was very straight forward. The analyst was to prepare a single dilution of the PE sample ampule contents to a specified volume, then analyze the sample, possibly in duplicate along with the regular sample load of the laboratory. There were to be no special procedures or measures taken on the sample that were different from what was routinely done with any other sample in the lab. When performed in this fashion, a statistical distribution of results can be assumed for all the tests within a PE sample study, and a good performance by the laboratory would be to get at least 80 to 85% of the individual analytes in the study correct. However, due to the emphasis that has been placed on acceptable laboratory PE results by clients and state and federal laboratory certification programs, the manner in which these samples are handled in the laboratory has been changed. What actually happens with them is that the laboratory technicians are alerted and ready well in advance of the arrival of the PE samples. The most capable technicians are assigned to spend a substantial amount of time analyzing and re-analyzing the samples. Techniques, such as direct injection of the concentrate or a dilution into the analytical instrument, preparation and analysis of a variety of dilutions, matrix spikes on the samples, microextractions, use of multiple methods, and other techniques invented by the analysts, are employed to insure that an acceptable result is generated. Many laboratories will share their results with other laboratories to help insure that the results are comparable. Some laboratories have been known to sub-contract analysis of the PE samples to other labs. In all, the PE samples are treated as anything but what a typical sample receives. The consequence of these actions is that the evaluation is not of the average performance of the laboratory but of the best answer that the lab can possibly generate. Major dislocations in the practice of the analysis of the samples from the original intents are obvious from the historical trends in scores and the distribution of scores for any of the recent tests[180]. It should not be surprising to anyone that the passing score for a good laboratory is now better than 95% of the analyte results being correct, with 100% correct not being uncommon.

---

[180] Burton, A.G., and D.E. Lawver, 1995. Evaluating Lab Performance. *Environmental Lab*, February, 1995. pp. 28-33.

Table 1-64. DMR QA Study 16 (1996) Chemical Analytes

Ampule(s)	Analytes
Trace Metals	Aluminum, Arsenic, Beryllium, Cadmium, Cobalt, Chromium, Copper, Iron, Mercury, Manganese, Nickel, Lead, Selenium, Vanadium, Zinc
Minerals	pH
Nutrients	Ammonia, Nitrate, Orthophosphate, Kjeldahl nitrogen, Total phosphorous
Demand	COD, 5 day BOD, TOC, 5 day carbonaceous BOD
Cyanide	Total cyanide
Residue	TSS
Phenolics	Total phenolics (4-AAP)
Oil & Grease	Oil & Grease
Chlorine	Total Residual Chlorine

DMR-QA Study 16
CHEMISTRY DATA

Analyte Name	EPA Use	Analyte No.	Sample No.	USEPA Labcode	Voluntary Analyte	Method Code	< / >	Quantity
TRACE METALS								
Aluminum	XC	001	1					µg/L
Arsenic	XC	002	1					µg/L
Beryllium	XC	003	1					µg/L
Cadmium	XC	004	1					µg/L
Chromium	XC	006	1					µg/L
Cobalt	XC	005	1					µg/L
Copper	XC	007	1					µg/L
Iron	XC	008	1					µg/L
Lead	XC	012	1					µg/L
Manganese	XC	010	1					µg/L
Mercury	XC	009	1					µg/L
Nickel	XC	011	1					µg/L
Selenium	XC	013	1					µg/L
Vanadium	XC	014	1					µg/L
Zinc	XC	015	1					µg/L

facsimile of EPA-422 (Cin) Rev. 3-96. Previous editions are obsolete.   Page 3 of 4

Figure 1-40. Example of the DMR QA Study 16 result reporting form.

There are differences in how the WP/DMR and WS QA studies are scored. The WP/DMR results obtained from the EPA Regional labs and selected state labs are used to generate Warning Limits and Acceptance Limits for the results for each target analyte. The Warning Limits are ±2 standard deviations from the mean and represent the 95% confidence level while the Acceptance Limits are ±3 standard deviations from the mean and represent the 99% confidence level. The possible evaluations that the lab receives for each analyte are "Acceptable," "Check for error," or "Not acceptable."

The WS PE samples scoring is described in 40 CFR 141 and is wrapped into the drinking water laboratory certification programs administered for the most part by the states. The true value is based on the quantity of analyte weighed out to prepare the check sample. In cases where the mean of the results obtained by the EPA regional and selected state labs does not match-up with the calculated true value, such as happened with fluoride in WS037, the analyte is deleted from the affected study. The only two possibilities for results for individual analytes in WS studies are "Acceptable" or "Not acceptable." These requirements have resulted in some absurd acceptance ranges, such as the range for beryllium in WS041, true value 2.58 µg/L, acceptance range 2.19-2.97 µg/L. At this concentration, the lab would normally report a single digit result, such as 1,

2, or 3. The study mandates reporting 3 significant figures whether justified scientifically or not, and laboratory results of 2 or 3 were translated by the study administrator to 2.00 or 3.00, which became unacceptable results.

Table 1-65. WS QA study acceptance criteria based on true value (40 CFR 141)

Analyte	Acceptance criteria
Antimony	±30%
Barium	±15%
Beryllium	±15%
Cadmium	±20%
Chromium	±15%
Copper	±10%
Lead	±30%
Mercury	±30%
Nickel	±20%
Selenium	±20%
Thallium	±30%
Cyanide	±25%
Fluoride	±10%
Nitrate	±10%
Nitrite	±15%
Total Trihalomethanes	±20%
Regulated VOC	±20% if >10 µg/L ±40% if <10 µg/L
Alachlor	±45%
Atrazine	±45%
Carbofuran	±45%
Chlordane	±45%
2,4-D	±50%
Dalapon	2 Std. Deviations[181]
Dibromochloropropane (DBCP)	±40%
Dinoseb	2 Std. Deviations
Diquat	2 Std. Deviations
Endothall	2 Std. Deviations
Endrin	±30%
Ethylenedibromide (EDB)	±40%
Glyphosate	2 Std. Deviations
Heptachlor	±45%
Heptachlor epoxide	±45%
Lindane	±45%
Methoxychlor	±45%
Oxamyl	2 Std. Deviations
Pentachlorophenol	±50%
Picloram	2 Std. Deviations

Continued on next page.

---

[181] Two standard deviations based on the results of the reference laboratories used in the QA Study. The reference labs are the EPA Regional labs and selected Primacy State labs.

Table 1-65. WS QA study acceptance criteria based on true value (40 CFR 141), *continued*

Analyte	Acceptance criteria
Simazine	2 Std. Deviations
Toxaphene	±45%
2,4,5-TP (Silvex)	±50%
Hexachlorobenzene	2 Std. Deviations
Hexachlorocyclopentadiene	2 Std. Deviations
Benzo(a)pyrene	2 Std. Deviations
PCB (as DCB)	0-200%
Di(2-ethylhexyl)adipate	2 Std. Deviations
Di(2-ethylhexyl)phthalate	2 Std. Deviations

There have never been EPA sponsored PE samples for microbiology associated with the WP or WS series. At least one of the commercial vendors (Environmental Resource Associates, ERA) has been providing PE samples for total and fecal coliform since 1995. The State of Florida requires annual participation in the ERA coliform testing program as part of laboratory certification. These samples consist of lypholyzed bacteria that are reconstituted by the laboratory in sterile water and tested. For drinking water the test is on a presence/absence basis. For wastewater, quantitation is required.

As of this writing (May, 1999), the EPA and NIST have not designated any approved commercial vendors of PE samples. The applicants are listed in Table 1-66. Some of the organizations applied for only a very limited range of PE analytes, while others applied for the entire suite. The approved list is expected in June or July, 1999. The WP040 and WS041 were the last PE samples sent out by EPA, and those were in the late summer and fall of 1998. For the interim period several states such as South Carolina, which requires participation in two studies of WS and WP each year have told certified labs to simply chose a commercial vendor, participate in the required study in the Spring of 1999, and submit the results to the State.

Table 1-66. Cost based suppliers of PE samples who applied to NIST for approval.

Supplier	Telephone
Absolute Standards, Inc	1-800-368-1131
AccuStandard	1-203-786-5290 (ext 117)
Analytical Standards, Inc	1-800-Audit44
APG	1-800-272-4442
CHRISOPE Technologies	1-800-256-4376 (ext 236)
Environmental Resource Associates	1-800-372-0122
Microcheck, Inc.	1-802-485-6600 (ext 26)
New York State DOH	1-518-485-5570
Protocol Analytical Supplies	1-732-627-0500
NSI Environmental Solutions	1-800-576-5690
SPEX CERTIPREP	1-732-549-7144 (ext 418)
ULTRA Scientific	1-401-294-9400

L. Evaluation of Laboratory Data

A review of performance evaluation (PE) sample results and the laboratory's quality assurance program are measures that should be performed prior to any contracted analysis with the laboratory. Although these reviews may lead to expectations that the candidate lab is competent to generate both analytically valid and legally defensible data, the reviews themselves give no indication as to the quality of the data that are reported on the specific samples. Evaluation of chemical laboratory data is the subject of recent books[182]. Evaluation of radiological data has been the subject of recent articles[183] and ANSI/ANS is preparing a guidance document[184]. In general, laboratory data are evaluated by comparison of the quality control results against measurement quality objectives that may be generic to the particular lab or they may be project specific. It must be emphatically stated as a basic premise that without quality control data there can be no confidence in analytical results. There are many instances in the literature of environmental research where completely unwarranted hypotheses and conclusions have been proposed that are based on laboratory data that are highly suspect due to laboratory contamination or other artifacts of analysis[185]. It is also very rare that researchers will publish retractions of their work when they do find out that the data are spurious.

Within the framework of the environmental industry, laboratory data must reflect correct identification and quantitation of target pollutants present in the sample while at the same time being obtained in compliance with the dictates of an approved method of analysis. To evaluate data, it is necessary for the reviewer to be familiar with both the project data needs and the referenced analytical methods.

---

[182] Berger, W., H. McCarty and R.-K. Smith, 1996. *Environmental Laboratory Data Evaluation*, Genium Publishing, Schenectady, NY; Smith, R.-K., 1999. *Lectures on Wastewater Analysis and Interpretation*, Genium Publishing, Schenectady, NY.

[183] Grega, K.K., and R.J. Vitale, 1995. "Validating Radiological Data." *Environmental Lab.* November, 1995. 7(7). pp. 14-18.

[184] Rucker, T.L., S.R. Salaymen, J. Griggs, C.K. Liu, D.E. McCurdy, A. Rosencrance, D.E. Vance, R. Wells, and R.W. Holloway. 1996. "ANSI/ANS Standard for Radioanalytical Data Validation. In *Proceedings of the Twelfth Annual Waste Testing and Quality Assurance Symposium*, EPA/ACS, Washington Hilton & Towers, Washington, D.C. 23-26 July, 1996. pg 88.

[185] Wallace, J.C., I. Basu, and R.A. Hites, 1996. "Sampling and Analysis Artifacts Caused by Elevated Indoor Air Polychlorinated Biphenyl Concentrations". *Environ. Sci. Technol.* 30(9). pp. 2730-2734.

Physical, Biological and General Chemical Parameters

I. PHYSICAL PARAMETERS

A. Solids (SM$_{18}$ 2540[*]; EPA 160)

Solids (also called residues) are an important characterization of drinking and waste-water, and one or another of the tests are normally required in all DMRs of NPDES permits. Conceptually simple tests, in practice the determinations can be tedious when attempting to dry the solid to a constant weight, the biggest problem stemming from bound water. Various classes of bound water are associated with solids, the difficulty in removing them decreases as one goes down the list:

- Chemically combined water such as in calcium hydroxide
- Water of crystallization, water occupying fixed positions in the crystal structure
- Water of hydration, water hydrogen bonded onto the crystal structure
- Occluded water, droplets of water encased by a solid coating
- Absorbed water, water in the body of the solid, also called pore water
- Adsorbed water, water on the surface of the solid

Solids are divided into classes with the class defined by how the test is performed. The general classes are total solids (TS), total suspended solids (TSS), total dissolved solids (TDS), total volatile solids (TVS), total volatile dissolved solids (TVDS), total volatile suspended solids (TVSS), settleable solids, and ash (fixed solids). It might be expected that total solids should equal total suspended solids plus total dissolved solids, TS = TSS + TDS, however this seldom works out in practice as the TS and TSS values are obtained from a 104 °C drying and the TDS at 180 °C. The volatile fractions are determined by the difference between the dried fraction and the ashed fraction and are often held to represent the organic part of the solid. However, loss of CO_2 from carbonates and bicarbonates and loss of volatile inorganic salts can give very misleading results. Other derivative measures, such as sludge volume index (SVI), are calculated from these fractions. The MDL of the analysis is dependent upon not only the volume or mass of the sample tested but also the minimum residual mass of the solid required. For example TS requires at least 2.5 mg residue, which, based on a 100 mL sample, gives a MDL of 25 mg/L. The MDL can be lowered by evaporating successive 100 mL portions in the same dish; however; the principle of diminishing returns quickly applies.

---

[*] The publication containing these methods can be accessed through the Tables in Section 1.II.

TS (SM$_{18}$ 2540 B, EPA 160.3) - A weighed portion is poured into a tared crucible and dried to a constant weight at 104 ± 1 °C. A minimum of 2.5 mg residue is required.

Settleable solids (SM$_{18}$ 2540 F, EPA 160.5) - A known volume, generally a liter, is allowed to sit in a graduated cone (Imhoff cone) for an hour. The settleable solids are read off in mL at the bottom of the cone.

TSS (SM$_{18}$ 2540 D, EPA 160.2) - Non-filterable (suspended) solids are determined by filtering a known volume through a tared glass fiber filter in a vacuum filtration apparatus, then drying the filter to a constant weight at 104 ± 1 °C. Recent WP series PE samples have included floating solids as part of the TSS check sample. Great care had to be taken to get the floating particles onto the glass fiber filter. A minimum of 2.5 mg residue is required for a detection of TSS.

TDS (SM$_{18}$ 2540 C, EPA 160.1) - Filterable (dissolved) solids are determined by evaporating a known volume of the filtrate from the TSS test in a tared crucible and drying at 180 ± 2 °C to a constant weight. A minimum of 2.5 mg residue is required. TDS detection limits are particularly sensitive to the 2.5 mg minimum residue because in many cases it is impossible to filter more than about 25 mL of water through the glass fiber filter. This results in MDLs of 100 mg/L and even higher in some cases.

Ash (SM$_{18}$ 2540 E, EPA 160.4) - Ignite TS residue at 550 ± 50 °C in a muffle furnace.

Volatile solids (SM$_{18}$ 2540 E, EPA 160.4) - This is the difference between the dried solids and the same sample further ignited at 550 ± 50 °C. Thus TVS = TS - ash. TVSS = TSS - TSS$_{ash}$. TVDS = TDS - TDS$_{ash}$.

SVI (SM$_{18}$ 2710 D) - A calculation that divides the result of the settleable solids (measured after 30 minutes) value by TSS. The units are mL/g.

Soils and dirts often need to be classified. Aside from the chemical composition, the size distribution of the soil particles affects the physical behavior. Sieving is a convenient method of characterization. A well-dried sample of the soil is shaken through a graded series of sieves, and the mass retained on each sieve is used to calculate the size distribution. Standard sieve sizes are listed in Table 2-1.

Table 2-1.   Standard sieve sizes

Sieve No.	Tyler Mesh No.	Millimeters	Inches
4	4	4.7	0.185
6	6	3.33	0.131
8	8	2.36	0.093
10	9	2.0	0.078
13	10	1.65	0.065
16	14	1.17	0.046
20	20	0.833	0.033
30	28	0.589	0.023
40	35	0.417	0.016
50	48	0.295	0.012
60	60	0.25	0.01
70	65	0.208	0.008
80	70	0.177	0.007
100	100	0.149	0.006

Continued on next page.

Table 2-1. Standard sieve sizes, *continued*

Sieve No.	Tyler Mesh No.	Millimeters	Inches
130	150	0.104	0.004
140	170	0.088	0.0035
200	200	0.074	0.0029
400	400	0.038	0.0015

The USDA standard size classifications of soils are: Gravel >2mm, sand particles 2-0.074 mm, silt 0.074-0.002 mm and, clay <0.002 mm[1]. The silts and clays are combined into "fines" in the ASTM classification. Other characteristics of soils include porosity, penetrability, compressibility, gas flux and diffusivity, and a large variety of water and hydraulic parameters[2].

Particle size is a parameter that relates to not only part of the characterization of soil samples, but is a necessary consideration in practical aspects of dealing with samples in the lab. For example, filtration is a common means of separating solids from liquids, and filter paper is frequently used. Knowing what will pass through the filter paper and what will be retained, ignoring any adsorption phenomena, is helpful in making the correct choice of paper size. The chart in Figure 2-1 relates size measurements to some items and concepts for which people have an innate feeling of "big" and "small."

[1] Winegardner, D.L. *Introduction to Soils for Environmental Professionals*. 1996. CRC Press, Boca Raton, FL.

[2] Klute, A. *Methods of Soil Analysis, Part 1 Physical and Mineralogical Methods*, 2nd Edition. 1986. ASA and SSSA, Madison, WI.

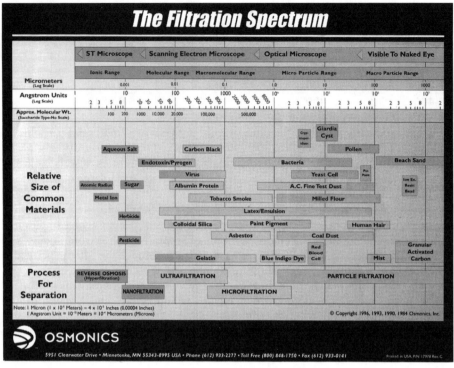

Provided Courtesy of Osmonics, Minnetonka, Minnesota USA

Figure 2-1. **Size of common objects.**

B. Moisture

The moisture content of samples is of interest when the results are to be reported on a dry weight basis. This determination involves weighing a portion of the sample in a tared crucible, drying to a constant weight at 104 ± 1 °C and then calculating the percent moisture by:

$$\text{percent moisture} = 100 - \left(\frac{\text{dry weight}}{\text{wet weight}} \times 100 \right)$$

$$\text{fraction solids} = \frac{\text{dry weight}}{\text{wet weight}}$$

$$\text{percent solids} = \frac{\text{dry weight}}{\text{wet weight}} \times 100$$

The reporting of results on a dry weight basis is performed by taking the test result and dividing by the fraction of solids.

$$\text{dry weight basis} = \frac{\text{wet result}}{\text{fraction solids}}$$

Some test methods, for example explosives residues in soils (Method 8330), dry the sample in the open air overnight prior to measuring out a portion for analysis. The final weight of the dried sample that is obtained depends on the local relative humidity. Samples dried in the arid Rocky Mountain regions will lose more water than the same samples dried in the very humid Southeast part of the United States. This sometimes will affect the comparability of the results from one laboratory to the next, and occasionally between duplicate determinations in the same laboratory. Drier samples result in higher target analyte values. Up to a two-fold difference in sample results have been noted that are attributable to this effect.

Often received in the laboratory are non-aqueous samples that require determination of water content. Gross amounts of water (greater than 1%) may be determined by weighing a portion of the sample, then doing azeotropic distillation with toluene in a Dean-Starke trap.

Amounts of water less than 1% down to the ppm level can be determined by Karl Fisher titration[3]. There are two versions of KF titration; the protic and the aprotic. Both are based upon the oxidation of sulfur dioxide to sulfate ion coupled with the reduction of iodine to iodide, a process that requires water to supply the oxygen atom for the sulfate product.

In the protic titration, the base most commonly used is pyridine, however any tri-substituted nitrogen base will work. One of the oxygen atoms on the final sulfate product comes from the alcohol solvent. The commercially available stench-free titrant solutions use bases other than pyridine, but the chemistry is the same.

Solvolysis
$$2ROH + SO_2 \longrightarrow RSO_3^- ROH_2^+$$

Buffer
$$Base + RSO_3^- ROH_2^+ \longrightarrow BaseH^+RSO_3^- + ROH$$

1:1 Redox titration
$$H_2O + I_2 + BaseH^+RSO_3^- + 2\,Base \longrightarrow$$
$$BaseH^+RSO_4^- + 2BaseHI$$

The aprotic procedure has fewer reagents, but is a bit more technically involved and has a 2:1 titration. Both oxygen atoms on the sulfate arise from water.

2:1 Redox titration
$$2H_2O + SO_2 + I_2 \longrightarrow H_2SO_4 + 2HI$$

Normal interferences include NH_3, RSH, Tl^+, Sn^{2+}, In^+, $S_2O_2^{2-}$ (thiosulfite anion), ascorbic acid, $HONH_2$ (hydroxylamine), all of which can reduce I_2. Other interferences include hydroxy and aminophenols and naphthols that are oxidized to quinoid structures.

Detection is performed by a number of techniques. The oldest is volumetric titration, which relies on the visual presence of excess I_2 for determination of the endpoint. Potentiometric detection is performed with two electrodes that sense the potential difference in $2e^- + I_2 \longleftrightarrow 2I^-$. With H_2O present there is no I_2, and a large potential difference exists. Without H_2O present the I_2 builds in concentration, and the potential

---

3 MacLeod, S.K. "Moisture Determination Using Karl Fisher Titrations." *Analytical Chemistry.* 1991. 63(10). pp. 557A-566A; Margolis, S.M., "Amperometric Measurement of Moisture in Transformer Oil Using Karl Fisher Reagents." *Anal. Chem*, 1995. 67(23). pp. 4239-4246; Cedergren, A., "Comparison Between Bipotentiometric and True Potentiometric End-point Detection using Rapidly Reacting Karl Fischer Reagents." *Anal. Chem.* 1996. 68(20). pp. 3679-3681; Cedergren, A., "Coulometric Study of Reaction Rates of Water in Pyridine- and Imidazole-Buffered Methanolic Karl Fischer Reagents Containing Chloroform." *Anal. Chem.* 68(20). pp. 3682-3687.

difference drops to zero, a deadstop titration. Amperometric detection is possible as there is no current flow without excess I_2 present and a "kickoff" endpoint current flow when I_2 becomes present.

The method is calibrated through titration of a known amount of sodium tartrate dihydrate, or better (if you happen to work in a pharmaceutical laboratory), Lincomycin HCl monohydrate. The common practice of adding water to anhydrous methanol with a microsyringe is quite imprecise.

C. Temperature (SM18 2550)

Temperature is a parameter that must be measured immediately after sampling. The thermometer must be either a certified thermometer or calibrated annually against an NIST traceable thermometer. It is suggested that glass thermometers be contained in metal thermometer holders. Glass thermometers come in two types: red fluid filled and silver mercury filled. The red fluids vary from alcohol to glycol mixtures depending on the temperature range of the thermometer. There is not much hazard associated with breaking these thermometers. However, the mercury-filled thermometers, which are generally regarded as more accurate, release dangerous mercury fumes on breaking. This presents a real problem with high background contamination if the lab is performing mercury analysis and the mercury-filled thermometer breaks indoors. There are also digital thermometers that operate on the thermocouple principle. These need to be calibrated just like the glass thermometers.

Temperature is a common monitoring parameter in the laboratory. Samples must be stored at the proper temperature, most often 4 °C. Waterbaths and ovens must be at the proper temperature for the performance of the various tests to be in compliance with the regulatory methods. These include mercury digestions, solids determinations, fecal coliform and BOD incubations, etc. The thermometers that monitor these temperatures must either be certified or calibrated against a certified NIST traceable thermometer at least annually. Temperature monitoring logs are kept for each instrument, which must be maintained at a set temperature. Figure 2-2 is an example of such a log.

TEMPERATURE MONITORING LOG

Device Monitored: Set-point/acceptance range:

Thermometer certificate or calibration number:

Date	AM reading	Initials/Time	PM reading	Initials/Time	Notes

Figure 2-2. Temperature monitoring log.

D. Turbidity (Nephelometry) (SM$_{18}$ 2130, EPA 180.1)

Turbidity is defined as suspended particulate matter in water. Acidic water is normally crystal clear, while basic/neutral water is turbid. The reason is that the oxides, hydroxides and carbonates of heavy metal ions found in basic conditions are insoluble substances, while the nitrates, chlorides and sulfates of the same metal ions present under acidic conditions are soluble. Further, acidic conditions are toxic to algae and other organisms, which can survive in very basic pH waters, creating turbidity.

Turbidity was originally measured with the Jackson candle turbidimeter. Test water is added to a tube until light from a standard candle at the bottom is extinguished. The minimum turbidity is 25 JTU (Jackson Turbidity Units).

More modern techniques use Nephelometers that measure scattered light at 90° to incident light with a photodetector. See Figure 2-3. The readings are in NTU's (Nephelometric Turbidity Units), which have no direct correlation with JTU's. Samples are quantitated *vs.* standards of freshly prepared polymer (hydrazine + hexamethylene-tetraamine, 1:10 w/w in water, 25 °C ± 3 °C, 24 hrs) or standard styrene divinylbenzene copolymer beads. The formazin is more repeatable. See Figure 2-4.

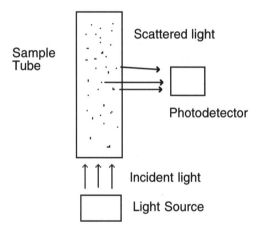

Figure 2-3.   Schematic of a nephelometer instrument for measuring turbidity.

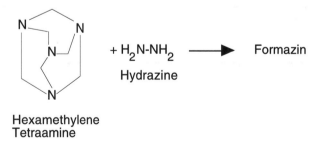

Figure 2-4.   Formazin polymer formation.

E. Conductivity (SM$_{18}$ 2510, EPA 120.1)

Conductivity is the inverse of resistance, which is the actual measured quantity in the lab. The units of measurement within the EPA complex are in μmhos/cm. The international units of conductivity are in millisiemens (mS) per meter, and some conductivity meters read in μS/cm. 1.0 μS/cm is exactly equal to 1.0 μmhos/cm. Freshly distilled water has a conductivity of 0.5 to 2.0 μmhos/cm, increasing on storage to 2 to 4 μmhos/cm due to dissolution of CO_2 and to a lesser degree NH_3. Potable water has values from 50 to 1500 μmhos/cm, while wastewaters may range to 10,000 μmhos/cm. Salt water exhibits a range of conductivity from 10000 to 100,000 μmhos/cm. Conductivity is a measure of ions present in the water, their charge, mobility, valence and relative concentration. The mobility of the ion is related to the concept of ionic atmosphere; the number and orientation of the solvent molecules in the immediate vicinity of the ion. Some ions have very highly structured atmospheres, and the physical movement of the ion and the atmosphere is retarded through the rest of the solvent. The ions H^+ and OH^-, on the other hand, have very high conductances in water solution as compared to other solvents due to the ability of the water molecules to dissociate into the ions. Thus transference of a charge due to H^+ or OH^- within water from one location to another does not require significant physical movement of the ion. Conductivity changes depend on the temperature of the sample. The temperature effect is complex with the exact nature of the ions in the sample affecting the magnitude of the temperature coefficient. These can range from 0.96 percent change/°C for a 5% sulfuric acid solution to 5.64 percent change/°C for a sugar syrup solution. Organic pollutants are generally not detected by conductivity measurements; however, a large organic content in the sample can severely depress the conductivity, compared to pure water solutions of similar ion concentration.

Measurement of conductivity is performed in a cell where the electrodes are rigidly fixed a constant distance from each other. The ideal cell has two electrodes of 1 cm^2 surface area fixed 1 cm apart. This ideal cell has a cell constant of 1.0/cm. Cells with small, widely separated electrodes will have cell constants > 1.0/cm, while closely spaced large electrodes will have cell constants < 1.0/cm. Electrodes with cell constants >1.0 are used for measurement of large conductivity. Electrodes with cell constants <1.0 are used for measurement of samples with low conductivity values.

The cell constant was important in the early days of conductivity measurement, where the direct reading of inverse resistance from the meter had to be multiplied by the cell constant to obtain the specific conductance of the sample.

Conductance = Reading x Cell Constant.

The cell constant was obtained by measuring the inverse resistance of a standard solution of known conductance, then dividing the known conductance value by the measured value. Today, in most approved regulatory methods, the conductivity values of the sample are given as a direct readout of the meter, calibrated by the measurement of standards immediately prior to the analysis. The cell constant is actually the slope of the calibration line. Although regular determination of the cell constant can serve as a preventative maintenance evaluation of the condition of the electrode, the daily calculation and recording of the cell constant serves no practical purpose.

II. BIOLOGICAL PARAMETERS

A. Fecal coliform *Escherichia coli*

The bacterial quality of water and its effect on public health is one of the original driving forces behind government supervision of water supplies. In the later part of the 1800's, water-borne diseases such as typhoid resulted in annual mortalities of approximately 35 per 100,000 population, with epidemics running at much higher rates. By the 1960's when disinfection of water systems was widely practiced, the annual death rate for typhoid had dropped to less than 10 for the whole population of the US (around 200,000,000).

The identification of pathogenic bacteria is a tedious and expensive process. Instead of testing for a suite of specific disease-causing organisms, examination of the water for an indicator organism is used to screen the sample. The coliform bacteria are characterized by being anaerobic and aerobic, gram negative, non-spore forming, rod shaped bacteria that ferment lactose within 48 hrs at 35 °C, producing carbon dioxide and acid. (See Figure 2-5.) The fecal coliforms exist in nature as part of the normal flora in the intestines of mammals and thus serve as an indicator that fecal contamination of the water has occurred. Normally what is intended when fecal coliform is mentioned is *Escherichia coli*., however other coliform genera that live in mammalian intestinal tracts include *Enterobacter, Klebsiella, Citrobacter* as well as the *Escherichia*. The coliforms are more hardy than almost all disease-causing bacteria, thus the absence of coliforms is a good indication of the lack of other pathogenic bacteria. The presence of coliforms indicates the possibility of other pathogens being present, but it is not diagnostic. When specific identification of *Escherichia coli* is needed there is a specific set of biochemical tests that can be performed for confirmation (SM_{18} 9225). Commercially available kits are commonly used for these identifications, for example Enterotube® II from Becton Dickinson; however, the logic of spending a lot of time to absolutely confirm the identity of a specific indicator organism is somewhat fuzzy when the objective is to reduce the presence of pathogenic organisms.

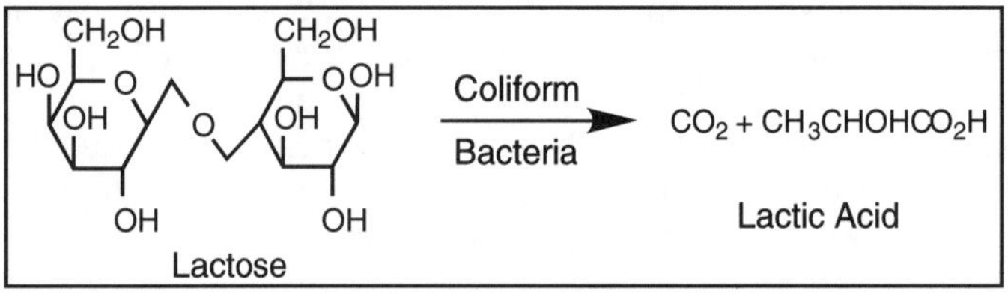

Figure 2-5. Fermentation of lactose by coliforms.

B. MPN tube tests (SM_{18} 9221)

The presumptive test consists of 5 repetitions of incubations in sterilized test tubes containing an inverted vial and a set volume (1.0 or 10.0 mL) of wastewater with 10.0 mL lauryl tryptose broth, which contains lactose. At least three decade (1:10 and 1:100) dilutions and repetitions are prepared. The minimum number of tubes used per test is 15. The inoculate is incubated at 35 °C ± 0.5 °C for 24 ± 2 hrs and examined for gas production, then incubated for a total of 48 ± 3 hrs and examined. Each positive tube (gas producing) is subjected to the confirmed test by transfer to a tube containing Brilliant Green Bile broth and incubated at 35 °C ± 0.5 °C for 24 ± 2 hrs and examined for gas production, then incubated for a total of 48 ± 3 hrs and examined. Positives are confirmed for fecal coliform by transfer to EC nutrient broth for 24 ± 2 hrs and 48 ± 3 hrs at $44.5\,°C \pm 0.2\,°C$. Positives are indicated by production of gas in an inverted vial. Most Probable Number of present organisms is determined from tables and depends on how many repetitions of which dilutions are confirmed positive. The completed test requires streaking a Eosin methylene blue agar plate with broth from a positive Brilliant Green Bile tube, incubation at $35\,°C \pm 0.5\,°C$ for 24 ± 2 hrs, then transfer of a typical colony (nucleated with or without a metallic sheen) to a lauryl tryptose fermentation tube and incubation for up to 48 ± 3 hrs and transfer of a typical colony to either a nutrient or plate count agar slant for up to 48 ± 3 hrs at $35\,°C \pm 0.5\,°C$. A positive completed test is indicated by gas production and gram negative rods.

Table 2-2. Formulations of common culture media for Coliforms

Lauryl Tryptose Broth	
Tryptose or Trypicase Peptone	20 g
Lactose	5.0 g
K_2HPO_4	2.75 g
KH_2PO_4	2.75 g
NaCl	5.0 g
Sodium lauryl sulfate	0.1 g
Preparation	35.6 g to 1 L

Brilliant Green Bile	
Peptone	10.0 g
Lactose	10.0 g
Oxgall or bile	20.0 g
Brilliant green	0.33 g
Preparation	40 g to 1 L

EC Nutrient Broth	
Tryptose or Trypticase Peptone	20.0 g
Lactose	5.0 g
Bile Salts #3 or Bile Salts mixture	1.5 g
K_2HPO_4	4.0 g
KH_2PO_4	1.5 g
NaCl	5.0 g
Preparation	37 g to 1 L

Eosin Methylene Blue agar	
Peptone	10.0 g
Lactose	10.0 g
K_2HPO_4	2.0 g
Agar	15.0 g
Eosin Y	0.4 g
Methylene Blue	0.065 g
Preparation	37.5 g to 1 L

Nutrient agar	
Peptone	5.0 g
Beef extract	3.0 g
Agar	15.0 g
Preparation	23 g to 1 L

Plate Count Agar	
Tryptone or Trypticase Peptone	5.0 g
Yeast Extract	2.5 g
Dextrose	1.0 g
Agar	15.0 g
Preparation	23.5 g to 1 L

For drinking water analysis, 10 tubes of double strength broth with 10.0 mL sample in each are tested. Positives are subjected to confirmation as above. A special MPN table for drinking water is used, however the MPN number can be calculated using the following equation:

$$\text{MPN/100 mL} = \frac{\text{no. of positive tubes x 100}}{\sqrt{\text{mL sample in neg. tubes x mL sample in all tubes}}}$$

Table 2-3. **MPN values for drinking water**

Number of positive tubes	MPN/100 mL	95% confidence limits
0	<1.1	0-3.0
1	1.1	0.03-5.9
2	2.2	0.26-8.1
3	3.6	0.69-10.6
4	5.1	1.3-13.4
5	6.9	2.1-16.8
6	9.2	3.1-21.1
7	12.0	4.3-27.1
8	16.1	5.9-36.8
9	23.0	8.1-59.5
10	>23.0	13.5-infinite

Table 2-4. **MPN/100 mL for five tube, three dilution series (10, 1.0, 0.1 mL)[1]**

Positives	MPN/100 mL	95% limits
0-0-0	<2	-
0-0-1	2	<0.5-7
0-1-0	2	<0.5-7
0-2-0	4	<0.5--11
1-0-0	2	<0.5-7
1-0-1	4	<0.5-11
1-1-0	4	<0.5-11
1-1-1	6	<0.5-15
1-2-0	6	<0.5-15
2-0-0	4	<0.5-13
2-0-1	7	1-17
2-1-0	7	1-17
2-1-1	9	2-21
2-2-0	9	2-21
2-3-0	12	3-28
3-0-0	8	1-19
3-0-1	11	2-25
3-1-0	11	2-25
3-1-1	14	4-34
3-2-0	14	4-34
3-2-1	17	5-46
4-0-0	13	3-31

Continued on next page.

[1] Table II-C-4, Microbiological Methods for Monitoring the Environment. EPA-600/8-78-017. December, 1978.

Table 2-4. **MPN/100 mL for five tube, three dilution series (10, 1.0, 0.1 mL)[2],**
continued

Positives	MPN/100 mL	95% limits
4-0-1	17	5-46
4-1-0	17	5-46
4-1-1	21	7-63
4-1-2	26	9-78
4-2-0	22	7-67
4-2-1	26	9-78
4-3-0	27	9-80
4-3-1	33	11-93
4-4-0	34	12-93
5-0-0	23	7-70
5-0-1	30	11-89
5-0-2	40	15-110
5-1-0	30	11-93
5-1-1	50	16-120
5-1-2	60	21-150
5-2-0	50	17-130
5-2-1	70	23-170
5-2-2	90	28-220
5-3-0	80	25-190
5-3-1	110	31-250
5-3-2	140	37-340
5-3-3	170	44-500
5-4-0	130	35-300
5-4-1	170	43-490
5-4-2	220	57-700
5-4-3	280	90-850
5-4-4	350	120-1000
5-5-0	240	68-750
5-5-2	500	180-1400
5-5-4	1600	640-5800

C. Membrane filter test (SM[18] 9222)

Sample volumes (100 mL for drinking water, less amounts are filtered for more
contaminated wastewater samples) are filtered through a 0.45 µm pore membrane with
drawn grids. The membranes are incubated in a water bath on an absorbent pad soaked
with M-FC (44.5 °C ± 0.2 °C for 24 ± 2 hrs and 48 ± 3 hrs) or M-Endo broth
(35 °C ± 0.5 °C for 24 ± 2 hrs and 48 ± 3 hrs). Positive FC colonies are blue in color
with a distinct metallic sheen on the M-FC nutrient. Positive coliform colonies are pink
to dark red with a metallic sheen on the M-Endo nutrient. At least five presumptive

---

[2] Table II-C-4, Microbiological Methods for Monitoring the Environment. EPA-600/8-78-017.
December, 1978.

coliform colonies must be confirmed by transfer to lauryl tryptose broth for incubation and examination for gas production.

Table 2-5. Media formulations for Fecal Coliforms

M-FC			M-Endo	
Tryptose or Biosate Peptone	10.0 g		Tryptose or Polypeptone	10.0 g
Proteose Peptone #3 or Polypeptone	5.0 g		Thiopeptone or Thiotone	5.0 g
Yeast Extract	3.0 g		Casitone or Trypticase	5.0 g
NaCl	5.0 g		Yeast Extract	1.5 g
Lactose	12.5 g		Lactose	12.5 g
Bile Salts #3 or Bile Salts mixture	1.5 g		NaCl	5.0 g
Aniline Blue	0.1 g		K_2HPO_4	4.375 g
Preparation	37 g to 1L		KH_2PO_4	1.375 g
			Sodium Lauryl Sulfate	0.050 g
			Sodium desoxycholate	0.1 g
			Sodium Sulfite	2.1 g
			Basic Fuchsin	1.05 g
			Preparation	48 g to 1L + 20 mL 95% ethanol

D. Presence-absence (P-A) Coliform Test (SM$_{18}$ 9221 D)

This is a one-step screening test using lauryl tryptose broth with bromocresol purple added as an acid-base indicator and 100 mL sample. Presence of coliform bacteria is suggested by a yellow color from the presence of acid in the broth after incubation. The test must be confirmed if positive.

Table 2-6. Presence-absence media formulation

P-A broth	
Dehydrated lactose broth	13.0 g
Dehydrated tryptose broth	17.5 g
Bromocresol purple	0.0085 g
Preparation	21.5 g to 1 L

E. Colilert™ Chromogenic Substrate Coliform Test (SM$_{18}$ 9223)

A patented, EPA approved (40 CFR 141.21, *Federal Register*, Wednesday, 10 June, 1992, Vol. 57, No. 122, pp. 24744-24747) one step P-A or MPN test for fecal coliforms. The sample is added to a dry mixture of o-Nitrophenyl-ß-D-galactopyranoside (ONPG, termed the chromogen), 4-Methylumbelliferyl-ß-D-glucuronide (MUG, called the fluorogen), either HEPES (4-[2-hydroxyethyl]-1-piperazineethanesulfonic acid) or phosphate buffer and essential nutrient salts, then incubated at 35-37 °C for 24 hrs. A yellow color from the chromogen indicates formation of ONP from digestion of ONPG (presence of the enzyme ß-D-galactosidase) and a blue fluorescence under 366 nm UV light from the fluorogen indicates formation of 4-methylumbelliferone from MUG (presence of enzyme ß-glucuronidase). These are the only sources of food for the bacteria in the medium, and fecal coliforms are the only bacteria capable of using both. For drinking water the test can be run on one 100 mL sample with results interpreted as in the P-A test, or on 10 tubes of 10 mL sample with results interpreted as in the MPN test. For wastewater the test is run in the same fashion as the MPN procedure.

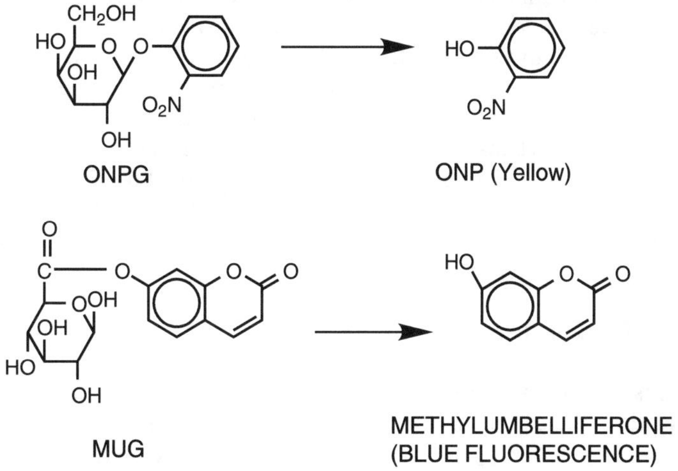

Figure 2-6. Chemistry of the Colilert P-A test.

Another approved version of this test is marketed as the Colisure™ test. It differs from Colilert by replacing the ONPG with chloro phenol red ß-galactopyranoside. Digestion of this material by bacteria containing ß-galactosidase is indicated by development of a red to magenta color from the original yellow. The presence of MUG in Colisure serves the same purpose as in Colilert.

The USEPA National Exposure Research Laboratory (NERL, formerly called EMSL) in Cincinnati, Ohio, has developed, and EPA has promulgated, a chromogen/fluorogen pair that is incorporated into a MI agar medium, for use with membrane filtration[3]. The fluorogen is MUG, however the chromogen is indoxyl-β-D-glucuronide which releases an intense blue on utilization by *E. coli*. The incubation time is 16-24 hrs at 35 °C. The test performs significantly better and in a shorter time than the traditional MF procedure.

F. Toxicity testing (EPA Methods 1001.0-1009.0)

There are two different approaches to evaluating environmental samples for contamination. The first approach is to determine *a priori* what chemical substances are dangerous to the environment, then test each sample for this list of bad boys. Most of us in the industry are familiar with this approach, as embodied in monthly analysis of our effluent for zinc, chromium, lead, 1,2-dichloroethane, and all the other substances on our permit. The advantages to this type of testing are that the laboratory knows what to look for in each sample, they can use identification techniques specific to the analytes of interest, and a multi-point calibration can be prepared for each analyte for reliable quantitation. The drawback is that regardless of how many analytes you test for, there is

---

[3] *Labcert Bulletin*, USEPA June, 1997; *Federal Register*, December, 1998

always the sneaking suspicion that you have overlooked something in the sample that is really harmful to the environment.

The alternate approach is to treat a living test organism with a portion of the sample and see if the creature exhibits any untoward effects. Toxic effects that are found are not only lethal effects (organism dies) but also reproductive- and growth-related. The effects may be irreversible or reversible, that is, permanent or the organism may recover. This approach is formalized in **Whole Effluent Toxicity** (WET) tests. The advantages here are that a lot of samples can be screened for toxicity in a short period of time. The disadvantages are that the actual results of a test on a particular effluent are somewhat dependent upon the little beastie selected for sacrifice. Further, assuming that toxicity in the sample is found, there is no indication of what exactly in the sample is responsible for the toxicity. However the ability to segregate effluents that exhibit toxicity from those that don't, means that efforts and resources to maintain statewide water quality can be concentrated upon the real problem areas.

Terms and definitions used in WET testing

WET testing is full of new terms and technical jargon that are unique to the procedures and interpretation of the results. Some of the more common terms are as follows:

- Toxicant (poison) - A substance that is harmful to living organisms due to detrimental effects on tissue, organs, or biological processes.

- Toxicology - The study of poisons and their effects on organisms.

- Dose Response curves - Dose is the amount of toxicant (mg/kg of body weight, or dilution factor) the organism is challenged with. Response is the biological effect on the organism, most commonly death. The curves are a plot of % response vs. log dose. One standard deviation on the curve runs from LD_{16} to LD_{84}. See Figure 2-7 for a general example.

- Lethal concentration (LC) - The toxicant concentration that kills a specified % of the test organisms after a set observation time, expressed as 48-h LC_{50}, where a 48-hour test was performed and 50% of the organisms died.

- Effective concentration (EC) - A point estimate of a toxicant concentration that produces an all or nothing effect on a given percentage of the test organisms. If the effect is death then the EC is equivalent to the LC and is expressed the same way, i.e. 48-h EC_{50}.

- Inhibition Concentration (IC) - A point estimate of a toxicant concentration that produces a set level of a graduated response for the population. For example when growth (body mass increase) is the response, an IC25 represents the toxicant concentration that produces a 25% reduction in growth for the test population. Within the population some individuals will be completely inhibited while others will be completely unaffected, however overall there is a 25% growth reduction.

- Acute toxicity - Short term lethal effects, generally 4 days or less for fish and 2 days for smaller organisms such as microcrustacea.

- Chronic toxicity - Longer term lethal or reproductive effects than acute toxicity. The response to a particular dose of a toxicant will vary from species to species.

Doses for chronic effects may be found at as little as 10^{-6} times the dose that results in acute effects.

- Immunity - Ability of a single organism to adjust metabolism to combat future exposures to a toxicant. Generally involves manufacture of antibodies that neutralize bacteria, viruses or other biological organisms. The body is generally unable to manufacture an antibody against a small molecule such as a pesticide like DDT or an atom such as mercury. Instead the antibody production is triggered by protein size molecules. Developers of immunoassay antibodies get around this problem by chemically attaching the toxicant, say atrazine, to a foreign protein, then injecting the modified protein into the organism. When the animal develops an antibody to the foreign protein the antibody receptor often will be able to bind to the toxicant without the attached foreign protein.

- Resistance - Shifting of the gene frequency in a population through attrition of susceptible individuals to leave only resistant organisms. The gene for resistance exists within the population prior to any exposure to the toxicant. The mechanism of resistance is generally the existence of one or more enzymes that can chemically degrade or change the toxicant to a harmless form.

- NOEC - No observable effect concentration, the maximum concentration of test substance that produces no effect. No effect is defined as no statistically significant difference between the controls and the test samples.

- LOEC - Lowest observable effect concentration, the lowest concentration of test substance that produces an effect. The lowest concentration that produces a statistically significant difference between the controls and the test samples.

- Reference toxicant - A standard material (potassium chloride, sodium dodecylsulfate, potassium dichromate, cadmium chloride, sodium chloride, etc.) that has a well characterized quantitative dose-effect on the test organism. Used as a quality control in toxicity tests.

- Screening test - An acute test or short-term chronic test performed with multiple replicates (10-20) at a single concentration of test material, generally the permit limit (IWC). Reported as "no observable effect - pass" (NOE) or "an effect - fail", in which case a definitive test must be performed.

- Definitive test - Multiple replicates of at least 5 different concentrations of test material, the concentrations must bracket the IWC and the end-point concentration.

- End-point - The observable effect of the test, generally limited to death, growth impairment, and/or reproductive success.

- Static non-renewal test - The test organism is exposed to a single portion of the test solution for the duration of the test. The test is limited due to shortage of dissolved oxygen and nutrients in the single portion of solution and the build-up of test organism waste products.

- Static renewal test - The test organism is exposed to fresh changes of the test material in water every day for the duration of the test.

- Flow through test - The test organisms are continuously exposed to fresh, recirculating solution of the test material during the test period.

- Instream water concentration (IWC) or receiving water concentration (RWC) - The concentration of the effluent in the receiving stream. Factors in the dilution of the effluent by stream at 7Q10 conditions. Generally a value of 5% is assumed, although for certain low-flow receiving streams the percentage may be much higher, up to the 90% or better level. Calculated by the equation:

$$IWC = \frac{\text{effluent flow}}{\text{effluent flow} + 7Q10 \text{ flow}} \times 100$$

- 7Q10 - Historical instream low flow rate; 7-day, 10-year minimum flow.

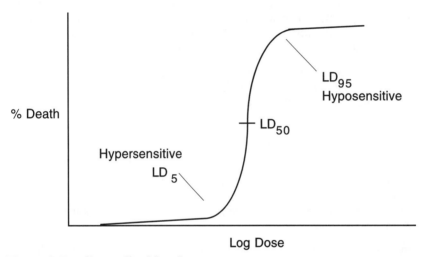

Figure 2-7. Generalized log dose-response curve.

Common test subjects for toxicity testing are the microcrustaceans represented by *Dafnia* sp. water fleas (fresh) (SM_{19} 8711). These organisms are very sensitive to pollutants in water and have been used for over a century. Another common group of test organisms are fish (SM_{19} 8910) represented by *Pimephales promelas* fathead minnows, *Salmo gairdneri* rainbow trout, and *Cyprinodon variegatus* sheepshead minnows. The promulgated EPA test methods for short-term estimates of chronic effects are listed in Table 2-7.

Table 2-7. EPA Methods for short-term estimates of chronic Whole Effluent Toxicity (WET)

Method[4]	Title
1000.0 (a)	Fathead minnow, *Pimephales promelas*, larval survival and growth test method
1001.0 (a)	Fathead minnow, *Pimephales promelas,* embryo-larval survival and teratogenicity test method
1002.0 (a)	Daphnid, *Ceriodaphnia dubia*, survival and reproduction test method
1003.0 (a)	Green alga, *Selenastrum Capricornutum*, growth test method
1004.0 (b)	Sheepshead minnow, *Cyprinodon variegatus*, larval survival and growth test method
1005.0 (b)	Sheepshead minnow, *Cyprinodon variegatus*, embryo-larval survival and teratogenicity test method
1006.0 (b)	Inland silverside, *Menidia beryllina*, larval survival and growth method
1007.0 (b)	Mysid, *Mysidopsis bahia*, survival, growth and fecundity test method
1008.0 (b)	Sea urchin, *Arbacia punctulata*, fertilization test method
1009.0 (b)	Red macroalga, *Champia parvula*, reproduction test method

Several manuals are available from EPA that detail the test procedures for WET testing. These include the documents in Table 2-8.

Table 2-8. EPA toxicity testing procedural manuals[5]

Short-term Methods for Estimating the Chronic Toxicity of Effluents and Receiving Water to Freshwater Organisms, Third Edition. July, 1994. EPA-600-4-91-002.
Short-term Methods for Estimating the Chronic Toxicity of Effluents and Receiving Water to Marine and Estuarine Organisms, Second Edition. July, 1994. EPA-600-4-91-003.
Methods for Assessing the Toxicity of Sediment-Associated Contaminants with Estuarine and Marine Amphipods. June, 1994. EPA/600/R-94/025.
Methods for Measuring the Toxicity and Bioaccumulation of Sediment-Associated Contaminants with Freshwater Invertebrates. June, 1994. EPA/600/R-94/024.
Manual for the Evaluation of Laboratories Performing Aquatic Toxicity Tests. January, 1991. EPA/600/4-90/031.
Methods for Measuring the Acute Toxicity of Effluents to Freshwater and Marine Organisms, Fourth Edition. 1993. EPA/600/4-90/027F.

The laboratory will generally maintain cultures of the test organisms, and verify through breeding records and frequent tests with reference toxicants that the cultures are disease-free and maintaining a certain level of toxicant sensitivity. Breeding and culture manipulation are scheduled so that large numbers of same-age organisms are available for each test that the lab performs. For *Ceriodaphnia*, suitable cohorts of test organisms are no more than 24 hours old and all born within 8 hours of each other. For minnows the larvae must be less than 48 hours old (preferably 24 hours) and all born within the same 24 hour time period.

---

[4] (a) *Short-term Methods for Estimating the Chronic Toxicity of Effluents and Receiving Water to Freshwater Organisms*, Third Edition, July, 1994. EPA-600-4-91-002; (b) *Short-term Methods for Estimating the Chronic Toxicity of Effluents and Receiving Water to Marine and Estuarine Organisms*, Second Edition, July, 1994 EPA-600-4-91-003

[5] An errata document has been published for these manuals, EPA-600/R-98/182, January, 1999, and been made official, *Federal Register* Vol 64, no. 21:4975-4978, Tuesday, 2 February, 1999.

Samples are normally collected as composite samples over 24 hours. Samples are to be chilled to 4 °C during and after the collection period. Sample holding times are 36 hours from the moment of the last aliquot collection until beginning of the testing. If static renewal tests are being performed, the same composite sample can be used for the initial set-up and the 24 and 48-hour renewals. This means that for the normal 7- to 8-day duration chronic test a total of 3 composite samples must be collected and sent to the lab. The normal sample size is 4 liters and within the industry the 1-gallon plastic "Cubitainers" or unused 1-gallon plastic milk jugs are widely employed. The containers are never reused.

Because of these organism age and holding time restrictions, there needs to be some measure of coordination between the lab and the sampling facility to insure that appropriate quantities of properly collected samples arrive when they are expected.

After initial characterization of the effluent for alkalinity, hardness, conductivity, residual chlorine presence, etc., the chronic tests are conducted by first filtering the entire sample through a 60 µm plankton net, and then performing a series of dilutions upon the effluent with the dilution water. The dilutions are chosen to cover the range of expected endpoints, from the undiluted effluent (100%) down to the no-effect concentration, say for instance 1% to 5%. At least five different concentration solutions are prepared, with no more than a multiplication factor of 2 difference in concentration between any two. Thus 100%, 50%, 25%, 12.5% and 6.25% might be the suitable for a particular effluent. The IWC must be within the range of the dilutions that are tested.

The next step is placing organisms in portions of the test solution in test chambers. When *Ceriodaphnia* are the test organisms, 50 mL plastic cups are the common test chambers, each test chamber contains about 15 mL of test solution and one organism. A minimum of 10 replicates are set-up for each concentration. A complete definitive test will then consist of at least 50 test organisms and 10 controls. When the minnows are used, test chambers are 500-1000 mL glass beakers containing about 250 mL test solution, each beaker will contain 10-15 embryo fish, and generally four replicates are set-up for each concentration. Thus each complete definitive test with a control will require about 300 fish. If a reference toxicant is set-up to run concurrently with the test samples (a very good procedure) it is also prepared in a minimum of ten replicates for *Ceriodaphnia* and four replicates for minnows at each of five concentrations.

Nutrient solution (food) is added to each test chamber. The completed racks of test chambers are then placed in a controlled temperature illuminated incubator. The illumination is set for a 16 hour on and 8 hour off photoperiod and the temperature is at 25 °C.

The next day, the number of surviving creatures and offspring are counted and recorded. For *Ceriodaphnia* the living test organisms (without brood) are transferred to a fresh portion of the test solution in a clean test chamber (static-renewal procedure). Nutrient is added and the test chambers placed back in the incubator. For the minnows, the dead fish are removed, the test chamber is cleaned of debris with a siphon, then the volume of the test solution is reduced by siphon to 15-20% of the original volume. Fresh test solution is carefully added to bring the volume back up to the original level, food is added and the test chambers replaced in the incubator.

This continues until the end of the test period 6-8 days later is reached. For the *Ceriodaphnia* the total number of surviving organisms for each test concentration are tallied along with the number of broods and total offspring for each adult. For the minnows, the number of surviving fish for each replicate are tallied and then the growth is determined. This is performed by placing all the surviving fish from a replicate in a tared weigh boat, drying at 60 °C for 24 hrs or 100 °C for 6 hrs, then weighing on an analytical balance. The total dry weight for the surviving fish in the replicate is divided by the original number of fish in the replicate to give the growth number. Average growth values are reported to the nearest 0.001 mg. This requires that a balance capable of weighing to 0.0001 g or better be used. Normal unimpaired growth weights for *Pimephales promelas* minnows should be 0.5-0.8 mg per fish.

These data are then plotted and processed using computerized statistical techniques to generate the LC, NOEC, and LOEC values. There are inherent differences in the statistics which unlie these results.

The LC results are generated from what are called point-estimation statistical techniques (Probit Analysis, Spearman-Karber Method, Trimmed Spearman-Karber Method, Graphical Method, or Linear Interpolation Method). The point-estimation assumes there is a regular dose-response relationship (Figure 2.7), and attempts to construct the best smooth curve through the data. Then the points corresponding to the LC_{25} and LC_{50} are read off the curve.

The NOEC and LOEC values are determined from hypothesis-testing statistical techniques (Dunnett's Test, a t-Test with the Bonferroni adjustment, Steel's Many-One Rank Test, or the Wilcoxon Rank Sum Test with the Bonferroni adjustment). These techniques attempt to answer the question of whether or not there is a significant difference between the results on the effluent and the results on the controls. The number that is reported corresponds to one of the dilutions that were performed in the test. The fineness of the scale of values reported for NOEC and LOEC depends entirely upon how close the concentrations of the dilutions were to each other. Thus if concentrations of 2000, 1000, 500, 250, and 125 were tested then LOEC/NOEC reported values are going to be limited to 2000, 1000, 500, 250, or 125. In many cases the lab will also report IC_{50} and IC_{25} values from the same data that generated the NOEC and LOEC values. As a rough approximation the IC_{50} will correspond to the LOEC, and the IC_{25} will correspond to the NOEC.

Although these various statistical treatments of the data can be performed by hand, in practice they are extraordinarily tedious and time-consuming. Computerized statistical packages have allowed much faster processing of the data, however even these packages are not automatic. There are certain decisions that have to be made by the statistician as to which statistical method is the most appropriate one to use for any particular set of data. These decisions, when confronted with non-normally distributed data or outliers, can have a drastic effect on the final results.

For the test to be considered acceptable, several control criteria must be met:

- the survival of the control organisms must be 80% or greater

- fathead minnows: the average dry-weight of the controls at 7 days must be 0.25 mg per fish or greater

- *Ceriodaphnia*: at least 60% of the control adults must have produced 3 broods by 7±1 days

- *Ceriodaphnia*: surviving control adults must have produced at least 15 offspring

If the minimum control requirements are not met or exceeded then the tests are invalid and must be repeated in their entirety.

Table 2-9. Reference toxicants and approximate endpoint results (data from references in Table 2-7 with exception of NaCl and $CuSO_4$ from in-house ASI data)

Organism	Toxicant	Test	Effect	Endpoint	Mean result
Ceriodaphnia dubia	NaPCP	7-day static renewal	Reproduction	IC_{25} IC_{50}	0.22 mg/L 0.30 mg/L
	NaCl	48-hr static	Death	LC_{50}	1750 mg/L
	NaCl	7-day static renewal	Reproduction	LOEC IC_{50} NOEC IC_{25}	1240 mg/L 1290 mg/L 621 mg/L 817 mg/L
	KCl	48-hr static	Death	LC_{50}	432 mg/L
Pimephales promelas	$CdCl_2$	7-day static renewal	Larval growth	NOEC	0.012 mg/L
	NaPCP	7-day static renewal	Larval growth	NOEC LOEC	0.179 mg/L 0.358 mg/L
	$CuSO_4$	7-day static renewal	Larval growth	LOEC IC_{50} NOEC	0.134 mg/L 0.116 mg/L 0.064 mg/L
	KCl	48-hr static	Death	LC_{50}	896 mg/L
	Silver	96-hr static	Death	LC_{50}	14 µg/L
	Endosulfan	96-hr static	Death	LC_{50}	2 µg/L
	SDS	96-hr static	Death	LC_{50}	8.6 mg/L
	NaPCP	96-hr static	Death	LC_{50}	0.14 mg/L
	Cadmium	96-hr static	Death	LC_{50}	0.15 mg/L

Reference toxicants are used to establish and monitor normal response of each test organism culture. The common reference toxicants for freshwater tests are sodium chloride (NaCl), potassium chloride (KCl), potassium dichromate ($K_2Cr_2O_7$), sodium pentachlorophenate (NaPCP), cadmium chloride ($CdCl_2$), copper sulfate ($CuSO_4$), and sodium dodecylsulfate (SDS). Normally a lab will chose one of these reference materials for each method and use it consistently. Sodium chloride is a common choice for *Ceriodaphnia*, while copper sulfate is a frequent choice for the freshwater minnows. The EPA methods require the laboratory to maintain control charts for the each of the endpoints (survival, growth, reproduction) for each test organism, for each method. At least one analysis of a reference toxicant is to take place each month, and the control chart limits are to be based upon the last 20 determinations with the reference toxicant. Some mean results for the common toxicants are presented in Table 2-9. An inability to generate acceptable reference toxicant results on the test organisms suggests that test results on your samples are also unreliable.

The EPA provides laboratories that perform toxicity tests, performance evaluation samples as a check on the lab's capability. These are part of the annual DMR QA Study. The check samples are supplied as a solid from which a stock solution and then a simulated effluent are prepared. The simulated effluent is diluted to give the 100%, 50%, 25%, 12.5% and 6.25% test solutions. The solids contain a selection of pure chemical toxicants that have been well characterized as to their effects upon the common organisms used in WET testing. The lab performs the toxicity tests upon their normal organism, then reports to the EPA the results as the percentage concentration of the simulated effluent required to produce a desired endpoint. The EPA generates acceptance limits for each organism for each endpoint at a variety of temperatures using either moderately hard synthetic freshwater (MHSF) or diluted mineral water (DMW), and grades the submitted results against the acceptance limits. Table 2-10 presents the true value and acceptance ranges for the PE samples provided in DMR QA Study 16 (1996).

Table 2-10. True values and acceptance limits for WET DMR QA Study 16. Results are expressed as percent of whole volume PE sample required to produce the indicated endpoint.

Organism, test	Endpoint, Temp[6]	True value	Acceptance limits
Fathead minnow, acute	LC_{50}-MHSF, 20 °C	41.9	DL-85.6
	LC_{50}-MHSF, 25 °C	43.7	DL-88
	LC_{50}-DMW, 25 °C	32.9	5.53-60.2
Fathead minnow, chronic	Survival, NOEC-MHSF	25.0	12.5-50.0
	Survival, NOEC-DMW	25.0	12.5-50.0
	Growth, NOEC-MHSF	25.0	12.5-50.0
	Growth, NOEC-DMW	25.0	12.5-50.0
	Growth, LC_{25}-MHSF	31.3	19.3-43.3
	Growth, LC_{25}-DMW	50.3	17.5-83
Ceriodaphnia, acute	LC_{50}-MHSF, 20 °C	38.2	8.0-68.4
	LC_{50}-DMW, 20 °C	28.6	2.3-54.8
	LC_{50}-MHSF, 25 °C	30.8	2.95-58.6
	LC_{50}-DMW, 25 °C	25.2	DL-51.7
Ceriodaphnia, chronic	Survival, NOEC-MHSF	25.0	12.5-50.0
	Survival, NOEC-DMW	12.5	6.25-25
	Reproduction, NOEC-MHSF	25.0	12.5-50.0
	Reproduction, NOEC-DMW	12.5	6.25-25
	Reproduction, IC_{25}-MHSF	28.2	14.5-41.9
	Reproduction, IC_{25}-DMW	14.8	10.7-18.8
Mysidopsis, acute	LC_{50}-40F, 20 °C	40.8	DL-82
Mysidopsis, chronic	Survival, NOEC-40F	25.0	12.5-50
	Growth, IC_{25}-40F	43.2	6.97-79.3
	Growth, NOEC-40F	25.0	12.5-50
Menidia beryllina, acute	LC_{50}-40F, 20 °C	21.6	DL-43.8

When toxicity test results are received it is important to interpret them with respect to the realities of the test. The tests are statistical evaluations of biological phenomenon. The single number you receive is not a hard, fast mathematical fact. Instead it is an estimate, and the bounds of uncertainty on that number are quite large, ±50% or better are quite normal. As an example, the DMR QA Studies are performed on pure water solutions of well-defined toxicants, normally mixtures of pure salts. But as illustrated in Table 2-10, the acceptance limits from the last study for the NOEC values were ± 1 concentration

---

[6]   MHSF - Moderately hard synthetic freshwater; DMW - 20% diluted mineral water; 40F - Synthetic seawater made up from Forty Fathom® sea salts.

level and the LC_{50} values ranged from less than 10% to over 50% effluent. The IC_{25} values from the chronic tests exhibited tighter acceptable ranges, however the absolute magnitude of the results depends greatly upon the water used for dilution. Thus even in the best circumstances, under the most tightly controlled conditions using a rigorously defined test sample, the size of the three-standard deviation precision renders the concept of accuracy in WET tests almost meaningless.

Putting these observations into useful guidelines, if the result of a WET test on your effluent lies at or very near the IWC or the permit limit, and indicates that you have a violation, there is a 50% probability that the result from a retest will indicate you do not have a violation. Thus it is not in your best interests to base major management decisions upon a single toxicity test result.

If a toxic effect is consistently found, then there are established procedures to isolate and identify the toxicant. The procedure is called a **Toxicity Identification Evaluation** (TIE). The reference documents are listed in Table 2-11. These procedures can be quite time-consuming and very expensive, however if they are followed exactly as presented in the EPA documents, frequently a compound or set of compounds will be discovered that are specifically responsible for the toxicity. Unfortunately there is tendency on the part of some consultants to short-cut the TIE procedures based on the mistaken belief that they know everything there is to know about the particular industrial effluent. The short-cut approach frequently will result in overlooking the major cause of the toxicity, while a systematic application of TIE procedures will almost always identify the major toxicant and probably many minor ones. Information may also be derived in the TIE which may shed light on how the toxicants interact to produce the overall toxic effect.

Table 2-11. USEPA TIE testing procedure manuals

Methods for Aquatic Toxicity Identification Evaluations. Phase I EPA/600/6-91/003
Methods for Aquatic Toxicity Identification Evaluations. Phase II EPA/600/3-88/035
Methods for Aquatic Toxicity Identification Evaluations. Phase III EPA/600/3-88/036
Characterization of Chronically Toxic Effluents. Phase I EPA/600/6-91/005F

Other toxicity protocols

Certain chronic toxic effects are of particular concern when humans are exposed to toxicants. These include:

- Mutagenesis - inheritable traits result from alteration of DNA; chemicals that cause mutations are known as mutagens. Often the traits are considered birth defects or give rise to cancer.

- Carcinogenesis - uncontrolled replication and growth of the organism's own cells. Most mutagens are also carcinogens. Biological alkylating and arylating chemicals such as guanidine can cause cancer. Most cancer-causing agents require metabolic activation and are thus classed as precarcinogens. Dioxin (2,3,7,8-tetrachlorodibenzodioxin) is probably a precarcinogen. Primary carcinogens require no activation.

- Teratogenesis - birth defects resulting from exposure to xenobiotics. Mutations in germ cells may give rise to teratogenesis, however the most common cause is damage to embryonic or fetal cells.

The Ames Test is commonly used for carcinogens. Mutant histidine requiring *Salmonella* bacteria are exposed to a mixture of homogenized liver tissue and the test chemical on an agar media that contains no histidine. The liver tissue serves to test for precarcinogens, compounds that are metabolically altered in the body to an active mutagen. If the test chemical is or becomes a mutagen, the bacteria mutate back to the ability to synthesize histidine and prosper, resulting in visible colonies on the agar surface. A 90% correlation exists between the ability to synthesize histidine and the actual mutagenic ability of the test compound.

Other testing procedures are found in the TSCA regulations, 40 CFR Subchapter R, Parts 702-799 (see TSCA discussion in Section 1-B). To a large extent these EPA methods are based in part or in whole upon OECD (Organization for Economic Co-operation and Development) Methods. A listing of the OECD procedures is presented in Table 2-12. OECD can be contacted on the Internet at www.OECD.org. Although finalized OECD methods must be purchased through the USA OECD office (202-785-6323, 2001 L Street, NW, Washington, DC 20036-4922; www.oecdwash.org), the proposed methods are available for downloading and review at the main OECD Website.

Table 2-12. OECD degradation and toxicity methods[7]

Method	Title
	Physical-Chemical Properties
101	UV-VIS Absorbance spectra
102	Melting point/melting range
103	Boiling point
104	Vapor pressure
105	Water solubility
106	Adsorption/desorption
107	Partition coefficient (n-octanol/water): shake flask method
108	Complex formation ability in water
109	Density of liquids and solids
110	Particle size distribution/fibre length and diameter distributions
111	Hydrolysis as a function of pH
112	Dissociation constants in water
113	Screening test for thermal stability and stability in air
114	Viscosity of liquids
115	Surface tension of aqueous solutions
116	Fat solubility of solid and liquid substances
117	Partition coefficient (n-octanol/water), HPLC method
118	Determination of the number-average molecular weight and the molecular weight distribution of polymers using gel permeation chromatography
119	Determination of the low molecular weight content of a polymer using gel permeation chromatography
120	Solution/extraction behavior of polymers in water

Continued on next page.

---

[7] OECD Guidelines for Testing of Chemicals, through the 10th Supplement, October, 1998.

Table 2-12. OECD degradation and toxicity methods[8], *continued*

Method	Title
	Effects on Biotic Systems
201	Alga, growth inhibition test
202	*Daphnia* sp. acute immobilization test and reproduction test
203	Fish, acute toxicity test
204	Fish, prolonged toxicity test, 14-day study
205	Avian dietary toxicity test
206	Avian reproduction test
207	Earthworm acute toxicity test
208	Terrestrial plants, growth test
209	Activated sludge, respiration inhibition test
210	Fish, early-life stage toxicity test
211	*Daphnia magna* reproduction test
212	Fish, short-term toxicity test on embryo and sac-fry stages
213	Honeybees, acute oral toxicity test
214	Honeybees, acute contact toxicity test
	Degradation and Accumulation
301	Ready biodegradability
301A	DOC die-away test
301B	CO2 evolution test
301C	Modified MITI test
301D	Closed bottle test
301E	Modified OECD screening test
301F	Manometric respirometry test
302	Inherent biodegradability
302A	Modified SCAS test
302B	Zahn-Wellens/EMPA test
302C	Modified MITI test
303A	Simulation test -Aerobic sewage treatment: coupled units test
304A	Inherent biodegradability in soil
305	Bioaccumulation
305A	Sequential static fish test
305B	Semi-static fish test
305C	Degree of bioconcentration in fish
305D	Static fish test
305E	Flow-through fish test
306	Biodegradability in seawater
	Health Effects
401	Acute oral toxicity
402	Acute dermal toxicity
403	Acute inhalation toxicity

Continued on next page.

---

[8] OECD Guidelines for Testing of Chemicals, through the 10th Supplement, October, 1998.

Table 2-12. OECD degradation and toxicity methods[9], *continued*

Method	Title
	Health Effects, *continued*
404	Acute dermal irritation/corrosion
405	Acute eye irritation/corrosion
406	Skin sensitization
407	Repeated dose 28-day oral toxicity study in rodents
408	Subchronic oral toxicity - rodent: 90-day
409	Subchronic oral toxicity - non-rodent: 90-day
410	Repeated dose dermal toxicity: 21/28-day
411	Subchronic dermal toxicity: 90-day
412	Repeated dose inhalation toxicity: 28/14-day
413	Subchronic inhalation toxicity: 90-day
414	Teratogenicity
415	One-generation reproduction toxicity
416	Two-generation reproduction toxicity
417	Toxicokinetics
418	Delayed neurotoxicity of organophosphorus substances following acute exposure
419	Delayed neurotoxicity of organophosphorus substances: 29-day repeated dose study
420	Acute oral toxicity - fixed dose method
421	Reproduction/developmental toxicity screening test
422	Combined repeated dose toxicity study with the reproduction/developmental toxicity screening test
423	Acute oral toxicity - acute toxic class method
424	Neurotoxicity study in rodents
425	Acute oral toxicity: up-and-down procedure
451	Carcinogenicity studies
452	Chronic toxicity studies
453	Combined chronic toxicity/carcinogenicity studies
	Genetic toxicity
471	*Salmonella typhimurium*, reverse mutation assay
(472)	*Escherichia coli*, reverse mutation assay
473	*In vitro* mammalian cytogenetic test
474	Micronucleus test
475	*In vivo* mammalian bone marrow cytogenetic test - chromosomal analysis
476	*In vitro* mammalian cell gene mutation test
477	Sex-linked recessive lethal test in *Drosophilia melanogaster*
478	Rodent dominant lethal test
479	*In vitro* sister chromatid exchange assay in mammalian cells
480	*Saccharomyces cerevisiae*, Gene mutation assay
481	*Saccharomyces cerevisiae*, mitotic recombination assay
482	DNA damage and repair, unscheduled DNA synthesis in mammalian cells *in vitro*

Continued on next page.

---

[9] OECD Guidelines for Testing of Chemicals, through the 10th Supplement, October, 1998.

Table 2-12. OECD degradation and toxicity methods[10], *continued*

Method	Title
	Genetic toxicity, *continued*
483	Mammalian germ cell cytogenetic assay
484	Mouse spot test
485	Mouse heritable translocation assay
486	Unscheduled DNA synthesis (UDS) test with mammalian liver cells *In vivo*

The toxicity screening of chemicals for endocrine disruptor effects (Section III.G) has been of increasing attention at EPA. A screening protocol has been proposed[11] and consists of a two tiered approach. The first tier is a rough screen to separate out those compounds that may demonstrate an effect from those that definitely do not. The second tier serves to generate a finer discrimination about the exact effects of the candidate compound.

Table 2-13. Proposed endocrine disruptor screening tests

Tier-1	
In vitro	Estrogen-receptor binding/transcription activation
	Androgen-receptor binding/transcription
	Steroidogenesis (substances that inhibit cytochrome P450 production of steroids)
	Placental aromatase inhibition (converts testosterone to estradiol)
In vivo	Rodent 3-day uterotrophic for estrogenicity
	Rodent 20-day pubertal female age of vaginal opening
	Rodent 5-7 day Hershberger assay for antiandrogens
	Rodent 14-day intact adult male reproductive organ inhibition
	Rodent 20-day thyroid/pubertal male to detect androgens and antiandrogens
	Frog metamorphosis (tail resorption)
	Fish gonadal recrudescence
Tier-2	
Mammalian	2-generation mammalian reproductive toxicity
	Alternative mammalian reproductive test or 1-generation
Other taxa	Avian reproduction (bobwhite quail and mallard)
	Fish life cycle (fathead minnows)
	Mysid life cycle (*Americamysis*)
	Amphibian development and reproduction (*Xenopus*)

---

[10] OECD Guidelines for Testing of Chemicals, through the 10th Supplement, October, 1998.

[11] Erickson, B., 1998. Screening and testing for endocrine disruptors. *Anal. Chem.* 70(17):528A-532A.

III. CHEMICAL PARAMETERS

A. pH (SM$_{18}$ 4500-H$^+$; EPA 150.1)

pH is defined as: pH = - log [H$^+$]. The scale in water ranges from 1 to 14, with 6 to 8 considered normal, or neutral. A more correct definition uses the activity of the hydrogen ion (a_H), which is equal to the single ion activity coefficient of the hydrogen ion (γ_H) times the molality ($m_H = \dfrac{mol}{kg}$).

$$pH = - \log (a_H) = - \log (\gamma_H m_H)$$

pH is measured either by electrodes attached to a pH meter or by pH-indicating paper.

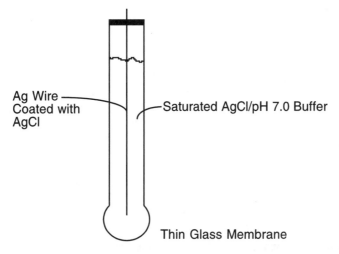

Ag Wire Coated with AgCl — Saturated AgCl/pH 7.0 Buffer

Thin Glass Membrane

Figure 2-8.   Single pole pH electrode.

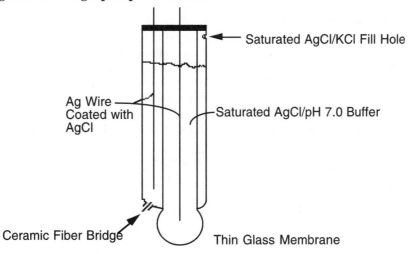

Saturated AgCl/KCl Fill Hole

Ag Wire Coated with AgCl — Saturated AgCl/pH 7.0 Buffer

Ceramic Fiber Bridge   Thin Glass Membrane

Figure 2-9. Combination pH electrode.

The best explanation for the operation of the thin glass membrane pH electrode is that the glass acts as a weak acid (GlassH). The existence of the pH 7.0 buffer inside the membrane maintains the inside of the membrane with a set number of anionic sites. When the outside of the membrane is placed in a solution at a different pH, the glass is either deprotonated or protonated relative to the inside of the glass. This sets up a potential across the membrane that is detected against the reference electrode and is proportional to the pH. The potential reading *vs* the reference electrode is sensitive to temperature, and the pH meter must be re-calibrated immediately before use.

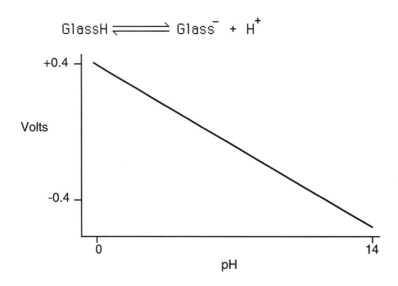

$$\text{GlassH} \rightleftharpoons \text{Glass}^- + \text{H}^+$$

Figure 2-10. pH plotted against potential for a pH electrode.

There are three effects of temperature upon the measurement of pH using an electrode. The first is an intrinsic relationship between temperature and the ionization constant of water. (See Figure 4-1 in Section 4.) The pH value of a neutral solution changes with temperature as presented in Table 2-14. This interdependence of temperature and ionization is also seen in the variation of the true pH value of the buffer solutions used for the calibration of the pH meter. Most commercially available buffers will have on the side of the label a chart of temperature *vs* true pH value.

Table 2-14. Temperature dependent pH variation of a neutral water solution

Temp °C	Neutral pH
0	7.49
20	7.09
25	7.00
30	6.92
40	6.77
60	6.51
70	6.40

The second effect relates to the relationship between temperature and measured potential differences[12]. A modification of the Nernst equation in simplistic form describes a direct temperature dependence that amounts to about 3.4% slope measurement difference for every 10 °C temperature change.

$$E_{measured} = E_{reference} - \frac{RT}{F} \log[H^+]$$

The third effect relates to the temperature dependent solubility of the salts contained in the buffer solution of the reference electrode. Calomel (Hg_2Cl_2) and silver chloride (AgCl) are the two most common salts found in reference electrodes. The reference voltage of the electrode is inversely related to the concentration of these salts in the filling solution and the concentration increases with increasing temperature. The effect is illustrated in Table 2-15.

Table 2-15. Reference electrode voltage variation with temperature due to increased solubility of silver chloride

Temp °C	Reference electrode mV
10	231
30	219
50	204
70	188
90	170

In most situations in the environmental laboratory, the extremes of pH (<2 for acidic conditions, and >12 for basic conditions) are not found in samples. Most natural water has a slightly acidic pH due to carbon dioxide saturation at pH = 6.35. See the following discussion on alkalinity for a more detailed look at carbon dioxide in water. Many tests in the lab require pH control, which is achieved through the use of buffers. A buffer is formed from either a weak acid and a salt of the acid, or a weak base and a salt of the base.

For a weak acid: HA $\longleftrightarrow$ H_3O^+ + A^-

$$K_a = \frac{[H_3O^+][A^-]}{[HA]} \quad ; \quad pK_a = - \log K_a$$

$$pH = pK_a - \log\frac{[HA]}{[A^-]} \quad \text{Henderson-Hasselbalch Equation}$$

Many different buffer systems are created and used in the laboratory. Table 2-16 gives a few of the more common. The pH of the equimolar solution is indicated as the pK_a. For other pH values that can be created from the buffer chemicals, the Henderson-Hasselbalch equation is used. However, the more common practice is to make an equimolar solution of the buffer chemicals then add acid or base as necessary to adjust the pH while it is being monitored with a pH meter.

---

[12] Frant, M., "The Effect of Temperature on pH Measurements." *American Laboratory*. July, 1995. pp. 18-23.

Table 2-16. Common laboratory buffer systems and their pK$_a$

Acid/conjugate base	pK$_a$
H$_3$PO$_4$ / KH$_2$PO$_4$	2.15
H$_3$Citric Acid / NaH$_2$Citrate	3.13
NaH$_2$Citrate / Na$_2$HCitrate	4.76
HOAc / NaOAc	4.76
H$_2$CO$_3$ / HCO$_3^-$	5.38
Na$_2$HCitrate / Na$_3$Citrate	6.40
KH$_2$PO$_4$ / Na$_2$HPO$_4$	7.20
Tris$^+$HCl / Tris	8.08
H$_3$BO$_3$ / Na$_3$BO$_3$	9.23
NH$_4$Cl / NH$_3$	9.25
NaHCO$_3$ / Na$_2$CO$_3$	10.33
Na$_2$HPO$_4$ / Na$_3$PO$_4$	12.4

Indicators are chemicals that exhibit a visual color change as the pH of the solution is varied. The operation of pH paper is dependent upon indicators absorbed on the paper. There is an equation similar to the Henderson-Hasselbalch equation for buffer solutions, which describes acid-base indicator transitions, based on pK$_{In}$.

$$pH = pK_{In} + \log \frac{[\text{Base form}]}{[\text{Acid form}]}$$

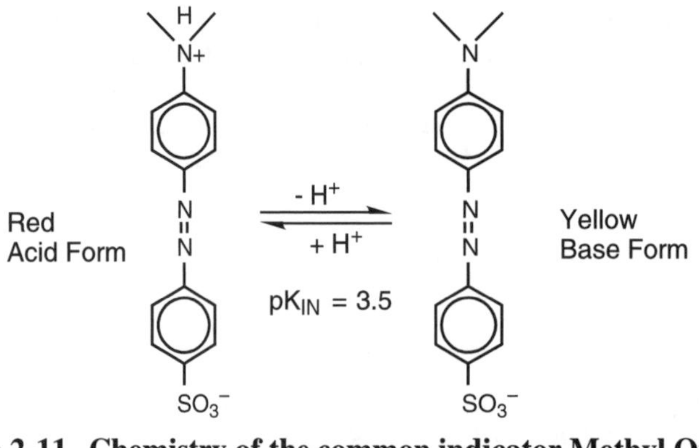

Figure 2-11. Chemistry of the common indicator Methyl Orange.

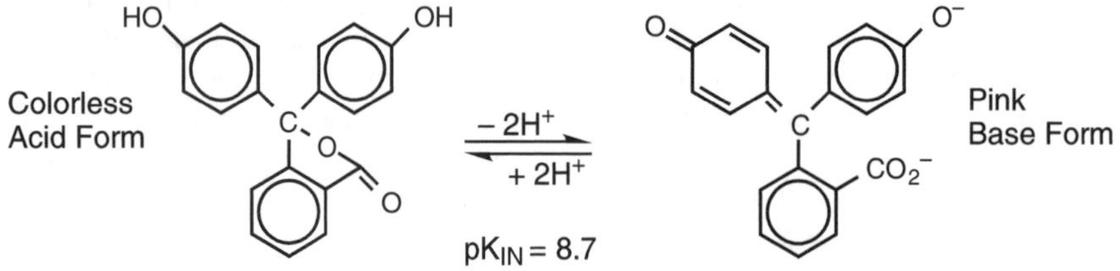

Figure 2-12. Chemistry of the common indicator phenolphthalein.

pH meters require calibration. Laboratories will often purchase calibration solutions at pH 4.0, 7.0, and 10.0 to use with the pH meter. These solutions and a number of other pH standards can be easily prepared from readily available compounds in the laboratory.

Table 2-17. Primary standards for pH calibration[13]

Primary Standard	Conditions	pH at 25 °C
Potassium hydrogen tartrate	saturated solution at 25 °C	3.557
Potassium dihydrogen citrate	0.10 mol/kg	3.776
Potassium hydrogen phthalate	0.05 mol/kg	4.005
$Na_2HPO_4 + KH_2PO_4$	0.025 mol/kg + 0.025 mol/kg	6.865
$Na_2HPO_4 + KH_2PO_4$	0.03043 mol/kg + 0.008695 mol/kg	7.413
Disodium tetraborate	0.010 mol/kg	9.180
$NaHCO_3 + Na_2CO_3$	0.025 mol/kg + 0.025 mol/kg	10.012

B. Alkalinity (SM$_{18}$ 2320; EPA 310.1)

Alkalinity is defined as the acid-neutralizing capability of water. It is reported as due to HCO_3^-, CO_3^{-2}, and OH^-, although borates, phosphates, ammonia, amines, silicates, organic carboxylates, and phenates (in humus) and other basic anions may contribute. Samples are titrated with standard H_2SO_4 or HCl ($0.02N$ or $0.1N$) to pH 8.3 (phenolphthalein or metacresol purple) for "carbonate" alkalinity and pH 4.5 (bromocresol green) for "bicarbonate" alkalinity. Results are expressed as "The alkalinity to pH ____ = ____ mg $CaCO_3$/L."

$$CO_{2(air)} <=> CO_{2(aq)} <=> HCO_3^-{}_{(aq)} <=> CO_3^{2-}{}_{(aq)} <=> CO_3^{2-}{}_{(solid)}$$

$$CO_{2(aq)} + H_2O \longleftrightarrow H_2CO_{3(aq)} \qquad K = \frac{[H_2CO_3]}{[CO_2]} = 2 \times 10^{-3} \text{ at } 25\text{ °C}$$

$$CO_2(aq) + H_2O \longleftrightarrow HCO_3^- + H^+ \qquad K = \frac{[H^+][HCO_3^-]}{[CO_2]} = 4.45 \times 10^{-7}$$

$$pK_{a1} = 6.35$$

$$HCO_3^- \longleftrightarrow CO_3^{2-} + H^+ \qquad K = \frac{[H^+][CO_3^{2-}]}{[HCO_3^-]} = 4.69 \times 10^{-11}$$

$$pK_{a2} = 10.33$$

Figure 2-13. Equilibrium chemistry of carbon dioxide in water.

---

[13] Kristensen, H. B., A. Salomon and G. Kokholm. "International pH Scales and Certification of pH." *Anal. Chem.* 1991. 63(18). pp. 885A–891A.

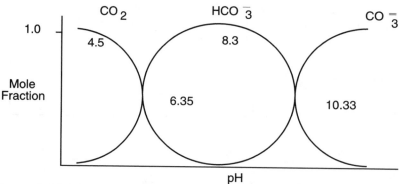

Figure 2-14. pH dependence of the mole fraction of carbonate, bicarbonate and carbon dioxide.

CO_2 saturation at 25 °C is 1.146 x 10^{-5} M (about 500 ppm), which results in pH = 5.65, not considering any disproportionation. For illustration purposes the alkalinity titration to pH 8.3 can be visualized as:

$$H_2SO_4 + CaCO_3 \longrightarrow \tfrac{1}{2} CaCO_3 \quad \text{for the carbonate fraction, and:}$$

$$H_2SO_4 + 2OH^- \longrightarrow H_2O \qquad \text{for the hydroxide fraction.}$$

The titration from pH 8.3 to pH 4.5 can be visualized as:

$$H_2SO_4 + \tfrac{1}{2} CaCO_3 \longrightarrow CO_2 \qquad \text{for the bicarbonate fraction, or}$$
one-half the carbonate fraction if the original pH was greater than 8.3.

By knowing the initial pH of the sample, the contribution of the different species can be easily determined.

A specific application of alkalinity concerns the narrow pH range (6.4 to 7.6) necessary for proper operation of an anaerobic digester. Total alkalinity to pH 4.3 includes all the bicarbonate contribution and 80% of the volatile organic acids. These contributions can be sorted by titration of the sample with acid to first pH 5.1 and then pH 3.5, using a pH meter[14]. The titration results are used to solve the following simultaneous equations:

$$A1 = \frac{[HCO_3^-]\{[H]_2-[H]_1\}}{[H]_2+K_1} + \frac{[VA]\{[H]_2-[H]_1\}}{[H]_2+K_2}$$

$$A2 = \frac{[HCO_3^-]\{[H]_3-[H]_1\}}{[H]_3+K_1} + \frac{[VA]\{[H]_3-[H]_1\}}{[H]_3+K_2}$$

where A1 and A2 are the molar amounts of the acid used to the first and second titration end-points; $[H]_{123}$ are the hydrogen ion concentrations of the initial sample and the first and second end-points, respectively; K_1 is the conditional dissociation constant of carbonic acid = 6.6 x 10^{-7}; and K_2 is the combined dissociation constants of the common volatile organic acids = 2.4 x 10^{-5}.

[14] G.K. Anderson and G. Yang. "Determination of Bicarbonate and Total Volatile Acid Concentration in Anaerobic Digesters Using A Simple Titration." *Water Environment Research.* 1992. 64(1). pp. 53-59.

The traditional determination of volatile organic acids in anaerobic digesters involves either isolation of the organic acids using a silica gel column with $CHCl_3$- butanol eluant and titration to phenolphthalein with standard base, or a more rapid process of titrating the sample to pH 4.0, noting the volume of standard acid used, then continued titration to pH 3.3 - 3.0. The sample is then boiled for 3 minutes and allowed to cool. Titration to pH 4.0 is performed with standard base, the volume noted, then continued to pH 7.0. The initial value of volatile organic acid alkalinity is = mL 0.050 N NaOH x 2500/mL sample used. If the calculated volatile acid alkalinity is greater than 180 mg/L, then the volatile acid content is the volatile acid alkalinity x 1.5. If the calculated volatile acid alkalinity is less than 180 mg/L, then the volatile acid alkalinity is the volatile acid alkalinity. Although very roughly determined these procedures give adequate results for wastewater plant process control.

C. Hardness (SM$_{18}$ 2340; EPA 130; or 200.7)

Defined as the sum of the calcium and magnesium concentrations, hardness is expressed as mg $CaCO_3$/L. Hardness may be calculated based on 2.497 [Ca] + 4.118[Mg] in mg/L, obtained from individual determinations of Ca and Mg by AA, ICP or other methods. The other common method is the 0.01M ethylenediaminetetraacetic acid (EDTA) complexometric titration. The pH of the sample is adjusted to pH 10.0, Eriochrome Black T is added as an indicator, and the solution becomes wine red. EDTA is a stronger complexing agent for magnesium and calcium than Eriochrome Black T. EDTA is used to titrate the sample. When all the ions are complexed to EDTA and none are available for the indicator, the end of the titration is signaled by the permanent blue of the uncomplexed Eriochrome Black T. The stoichiometry for EDTA to calcium and magnesium ions is 1:1.

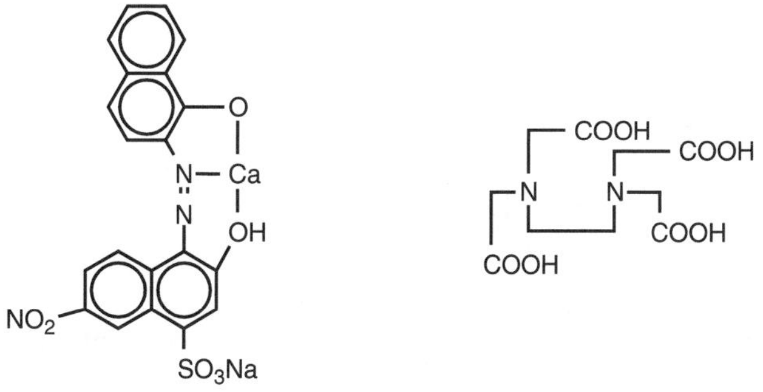

Erichrome Black T   EDTA

Figure 2-15. Reagents used in hardness titration.

D. Langelier's Index

Langelier's Index is a measure of the saturation state of water with respect to calcium carbonate. A value of zero indicates that the water is in thermodynamic equilibrium with calcium carbonate. A negative value indicates that the water is corrosive with respect to precipitated calcium carbonate. A positive Langelier's Index indicates that the water is oversaturated with calcium carbonate, and it will precipitate or be "encrustive." A positive value is the desired state as the precipitated calcium carbonate tends to passivate metal water lines from dissolution of copper and lead.

The Index is calculated as follows:

$$LI = pH_{sample} - pH_{saturation}$$

$$pH_{saturation} = A + B - log[Ca^{+2}] - log[alkalinity]$$

where:

[Ca^{2+}] and [alkalinity] are in terms of $CaCO_3$ in mg/L

A = constant for water temperature in °C

B = constant for TDS in mg/L

Table 2-18. Langelier's Index Values for A

Temperature °C	A
0	2.60
4	2.50
8	2.40
12	2.30
16	2.20
20	2.10

Table 2-19. Langelier's Index Values for B

TDS mg/L	B
0	9.70
100	9.77
200	9.83
400	9.86
800	9.89
1000	9.90

E. Dissolved oxygen (SM$_{18}$ 4500-O)

Wet chemical methods exist, however, most dissolved oxygen determinations are performed using one of a variety of oxygen-specific electrodes. The older style electrodes required vigorous stirring of the sample solution, due to a net consumption of O_2 from the sample:

Cathode reaction	$O_2 + 4H^+ + 4e^- \longrightarrow 2H_2O$
Anode reaction	$2\ Pb + 2H_2O \longrightarrow 2PbO + 4H^+ + 4e^-$
Net	$O_2 + 2Pb \longrightarrow 2PbO$ (Clark type DO probe)

The most modern electrodes rely on the following, with no net consumption of O_2:

Cathode reaction	$O_2 + 4H^+ + 4e^- \longrightarrow 2H_2O$
Anode reaction	$2H_2O \longrightarrow O_2 + 4H^+ + 4e^-$
Net	zero

The system is separated from the sample by a polyethylene and/or fluorocarbon membrane that allows diffusion of O_2. Introduction of O_2 to the system across the membrane causes increased current to maintain the higher presence of O_2. The fluctuations in current are related to the DO level through calibration with a standard, either air or air-saturated water. The calibration of the electrodes is subject to local temperature and atmospheric pressure, which can fluctuate in a significant fashion during the course of a single day. The most accurate calibration is to determine the DO of a sample with the Winkler titration, then use that value to adjust the electrode.

Winkler Method (azide modification) for DO: $Mn(II)SO_4$ is added to the sample followed by a strongly basic solution of NaN_3 and KI (alkaline-azide-iodide or AIA solution). If the precipitate is white at this point, the lack of DO is indicated, a brown precipitate of Mn^{4+} forms if oxygen was present. The precipitate is allowed to settle, and the sample acidified. After the addition of acid the sample is considered preserved and can be transported back to the laboratory. The released I_2 (I_3^-) is titrated with PhAsO (or thiosulfate) with starch as the indicator or until it is colorless. Most titration procedures use only a portion of the sample, generally 203 mL of the 300 mL in the BOD bottle. The odd volume is due to the addition of the 2 mL of manganous sulfate solution and 2 mL of AIA solution, which displace 4 mL of DO containing sample. 2/3 of 4 mL is rounded to 3 mL. The addition of the acid is performed after the floc has settled, which contains the information on the original DO level, and no dilution correction is necessary.

$$2Mn^{2+} + 4OH^- + O_2 \longrightarrow 2MnO(OH)_2 \qquad \text{base conditions}$$

$$NaN_3 + H^+ \longrightarrow HN_3 + Na^+ \qquad \text{acid conditions}$$

$$HN_3 + NO_2^- + H^+ \longrightarrow N_2 + N_2O + H_2O \qquad \text{prevents } I^- \text{ oxidation by } NO_2^-$$

$$MnO(OH)_2 + 6I^- + 6H^+ \longrightarrow Mn^{2+} + 2I_3^- + 3H_2O \qquad \text{oxidation of iodine}$$

$$2H_2O + I_3^- + PhAsO \longrightarrow 2HI + I^- + PhAs(OH)_2O \qquad \text{titration analysis}$$

Figure 2-16. Chemistry of the Winkler DO method.

F. Biochemical Oxygen Demand (BOD) (SM$_{18}$ 5210)

BOD measures the amount of oxygen required for bacteria and other microorganisms to metabolize waste material in a water stream. The material metabolized may be organic substances or some inorganics such as iron(II) and sulfides. The organic material can be subdivided into carbonaceous and nitrogenous demand. Nitrogen oxidation can be in-hibited through the addition of 2-chloro-6-trichloromethyl pyridine (TCMP), methylene blue or allylthiourea[15]. If nitrogen inhibition is performed the test is called CBOD (carbonaceous biochemical oxygen demand). A subscript is added to the initials to indi-cate the length of time in days the test was conducted; BOD_5 is the standard. In short the test calls for measurement of the DO, incubation for 5 days at constant temperature (20 °C) in the dark, measurement of DO, and comparison of the before and after values of DO to give BOD. Distilled water at 20 °C is saturated with oxygen at approximately 9 mg/L. The BOD of wastewater normally exceeds this by a factor of 10 to 10,000, thus dilutions are performed to obtain usable results.

---

[15] Young, J.C., "Chemical Methods for Nitrification Control." *J. Water Pollution Control Fed.* 1973. 45. p. 639.

Samples are stored at 4 °C with no preservative, for a limit of 48 hours. Samples are warmed to 20 °C, neutralized to pH 6.5 - 7.5 with H_2SO_4 or NaOH of such a strength that the volume does not exceed 0.5% of the sample. Na_2SO_3 can be added to destroy residual chlorine and other oxidizers. (Excess Na_2SO_3 will exert a BOD). Dilutions are prepared with neutralized distilled water containing nutrients and saturated with DO. Range of dilutions is 1.0% or less for strong industrial wastes, 1 to 5% for raw and set-tled wastewater, 5 to 25% for biologically treated effluent, 25% to 100% for polluted river waters. In BOD bottles (300 mL capacity, tapered water seal stopper) the sample is placed along with nutrients (Ca, Mg, Fe salts, and phosphate buffer), DO saturated dilu-tion water and a multi-organism seed. DO is measured. Bottles are sealed and incubated in the dark for 5 days at 20 °C ± 1 °C. DO is again measured after 5 days. The BOD re-quirement of the seed is subtracted, then the BOD calculated. Usable dilutions have initial DO 7-9 mg/L and final values >1 mg/L. A minimum corrected depletion between initial and final DO of 2.0 mg/L is required to calculate the BOD.

A novel variation on the traditional BOD procedure has been reported[16] that uses an immobilized microorganism coupled with an oxygen sensor to yield a biosensor capable of determining a value up to approximately 110 mg/L BOD. Although the results were not identical with the traditional BOD, a correlation could be demonstrated. The quick determination of the results makes this type of instrument very attractive for process control.

A major technical problem of the BOD_5 procedure results from the initial limited amount of oxygen in the sample. A modification of the procedure[17] uses a headspace in the sealed system to replenish the oxygen consumed in the sample and gives a much longer dynamic range for each test bottle. Thus headspaces of 5, 10 and 15 mL give ranges of 8-51, 18-120 and 36-241 mg/L BOD for a 28 mL container. The performance of the modified test is essentially the same as the traditional procedure with measured parameters of headspace volume and oxygen saturation at the beginning of the test and dissolved oxygen at the end of the test. The mathematics of this procedure are somewhat more involved, having to take into account the initial and final number of moles of oxygen in the system and the Henry's Law constant for oxygen.

$$HBOD = \frac{V_g M p_i 10^3}{[V - V_g]RT} (1 - c_f/c_{sat}) + (c_i - c_f)$$

where:

V is the total volume of the sealed system,

V_g is the volume of the headspace,

M is the molecular mass of oxygen,

p_i is the initial partial pressure of oxygen,

R is the gas constant, 0.0821 Latm/molK,

T is temperature in Kelvins, and,

c_i, c_f, and c_{sat} are the initial, final, and saturation levels of dissolved oxygen.

---

[16] Preininger, C., I. Klimant and O.S. Wolfbeis. "Optical Fiber Sensor for Biological Oxygen Demand." *Analytical Chemistry*. 1994. 66(11). pp. 1841-1846.

[17] Logan, B.E. and G. A. Wagenseller "The HBOD test: A New Method for Determining Biochemical Oxygen Demand." *Water Environment Research*. 1993. 65(7). pp. 862-868.

Many factors influence BOD_5 results. These include the presence of toxic materials in the sample and the exact nature of the seed. Further, metabolized material may be toxic at high concentrations, while a nutrient at lower levels. It is possible to control the method by using glucose-glutamic acid or KHP as the standard and thus QC can be applied in a rigorous fashion. A 300 mg/L GGA standard gives a BOD_5 of 198 $\pm$ 30.5 mg/L, and a $CBOD_5$ of 164 $\pm$ 30.7 mg/L.

KHP:

$$2KC_8H_5O_4 + 15O_2 + 2H^+ \longrightarrow 16CO_2 + 6H_2O + 2K^+$$

Glucose:

$$C_6H_{12}O_6 + 6O_2 \longrightarrow 6CO_2 + 6H_2O$$

Glutamic acid:

$$2C_5H_9NO_4 + 9O_2 \longrightarrow 10 CO_2 + 6H_2O + 2NH_3$$

Ammonia oxidation:

$$2NH_3 + 4O_2 \longrightarrow 2NO_3^- + 2H_2O + 2H^+$$

Figure 2-17. Chemistry of oxidation of KHP and glucose-glutamic acid.

G. Chemical Oxygen Demand (COD) (SM_{18} 5220; EPA 410.1)

Chemical oxidation of the sample with the strong oxidant dichromate, results in almost complete (>95%) oxidation of organic materials. Values are almost always higher than BOD values. Materials that resist chemical oxidation include some volatile chemicals (they don't remain in the oxidation flask when heated), hydrocarbons, pyridine, and ammonia. A variety of inorganic ions are also oxidized, such as Fe^{+2}, S^{-2}, Mn^{+2}, etc.

A sample of wastewater (20 mL) is strongly acidified with sulfuric acid containing Ag_2SO_4 (a catalyst). A known amount of $K_2Cr_2O_7$ is added, and mercuric sulfate ($HgSO_4$ 0.4 g/20.0 mL sample). The mercuric sulfate removes interfering chloride ions that can precipitate the silver catalyst. Chloride ion can be oxidized to chlorine by dichromate, and thus exert a COD on the sample. The mixture is refluxed for 2 hours. After cooling, ferroin indicator (1,10-phenanthroline ferrous sulfate) is added, and the residual dichromate titrated with ferrous ammonium sulfate (FAS). The ferroin indicator forms an intense color in the presence of ferrous ions (Fe^{+2}), and is colorless with only Fe^{+3} present. The titration end-point is indicated by the solution change from greenish blue to orange brown. Each mL of a 0.25N solution of $K_2Cr_2O_7$ (22.259 g/1.0 L) consumed is equivalent to 2.0 mg/L COD if a 20.0 mL sample is used.

The test can also be performed with a spectrophotometer by measuring either the decrease in absorbance of the dichromate ion or the increase in absorbance of the Cr^{+3} ion (SM_{18} 5220 D; EPA 410.4). The reaction is exactly the same as the titrimetric method; however, it is conducted in a screwtop test tube or cuvette. The reflux is replaced by heating the closed test tube in a heating block. The colorimetric method is preferred these days because of the decreased amount of hazardous reagents (chromium, mercury and silver, and the associated disposal costs) and reduced sample size used in the test with an improvement in detection level and precision. Use of greater than 1 cm cells can reduce MDL to be equivalent to titration.

Oxidation equivalents; one mole of dichromate is equivalent to 1.5 mole of O_2:

$$Cr_2O_7^{2-} + 8H^+ \longrightarrow 2Cr^{3+} + 4H_2O + 3(O°) ;$$

Titration reaction:

$$Cr_2O_7^{2-} + 14H^+ + 6Fe^{2+} \longrightarrow 2Cr^{3+} + 6Fe^{3+} + 7H_2O$$

Figure 2-18. Chemistry of COD reaction and titration.

The COD reaction is standardized by using potassium hydrogen phthalate as the test material. The COD procedure is one of the few tests that uses a primary standard as the major reagent and is standardized against a primary standard (KHP). Potassium dichromate is a primary standard and available in very high purity at a reasonable cost as is KHP. Primary standards are very precious materials in analytical chemistry because there are so few. Primary standards have the following properties:

- They are chemically stable and have very long shelf lives at room temperature.
- They are readily available.
- They are solids and easily purified.
- Their chemistry is well defined.
- They do not form hydrates upon storage nor tend to absorb water.

$$2KC_8H_5O_4 + 10K_2Cr_2O_7 + 41H_2SO_4 \longrightarrow 16CO_2 + 46H_2O +$$
$$10Cr_2(SO_4)_3 + 11K_2SO_4$$

Figure 2-19. Reaction of KHP in the COD procedure.

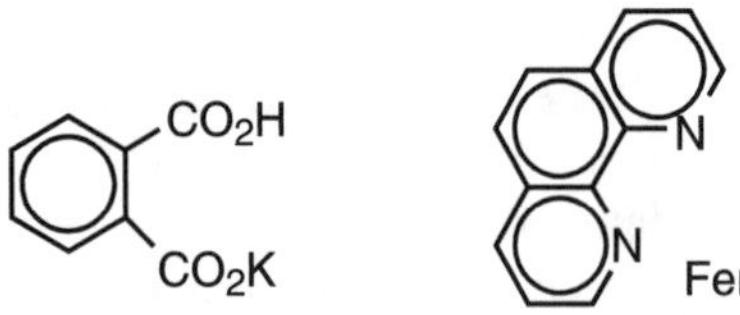

Ferroin Indicator

Figure 2-20. Structures of potassium hydrogen phthalate (KHP) and ferroin indicator.

Table 2-20. KHP used as a 300 mg/L solution as standard for a number of tests

Test	Analytical Value
BOD$_5$	240 mg/L
Dichromate COD	353 mg/L
TOC	141 mg/L
Total Acidity	74 mg/L (as $CaCO_3$)
Normality	0.00149 N
Total Solids	300 mg/L
Fixed Solids	100 mg/L
Volatile Solids	200 mg/L
Potassium	57.5 mg/L
Conductivity at 25 °C	168
pH	4.4

H. Metals (SM$_{18}$ 3000s; EPA 200s and 7000s)

1. Preparation (digestion) - All samples for metals analysis, except for drinking water samples, must be subjected to one of a variety of digestion procedures. (To achieve the drinking water MDLs, which are based on the MCLs, may require up to a 10-fold concentration.) A very informative reference[18] describes many types of digestions including open and closed systems, fusions, sintering, thermal procedures, gas streams, gaseous halogens and hydrogen halides, and pyrohydrolysis.

a. Open Air (Hotplate) Digestions – The most commonly used digestion procedure is a hotplate digestion exposed to the atmosphere with nitric acid (SM$_{18}$ 3030E). Other additives used in the procedure include:

- Nitric and hydrochloric acids (SM$_{18}$ 3030F)

- Nitric and sulfuric acids (SM$_{18}$ 3030G)

- Nitric and perchloric acids (SM$_{18}$ 3030H)

- Nitric, perchloric, and hydrofluoric acids (SM$_{18}$ 3030I).

The corresponding EPA approved methods include nitric acid (EPA 3005), nitric and hydrochloric acids (EPA 3010), nitric and hydrochloric acids, and hydrogen peroxide (EPA 3050).

The digestion procedure is frequently the place of procedural breakdown when samples produce erratic results as indicated by poor spike recoveries or lack of precision when comparing duplicate determinations. Contrary to most beliefs, metals are not totally inert and stable solids. At temperatures slightly higher than 150 to 200 °C, readily achieved on a hotplate or other heating surface, many metal analytes will volatize and be lost. Technicians who allow their digestions to boil dry, with a little bit of dark brown crud left in the bottom of the container, may be astonished to know that the brown residue frequently consists of mainly polymerized organic humic debris, rather than a quantitative recovery of the metal target analytes. Further, the residue, when it does contain the target analytes, may have transformed them into an insoluble form, that simple dilution to volume with reagent grade water will not solubilize.

Method 3050: Acid Digestion of Sediments, Sludges and Soils.

One to two grams of material is heated with 10 mL of 1:1 HNO_3, then heated with two additional portions of 5 mL concentrated HNO_3, then the volume reduced to 5 mL. Two mL water and 3 mL 30% H_2O_2 is added and the sample heated. Additional peroxide is added in 1 mL increments, with heating, to no more than 10 mL total. For some metal analytes concentrated HCl is added, and the sample heated. The digestate is filtered and diluted to 100 mL for analysis. The method is applicable to most metals by ICP, flame or graphite furnace AA. A recent article has suggested that the methodology is not universally applicable due to the insolubility of several metal forms[19]. The observations on the solubilization of lead, silver, antimony, chromium, molybdenum, and selenium are especially interesting because, if proven correct, the EPA methods 3020 and 3050 may be completely inappropriate for digestion of these metals.

---

[18] Sulcek, Z, and P. Ponondra. *Methods of Decomposition in Inorganic Analysis*. 1989. CRC Press. Boca Raton, FL.

[19] Kimbrough, D.E. and J. Wakakuwa. "A Study of the Linear Dynamic Ranges of Several Acid Digestion Procedures." *Environ. Sci. Technol.* 1992. 26(1). pp. 173-178.

The digestion of silver from solid samples using a variety of different procedures was examined[20]. Factors found to be important included maintenance of the digestion temperature at 95 °C and use of an excess of hydrochloric acid in the solution. The prefered conditions are those of the ASTM D3974 procedure, where 1 g of sample is reacted in 20 mL of water with 0.5 mL nitric acid and 5.0 mL hydrochloric acid, a 1:10 ratio of acids rather than the 1:1 ratio specified in the EPA procedures. The requirement for a large excess of HCl is attributed to the HCl-H_2O azeotrope boiling point of 109 °C as compared to the BP of the nitric acid azeotrope (121 °C).

Digestions for arsenic in ore samples are described in Methods 108A, 108B and 108C of 40 CFR 61, Appendix B of the Air regulations. The first method uses nitric and hydrofluoric acids in a bomb, and the second a combination of nitric, hydrochloric, hydrofluoric, and perchloric acids in Teflon beakers on a hotplate, both followed by instrumental analysis. Method 108C describes a digestion procedure with nitric, hydrochloric, hydrofluoric, perchloric, and sulfuric acids in an Erlenmeyer flask on a hotplate, followed by distillation of arsenic as the chloride and analysis by a molybdenum blue colorimetric method.

b. Microwave Digestions – Other variations use a microwave oven to affect the digestion with acid (EPA 3015 and 3051). The major advantages to the microwave digestion lie in the very rapid heating to a suitable digestion temperature and the use of a closed system, which minimizes losses of volatile target analytes such as arsenic and selenium[21]. The EPA methods offer a procedure for calibrating the power output of the oven by measuring the temperature increase of a plastic vessel of water in the oven. The power output is then related to the desired temperature increase in the digestion vessels. Figure 2-21 is a diagram of a microwave digestion vessel. This technique in practice gives erratic digestion results, particularly when differing numbers of samples are digested in different batches, and a variety of different acid mixtures are used. As the EPA methods specify a set temperature objective during the digestion, use of either a temperature-sensing thermocouple or a pressure-sensing transducer as a positive indicator of successful digestion is well worth the slight additional initial investment. Temperature monitoring is discussed in the EPA methods, but no mention of pressure monitoring is made, and no conversion data from temperature set points to pressure set points are provided. Table 2-21 of water pressures in psi and mm Hg for pure water at a variety of temperatures can be used as a guide for the pressure set points for aqueous samples. Since the aqueous digestion solution is dilute acid rather than pure water, 5 psi are subtracted from the pure water value to approximate the desired digestion temperature[22].

---

[20] Cohen, R.J., A.J. Meyer, E. O'Bryan, J. Kunze and S. Kunze. "An Improved Digestion Method for Silver Analysis in Solid Samples." *Am. Environ. Lab.* 1996. 6/96. pp. 28-29.

[21] Kingston, H.M., and C.B. Jassie. "Introduction to Microwave Sample Preparation Theory and Practice." American Chemical Soc. Washington, DC. 1988. ISBN -0-8412-1450-6.

[22] As of 1 July, 1993, Microwave digestion is allowed for wastewater samples for aluminum, arsenic, chromium, copper, lead, nickel, iron, selenium, zinc, barium and a few other metals. 40 CFR 136, Table 1B, footnote 36.

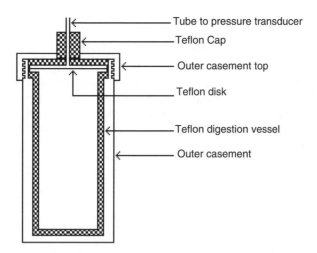

Figure 2-21. Microwave digestion vessel.

Table 2-21. Vapor pressure of pure water at a variety of temperatures

°C	mm Hg	psi	°C	mm Hg	psi
20	17.5	0.34	110	1075	20.8
30	31.8	0.62	120	1489	28.8
40	55.3	1.07	130	2026	39.2
50	92.5	1.79	140	2711	52.4
60	149	2.88	150	3570	69.0
70	234	4.53	160	4636	89.6
80	355	6.87	170	5941	115
90	526	10.2	180	7520	145
100	760	14.7	190	9413	182

For example the first setpoint for the aqueous microwave digestion using nitric acid (method 3015) is 160 °C for 10 minutes. The corresponding pressure from the Table is 90 psi, which is reduced by 5 psi to 85 psi, which becomes the first setpoint. The second setpoint is 170 °C, which corresponds to 110 psi as the setpoint.

The solids digestion (method 3051) is performed in constant boiling nitric acid (120 °C) with setpoints of 175 °C and 180 °C with a pressure peak of less than 6 atmospheres (88 psi). The vapor pressure curve of the 70% nitric acid is very similar to that of pure water, but offset 20 °C. The pressure of the 70% nitric acid is 14.7 psi at 120 °C, which is the same as that of pure water at 100 °C. We have found that the subtraction of 5 psi from the pure water setpoint works very well for solids digestion. Thus a setpoint of 85 psi for 10 minutes duration gives very good results.

There are some metal target analytes that are more efficiently recovered under basic conditions rather than acidic. A recipe for basic digestions in the microwave has been published[23].

---

[23] Zehr, B., J.P. VanKuren, and H.M. McMahon. "Inorganic Microwave Digestions Incorporating Bases." *Anal. Chem.* 1994. 66(13). pp. 2194-2196.

Method 3051: Microwave Assisted Acid Digestion of Sediments, Sludges, Soils and Oils.

Up to 0.5 grams of material is digested in 10 mL HNO_3 in a Teflon® vessel for 10 minutes in a microwave. Either temperature or pressure must be monitored to determine successful digestion. The digestate is suitable for analysis of a number of metals as indicated in Table 2-22. Modifications of the method suggested by the microwave vendors include a nitric-hydrochloric acid digestion and a nitric-hydrochloric-hydrofluoric acid digestion. SW-846 draft method 3052 describes the latter digestion procedure. It is recognized that the digestion procedure in method 3051 does not recover all the metals in a sample, and the results are defined by the test. The hydrofluoric acid mixture is a more vigorous digestion, reducing the silicon- and aluminum- based soil matrix to the soluble state. The digestate is reflective of total metals content, except for several metals, such as calcium, which forms insoluble fluorides, and boron, as borate is added as the final reagent in the process.

Table 2-22. Metals that can be digested by microwave techniques

Aluminum	Barium	Chromium	Lead	Molybdenum	Silver	Thallium
Antimony	Beryllium	Cobalt	Magnesium	Nickel	Sodium	Vanadium
Arsenic	Cadmium	Copper	Manganese	Potassium	Strontium	Zinc
Boron	Calcium	Iron	Mercury	Selenium		

c. Volatilization of Metal Analytes from Samples – In the above discussion of sample preparation techniques, the purpose is to obtain and retain the target analytes in a solution for ease of introduction by pipetting or suction into the instrument. Some analytes such as selenium, arsenic and antimony are quite challenging to keep in the solution due to inadvertent volatilization from the digestion mixture. By altering the sample introduction part of the instrument to allow analysis of gas streams, techniques of sample preparation that intentionally generate the metal analytes in volatile forms can be used effectively. These procedures, in general, must be tailored to the individual analyte but have the great advantage of a substantial reduction in the level of background noise and matrix interferences from the sample. This can allow routine analysis of certain metals at the part per trillion and lower levels.

The most frequent application of this idea is the cold vapor analysis of mercury from samples. Mercury has the property of existing in the elemental state as a relatively volatile liquid at room temperature and can easily be purged from the sample, discussed further in the next subsection (2.III.I). All the other encountered metal analytes exist in the elemental form as relatively non-volatile solids. However, select compounds of other metal analytes are volatile and can be purged from the rest of the sample by an inert gas stream. Candidate compounds[24] are select metal hydrides (As[25], Bi[26], Ge, Sb, Sn, Se,

---

[24] Reviews: Yan, P.-X., and Z.-M. Ni. *Anal. Chim. Acta.* 1994. 291. pp. 89-105; Dedina, J., and D.L. Tsalev. *Hydride Generation Atomic Absorption Spectrometry*, 1995. John Wiley & Sons, New York, NY.

[25] Chen, H., I.D. Brindle and X-C. Le. "Prereduction of Arsenic(V) to Arsenic (III), Enhancement of the Signal and Reduction of Interferences by L-Cysteine in the Determination of Arsenic by Hydride Generation." *Anal. Chem.* 1992. 64(6). pp. 667-672.

[26] Hahn, M.H., K.A. Wolnik, F.L. Ficke and J.A. Caruso. "Hydride Generations/Condensation System with an Inductively Coupled Plasma Polychromator for Determination of Arsenic, Bismuth, Germanium, Antimony, Selenium, and Tin in Foods." 1982. *Anal. Chem.* 54(7). pp. 1046-1052.

Pb[27], Tl[28], In[29], Cd[30] and Cu[31]), chlorides (Bi, Cd, Ge, Mo, Pb, Sn, Tl, As, and Zn), fluorides (W, Mo, U, V, Re, and Ge), diketonates (Cr, Fe, Zn, Co, Mn, Cu, Ni, and Pb), and dithiocarbamates (Co and Cu), as well as several organometallic materials (tetraethyl-Pb[32] and diethyl-Cd[33]). Determinative techniques have ranged from the traditional colorimetric method for arsenic to cold vapor AA, FLAA, GFAA, ICP-AES and ICP-MS. Environmental methods have been promulgated for analysis of antimony (EPA method 7062), arsenic (EPA 206.3 and 7061A, SM 3114) and selenium (EPA 270.2 and 7741A, SM 3114) as the hydrides; however, as the above list of metals demonstrates, the possibilities have been barely touched.

2. Instrument Analysis

a. Atomic absorption (AA) spectrometry - A low temperature method that uses a flame to atomize elements up to 2000 °C. This is a very good technique for easily atomized metals such as the alkali and alkaline earth metals. AA is used to directly determine calcium and magnesium for hardness. Various combustion gas combinations are in use with air-acetylene being the most common. Higher temperatures can be obtained through use of nitrous oxide-acetylene. The AA is also used with a quartz cell in place of the burner head for determination of mercury by the cold vapor technique and selenium, arsenic, and several other metals by the volatile hydride technique. The cell is heated to about 900 °C for determination of metal hydrides. AsH_3 can be determined by using $NaBH_4$ in a highly automated method[34].

---

[27] Valdes-Hevia y Temprano, M.C., B.A. Fernandez, M.R. Fernandez de la Campa, and A. Sanz-Medel. *Anal. Chim. Acta.* 1993. 283. pp. 175-182.

[28] Ebdon, J., P. Goodall, S.J. Hill, P. Stockwell, and K.C. Thompson. *J. Anal. At. Spectrom.* 1995. 10. pp. 317-320.

[29] Liao, Y. and A. Li. *J. Anal. At. Spectrom.* 1993. 8. pp. 633-636.

[30] Sanz-Medel, A., M.C. Valdes-Hevia y Temprano, N. B. Garcia, and M.R.F. de la Campa. *Anal. Proc.* 1995. 32. pp. 49-52; Xiao-Wei, G., and G. Xu-Ming. *J. Anal. At. Spectrom.* 1995. 10. pp. 987-991. Sanz-Medel, A., MC. Valdes-Hevia y Temprano, N.B. Garcia, and M.R.F. de la Campa. "Generation of Cadmium Atoms at Room Temperature Using Vesicles and its Application to Cadmium Determination by CVAA." *Anal. Chem.* 1995. 67(13). pp. 2216-2223.

[31] Sturgeon, R.E., J. Liu, V.J. Boyko, and V.T. Luong. "Determination of Copper in Environmental Matrices Following Vapor Generation." *Anal. Chem.* 1996. 68(11). pp. 1883-1887.

[32] Sturgeon, R.E., S.N. Willie, and S.S. Berman. *Anal. Chem.* 1989. 61. pp. 1867-1869; Edbon, L., P.Goodall, S.J. Hill, P. Stockwell, and K.C. Thompson. *J. Anal. At. Spectrom.* 1994. 9. pp. 1417-1421.

[33] D'Ulivo, A., and Y. Chen. *J. Anal. At. Spectrom.* 1989. 4. pp. 319-322.

[34] Chen, H., I.D. Brindle and X-C. Le. "Prereduction of Arsenic (V) to Arsenic (III), Enhancement of the Signal and Reduction of Interferences by L-Cysteine in the Determination of Arsenic by Hydride Generation." *Anal. Chem.* 1992. 64(6). pp. 667-672.

Table 2-23. Method numbers for FLAA (Direct Aspiration) metals procedures

Metals	W/WW Method	SW-846 Method[35]
Aluminum	202.1	7020
Antimony	204.1	7040
Barium	208.1	7080
Beryllium	210.1	7090
Cadmium	213.1	7130
Calcium	215.1	7140
Chromium	218.1	7190
Cobalt	219.1	7200
Copper	220.1	7210
Iron	236.1	7380
Lead	239.1	7420
Lithium	-	7430
Magnesium	242.1	7450
Manganese	243.1	7460
Molybdenum	246.1	7480
Nickel	249.1	7520
Potassium	258.1	7610
Silver	272.1	7760
Sodium	273.1	7770
Strontium	-	7780
Thallium	279.1	7840
Tin	282.1	7870
Titanium	283.1	-
Vanadium	286.1	7910
Zinc	289.1	7950

Graphite Furnace Atomic Absorption (GFAA) - Uses a small graphite tube with electrothermal heating to atomize the metals. Usable temperature range is up to 2800 to 3000 °C. The heating can be programmed to achieve a thermal ashing of the sample prior to atomization. Detection limits are 100 to 10,000 times lower than with flame AA for many metals due to elimination of the flame as a background interferent. Interferences that are seen include creation of smoke clouds and the resulting non-specific absorption due to improper choice of ashing and vaporization temperature programs. Background correction is normally required due to interferences from high solids content and spectral interferences. Common techniques for background correction are the deuterium continuum source correction and Zeeman background correction. The advantages of the Zeeman system over the deuterium system have been discussed in detail with examples of actual analytical situations[36]. In general, the deuterium background correction is ineffective when there are high levels of organic materials in the sample digestate. Although EPA and *Standard Methods* procedures require the use of liquid

---

[35] All these methods are deleted from Update IV, 3rd Edition of SW-846 in favor of the new general method 7000B for FLAA.

[36] Flajnik-Rivera, C., and F. Delles. "Evaluation of Deuterium and Zeeman Background Correction with the Presence of Spectral Interferences." *Am. Environ. Lab.* 1996. 3/96. pp. 24-27.

digestates of samples for analysis, techniques for direct analysis of solids have been published[37].

Table 2-24. Method numbers for GFAA metals procedures

Metals	W/WW Method	SW-846 Method[38]
Aluminum	202.2	-
Antimony	204.2	7041
Arsenic	206.2	7060
Barium	208.2	7081
Beryllium	210.2	7091
Cadmium	213.2	7131
Chromium	218.2	7191
Cobalt	219.2	7201
Copper	220.2	7211
Iron	236.2	7381
Lead	239.2	7421
Manganese	243.2	7461
Molybdenum	246.2	7481
Nickel	249.2	-
Selenium	270.2	7740
Silver	272.2	7761
Sodium	273.2	-
Thallium	279.2	7841
Tin	282.2	-
Titanium	283.2	-
Vanadium	286.2	7911
Zinc	289.2	7951

Sensitivity for determination of specific elements can be increased dramatically through use of the GFAA in a fluorescence mode, where excitation of analyte atoms in the furnace occurs at one wavelength and detection is performed at another. Lead has been determined[39] using the technique at the 10 pg/L level. The excitation source was a laser tuned to 283.3 nm while detection was performed at the lead fluorescence line at 405.7 nm.

b. Inductively Coupled Argon Plasma (ICP or ICAP) Emission Spectrometry and Mass Spectrometry - Operating in the 6000 to 10,000 °C range for excitation of the analyte atoms, two instrument designs are commercially available for analysis of the emission lines, the sequential and the simultaneous. The sequential is the slower but can examine many more elements by passing the diffracted emission spectrum across a photodetector. The simultaneous ICP has set detectors along the optical bench; however, automatic movement of the spectrum shifter for background correction results in small

[37] Freedman, Y., D. Ronen, and G.L. Long. "Determination of Cu and Cd Content of Groundwater Colloids by Solid Sampling GFAA." *Environ. Sci. Technol.* 1996. 30(7). pp. 2270-2277.

[38] All these methods are deleted from Update IV, 3rd Edition of SW-846 in favor of the new general method 7010 for GFAA.

[39] Wagner, E.P., B.W. Smith and J.D. Winefordner. "Ultratrace Determination of Lead in Whole Blood Using Electrothermal Atomization Laser-Excited Atomic Fluorescence Spectrometry." *Anal Chem.* 1996. 68(18). pp. 3199-3203.

scans around each detector. Elements that have emission lines falling within the range of the spectrum shifter can also be analyzed. Normally a 28-element instrument can be programmed to assay up to 50 elements or more. Newer design plasma emission instruments use a photo diode array to simultaneously obtain a complete emission spectrum from a sample (TJA IRIS instruments). The ability to identify and quantitate elements from a large set of emission lines offers improved accuracy in analysis. It is possible to examine certain difficult elements such as thallium, selenium, and arsenic on the more modern ICP instruments, however the common practice is to perform these by GFAA.

ICP emission spectrometry is subject to many interferences[40] due to the large number of emission lines that most elements exhibit. Interference correction factors are widely employed to control these spectral overlaps. These are used by measuring the amount of interfering element in the sample, multiplying the amount by the correction factor and subtracting (or in some cases adding) the result from the apparent amount of the target element. A number of generic correction factors are presented in Table 2-25.

Table 2-25. Generic ICP interference correction factors

Analyte	nm	Al	Ca	Cr	Cu	Fe	Mg	Mn	Ni	Ti	V
Al	308.22	-	-	-	-	-	-	0.21	-	-	1.4
Sb	206.83	0.47	-	2.9	-	0.08	-	-	-	0.25	0.45
As	193.696	1.3	-	0.44	-	-	-	-	-	-	1.1
Ba	455.40	-	-	-	-	-	-	-	-	-	-
Be	313.04	-	-	-	-	-	-	-	-	0.04	0.05
B	249.77	0.04	-	-	-	0.32	-	-	-	-	-
Cd	226.50	-	-	-	-	0.03	-	-	0.02	-	-
Ca	317.93	-	-	0.08	-	0.01	0.01	0.04	-	0.03	0.03
Cr	267.72	-	-	-	-	0.003	-	0.04	-	-	0.04
Co	228.62	-	-	0.03	-	0.005	-	-	0.03	0.15	-
Cu	324.75	-	-	-	-	0.003	-	-	-	0.05	0.02
Fe	259.94	-	-	-	-	-	-	0.12	-	-	-
Pb	220.35	0.17	-	-	-	-	-	-	-	-	-
Mg	279.08	-	0.02	0.11	-	0.13	-	0.25	-	0.07	0.12
Mn	257.61	0.005	-	0.01	-	0.002	0.002	-	-	-	-
Mo	202.03	0.05	-	-	-	0.03	-	-	-	-	-
Ni	231.60	-	-	-	-	-	-	-	-	-	-
Se	196.03	0.23	-	-	-	0.09	-	-	-	-	-
Si	288.16	-	-	0.07	-	-	-	-	-	-	0.01
Na	588.99	-	-	-	-	-	-	-	-	0.08	-
Tl	190.86	0.30	-	-	-	-	-	-	-	-	-
V	292.40	-	-	0.05	-	0.005	-	-	-	0.02	-
Zn	213.86	-	-	-	0.14	-	-	-	0.29	-	-

Reference : USEPA Method 6010, SW-846, 3rd Edition, September, 1986

The weakness in this approach is the necessity to measure the interfering element, which is itself subject to interferences and may not even be an analytical line on the instrument. The published methods in general only mention a few of the most common interferences. A frequent occurrence is that the analytical lines listed in the method for the target elements are different from those on the instrument, and reference lists of described spectral overlaps should be available for consultation. The operational software

---

[40] Olesik, J.W. "Fundamental Research in ICP-OES and ICPMS." *Anal. Chem.* 1996. 68(15). pp. 469A-474A.

for the instrument often have interference lists imbedded in them. A common technique to check for spectral interferences in a sample is to perform a wavelength scan and visually inspect each signal to see if there are overlapping emission lines at either the analytical signal or at the background correction point. This can take up to 5 minutes for each sample and most production labs are not willing to take this additional time for the analysis. Although it is possible to optimize the sensitivity of the ICP emission spectrometer through better optics, diffraction gratings, and plasma viewing designs, in the end it is the overwhelming problems of spectral interferences that places a limit on how low the detection levels can go.

In addition to the spectral interferences, the sample introduction into the plasma torch has a great bearing on the results. Two areas of special concern are samples with high dissolved solids content and viscosity (percent acid content) matching of the sample and calibration standards. Most sample introduction devices use a high velocity carrier gas to blast the entering liquid sample stream into a fine mist (the nebulizer). Baffles or skimmers are placed in the path of the mist to collect the larger droplets and allow only a very fine mist to reach the torch. The solids content and viscosity of the sample affect the efficiency of the nebulization and the interaction of the formed mist with the baffles. There can be great differences in the amount of sample actually introduced into the torch from one sample to the next. The solids content of the mist reaching the plasma can also effect the temperature profile within the torch. The volatilization of the solids from the particles can create local cold spots and decrease the emission efficiency of the analyte elements. Droplets with very high solids content can actually crystallize around a microdroplet of water (occluded water) then explode within the torch creating a significant disturbance in the plasma flow dynamics.

The alternative detector for the ICP is to introduce the atoms from the plasma into a mass spectrometer (EPA methods 200.8 and 6020). The mass range of the elements extends from 1 to around 250, so that, compared to the mass spectrometer used for organics analysis, more time is available for acquiring data for each mass, resulting in excellent sensitivity. Most elements can be detected. However, the ICP-MS is not interference free. Isotopes of different elements can have the same mass (isobaric interference), although the interference can be detected by examining ratios of the isotope peaks of the target element. Polyatomic isobaric interferences also occur where atom clusters with the appropriate mass/charge ratio can coincide with the mass of the target analyte. Some of these are listed in Table 2-26. Another problem is that not all elements enter the mass spectrometer as single atoms, and the ratio of the various forms of the element that reach the mass analyzer can be concentration dependent. Ion transmission efficiencies through the mass analyzer are concentration dependent and serve as a source of interference. Internal standards of scandium-45, yttrium-89, indium-115, terbium-159 and bismuth-209 are used to minimize the sample introduction and ion transport variations.

Table 2-26. Examples of polyatomic interferences found in ICP-MS

Ion Cluster	Mass		Ion Cluster	Mass
NH^+	15		OH^+	17
OH_2^+	18		C_2^+	24
CN^+	26		CO^+	28
N_2^+	28		N_2H^+	29

Continued on next page.

Table 2-26. Examples of polyatomic interferences found in ICP-MS, *continued*

Ion Cluster	Mass		Ion Cluster	Mass
NO^+	30		NOH^+	31
O_2^+	32		O_2H^+	33
$^{36}ArH^+$	37		$^{38}ArH^+$	39
$^{40}ArH^+$	41		CO_2^+	44
CO_2H^+	45		ArC^+	52
ArO^+	52		ArN^+	54
$ArNH^+$	55		ArO^+	56
$ArOH^+$	57		$ArAr^+$	76, 78, 80
ClO^+	51, 53		$ClOH^+$	52, 54
$ArCl^+$	75, 77		SO^+	48, 50
SOH^+	49, 51		SO_2^+, S_2^+	64
ArS^+	72, 74		PO^+	47
POH^+	48		PO_2^+	63
ArP^+	71		$ArNa^+$	63
ArK^+	79		$ArCa^+$	80
TiO	62-66		ZrO	106-112
MoO	108-116			

c. Anodic stripping voltametry – Anodic stripping voltametry is a two part electrochemistry process[41]. The first part is an electrolysis that serves to reduce the metal ions and deposit them as an amalgam in a mercury cathode. This serves a concentration function by removing the analyte ions from solution and placing them in the confines of the tiny mercury electrode. The polarity of the cell is then reversed so that the mercury electrode is now the anode. The voltage (potential) of the cell is scanned, and the current monitored. A spike in the current will occur at the dissolution potential for each of the analytes in the mercury electrode. The size of the spike is related to the original concentration of the analyte in the sample. By constructing the analytical electrode of platinum or carbon and spinning a thin film of mercury on it (rotating disk electrode) quite low detection limits can be achieved on the order of those routinely observed with GFAA. A distinct advantage is the ability to determine a number of different analytes in one procedure. Use of a gold electrode allows determination of mercury in ASV.

Quantitative results obtained with the technique depend on exact duplication of conditions for calibration standards and samples. Buffer control of pH can prevent some problems due to precipitation of insoluble hydroxides. Unexpected cations, such as gold, in the sample can lead to formation of alloys other than the desired amalgams. Dissolution potentials for these alloys, for example AuCd, Au_3Cd and AuZn, can lead to spurious peaks in the current-potential profile. As with most analyses, use of regular matrix spikes, especially with unfamiliar samples, can help detect anomalous results.

Anodic stripping voltametry methods have been published by EPA for arsenic (7063) and mercury (7472) as part of Update IV, 3rd Edition of SW-846.

d. Ion Selective Electrodes and Optodes – Optodes are devices used in conjunction with a spectrophotometer or colorimeter to measure metal cation concentrations. The

---

[41] Rieger, P.H. *Electrochemistry*, 2nd Edition, Chapman & Hall, New York, NY. 1994.

sensor consists of an organic polymer film that is in direct contact with the aqueous sample. The film contains a neutral ionophore that is capable of selectively chelating the target cation, and a chromoionophore, a colored pH indicator in disguise. The pH indicator is initially in the H^+ state. When the ionophore removes an analyte cation from the aqueous sample, the pH indicator gives up an H^+ to the aqueous sample so that the organic polymer remains electrically constant. The chromoionophore is chosen to have a distinct change in absorbance related to loss of the H^+. The optode is mounted in the lightpath of the colorimeter, and a selected wavelength used to monitor the absorption of the chromoionophore. Changes in the absorbance in the chromoionophore correspond indirectly to target analyte concentration in the aqueous sample. The sample is buffered to a value suitable to the pK_a of the chromoionophore. An ionophore and chromoionophore used for silver ion detection are illustrated in Figure 2-22. Recent publications have discussed the development of optodes for Ag[42], Pb[43], Hg[44] and U[45] ions in solution as continuous monitoring devices.

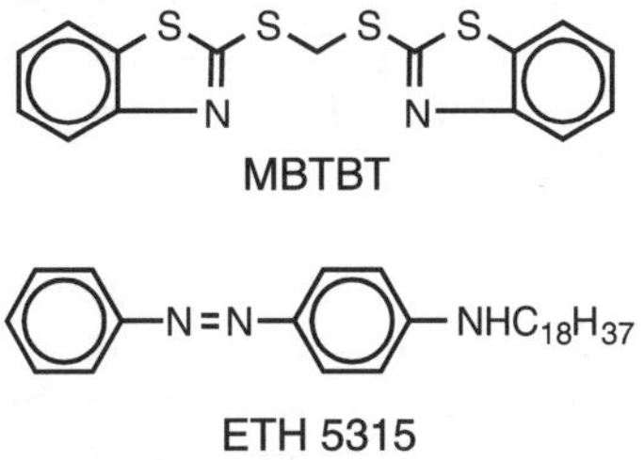

MBTBT

ETH 5315

Figure 2-22. Ionophore (MBTBT) and chromoionophore (ETH 5315) used in an optode for silver ion detection.

e. Metal analyte speciation – One aspect of speciation of metal analytes is determination of the dissolved fraction as compared to the total content of the sample. Traditionally this has been accomplished by filtration of the sample through a 0.45 μm pore size membrane, followed by either direct analysis by AA, ICP-AES, or ICP-MS. Aside from the normal concerns of contamination associated with having an additional step in sample processing,[46] a recent paper[47] has addressed the question of what is actually being measured.

The determination of hexavalent chromium (Cr^{6+}) as compared to the amount of total chromium in the sample has for many years been a compliance monitoring parameter. Hexavalent chromium is recognized as a potent carcinogen, while other forms of chromium, such as the frequently found trivalent chromium (Cr^{3+}), are essential nutri-

[42] Lerchi, M., F. Orsini, Z. Cimerman, E. Pretsch, D.A. Chowdhury and S. Kamata. "Selective Optical Sensing of Silver Ions in Drinking Water." *Anal Chem.* 1996. 68(18). pp. 3210-3214.

[43] Lerchi, M., E. Bakker, B. Rusterholz and W. Simon. "Lead-Selective Optodes Based on Neutral Ionophores with Subnanomolar Detection Limits." *Anal. Chem.* 1992. 64(14). pp. 1534-1540.

[44] Lerchi, M., E. Reitter, W. Simon, E. Pretsch, D.A. Chowdhury, and S. Kamata, 1994. "Bulk Optodes Based on Neutral Dithiocarbamate Ionophores with High Selectivity and Sensitivity for Silver and Mercury Cations." *Anal. Chem.* 66(10). pp. 1713-1717.

[45] Lerchi, M., E. Reitter, and W.Simon. *Fresenius J. Anal. Chem.* 1994. 348. pp. 272-276.

[46] In 1995, the primary supplier of a popular membrane realized that the membranes were contaminated with antimony and had to adjust their manufacturing process.

[47] Horowitz, A.J., K.R. Lum, J.R. Garbarino, G.E.M. Hall, C. Lemieux, and C.R. Demas. "Problems Associated with using Filtration to Define Dissolved Trace Element Concentrations in Natural Water Samples." *Environ. Sci. Technol.* 1996. 30(3). pp. 954-963.

ents and, while not benign, present substantially less of a hazard. Hexavalent chromium can be determined using diphenylcarbazide in a simple colorimetric test (EPA methods 218.5 and 7196A), ion chromatography (EPA methods 218.6, 1636 and 7199), differential pulse polarography (EPA method 7198) and a chelation/extraction AA procedure (EPA methods 218.4 and 7197).

The term speciation means determination of the different states of the analyte that are present in the sample. The potential states of interest could include the zero-valent state (elemental), and different valence states of both inorganic and organometallic compounds of the analyte. Mercury presents a case where elemental, inorganic and organic forms can easily co-exist in the same sample[48]. Other than chromium, there are not a lot of promulgated procedures for speciation of metal analytes. The available few include methods EV-024/EV-025 for total and organotin in wastewater, and methods 1 and 2 of 40 CFR Part 80, App. B for lead in gasoline.

Although the concept of speciation is easy to understand, the analytical protocols that need to be used are not as simple as represented by hexavalent chromium determination. For many of the potential analytes, the different valence states can be easily interconverted, especially during the sample preparation. Further colorimetric tests, although specific for a particular metal valence, may not offer sufficient sensitivity to be of any use for trace contaminant determination.

Most efforts in the speciation of metals have been directed toward direct analysis of aqueous samples with minimal sample preparation, relying instead upon a chromatographic separation of the analytes of interest followed by a variety of detection schemes. LC-ICPMS[49] and ion exchange chromatography-MS[50] have been proven useful for speciation of Pb, Hg, As, Se, and Cr. HPLC-AA has been used for As[51]. Capillary electrophoresis with amperometric detection or coupled to ICP-AES[52] or ICP-MS[53] has been used successfully for the speciation of mercury[54], organotins[55], arsenic

---

48 Galbreath, K.C., and C.J. Zygalicke, 1996. "Mercury Speciation in Coal Combustion as Gasification Flue Gases." *Environ. Sci. Technol.* 30(8). pp. 2421-2426, and many references therein.

49 Shum, S.K.C., H.M. Pang, and R.S. Houk. "Speciation of Mercury and Lead Compounds by Microbore Column LC-ICPMS with Direct Injection Nebulization." *Anal. Chem.* 1992. 64. pp. 2444-2450; Shum, S.K.C., R. Neddersen, and R.S. Houk. *Analyst.* 1992. 117. pp. 577-582; Gjerde, D.T., D.R. Wiederin, F.G. Smith, and B.M. Mattson. *J. Chromatogr.* 1993. 640. pp. 73-78; Shum, S.C.K., and R.S. Houk. "Elemental Speciation by Anion Exchange and Size Exclusion Chromatography with Detection by ICPMS with Direct Injection Nebulization." *Anal. Chem.* 1993. 65. pp. 2972-2976.

50 Corr, J.J., and J.F. Anacleto. "Analysis of Inorganic Species by Capillary Electrophoresis-Mass Spectrometry and Ion Exchange Chromatography-Mass Spectrometry Using an Ion Spray Source." *Anal. Chem.* 1996. 68(13). pp. 2155-2163.

51 Manning, B.A. and D.A. Martens. "Speciation of As(III) and As(V) in Sediment Extracts by HPLC-Hydride Generation AA Spectrometry." *Environ. Sci. Technol.* 1997. 31(1). pp. 171-177.

52 Olesik, J.W., J.A. Kinzer, and S.V. Olesik, 1995. "CE-ICP Spectrometry for Rapid Elemental Speciation." *Anal. Chem.* 67(1):1-12.

53 Lui, Y., V. Lopez-Avila, J.J. Zhu, D.R. Wiederin, and W.F. Beckert. "Capillary Electrophoresis Coupled On-Line with ICP-MS for Elemental Speciation." *Anal. Chem.* 1995. 67(13). pp. 2020-2025; Lu, Q., S.M. Bird, and R.M. Barnes. "Interface for Capillary Electrophoresis and ICP-MS." *Anal. Chem.* 1995. 67(7). pp. 2949-2956.

54 Lai, E.P.C., and E.Dabek-Zlotorzynska. "Capillary Electrophoresis wih Amperometric Detection for Mercury Speciation." *Am. Environ. Lab.* 1996. 6/96. pp. 1,6,8.

55 Liu, Y., V. Lopez-Avila, M. Alcaraz, and W.F. Beckert. "Determination of Organotin Environmental Samples by Supercritical Fluid Extraction and GC-AED." *J. High. Resolut. Chromatogr.* 1993. 16(2). pp. 106-112; Liu, Y., and V. Lopez-Avila. *J. High Resolut. Chromatogr.* 1993. 16. pp. 717-720.

and selenium. GC-AES has been reported as a useful tool for analysis of organomercury species[56].

When sample preparation has been addressed, supercritical fluid extraction of solid samples using carbon dioxide modified with dithiocarbamates, diketones or tributyl-phosphate, was found to be useful for isolation of inorganic mercury and organo-mercurials, lanthanides, uranium, and thorium[57]. EPA has a speciation method for mercury (EPA draft method 3200) under consideration that uses a sequential series of extractions with toluene and then acidic water solutions of increasing oxidizing strength. Each solution is then analyzed for total mercury. Sequential extractions and hydride AA have been used for selenium speciation[58].

Dr. Skip Kingston has recently presented an innovative (and patented) approach to speciation[59] using ion chromatography-ICP/MS as the determinative instrument. He has termed the technique "Speciated Isotope Dilution Mass Spectrometry." The method requires an available pure isotope for each of the common valence states of the analyte. Each of the isotopes is used to prepare a single pure standard of one of the valences of the element. The sample is spiked with a known amount of each of the isotopically labeled valence states. The sample is then prepared/analyzed and the amounts of each isotope in each form are determined. Based on the natural abundance of the isotopes of the analyte and the valence distribution found in the spiked sample, the original amounts of each species can be computed. This very nicely takes into account any interconversion of the analyte forms that occurs during the sample preparation. For example, chromium naturally has the abundance of ^{50}Cr 4.35%, ^{52}Cr 83.79%, ^{53}Cr 9.50% and ^{54}Cr 2.36%. A Cr(III) spike is prepared from ^{50}Cr with 93.1% abundance and a Cr(VI) spike from ^{53}Cr with 97.7% abundance. Examination of the $^{50}Cr/^{52}Cr$, $^{50}Cr/^{53}Cr$, and $^{50}Cr/^{53}Cr$ ratios for the separated Cr(III) and Cr(VI) peaks allows calculation of the original amount of the two species in the sample. Interconversion percents for the two species ranged from 14 to 40% depending on the sample matrix and how the sample was

56   Donais, M. K., P.C. Uden, M.M. Schantz, and S.A. Wise. "Development, Validation and Application of a Method for Quantification of Methylmercury in Biological Marine Samples using GC-AES." *Anal. Chem.* 1996. 68(21). pp. 3859-3866; Cai, Y., R. Jaffe and R. Jones. "Ethylmercury in the Soils and Sediments of the Florida Everglades." *Environ. Sci. Technol.* 1997. 31(1). pp. 302-305.

57   Smart, N., Y. Lin, and C.M. Wai,. "Supercritical Fuid Extraction of Metal Ions from Solid Samples." *Am. Environ. Lab.* 1996. 2/96. pp. 38-42; Lin, Y., R. Brauer, K.E. Laintz, and C.M. Wai. "Supercritical Fluid Extraction of Lanthanides and Actinides from Solid Materials with a Fluorinated Diketone." *Anal. Chem.* 1993. 65. pp. 2549-2551; Wai, C.M., Y. Lin, R. Brauer, S. Wang, and W.F. Beckert. "Supercritical fluid extraction of organic and inorganic mercury from Solid Materials." *Talanta.* 1993. 40. pp. 1325-1329; Lin, Y., and C.M. Wai. "Supercritical Fluid Extraction of Lanthanides with Fluorinated Diketones and Tributylphosphate." *Anal. Chem.* 1994. 66. pp. 1971-1975; Lin, Y., C.M. Wai, F.M. Jean, and R.D. Brauer. "Supercritical Fluid Extraction of Thorium and Uranium Ions From Solid and Liquid Materials with Fluorinated Diketones and Tributylphosphate." *Environ. Sci. Technol.* 1994. 28. pp. 1190-1193.

58   Martens, D.A., and D.L. Suarez. "Selenium Speciation of Soil/Sediment Determined with Sequential Extractions and Hydride Generation Atomic Absorption Spectrometry." *Environ. Sci. Technol.* 1997. 31(1). pp. 133-139.

59   Kingston, H.M., D. Huo, S. Chalk and P.J. Walter. "The Accurate Determination of Species by Speciated Isotope Dilution Mass Spectrometry: Exemplified by the Evaluation of Chromium (VI) in Soil." *Proceedings of the 12th Annual Waste Testing and Quality Assurance Symposium*, 23-26 July, 1996, Washington, DC. 1996. pp 112-119; U.S. Patent Number 5,414,259, "Method of Speciated Isotope Dilution Mass Spectrometry," Granted 9 May, 1995.

prepared. This procedure has been adopted into SW-846 (Update IV, 3rd Edition) as Method 6800.

3. Recent EPA Metals Methods and Monitoring Requirements

The EPA has published the *Manual for the Determination of Metals in Environmental Samples,* and a supplement[60] in a movement to consolidate methods from the various offices in EPA. Most of the methods in the supplement are updated revisions of methods in the original manual; however, Method 200.15 is entirely new.

Table 2-27. Contents of Manual for the Determination of Metals in Environmental Samples. Methods marked with an * are in the Supplement.

Method	Title
200.1	Determination of acid-soluble metals
200.2*	Sample preparation procedure for spectrochemical determination of total recoverable elements
200.3	Sample preparation procedure for spectrochemical determination of total recoverable elements in biological tissues
200.7*	Determination of metals and trace elements in water and wastes by inductively coupled plasma - atomic emission spectrometry
200.8*	Determination of trace elements in water and wastes by inductively coupled plasma - mass spectrometry
200.9*	Determination of trace elements by stabilized temperature graphite furnace atomic absorption spectrometry
200.10	Determination of trace elements in marine waters by on-line chelation preconcentration and inductively coupled plasma - mass spectrometry
200.11	Determination of metals in fish tissue by inductively coupled plasma - atomic emission spectrometry
200.15*	Determination of metals and trace elements in water by ultrasonic nebulization inductively coupled plasma-atomic emission spectrometry.
218.6*	Determination of dissolved hexavalent chromium in drinking water, groundwater, and industrial wastewater effluents by ion chromatography
245.1*	Determination of mercury in water by cold vapor atomic absorption spectrometry
245.3	Determination of inorganic mercury (II) and selected organomercurials in drinking and groundwater by HPLC with electrochemical detection
245.5	Determination of mercury in sediment by cold vapor atomic absorption spectrometry
245.6	Determination of mercury in tissues by cold vapor atomic absorption spectrometry

The average metals laboratory that analyzes environmental samples has problems with laboratory contamination. The most frequently found contaminants are zinc, nickel, iron, aluminum and copper. These analytes are ubiquitous as contaminants and can actually be used as a hallmark of the technical competence of the laboratory. Although the GFAA, ICP-AES and ICP-MS have the ability to measure very low levels of these analytes, laboratories without clean room facilities that claim routine reporting limits for copper, nickel and zinc of less than 20 µg/L or iron and aluminum limits of less than 50 µg/L are probably overstating their capabilities.

The establishment of the water quality criteria for metals as monitoring goals has run directly into the problem of laboratory contamination. A series of trace metal

---

[60] *Methods for the Determination of Metals in Environmental Samples*, Supplement I, EPA-600/R-94/111, May 1994.

determination methods, 1631, 1632, and 1637 through 1640, have been distributed from the Office of Water in support of the clean metals monitoring program. Associated with these methods, EPA has distributed guidance on clean metals sampling, the establishment and maintenance of a clean-room facility in the analytical lab, and data evaluation techniques for users of lab data. These methods and guidance documents have been distributed by EPA Office of Water as a set on a 3.5 inch disks for use with Word Perfect. See Table 2-28.

Table 2-28. Metals methods and associated guidance for the clean metals program

Method	Title
1631	Mercury in water by oxidation, purge and trap, and cold vapor atomic fluorescence spectrometry EPA 821-R-95-027, April 1995 (draft)
1632	Determination of inorganic arsenic in water by hydride generation flame atomic absorption EPA 821-R-95-028 April 1995 (draft)
1636	Determination of hexavalent chromium by ion chromatography EPA 821-R-95-029 April 1995
1637	Determination of trace elements in ambient waters by chelation preconcentration with graphite furnace atomic absorption EPA 821-R-95-030, April 1995
1638	Determination of trace elements in ambient waters by inductively coupled plasma-mass spectrometry EPA 821-R-95-031, April 1995
1639	Determination of trace elements in ambient waters by stabilized temperature graphite furnace atomic absorption EPA 821-R-95-032 April 1995
1640	Determination of trace elements in ambient waters by on-line chelation preconcentration and inductively coupled plasma-mass spectrometry EPA 821-R-95-033, April 1995
-	Guidance on establishing trace metal clean rooms in existing facilities EPA 821-B-95-001 April, 1995 (draft)
1669	Sampling ambient water for determination of trace metals at EPA water quality criteria levels and Quality Control Supplement for Determination of Trace Metals at EPA Water Quality Criteria Levels using EPA Metals Methods. EPA 821-R-95-034, April 1995
-	Guidance on the documentation and evaluation of trace metals data collected for clean water act compliance monitoring EPA 821-B-95-002, April 1995

I.   Mercury by cold vapor (SM$_{18}$ 3500-Hg B; EPA 245.1 and 7470)

An ongoing concern in mercury analysis has concentrated on the collection and preservation of samples[61]. Unpreserved or acid-preserved samples must be collected in borosilicate glass containers with Teflon® liners to prevent loss of mercury through disproportionation and volatilization. Samples preserved with 5.0% HNO_3 and 0.05% $K_2Cr_2O_7$ were stable for up to 6 months in glass or 30 days in polyethylene containers. Polypropylene containers were found to be totally unsuitable unless preservation also included HCl to form the stable, soluble $HgCl_4^{-2}$.

The addition of the H_2SO_4, HNO_3, and $KMnO_4$ serve to oxidize the mercury and organomercurials to inorganic Hg(II). The oxidation is insured to go to completion through the further addition of the K_2SO_5. The addition of the NaCl-hydroxylamine reduces the excess permanganate without reducing the mercury and transforms the oxidized mercury to the insoluble (and non-volatile) $HgCl_2$. Final addition of the $SnSO_4$

---

[61] Hamlin, S.N. "Preservation of Samples for Dissolved Mercury." *Water Resources Bulletin.* 1989. 25(2). pp. 255-262.

(or $SnCl_2$) solution reduces the mercury to the volatile elemental state and allows it to be swept through the AA analysis cell.

$$\text{"Hg"} \;-\; \text{oxidized} \longrightarrow Hg^{+2}$$

$$Hg^{+2} + Sn^{+2} \longrightarrow Hg^0 + Sn^{+4}$$

Once in the cell the mercury can be determined by either atomic absorption or by the more sensitive atomic fluorescence technique (EPA Methods 1631 and 245.7), either determination improved by the gold foil amalgamation procedure. This is simply allowing the mercury atoms coming off the sample to be initially collected on a gold surface as an amalgam, then thermally desorbing the mercury into the detector. The effect of this is to turn a diffuse mercury signal that passes through the detector over a period of up to 30 seconds or more into a very tightly compressed band of mercury with a detector transit time of less than 5 seconds. This effect is analogous to the increased signal-to-noise response and resulting sensitivity improvement seen when an analyst changes from packed column to capillary column in GC and GC-MS organics analysis. Successful use of the fluorescence instrument at the low ppt levels requires strict attention to sample preparation and reduction of laboratory contamination. As a number of common laboratory procedures, for example COD, use mercury compounds as reagents, and a broken mercury thermometer can make a permanent contribution to the ambient mercury background, the attention to laboratory contamination may extend to sample preparation in positive pressure glove boxes or isolated clean rooms.

J. Residual Chlorine (SM$_{18}$ 4500-Cl; EPA 330)

Chlorination is used to disinfect drinking water and remove some organic and nitrogen contaminants. The reaction of chlorine with certain organics leads to additional pollution problems such as chlorinated phenols and trihalomethanes. Trihalomethane (THM) potential (EPA method 510.1, Reference 27) uses 3,5-dihydroxybenzoic acid reacted with excess hypochlorite as the standard precursor for THMs in the method calibration. These reactions are illustrated in Figure 2-23. One of the most potent direct-acting mutagens ever evaluated in Ames Tester Strain TA100, 3-chloro-4[dichloromethyl]-5-hydroxy-2(5H)-furanone (MX for short) is produced in water from the action of chlorine on 3,5-dihydroxybenzaldehyde, a lignin derivative[62]. Chloroform is a side product of the reaction (Figure 2-24).

---

[62] Kronberg, L., and R. Franzen. "Determination of Chlorinated Furanones, Hydroxyfuranones and Butenedioic Acids in Chlorine-Treated Water and in Pulp Bleaching Liquor." *Environmental Sci. Technol.* 27(9). 1993. pp. 1811-1818.

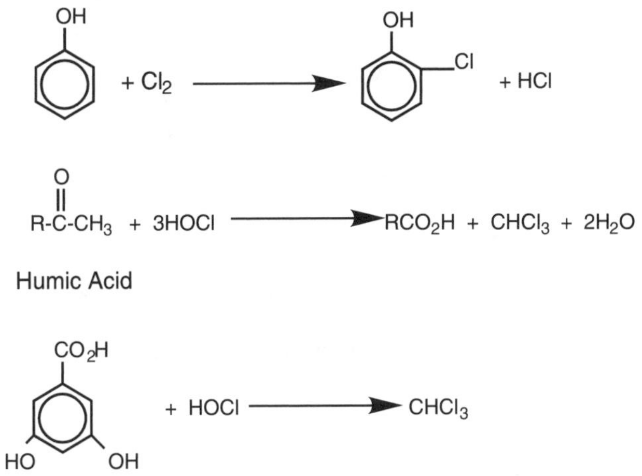

Figure 2-23. Reactions of organic materials with chlorine to produce pollutants.

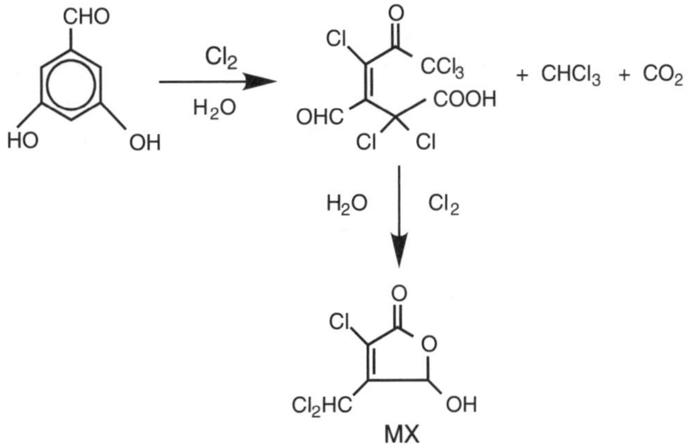

Figure 2-24. Production of MX by reaction of chlorine with 3,5-dihydroxybenzaldehyde.

Chemical preservation of samples often requires removal of residual chlorine to eliminate destruction of target analytes through the above types of reactions. The most common agents used for removal of residual chlorine are sodium thiosulfate, sodium sulfite and ascorbic acid. The reaction of thiosulfate with chlorine is described below and is limited to a 2:1 molar ratio, although in the presence of acid a 1:1 neutralization reaction can occur. Ascorbic acid on the other hand has a 1:1 stoichiometric initial reversible reaction with chlorine to form dehydroascorbic acid. In the presence of additional oxidant the dehydroascorbic acid irreversibly ring opens to 2,3-diketogulonic acid, which consumes further multiple equivalents of oxidant to result in a variety of five or less carbon products[63].

---

63 Deutsch, J.C, C.R. Santhosh-Kumar, K.L. Hassell, and J.F. Kolhouse. "Variation in Ascorbic Acid Oxidation Routes in H_2O_2 and Cupric Ion Solution as Determined by GC/MS." *Anal. Chem.* 66(3). 1994. pp. 345-350.

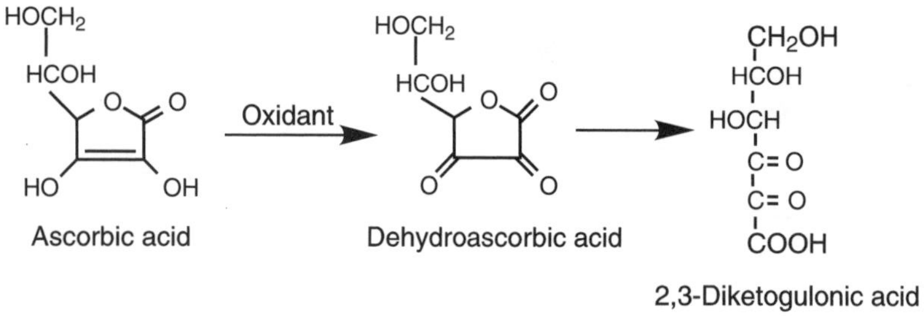

Figure 2-25. Neutralization of residual chlorine with ascorbic acid.

1. Breakpoint Chlorination

In addition to the reactions with organic chemicals and organic matter such as bacteria, algae, and viruses, chlorine is used to remove ammonia from water. The reactions of chlorine with ammonia are illustrated in Figure 2-26. Some of the intermediate compounds formed in this series are potent biocides, but not as effective as chlorine or hypochlorous acid. Mono-chloramine is an example. In many tests for residual chlorine, the mono- and di-chloramines react as if they were chlorine and contribute to the observed result. In the presence of ammonia, added chlorine reacts with it to form mono-chloramine, which tests as chlorine. When all the ammonia has been converted to mono-chloramine, the observed test results hit a maximum. Further addition of chlorine forms di-chloramine, which reacts with mono-chloramine to form nitrogen and the observed residual decreases. When all of the ammonia has been oxidized to nitrogen, the residual chlorine test hits a minimum, and with addition of more chlorine, HOCl begins to accumulate, and the breakpoint is passed.

$$Cl_2 + H_2O \longrightarrow HOCl + HCl$$

$$HOCl + NH_3 \longrightarrow NH_2Cl + H_2O$$

$$NH_2Cl + HOCl \longrightarrow NHCl_2 + H_2O$$

$$NHCl_2 + NH_2Cl \longrightarrow N_2 + 3HCl$$

Figure 2-26. Reactions of chlorine with ammonia.

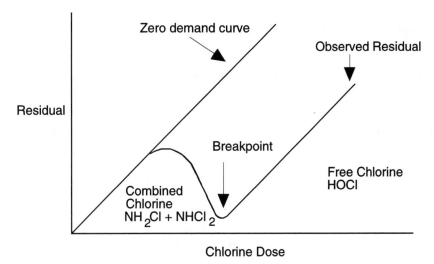

Figure 2-27. Breakpoint chlorination curve.

2. Determination of Residuals

Virtually all methods will have interference from ClO_2, molecular and HOX forms of bromine and iodine, permanganate, H_2O_2 and ozone. As mentioned above, mono-, di- and tri-chloramines will also contribute to the observed results in several of the procedures[64]. NO_2^- interferes in some test procedures, particularly iodine-based methods, through both direct oxidation of iodide to iodine and in-direct involvement of dissolved oxygen in the sample in the oxidation of iodide[65].

$$2NO_2^- + 2I^- + 4H^+ \longrightarrow 2NO + I_2 + 2H_2O$$

$$O_2 + 2NO \longrightarrow 2NO_2$$

$$4H^+ + 4I^- + 2NO_2 \longrightarrow 2I_2 + 2H_2O + 2NO$$

Nitrite interference is commonly countered by the addition of sulfamic acid and phosphoric acid. However, if thiosulfate is present, competing reactions are set up with the thiosulfate winning.

$$NH_2SO_3H + HNO_2 \longrightarrow H_2SO_4 + N_2 + H_2O$$

$$2S_2O_3^{2-} + 2HNO_2 + 2H^+ \longrightarrow S_4O_6^{2-} + 2NO + 2H_2O$$

Iodometric direct (Iodometric titrations) - Potassium iodide reacts with chlorine and other oxidizers to form iodine, which is titrated with thiosulfate in the presence of a starch indicator.

---

[64] Derrigan, J., L.Y. Lin and J.N. Jensen. "Comparison of Free and Total Chlorine Measurement Methods in Municipal Wastewaters." *Water Environment Reasearch*. 1993. 65(3). pp. 205-212.

[65] Dietz, E.A. Jr., R. Cortellucci, and M. Williams. "A Study of Analysis Errors Caused by Nitrite and Free Available Chlorine During Iodometric Titration of Total Residual Chlorine in Wastewater." *Water Environ. Res.* 1996. 68(6). pp. 974-980.

$$Cl_2 + 2KI \longrightarrow I_2 + 2KCl$$

$$I_2 + 2Na_2S_2O_3 \longrightarrow 2NaI + Na_2S_4O_6 \ (1:2 \ \text{titration})$$

Iodometric indirect (Iodimetric titrations) - A known amount of thiosulfate or phenylarsine oxide is added to the sample, then the excess, which is not required for reaction with chlorine or other oxidizing agents, is determined by titration with an iodine solution.

$$Cl_2 + PhAsO \longrightarrow 2Cl^- + PhAsO(OH)_2 \quad \text{or}$$

$$Cl_2 + 2S_2O_3^{2-} \longrightarrow 2Cl^- + S_4O_6^{2-}$$

Excess PhAsO or $S_2O_3^{2-}$ is titrated with standard I_3^- or IO_3^- and starch indicator. The technique is particularly prone to interferences from nitrite present in the sample and also to the exact form of residual chlorine. Thiosulfate tends to give much lower values than PAO due to some over-oxidation of the thiosulfate to sulfate[66] by free chlorine. This can be counteracted by addition of dimethylamine to the sample prior to thiosulfate reagent addition.

$$S_2O_3^{2-} + 4Cl_2 + 5H_2O \longrightarrow 2SO_4^{2-} + 8Cl^- + 8H^+$$

3. Iodine and thiosulfate solutions

Molecular iodine is not soluble in water to any appreciable degree. To obtain iodine in solution for titrations, the iodine is reacted with excess iodide ion to form the triiodide ion (I_3^-), which is very soluble and reacts as if it were molecular iodine. A handy source of iodine is from potassium biiodate, $KH(IO_3)_2$, which is a primary standard. Iodine forms in the presence of acid.

$$KH(IO_3)_2 + 10KI + 11H^+ \longrightarrow 6I_2 + 6H_2O + 11K^+$$

Excess KI reacts with the formed I_2 to form I_3^- (triiodide ion), which titrates as if it were I_2. The potassium biiodate is used as a primary reference to form a known amount of I_2 for standardization of the thiosulfate. Thiosulfate solutions are not stable when first made. The titer seems to rise over a period of two to three days, then drop, then stabilize after two or more weeks. The reason behind this behavior is the instability of thiosulfuric acid, which forms from any acid in the water used to make the solution or from absorption of atmospheric carbon dioxide. The thiosulfurous acid decomposes to form sulfur and sulfurous acid, which reacts with iodine in a 1:1 titration instead of the 2:1 reaction of thiosulfate and the titer appears to rise. The sulfurous acid slowly reacts with dissolved oxygen to form sulfuric acid, which is inactive in the iodine titration, and the titer drops. The sulfuric acid transfers the protons to a thiosulfate ion, forming the weaker acid. The cycle continues until all the dissolved oxygen is consumed at which point the titer stabilizes, or until someone opens and shakes the bottle.

---

[66] Dietz, E.A. Jr., R. Cortellucci, and M. Williams. "A Study of Analysis Errors Caused by Nitrite and Free Available Chlorine During Iodometric Titration of Total Residual Chlorine in Wastewater." *Water Environ. Res.* 1996. 68(6). pp. 974-980.

$$S_2O_3^{2-} + 2H^+ \longrightarrow H_2S_2O_3$$

$$H_2S_2O_3 \longrightarrow H_2SO_3 + S$$

$$I_2 + H_2SO_3 + H_2O \longrightarrow 2HI + H_2SO_4 \quad \text{(1:1 titration)}$$

$$2H_2SO_3 + O_2 \longrightarrow H_2SO_4 \qquad \text{(inactive in I}_2\text{ titrations and titer drops)}$$

$$H_2SO_4 + S_2O_3^{2-} \longrightarrow H_2S_2O_3 + SO_4^{2-}$$

Figure 2-28. Chemistry of thiosulfate solutions.

Sodium thiosulfate solutions are also prone to developing bacterial and fungus growth. Sodium hydroxide is commonly used as an additive to the solutions to prevent growth and to neutralize any acid. Concentrated stock solutions of sodium thiosulfate are more stable toward growth and acid degradation; however, working solutions are very sensitive and need to be prepared and standardized daily.

4. Amperometric titration.

Two models are available. The single electrode model monitors a Pt electrode *vs.* a silver reference electrode. A small voltage is applied across the electrodes, and as long as an oxidizing agent (Cl_2) is present, a current flows through the cell. Phenylarsineoxide (PAO) titrant is added, and the current decreases, reaching zero when all the oxidizing agent is exhausted. A back titration is also possible by adding an excess of PAO then titrating the excess PAO with iodine until current appears. A dual electrode model is also available that operates on a steady state current flow principle: current is proportional to the concentration of oxidizing agent Cl_2.

$$\text{Cathode Rxn:}\quad Cl_2 + 2e^- \longrightarrow 2Cl^-$$

$$\text{Anode Rxn:}\qquad 2Cl^- \longrightarrow Cl_2 + 2e^-$$

PAO, in the absence of KI, reacts only with Cl_2 and HOCl at pH 7, thus reading only residual chlorine. Addition of 50 mg/L KI at pH 7 allows titration of monochloramine, and addition of 250 mg/L KI at pH 4 allows titration of dichloramine. Addition of larger amounts of KI and allowing the sample to sit for several minutes makes NCl_3 chlorine available for titration. Stepwise analysis of the differing Cl residuals is thus possible from assay of a single sample.

Amperometric titrators are available commercially and are the standard for analysis of chlorine residuals both free and combined.

5. DPD Ferrous Titrimetric

N,N-diethyl phenylenediamine (DPD) is oxidized with Cl_2 or HOCl or OCl^- (I_2 and other strong oxidants) to a stable red-colored radical cation called a Würster dye[67]. At pH 6.2 to 6.5 the reaction is rapid and reversible, with the red color titrated with the reducing agent ferrous ammonium sulfate, $Fe(NH_4)_2(SO_4)_2$ [FAS] to a sharp endpoint. Little interference from the combined chloramines is seen in the absence of iodide. Addition of

---

[67] Harp, D.L., "Measuring Trace Levels of Total Residual Chlorine in Wastewater." *Water Environment Laboratory Solutions*. 1994. January/February. pp. 4-5.

a small crystal of KI allows titration of monochloramine. Addition of more KI gives the dichloramine contribution, similar to the amperometric titration.

The buffer is a Na_2HPO_4/KH_2PO_4 system with EDTA added to remove heavy metal ion catalysis interference. Oxidized manganese will interfere with the determination and is accounted for by addition of thioacetamide to remove all chlorine contribution, then addition of DPD and titration as a blank.

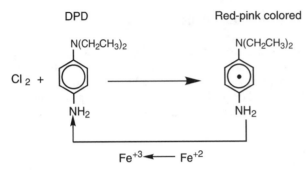

Figure 2-29. Chemistry of DPD-FAS chlorine determination.

6. DPD Colormetric

Addition of excess DPD with buffer gives a red color, the intensity of which is proportional to the concentration of Cl_2 or HOCl. The intensity is read on a spectrophotometer at 515 nm or compared visually to standards. There is good evidence that values of greater than 1 mg/L residual chlorine obtained from the DPD colorimetric procedure are in fact low estimates due to over oxidation of the DPD to a colorless anion[68]. The titration procedure is not affected by the overoxidation of DPD as FAS is capable of reducing the colorless anion back down to DPD.

7. Syringaldazine (FACTS)

Free residual chlorine (Cl_2 or HOCl) reacts 1:1 with 3,5-dimethoxy-4-hydroxy-benzaldazine (syringaldazine) at pH 6.5 to 6.8 to form a colored species with an absorption maximum at 530 nm. The colored product has limited solubility in water, and 2-propanol is used to keep it in solution. The only interferences in the method are I_2, Br_2 and O_3, and the combined chloramines are non-reactive. The method is known as the Free Available Chlorine Test, Syringaldazine (FACTS).

---

[68] Gordon, G., D.L. Sweetin, K. Smith and G.E. Pacey. "Improvements in the DPD Method for Determination of Free and Combined Residual Chlorine Through use of FIA." *Talanta.* 1991. 38(2). pp. 145-149.

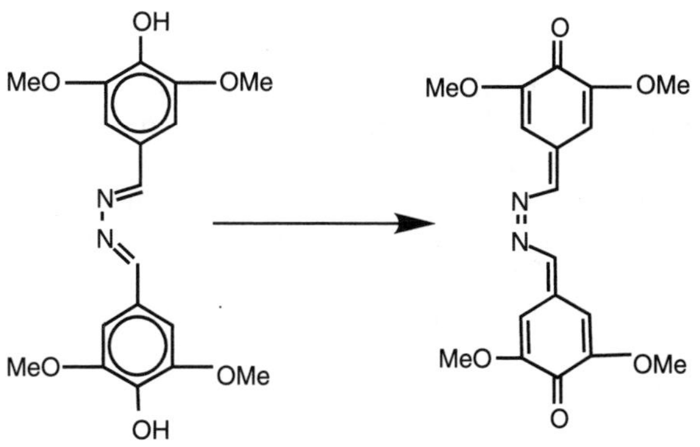

Figure 2-30. FACTS chemistry.

8. Orthotolidine

Not currently used due to the toxic nature of *o*-Tolidine, it offers quick reaction with residual chlorine species to form a colored product, which is read on a spectrophotometer.

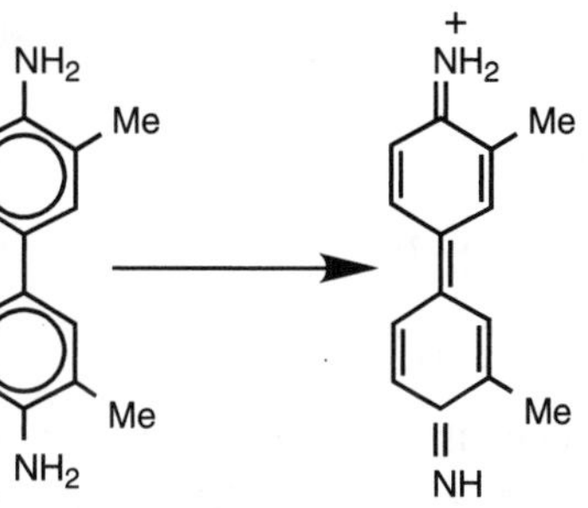

Figure 2-31. Orthotolidine reaction with chlorine.

9. Leuco Crystal Violet

Again, this is an out-dated method. LCV reacts instantly with free chlorine to develop a blue color and can be read spectroscopically within 5 minutes. Addition of I^-, reacts with the combined chlorine species to form I_2, which reacts with LCV to form Crystal Violet (Basic Violet 3), a violet color stable for days and read spectroscopically.

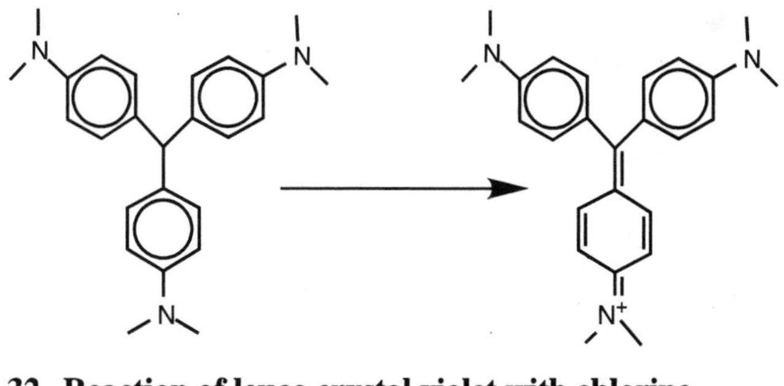

Figure 2-32. Reaction of leuco crystal violet with chlorine.

10. Methyl Orange

This is a method that in a comparison study, ranks very high in accuracy and precision for determination of chlorine free and combined residuals, yet has never caught on. Methyl Orange (Acid Orange 52, C.I. 13025, CAS 547-58-0) is decolorized instantly by free chlorine (or HOCl) on a 1:2 molar basis. The reaction is much slower with combined chlorine. The reaction can be used as a self-indicating titration method using 0.005% M.O. solution where 1.00 mL M.O. solution is equivalent to 21.9 mg Cl_2. The method can also be performed as a absorbance method with a spectrophotometer. M.O. is a primary standard, and solutions are stable for long periods of time, while maintaining their titer. The initial addition compound reacts further with Cl_2 to form nitrogen gas.

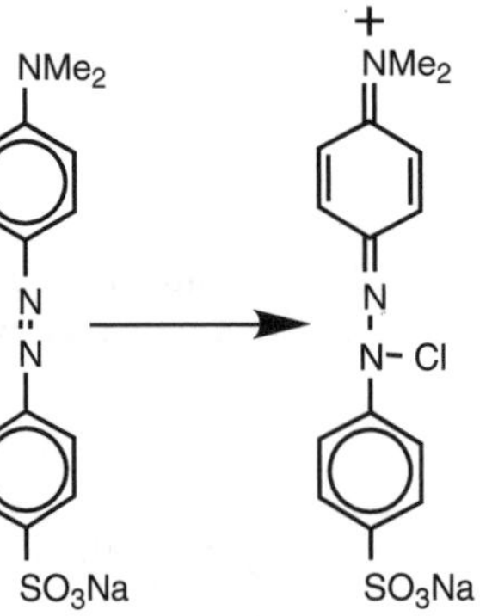

Figure 2-33. Methyl orange determination of residual chlorine.

11. Inorganic disinfection by-products

The three most common inorganic disinfection by-products of concern are chlorite (ClO_2^-), chlorate (ClO_3^-) and bromate (BrO_3^-). They titrate as total residual chlorine in some of the above test procedures and thus serve as interferences. They also are contaminates of concern of and by themselves in drinking water. A suitable test procedures that has been approved for use on drinking water samples is ion chromatography (EPA Method 300.0). Capillary ion electrophoresis has also been demonstrated as an effective analytical tool.

The inorganic disinfection by-products are not commonly created in the disinfection process. They are generally introduced to the water supply as co-contaminants of the disinfection chemicals, particularly the hypochlorite solutions, used to treat the water.

$$2NaClO_2 + Cl_2 \longrightarrow 2ClO_2 + 2NaCl$$
Production of chlorine dioxide

$$2ClO_2 + H_2O \longrightarrow 2H^+ + ClO_2^- + ClO_3^-$$
Disproportionation at pH >11

$$ClO_2 + e^- \longrightarrow ClO_2^-$$
Neutral pH partial reaction with thiosulfate or PAO

$$ClO_2 + 4H^+ + 4e^- \longrightarrow Cl^- + 2H_2O$$
$$4I^- \longrightarrow 2I_2 + 4e^-$$

At pH of 2 or lower pH adjustment allows selective determination by FAS-DPD titration[69].

K. Total organic carbon (TOC) (SM₁₈ 5310; EPA 415 and 9060)

Carbon fractions found in water are:

- Total Carbon (TC) - all forms of carbon, convert to CO_2 over heated cobalt oxide catalyst (900 °C), or persulfate -UV light oxidation to CO_2, determine CO_2 by infrared absorption or FID.
- Inorganic Carbon (IC) - carbonate, bicarbonate and dissolved CO_2, acidify and gas purge CO_2, determine by IR or FID.
- Total Organic Carbon (TOC) - covalently bonded carbon, determined as TC - IC.
- Dissolved Organic Carbon (DOC) - passes a 0.45 μm filter, assay as TC - IC.
- Nondissolved Organic Carbon (NDOC) - retained by 0.45 μm filter, assay as TC - IC.
- Purgeable Organic Carbon (POC) - fraction of TOC removed by gas stripping, determine as TC - IC - NPOC.
- Nonpurgeable Organic Carbon (NPOC) - residue after gas stripping, assay as TC.

In water IC is many times greater than TOC. IC is removed by acidifying the sample and then gas stripping to remove CO_2. This also results in a loss of POC. Carbon determinations after IC removal are actually NPOC values; however, POC is generally very small (negligible) in most samples, although this is not believed to be true when analyzing landfill leachates[70]. Pretreatment of the sample defines the fraction assayed.

All procedures call for the conversion of the carbon to CO_2 then determination of CO_2 by either gas chromatography (after reduction to methane and FID), nondispersive infrared spectrometry, or determination of conductance after dissolution in ultrapure water. As far as being an indicator of organic contamination, TOC is generally not very useful as a high background is normal due to the presence of large amounts of humic acids and fulvic acids. A further problem exists in interpretation of the results. Most regulated organic compounds (VOCs, pesticides, BNAs) and background organics have from 39-50% carbon, while petroleum hydrocarbons, oil, and grease exhibit above 75% carbon. TOC has been used as an alternative to BOD or COD characterization of wastewater; however, the relationship varies for every wastewater source. Assuming a relationship has been determined, TOC becomes a very rapid monitoring tool as an analysis is completed in minutes rather than hours or days.

L. Total Organic Halide (TOX) (SM₁₈ 5320; EPA 9020)

Four steps are used in the analysis. The sample is introduced as a water solution of known volume into an activated carbon column. Inorganic halides (Cl, Br, and I) are

---

[69] Adam, L.C. and G. Gordon. "Direct and Sequential Potentiometric Determination of Hypochlorite, Chlorite and Chlorate Ions when Hypochlorite Ion is Present in Large Excess." *Anal. Chem.* 1995. 67(3). pp. 535-540.

[70] Levine, A.D., and L.R. Kroemer. "TOC and TOX as Indicator Parameters for Organic Contaminants in Landfill Leachate." *Waste Management and Research.* 1989. 7. pp. 337-349.

removed by washing with a nitrate ion solution. The residual organic halogen compounds remaining on the column are pyrolyzed to HCl, HBr, and HI and detected with a microcoulometric titration cell. The titration cell consists of a constant concentration of silver ions in acetic acid solution maintained by a constant electric potential through a silver electrode. As the hydrogen halides dissolve in the acetic acid, solid silver halide precipitates, and the electric current rises to maintain the silver ion concentration. The applied current is integrated over the pyrolysis period and is proportional to the moles of halide on the column.

Method 9021 (SW-846) purges an aqueous sample with carbon dioxide into the pyrolysis chamber to determine the volatile total organic halide. A draft method (9023) for extractable organic halides (EOX) is currently under consideration for inclusion in SW-846. The organohalide compounds are desorbed from a solid sample by sonication in ethyl acetate, then an aliquot of the ethyl acetate solution is introduced into the pyrolysis oven.

M. Surfactants (SM$_{18}$ 5540; EPA 425)

Surfactants consist of three basic types: anionic (RSO_3^-Na), cationic ($RMe_3N^+Cl^-$), and nonionic ($R[OCH_2CH_2]_nOH$) where R is from 10 - 20 carbons long and "n" can range to the thousands. The charged end of the molecule imparts water solubility and the organic end non-polar solubility. The presence of the ether oxygens in the non-ionic surfactants allows chelation of cationic materials and promotes further solubilization. There are also surfactants that are mixed anionic/non-ionic materials, formed by attaching a sulfate ester to the terminal hydroxy group of the non-ionic molecule. Some surfactants are noted for the production of very tenacious foams, presenting major problems in waterways downstream from effluent points. Others are designed to produce no foam, while still performing the detergent function.

Sublation is a process that removes water from the surfactant and produces a dry form of the material for analysis. The technique consists of covering a sample of surfactant containing water with ethyl acetate (a polar organic solvent) and bubbling N_2 gas up through the sample. The surfactant forms a foam on contact with the N_2 in the water, then dissolves into the organic layer as the bubbles rise. Two changes of the organic layer are sufficient to remove most of the surfactants. Evaporation of the ethyl acetate leaves the surfactant as a dried residue. The equipment is illustrated in Appendix C.

Methylene blue active substances (MBAS) are anionic surfactant specific. Methylene blue is a cationic organic dye. In the presence of an acidified solution of an anionic surfactant, the resulting ion-pair is non-polar soluble and can be extracted into chloroform. The intensity of the methylene blue in the chloroform layer is proportional to the anionic surfactants present. Carboxylic soaps are not strong enough to be extracted with methylene blue, however the sulfonate (RSO_3^-), sulfate ester ($ROSO_3^-$), and sulfated non-ionics ($R[OCH_2CH_2]_nOSO_3^-$) are extracted. The absorption curve at 652 nm is calibrated by extracting known amounts of linear alkylbenzene sulfonate (LAS), which is assumed to have a molecular mass of 318 g/mol. Results are reported in units of mg MBAS/L (calculated as LAS). A useful innovation is the use of microextraction for preparation of the 10-point calibration curve[71].

---

[71] Craig, C. A., and O. L. Salvador. "Microextraction for Preparing Calibration Standards for Methylene Blue Active Substances (MBAS)." *American Environmental Laboratory*. Feb., 1992. pp. 42-44.

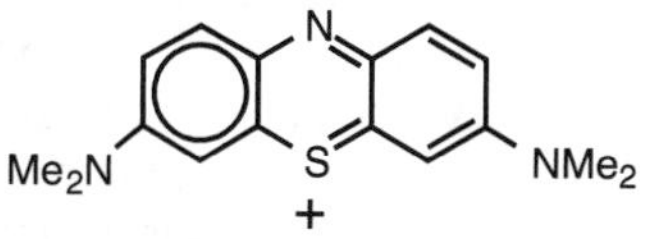

Figure 2-34. Structure of methylene blue.

Cobalt thiocyanate active substances (CTAS) are nonionic surfactants. Cationic and anionic surfactants are removed from the sublation residue by dissolution in MeOH and passage through a ion-exchange column containing both anionic and cationic resins. Solvent exchange to water is followed by treatment with cobalt thiocyanate and extraction with methylene chloride. Nonionic surfactants will coordinate to the cobalt and render it nonpolar soluble (the methylene chloride layer). Measurement of the absorbance of the methylene chloride cobalt solution at 620 nm is directly proportional to the molar amount of nonionic surfactant present. The method is calibrated by measuring the absorption of cobalt complexes of known amounts of a standard nonionic surfactant ($C_{12-18}[OCH_2CH_2]_{11}OH$).

There are many other techniques that can be used for surfactant analysis[72], some are substantial improvements over the MBAS and CTAS procedures. Bismuth iodide active substances (BIAS) uses Dragendorff reagent (barium tetraiodobismuthate) to form a precipitate with surfactants followed by potentiometric titration of the remaining bismuth in solution with pyrrolidine dithiocarbamate. The BIAS precipitate forms in a constant ratio of one barium to 9.8 ether oxygens and experimentally produces less variation than CTAS. The Potassium Picrate Active Substances (PPAS)[73] procedure was recently published. The sublatted residue is dissolved in ethylene dichloride, potassium picrate solution added then extracted into methylene chloride. The extract is read spectrophotometrically. The authors report a detection limit of 0.1 mg/L and fewer interferences than BIAS or CTAS. Surfactants can be qualitatively and semi-quantitatively determined by thin layer chromatography, TLC (Swisher, 1987). Gas chromatographic analytical techniques include derivatization as a trimethylsilane ester or acetate and fission with HBr (Cross, 1987). High pressure liquid chromatography, HPLC, is the most common instrumental technique[74,75]. The surfactants are reacted with phenyl isocyanate or one of a variety of acetylation reagents to form a HPLC compatible material. Detection is by UV, FID, or MS. A number of HPLC references for anionic and other surfactants are listed in *Anal. Chem.* 1992. 64(6). pp. 583-589.

---

[72] Talmage, S.S. *Environmental and Human Safety of Major Surfactants*, Lewis Publishers, Boca Raton, FL. 1994. ISBN 1-56670-017-5; Swisher, R.D., *Surfactant Biodegradation*, 2nd Ed, 1987. Marcel Dekker, NY; Cross, J. *Nonionic Surfactants: Chemical Analysis*. 1987. Marcel Dekker, NY; Midwidsky, B, and D.M. Gabriel. *Detergent Analysis*. 1982. Halstead Press, NY.

[73] Favretto, L., B. Stancher, and F. Tunis. "An Improved Method for the Spectrophotometric Determination of Polyoxyethylene Non-Ionic Surfactants in Waters as Potassium Picrate Active Substances." *Intl. J. Environ. Anal. Chem.* 1983. 14. pp. 201-214.

[74] Schmitt, T.M., M.C. Allen, D.K. Brain, K.F. Guin, D.E. Lemmel and Q.W. Osburn. "HPLC Determination of Ethoxylated Alcohol Surfactants in Wastewater." *J. Am. Oil Chem. Soc.* 1990. 67. pp. 103-109.

[75] Kiewiet, A.T., J.M.D. van der Steen, and J.R. Parsons. "Trace Analysis of Ethoxylated Nonionic Surfactants in Samples of Influent and Effluent of Sewage Treatment Plants by HPLC." *Anal. Chem.* 1995. 67(23). pp. 4409-4415.

Capillary electrophoresis has been examined for analysis and characterization of surfactants. Anionic sulfate and sulfonate surfactants have been determined using an naphthalenesulfonate electrolyte[76]. An alternate recipe uses a non-aqueous electrolyte[77].

Branched nonylphenol (CAS 84852-15-3) is the most common toxic degradation product of alkylphenol ethoxylates (APE), a sub-class of the non-ionic surfactants. Nonylphenol has been implicated as a significant endocrine disruptor in the environment. Analyses of APE precursors to nonylphenols are discussed above. One technique reacts the isolated surfactant to form a bromide followed by analysis by GC-MS[78]. Another technique uses acetylation with acetic anhydride (SFE extraction and acetylation for sludge and solid samples), liquid-liquid extraction and determination of the acetate by GC-MS in the SIM mode. Detection limits were estimated as 0.1 μg/L for aqueous samples and 0.1 mg/kg for solid matrices[79].

EDTA, ethylene diamine tetraacetic acid, is a small molecule chelation agent for cations and one member of a class of chelation agents. The structure is shown in Figure 2-15, in conjunction with its use as a reagent in the hardness titration. Another chelation reagent is DTPA, diethylenetriamine pentaacetic acid. These types of materials exhibit human toxicity and are becoming of interest as pollutants. Analysis has been performed by HPLC[80]. Other chelation agents include the polyphosphonates, which bear the Dequest[81] trademark. Some of these materials are illustrated in Table 2-29. Capillary electrophoresis has been used for analysis[82].

Table 2-29. Commonly encountered chelation agents

Name	Initials	Structure
Ethylenediamine tetraacetic acid	EDTA	$(HO_2CCH_2)_2NCH_2CH_2N(CH_2CO_2H)_2$
Diethylenetriamine pentaacetic acid	DTPA	$(HO_2CCH_2)_2N(CH_2)_2NH(CH_2)_2N(CH_2CO_2H)_2$
Nitrilo triacetic acid	NTA	$N(CH_2CO_2H)_3$
Dequest[83] 2010	HEPD	$CH_3CH(PO_3H_2)_2$
Dequest 2006	ATMP	$N(CH_2PO_3H_2)_3$
Dequest 2041	EDTMP	$(H_2O_3PCH_2)_2NCH_2CH_2N(CH_2PO_3H_2)_2$
Dequest 2060	DETPMP	$H_2O_3PCH_2N[CH_2CH_2N(CH_2PO_3H_2)_2]_2$
Triethanolamine		$N(CH_2CH_2OH)_3$

[76] Shamsi, S.A. and N.D. Danielson. "Naphthalenesulfonates as Electrolytes for Capillary Electrophoresis of Inorganic Anions, Organic Acids and Surfactants with Indirect Photometric Detection." *Anal. Chem.* 1994. 66(21). pp. 3757-3764.

[77] Salimi-Moosavi, H., and R.M. Cassidy. "Application of Nonaqueous Capillary Electrophoresis to the Separation of Long-Chain Surfactants." *Anal. Chem.* 1996. 68(2). pp. 293-299.

[78] Fendinger, N.J., D.C. McAvoy, W.M. Begley and W.S. Eckhoff. "Measurement of Alkyl Ethoxylate Surfactants in Natural Waters." *Environ. Sci. Tech.* 1995. 29(4). pp. 856-863.

[79] Lee, H.-B., and T.E. Peart. "Determination of 4-Nonylphenol in Effluent and Sludge From Sewage Treatment Plants." *Anal. Chem.* 1995. 67(13). pp. 1976-1980.

[80] Nowack, B., F.G. Kari, S.U. Hilger and L. Sigg. "Determination of Dissolved and Adsorbed EDTA Species in Water and Sediments by HPLC." *Anal. Chem.* 1996. 68(3). pp. 561-566.

[81] Monsanto Co., St. Louis, MO.

[82] Shamsi, S.A. and N.D. Danielson. "Ribonucleotide Electrolytes for Capillary Electrophoresis of Polyphosphates and Polyphosphonates with Indirect Photometric Detection." *Anal. Chem.* 1995. 67(11). pp. 1845-1852.

[83] Trademark of Monsanto Company, St. Louis, MO

N. Oil & Grease (SM$_{18}$ 5520; EPA 413; EPA 1664)

What is assayed in an oil-and-grease determination depends to a large extent on how the measurement is made. The gravimetric methods depend on solubility in 1,1,2-trichloro-trifluoroethane (Freon 113), and a lack of volatility when the sample is evaporated. The total petroleum hydrocarbon (TPH) method measures only material with C-H bonds that are soluble in Freon 113. Various classes of materials that are measured as oil & grease include fatty acids, esters and amides, animal and plant waxes, triglycerides, phosphono-lipids, chlorophylls and other synthetic and natural dyes and pigments, essential oil components, surfactants, and a range of petroleum hydrocarbon derived products.

With the gravimetric method, the sample is extracted with Freon 113, and water is removed by passage through anhydrous Na_2SO_4, and evaporated to dryness. The material is then measured by weight. A modification of the method using a Soxhlet extractor allows processing of soils and sludges (EPA Method 9071B, Update IIIA, SW-846, April, 1998). Anhydrous $MgSO_4$ is used for drying the sludge prior to soxhlet extraction.

For the total petroleum hydrocarbons method, the sample is extracted with Freon 113, dried by passage through anhydrous Na_2SO_4, passed through a column of silica gel to remove non-hydrocarbons, and the absorbance measured from 3200 cm^{-1} to 2700 cm^{-1} on an infrared spectrophotometer *vs.* a solvent blank. Freon 113 is used because it has no IR absorbance in the analytical range. A reference oil containing iso-octane, hexadecane and chlorobenzene (37.5 : 37.5 : 25) is used to prepare a calibration curve. Omission of the silica gel column gives the "Partition - Infrared" method for determination of oil and grease. Other possibilities include the development by Buck Scientific of a quartz IR cell that uses no solvent in the IR analysis of TPH[84].

During the Summer of 1994, EPA announced draft method 1664 for oil & grease (hexane extractable material - HEM) and total petroleum hydrocarbon (silica gel treated hexane extractable material - SGT-HEM) analysis, then revised as a draft method in 1995 and 1996. The Freon 113 has been replaced by hexane, however a separatory funnel extraction remains the basis of the procedure. The method is written in a performance based modification fashion, and several possible alternates are mentioned. These consist of a continuous liquid-liquid extraction or solid phase column/disk for isolation of the target analytes, followed by elution with a suitable organic solvent. Several determinative methods are specifically excluded as allowable performance based modifications of Method 1664. Excluded are use of IR or immunoassay for determination of the residue. Method 1664 includes very strict quality control and method performance criteria as measuring sticks for what is an allowable modification and what is not. These QC include initial and continuing demonstrations of ability (IPR - Initial Precision and Recovery, and OPR - Ongoing Precision and Recovery), matrix spike, matrix spike duplicate, and blank analysis every 20 samples. The method includes specified acceptance ranges for MS/MSD and method detection/reporting limit. Method 1664 was promulgated on 14 May, 1999 in the Federal Register (Vol 64, Num 93 pp 26315-26327).

---

[84] DeMenna, G. "Determination of Oil and Grease by Evaporation of Solvent in a Quartz Cell in An Infrared Spectrophotometer." In *Oil and Grease Workshop*, EPA-821-R-93-014, Sept., 1993, p. 7 and Appendix G. As part of 16th Annual EPA Analytical Conference, May 4-6, 1993. Norfolk, Va.

See Sections 3 and 4 for further information on petroleum hydrocarbon classification and analysis.

O. Total phenols (SM$_{18}$ 5530; EPA 420)

Phenols are important industrial pollutants from a wide range of manufacturing processes. Wood, after hydrolysis, is a major source of phenols. Phenols are important because they are in themselves harmful, and during water chlorination are easily transformed into chlorophenols and then further transformed into dioxins. Phenols are organic acids and are quite soluble in mildly alkaline water. The parent compound, phenol, was the first disinfectant used in surgery by Lister (1885). Many different phenols are used in disinfectants for industrial use, in hospitals and in food preparation facilities. Phenols are often absorbed through the skin, and are active CNS agents as well as general protoplasmic poisons.

Phenols can be purified (interferences removed) by extraction of a basic solution with an organic solvent such as methylene chloride or chloroform, then acidification of the water layer and steam distillation of the phenols. Phenols are detected by reaction with 4-aminoantipyrine (4-AAP) in the presence of potassium ferricyanide, $K_3Fe(CN)_6$ to give a colored antipyrine dye that is measured spectrophotometricly. The absorbance can be read directly at 500 nm in the water solution, or extracted into chloroform and read at 460 nm for increased sensitivity. A drawback to this method is that para-substituted phenols are unreactive and not measured. Further, some types of phenol, such as the nitrophenols, are deactivated toward reaction due to the ring electronics.

Phenols can be individually detected and assayed by GC, as discussed in Section 3. Some of the phenols are listed as hazardous wastes.

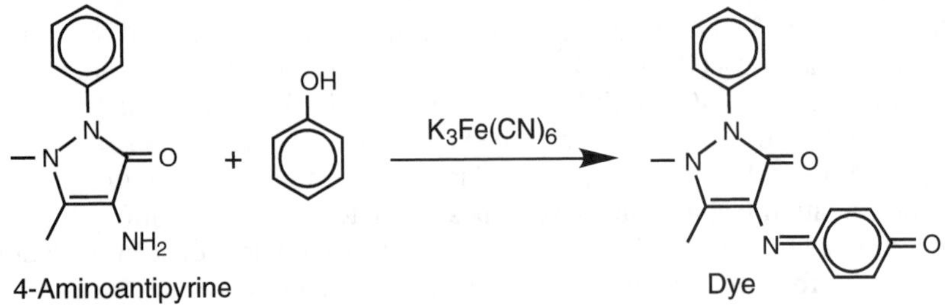

Figure 2-35. 4-AAP reaction for analysis of total phenols.

The preparation of standards for total phenols analysis is somewhat of a problem. Phenol itself is extremely hydroscopic with even samples that do not appear to be wet containing 8 to 10% water. After the standard is prepared according to the method (either *Standard Methods* or EPA 420.1) the concentration must be verified. *Standard Methods* offers a procedure based on the bromination of phenol. Bromate ion reacts with bromide to form free bromine. In the presence of acid and phenol, tribromophenol is formed, which precipitates. The original amount of bromate in the reaction solution is determined by titration of a portion of the mixed bromate/bromide reagent with iodine and sodium thiosulfate. The remaining bromate after the reaction has gone to completion is determined by titration and the consumed bromate determined by the difference. There is a 1:1 relation between the amount of bromate consumed and the phenol initially present in the standard.

$$BrO_3^- + 5Br^- + 6H^+ \longrightarrow 3Br_2 + 3H_2O$$

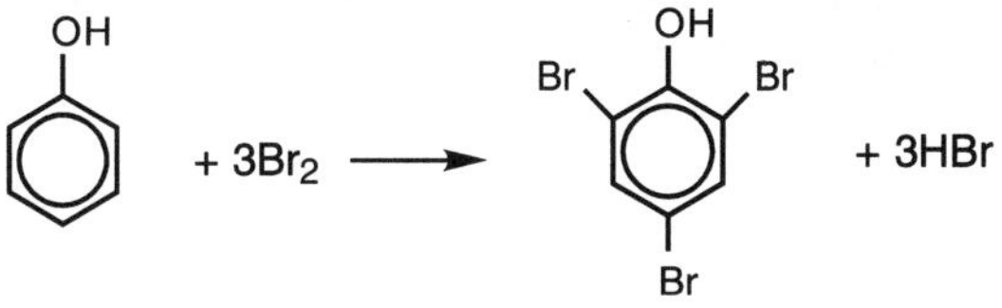

$$Br_2 + 2I^- \longrightarrow 2Br^- + I_2$$

$$I_2 + 2Na_2S_2O_3 \longrightarrow 2I^- + 2Na^+ + Na_2S_4O_6$$

Figure 2-36. Standardization of phenol solutions

P. Cyanide (SM$_{18}$ 4500-CN; EPA 335 and 9010/9014)

Cyanide salts and the molecular HCN are all highly poisonous, with a fatal dose for humans on the order of 50-60 mg. HCN was used during WWII for the mass extermi-nations in Nazi Death Camps. Fish are even more sensitive to cyanide and concentra-tions as low as 0.02 mg/L are fatal, whereas humans can tolerate 0.20 mg/L in drinking water. Cyanide reacts with ferricytochrome oxidase to keep the Fe^{+3} active center from being reduced to Fe^{+2}, which is required as a first step in O_2 utilization in cell mitochondria. Cyanide is one of the two compounds listed under Characteristic of Reactivity in Hazardous Material Characterization 40 CFR, 261.23. The other is sulfide.

HCN is more toxic than CN$^-$, and the pH of most waters are less than the pK_a of HCN, thus most of the free cyanide exists in the form of HCN. The situation is different when considering metal complexes of cyanide such as $Fe(CN)_6^{4-}$ and $Fe(CN)_6^{3-}$, which are very common forms of cyanide encountered, as most wastewater will contain some dissolved iron. The dissociation of these complexes is close to zero, and the toxic hazards are much less. Other complexes such as $Hg(CN)_2$, $Zn(CN)_4^{2-}$, $Ag(CN)_2^-$, $Cu(CN)_4^{3-}$ and $Ni(CN)_4^{2-}$ are not dissociated to any large degree in environmental samples, but are still toxic as the complex. Further, even complexes such as the relatively stable $Fe(CN)_6^{3-}$ are labile in the presence of ultraviolet radiation, such as direct sunlight, in dilute solutions.

In evaluating the health risks and thus the availability of cyanide in samples, it becomes necessary to distinguish between bound and free cyanide. Analysts use the recovery of cyanide from acidified samples as a measure of availability. The Weak Acid Dissociation (WAD) cyanide procedure, where the sample is acidified to pH 4.5 and the cyanide removed by distillation, will recover all forms of bound cyanide except mercury and iron complexes. The use of complexing ligands has also been evaluated for dis-placement of cyanide[85]. Ligands explored were EDTA (ethylenediamine tetraacetic acid), EGTA (ethylene bis[oxyethylenenitrilo]tetraacetic acid), CDTA (1,2-diaminocy-clohexane tetraacetic acid), dithizone (diphenylthiocarbazone), TEP (tetraethylene-pentaamine), and Tiron (4,5-dihydroxy-1,3-benzene disulfonic acid disodium salt). The

---

[85] Sebroski, J.R., and R.H. Ode. "Method Comparison and Evaluation for the Analysis of Weak Acid-Dissociable Cyanide." *Environ. Sci. Technol.* 1997. 31(1). pp. 52-57.

TEP/dithizone combination was found to be effective for all WAD complexes including $Hg(CN)_2$.

Typical removal of cyanide from wastewater consists of alkaline chlorination, which proceeds through several steps to innocuous products. The first step in the process is formation of cyanogen chloride.

$$NaCN + Cl_2 \longrightarrow CNCl + NaCl$$

$$CNCl + 2NaOH \longrightarrow NaCNO + NaCl + H_2O$$

$$2NaCNO + 4NaOH + 3Cl_2 \longrightarrow 6NaCl + 2CO_2 + N_2 + 2H_2O$$

or $\quad 2NaCNO + 6NaOH + 3Cl_2 \longrightarrow 2NaHCO_3 + 6NaCl + N_2 + 2H_2O$

Figure 2-37. Chlorination chemistry of cyanide.

Cyanogen chloride (CNCl) is at least as toxic a gas as HCN, and of limited solubility in water. The decomposition of CNCl to cyanate ion (much less toxic) is slow at pH < 9 in the absence of excess Cl_2. CNO^- (cyanate ion) is about 1000 times less toxic than cyanide. The removal of cyanide ion by alkaline chlorination from metal complexes such as cobalt, nickel, silver, and copper is slow at best. Intractable complexes such as $Fe(CN)_6^{-3}$ are essentially non-reactive. These complexes can be destroyed through electrolysis. The process is illustrated for removal of cyanide from a copper plating bath.

Anode

$$Cu(CN)_3^{2-} + 6OH^- \longrightarrow Cu^{2+} + 3CNO^- + 3H_2O + 7e^-$$

$$CN^- + 2OH^- \longrightarrow CNO^- + H_2O + 2e^-$$

$$CNO^- + 4H_2O \longrightarrow 2CO_2 + N_2 + 2H_2O + 6e^-$$

Cathode

$$Cu^+ + e^- \longrightarrow Cu$$

Figure 2-38. Electrolytic decomposition of cyanide.

It thus becomes of interest to distinguish between Total Cyanide and Cyanide Amenable to Chlorination.

1. Total cyanide

A sample is strongly acidified with H_2SO_4 and sweep distilled with N_2 into a NaOH solution-filled bubbler trap. The total cyanide in the trap is measured by four methods.

1) Titration with $AgNO_3$ to form the soluble complex $Ag(CN)_2^-$. The end of the titration is signaled with the silver-sensitive indicator, p-dimethylamino-benzalrhodanine, which turns from yellow in the absence of silver to salmon color in the presence of uncomplexed silver.

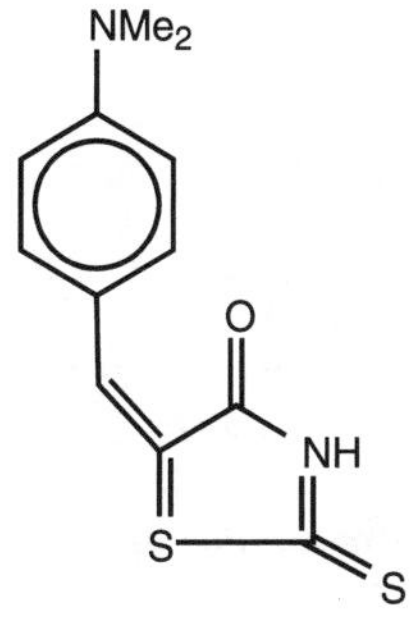

Figure 2-39. Structure of dimethylaminobenzalrhodanine.

2) Reaction with Chloramine-T to form CNCl, followed by reaction with pyridine-barbituric acid reagent to form a deep red-blue dye, the intensity of which is measured on a spectrophotometer at 578 nm.

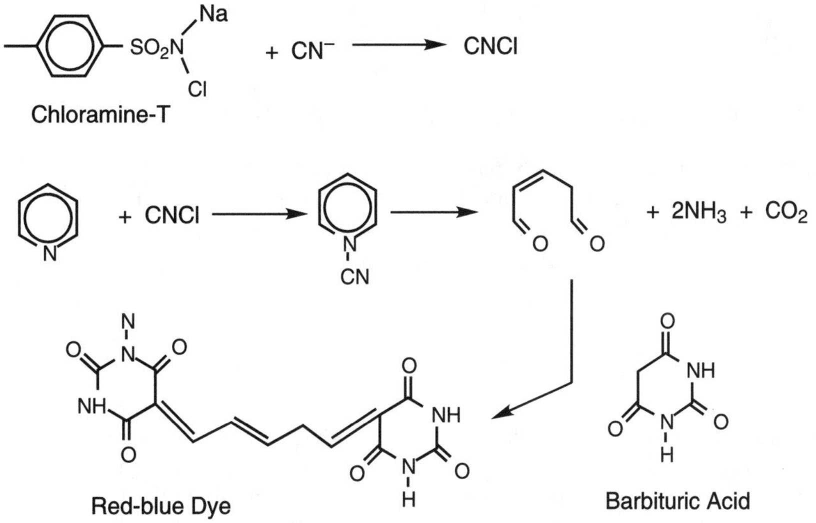

Figure 2-40. Chemistry of pyridine-barbituric acid cyanide determination.

3) Reaction with chlorine to form CNCl, followed by reaction with pyridine and pyralozone to form a blue-colored species that is measured spectrophotometricly at 612 nm.

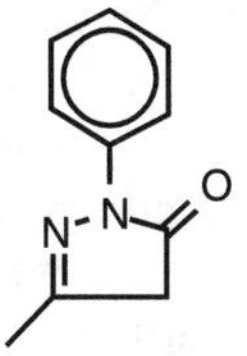

Figure 2-41. Structure of pyralozone used in colorimetric cyanide determination.

4) Use of CN⁻ selective electrode to determine concentration is very rapid but subject to interferences that are removed by the distillation step above. The cyanide sensing membrane will dissolve at cyanide concentrations above 10 mg/L.

For cyanides amenable to chlorination both direct and indirect methods are used:

- The direct method is basically the same as the second method above under Total Cyanide, except the initial distillation step is skipped. Many interferences exist in this procedure with the notable inclusion of thiocyanate, which assays as cyanide. A separate SCN⁻ determination is made, and the result subtracted from the apparent CN⁻ result.

- The indirect method involves addition of $Ca(OCl)_2$ to the basic solution until a drop tests blue when applied to a KI-starch test paper, indicating excess chlorine present. Sodium thiosulfate is then added until the solution tests colorless with KI-starch paper. The sample is then strongly acidified and sweep distilled into a NaOH solution. The trap contents are assayed for CN⁻ by any of the methods under Total Cyanide. The value obtained is the cyanide NOT amenable to chlorination. A concurrent sample is run for Total Cyanide. The difference between the two values is the Cyanide Amenable to Chlorination.

Q. Sulfide (SM$_{18}$ 4500-S^{2-}; EPA 376 and 9030/9034)

Sulfide (S^{2-}), is one of the species of sulfur that occur in environmental samples. Sulfide is the most reduced form of sulfur, capable of being oxidized to elemental sulfur (S_8) and then on to sulfite and finally sulfate. Corresponding organic forms of sulfur can also exist in a number of oxidation states and bonding schemes.

$$S^{2-} \;\overset{2e^-}{\longleftrightarrow}\; S° \;\overset{4e^-}{\longleftrightarrow}\; SO_3^{2-} \;\overset{2e^-}{\longleftrightarrow}\; SO_4^{2-}$$

sulfide   sulfur   sulfite (S^{4+})   sulfate (S^{6+})

Sulfate and sulfite analyses are discussed in Section 5.

Sulfide, such as sodium sulfide, is a fairly strong base that can be converted to the volatile weak acid H_2S. In a waste, acid convertable sulfide, along with cyanide, are the hazardous chemicals under the Characteristic of Reactivity. H_2S is more toxic than HCN, with a level of 1000 ppm in air resulting in very rapid human death. H_2S affects the CNS, and death results from respiratory system paralysis. The gas occurs naturally in decomposition of organic matter in swamps, bogs, and tidal flats; from active volcanoes; and is a common contaminant in natural gas. In 1950, 22 people were killed in Poza Rica, Mexico when a flare used to burn-off H_2S from a well extinguished, releasing toxic amounts of the gas. Nine people were killed in Denver City, Texas in 1975 when H_2S blew out of a secondary petroleum recovery well. The gas has a foul rotten egg smell, yet fatal gassings may occur because H_2S incapacitates the ability to smell by irreversibly reacting with the metal atoms in the proteins responsible for odor detection. Hydrogen sulfide is a product of anaerobic bacterial metabolism of sulfate and is common in wastewater. Hydrogen sulfide is converted to sulfuric acid on contact with concrete surfaces in the presence of air and is a common cause of concrete pipe corrosion in sewer systems.

Samples for sulfide determination are collected and preserved with either $Zn(OAc)_2$, which forms the insoluble ZnS, or $CdCO_3$ to form CdS, and basified with sodium hydroxide to pH >12. The sample should be then stored, in the dark and cool, until assay. Interferences can be removed from the sample (and the sample concentrated) by carefully withdrawing the supernatant liquid from the ZnS or CdS precipitate, and either replacing the removed water with deionized water or leaving at the lesser volume for concentration. As an alternative (and required in the Reactivity Characteristic) H_2S can be sweep distilled from the sample by strongly acidifying the sample and trapping the H_2S removed in a NaOH solution in a bubbler trap.

Sulfide is assayed by one of five methods, the last two being particular to wastewater generated from the leather tanning and finishing point source category (40 CFR 425):

1) S^{2-} reacts with I_2 to produce elemental sulfur. Excess standardized I_2 solution is added to the sample, and the excess I_2 titrated with standardized sodium thiosulfate with starch as indicator. This technique is particularly prone to false positive interferences due to other reduced substances in environmental samples, however it is good method for standardizing sulfide solutions.

$$S^{2-} + I_2 \longrightarrow S° + 2I^-$$

2) Methylene blue method - S^{-2} reacts with dimethylphenylenediamine and ferric chloride ($FeCl_3$) in a strongly acidic solution to form the dye methylene blue. The excess color due to $FeCl_3$ is removed by addition of diammonium hydrogen phosphate, $(NH_4)_2HPO_4$. Centrifugation is often required to remove the formed floc so that the test can be read colorimetrically. The color is read on a spectrophotometer at 664 nm against standards.

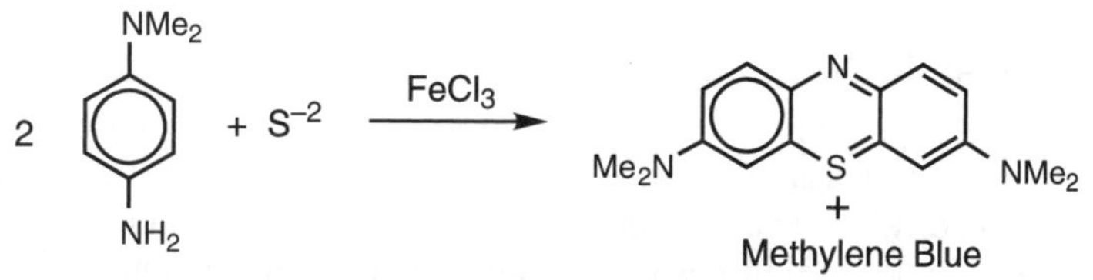

Figure 2-42. Chemistry of methylene blue formation as a sulfide assay.

3) A newer method uses a sulfide selective electrode to determine the sulfide contents in the NaOH trap from the distillation procedure.

4) The sulfide-containing sample is buffered to pH 9.3 with an ammonia buffer, then titrated with potassium ferricyanide in the presence of ferrous dimethylglyoxime indicator and barium chloride. The ferricyanide serves to oxidize the sulfide to sulfur with the endpoint indicated by permanent disappearance of the pink ferrous dimethylglyoxime color. Barium chloride serves to remove sulfite interference. (Appendix A to 40 CFR 425).

5) The modified Monier-Williams method (Appendix B, 40 CFR 425) first isolates the sulfide from the sample by strong acidification and sweep-distillation with nitrogen, passes the gas through a pH 7 potassium phosphate buffered scrubber to remove interfering sulfur dioxide, and finally traps the hydrogen sulfide in an alkaline peroxide scrubber as sulfate. The sulfate is determined by either a gravimetric or a turbidimetric determination with barium chloride.

R. Nitrogen (SM$_{18}$ 4500-N; EPA 351)

Nitrogen is an essential nutrient in biological systems. The biologically important forms of nitrogen are organic nitrogen (proteins, amino acids, DNA, etc.), ammonia, nitrite (NO_2^-), nitrate (NO_3^-), and nitrogen gas. Degradation of organic nitrogen (urea, alkaloids, aminoacids and proteins) in treatment plants proceeds in stepwise fashion to first ammonia in an anaerobic biological process. Subsequent aerobic transformations convert the ammonia biologically to nitrite by bacteria of the *Nitrosomonas* group, and then on to nitrate by members of the *Nitrobacter* group. This overall process is termed "nitrification." Under anaerobic conditions, nitrate and nitrite are converted biologically to nitrogen gas, or rarely ammonia, in the "denitrification" process. Animals can only bioassimilate organic nitrogen as a nitrogen source; however, bacteria and plants can use the other forms to make organic nitrogen[86]. Nitrite is of special interest due to the reaction with organic nitrogen to form the carcinogenic nitrosamines. Nitrite in drinking water is the cause of methemoglobinemia in human babies.

The TKN method for nitrogen determination is limited to ammonia and organic nitrogen in the -3 valence (amines). Total nitrogen methods have recently been published in *Standard Methods* 20th Edition. The techniques digest all nitrogen forms (except nitrogen gas) to nitrate using either a buffered (pH 8.5) UV-persulfate or a heated strong alkaline persulfate procedure. The nitrite is then analyzed by a nitrate selective electrode or traditional cadmium reduction and colorimetric determination of the nitrite. The Supplement to the 20th Edition of *Standard Methods* presents an oxidative digestion using persulfate and sulfuric acid that produces nitrate as the final determinative analyte. This digestion also serves as a suitable procedure for total phosphorus determination.

S. Ammonia (SM$_{18}$ 4500-NH$_3$; EPA 350)

Ammonia analysis is normally performed on distilled samples, except in the case of drinking water or highly purified wastewaters. Distillation consists of addition of a pH 9 borate buffer and distillation of water and ammonia with trapping into either boric acid (H_3BO_3) or sulfuric acid solution. In samples with a high organic nitrogen content the sample may be buffered to pH 7.2 - 7.4 with phosphate buffer to minimize decomposition of the organic nitrogen to ammonia. After the sample is distilled, one of four major methods is used to determine the ammonia present:

1) Back titration with sulfuric acid to the original pH of the boric acid trap.

$$NH_3 + H_3BO_3 \longrightarrow NH_4^+H_2BO_3$$
$$2NH_4H_2BO_3^- + H_2SO_4 \longrightarrow H_3BO_3 + (NH_4)_2SO_4$$

2) Reaction with Nessler's reagent (K_2HgI_4 from KI and HgI_2)

$$NH_3 + K_2HgI_4 + OH^- \longrightarrow NH_2Hg_2OI + KI + H_2O$$

The yellow-brown complex absorbs light over a wide range, and a number of wavelengths are used to make spectrophotometric determinations over a wide range of concentrations. Low NH_3 concentrations (up to 5 mg/L) are read at 400-425 nm, while values to 10 mg/L are read at 450-500 nm. Significant deviations from Lambert-Beer's Law (Abs = abc) can occur. The technique is also used for a

---

[86] Sawyer, C.N., P.L. McCarty and G.F. Parkin. *Chemistry for Environmental Engineering*, 4th Edition. 1994. McGraw-Hill, Inc. New York, NY.

visual determination of the ammonia levels in water. For this use permanent color standards are prepared in Nessler tubes with increasing amounts of potassium chloroplatinate (K_2PtCl_6) and cobalt chloride solutions. Due to waste disposal problems of the mercury reagent this method is being phased out.[87]

3) The phenate method involves the reaction of ammonia with hypochlorite and alkaline phenol in the presence of $MnSO_4$ to form indophenol - a vivid blue dye which is read at 630 nm with a spectrophotometer. A variation on the method uses sodium salicylate in the presence of a nitroferricyanide catalyst to form the blue indosalicylate, that in the presence of the yellow nitroferricyanide gives a green color.

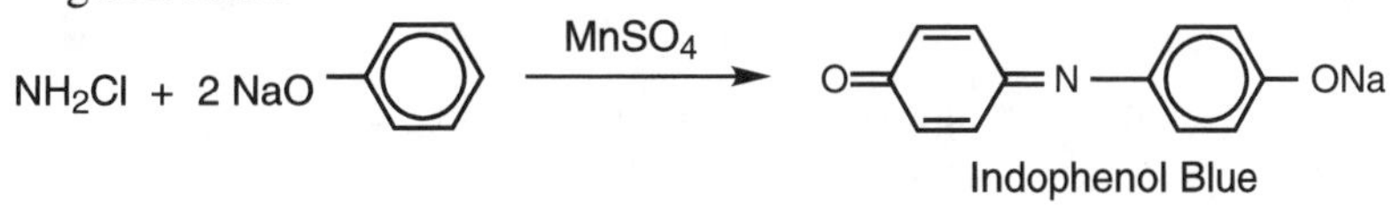

Indophenol Blue

Figure 2-43. Phenate method for ammonia determination.

4) The ammonia-selective electrode has the widest dynamic range (0.1-1000 mg/L) of any of the methods, is the fastest method, and many samples do not need to be distilled. Wastewater and water regulations require that a comparison of distilled and non-distilled results from samples be made prior to any abandonment of the distillation. Mercury and silver ions in the sample are a distinct interference due to complexation with ammonia.

T. Nitrite (SM$_{18}$ 4500-NO$_2$; EPA 354)

NO_2^- in the presence of acid reacts with amines, particularly aromatic amines, to form diazonium salts. Diazonium salts are very reactive and can couple with other aromatic systems to form colored azo-dyes. Coupling agents in current use include gentisic acid, chromotropic acid, and the very common N-napthyl-ethylenediamine dichloride (NED).

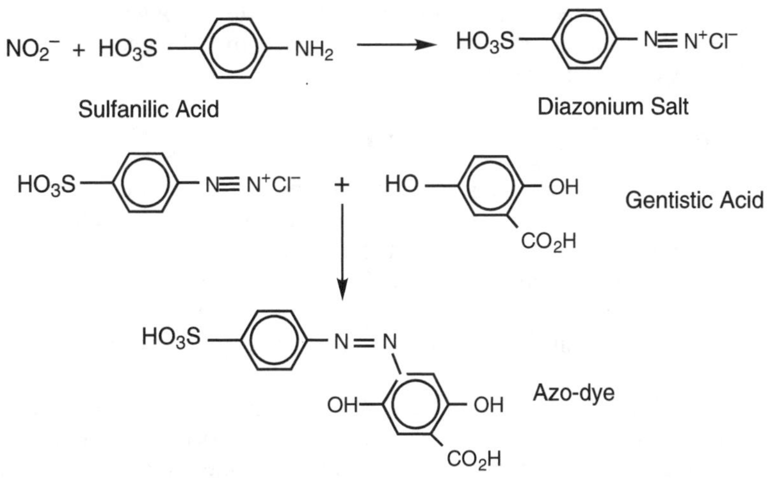

Figure 2-44. Chemistry of nitrite colorimetric analysis.

---

[87] The 19th Edition of *Standard Methods* dropped determination of ammonia by Nesslerization due to the mercury waste disposal problem.

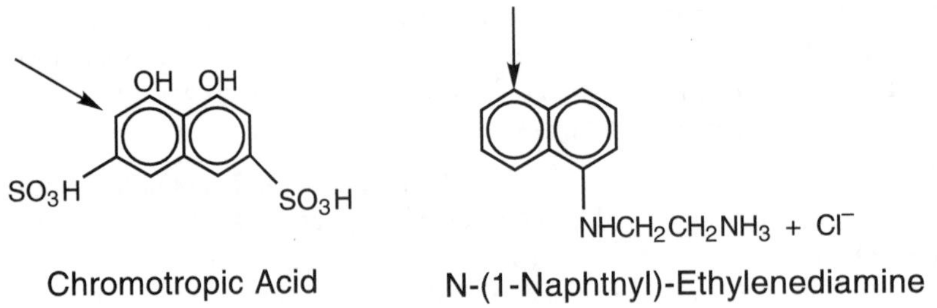

Chromotropic Acid   N-(1-Naphthyl)-Ethylenediamine

Figure 2-45. Coupling site with other nitrite colorimetric reagents to form azo dyes.

Nitrite can also be detected by the time-worn ferrous brown ring test.

$$2H^+ + 2FeSO_4 + 2HNO_2 \longrightarrow 2Fe^{3+} + 2NO + 2H_2O$$

$$NO + FeSO_4 \longrightarrow NOFeSO_4 \text{ (green-brown color) determined colorimetrically}$$

Nitrite has been determined in marine samples by addition of an acidic solution of 2,4-dinitrophenylhydrazine to form 2,4-dinitrophenylazide[88]. The azide reaction is complete within 5 minutes and it is then determined by HPLC with UV detection. The azide is stable for up to 4 weeks when stored cold and in the dark. Quantitation limits are reported as on the order of 5 ng/L.

U. Nitrate (SM$_{18}$ 4500-NO$_3$; EPA 352)

Nitrate can be determined along with nitrite by ion chromatography and capillary electrophoresis. Nitrate ion also has a UV absorbance, that in the absence of Cr^{6+}, organic matter, and other interfering absorbers, can be used for quantification. The Supplement to the 20th Edition of *Standard Methods* presents a modified dual wave length UV procedure that minimizes interferences. An electrode that is somewhat selective for nitrate is also available and useful as a screening test. However most of the common nitrate quantitative tests first reduce nitrate to nitrite by Cd-Hg amalgam, Cd-Cu alloy, or hydrazine sulfate and then test for nitrite.

V. Total (Kjeldahl) (SM$_{18}$ 4500-N$_{org}$; EPA 351)

The Kjeldahl method for determining nitrogen is one of the oldest quantitative test procedures known. First published in 1883, it quantitates organic and ammonia nitrogen by conversion of the organic nitrogen to ammonia with hot concentrated sulfuric acid, catalyzed by salts of Hg, Cu, or Se (sometimes with H_2O_2 added). (Most organic nitrogen is in the form of amides or primary amines.) Excess NaOH is added, and the liberated NH_3 is distilled into a trap containing a standard amount of acid. The excess acid is back-titrated with base.

The values obtained from the TKN procedure are in terms of mass nitrogen per liter or kilogram of sample. For many years conversion factors have been used on these results to give related numbers representing protein content of the sample. Some factors are 6.25% for meat protein, 6.38% for dairy protein and 5.7% for grain protein.

---

[88] Kieber, R.J., and P.J. Seaton. "Determination of Subnanomolar Concentrations of Nitrite in Natural Waters." *Anal. Chem.* 1995. 67(18). pp. 3261-3264.

Modifications of the method by addition of reducing substances prior to the digestion with sulfuric acid allow determination of azo-, nitro-, nitrite, nitrate and aromatic amine containing nitrogen compounds. An example is reaction with Devarda's metal (45% Al, 5% Zn, 50% Cu) in strongly basic media[89]:

$$3NO_3^- + 8Al + 5OH^- \longrightarrow 8AlO_2^- + 3NH_3$$

An oxidative digestion using persulfate and sulfuric acid has been used to produce nitrate as the final determinative analyte. This digestion also serves as a suitable procedure for total phosphorus determination.

W. Phosphorus (EPA 365; SM$_{18}$ 4500-P)

Phosphorus in the phosphate oxidation state is a key nutrient in water systems. It occurs in many forms, both organic and inorganic, soluble and mineral. One of the more important insoluble phosphate minerals is hydroxyapatite - $Ca_5(PO_4)_2OH$. The monomeric phosphate anion is called orthophosphate. The phosphate ion exists as four different salts with many different names. An example of the sodium series follows.

Table 2-30. Forms and names of mono-phosphates

Form	Name
H_3PO_4	Phosphoric acid Orthophosphoric acid
NaH_2PO_4	Sodium dihydrogen phosphate Sodium biphosphate Sodium phosphate monobasic Acid sodium phosphate Monosodium orthophosphate
Na_2HPO_4	Disodium hydrogen phosphate Sodium hydrogen phosphate Sodium phosphate dibasic Disodium orthophosphate Disodium phosphate Phosphate of soda
Na_3PO_4	Sodium phosphate tribasic Trisodium phosphate Sodium phosphate Trisodium orthophosphate

Linear strings of phosphates are called polyphosphates. Pyrophosphate is the simplest condensed polyphosphate. Polyphosphates up to 16 units long are common and well known. The metaphosphates are either cyclic structures or branched linear structures. The trimeta- and tetrametaphosphates are common cyclic structures, with structures known to contain up to 10 phosphate units. The common chemical sodium hexametaphosphate is not a well-defined single chemical, but rather a mixture of polymeric metaphosphates.

---

[89] Method 892.01, 15th Edition of *Official Methods of Analysis*, AOAC. Volume 1. pp. 19-20.

Table 2-31. Forms, names, and structures of inorganic phosporus

Form	Name	Structure
PO_4^{3-}	ortho-phosphate	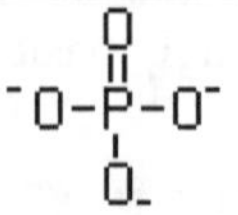
$P_2O_7^{4-}$	pyrophosphate	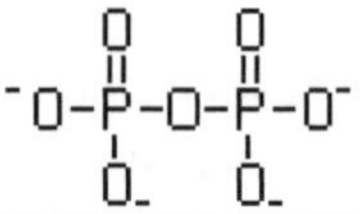
$P_3O_{10}^{5-}$	tripolyphosphate	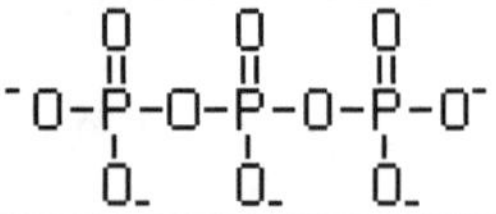
$P_3O_9^{3-}$	trimetaphosphate	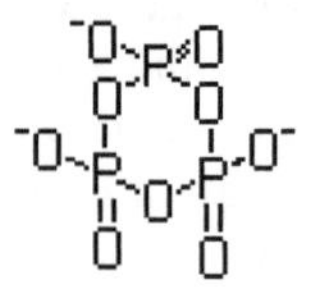
HPO_3^{2-}	phosphite (phosphonate)	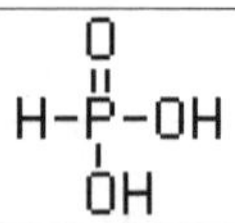
$H_2PO_2^-$	hypophosphite (phosphinate)	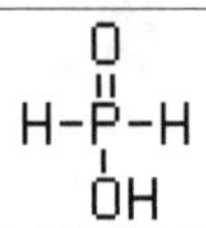

Organic phosphorus can have a large variety of organic attachments to the basic PO_4 system. Examples are DNA, RNA, phospholipids, and adenosine triphosphate (ATP).

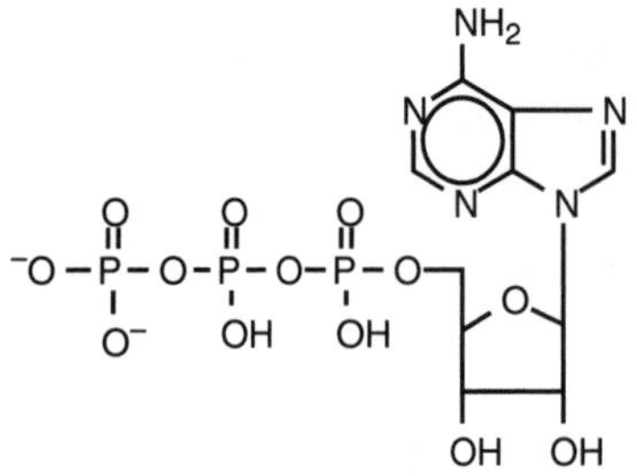

Figure 2-46. Structure of ATP, an organic phosphate.

The analysis of phosphate depends on the pretreatment of the sample. The simplest analysis is reaction of the sample with molybdate to form a phosphomolybdate that can be determined colorimetrically, or followed by reduction with one of a number of mild reducing agents such as $SnCl_2$, hydrazine, or ascorbic acid to form a heteropoly blue, which is determined colorimetrically. The latter procedure is the more sensitive. The direct analysis determines reactive phosphorus, which is primarily orthophosphate, but may contain some polyphosphate. The condensed phosphates can be hydrolyzed with acid and heated to orthophosphate and then determined, giving acid-hydrolyzable phosphorous; however, this also gives some of the organic phosphorus. Total phosphorus requires oxidative hydrolysis with heating to convert all phosphorus forms to orthophosphate. The persulfate oxidation is the most common and the mildest; nitric-sulfuric acid or perchloric acid digestions are more rigorous. See Section 2.III.R for a combined nitrogen-phosphorus digestion procedure.

$$PO_4^{3-} + 12(NH_4)_2MoO_4 + 12H^+ \longrightarrow (NH_4)_3PO_4(MoO_3)_{12} + 21NH_4^+ + H_2O$$

Ammonium molybdate Ammonium phosphomolybdate

$$PO_4^{3-} + (NH_4)_6Mo_7O_{24} \cdot 4H_2O \longrightarrow (NH_4)_3PO_4(MoO_3)_{12} \text{ (unbalanced reaction)}$$

Ammonium molybdate tetrahydrate

Figure 2-47. Formation of phosphomolybdate from phosphate.

The first step of the analysis is formation of the phosphomolybdate. The phosphomolybdate (heteropoly acid) has all the molybdenum in the +6 oxidation state. Reaction with a mild reducing agent forms the molybdenum heteropoly blue. The blue was believed to have the same structure as the heteropoly acid with two of the molybdenums in the +5 state and the other 10 molybdenums in the +6 state. Recent work has indicated that the blue actually is a huge donut-shaped poly-anion containing dozens of MoO_3 subunits[90]. The blues can accommodate up to 6 extra electrons and thus are prone to over reduction. The blue color is due to the trapped electrons being loosely associated with the reduced atoms. Variations on the procedure use antimony in the formation of the phosphomolybdate (as in the EPA methods), followed by reduction.

$$PO_4^{3-} + KSbOC_4H_4O_6 + 12(NH_4)_2MoO_4 + XH^+ \longrightarrow SbOPO_4(MoO_3)_{12}$$

Another variation uses ammonium metavanadate to produce the heteropoly acid, which is directly read colorimetrically without further reduction, for a high level determination (1-20 mg/L). This is used in the Hach method and SM 4500-P C.

$$PO_4^{3-} + NH_4VO_3 + (NH_4)_6Mo_7O_{24} \cdot 4H_2O \longrightarrow PO_4VO_3Mo_{16}O_{48}^{4-}$$

The above procedures give either reactive phosphate or total phosphate as results. On the other hand the analytical task may involve characterization of a sample to determine exactly the source of the phosphate pollution. This "fingerprinting" can be accomplished by thin layer chromatography (TLC) or more definitively by ion chromatography or capillary ion electrophoresis[91].

---

[90] Muller, A, J. Meyer, E. Krickemeyer and E. Diemann, *Angew. Chem. Int. Ed. Engl.* 1996. 35. pp. 1206.

[91] Shamsi, S.A. and N.D. Danielson. "Ribonucleotide Electrolytes for Capillary Electrophoresis of Polyphosphates and Polyphosphonates with Indirect Photometric Detection." *Anal. Chem.* 1995. 67(11). pp. 1845-1852.

X. Fluoride (SM$_{18}$ 4500-F$^-$; EPA 340)

There are three common techniques used for fluoride determinations, the SPADNS and complexone colorimetric methods and the ion-selective electrode method. All the techniques are subject to interferences, and complexed fluorides such as fluoroborates in general do not react well. For these reasons all samples for fluoride determination should be distilled. The distillation consists of strong acidification of the sample with concentrated sulfuric acid and addition of soft glass beads. This converts the fluoride to hexafluorosilicic acid, which is then distilled out of the sample and collected in a water solution. The addition of silver sulfate to the reaction pot serves to remove chloride interferences as silver chloride.

The SPADNS method measures the absorbance of an initial complex between zirconium ion and the dye sodium 2-(parasulfophenylazo)-1,8-dihydroxy-3,6-naphthalene disulfonate (SPADNS) and the subsequent bleaching of the complex due to reaction with fluoride ion.

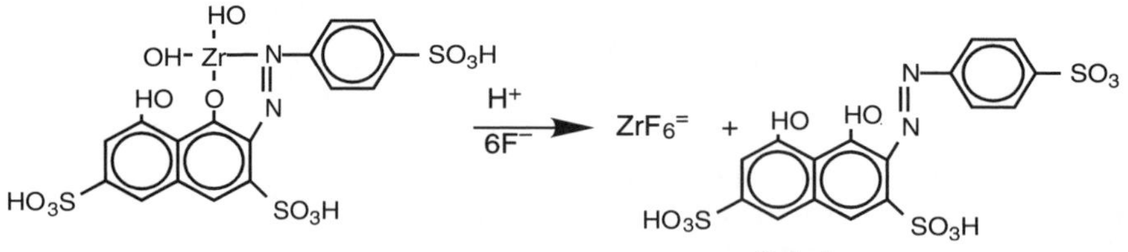

Figure 2-48. Bleaching reaction of fluoride on zirconium-SPADNS reagent.

The SPADNS calibration is one of the few encountered in environmental general chemical analysis that has a negative slope, i.e. the absorbance decreases with increasing amount of analyte. The colorimetric calibration is best set at zero with a reference blank, which contains all the reagents except the zirconium. Unfortunately the commercially available SPADNS reagent is a mixed reagent and already contains zirconium. The analyst is allowed to either set the absorbance of the blank sample at an arbitrary absorbance between 0.200 and 0.500 or to pick one of the high standards and set the absorbance at zero. Regardless of the zeroing procedure, the calibration curve has a distinct curve, being approximately linear from 0.1 mg/L to 2.0 mg/L fluoride. Since the analyst is setting the calibration, the maximum range of the calibration curve should be utilized. Absorbance values obtained from setting zero at 3.5 mg/L fluoride and the associated curve are illustrated in Table 2-32 and Figure 2-49.

Table 2-32. Absorbance data obtained from SPADNS procedure with 3.5 mg/L fluoride standard set at zero absorbance

Absorbance	F$^-$ mg/L
.922	0.00
.878	0.10
.722	0.50
.524	1.00
.190	2.00
.093	2.50
.026	3.00
.001	3.50

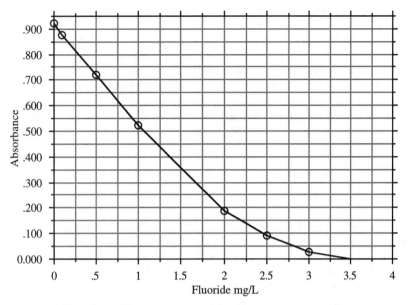

Figure 2-49. SPADNS Fluoride calibration curve.

The automated complexone reaction generates a colorimetric response read at 620 nm through reaction of lanthanum ion, Alizarin fluorine blue and fluoride ion. The auto-analyzers that use this chemistry all incorporate an initial distillation step.

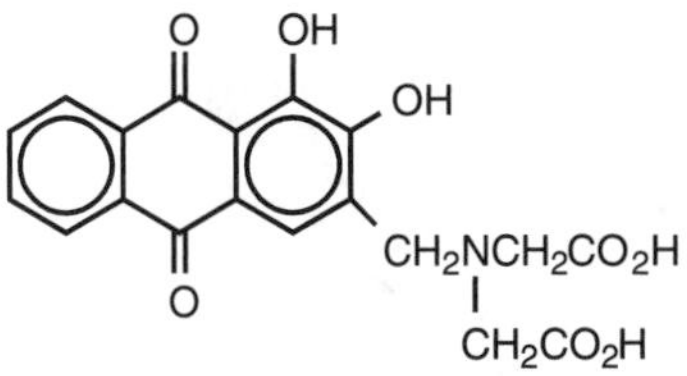

Alizarin Fluorine Blue

Figure 2-50. Structure of Alizarin fluorine blue.

The fluoride-selective electrode consists of a lanthanum (III) fluoride single crystal doped with trace amounts of europium (II) fluoride to serve as the electrical barrier between the inside of the electrode and the sample. The doping of the crystal is necessary to provide electrically conducting defects in the medium. The supporting electrolyte inside the electrode is sodium chloride/sodium fluoride at 0.1 M each. An electrical imbalance is created across the single crystal when the outside of the crystal is immersed in a solution of different fluoride activity, which generates a measurable voltage difference. The device is sensitive to total ion activity and is particularly sensitive to hydroxide concentration. Thus a pH 5.0 buffering solution, TISB (total ion strength buffer), is added to each sample and standard. TISB also contains cyclohexylene-diaminetetracetic acid (CDTA) as a cation complexing agent to free complexed fluoride ions for determination.

Y. Chloride (SM$_{18}$ 4500-Cl$^-$; EPA 325; EPA 9250, 9251, 9253).

Determination of chloride with mercury has been a time-tested reliable technique, however, due to the increasing awareness of mercury's toxic effects, these methods have been falling out of favor with more environmentally conscious laboratories. Thus the EPA has dropped Method 9252 from SW-846. The mercury-based methods depend upon removal of mercury (II) ion from a reaction mixture as the soluble, stable mercuric chloride. The automated ferricyanide methods react the chloride ion with mercuric thiocyanate to free thiocyanate ion, which further reacts with ferric ion, forming the highly colored red ferric thiocyanate ion.

$$2Cl^- + Hg(SCN)_2 \longrightarrow HgCl_2 + 2SCN^-$$
$$SCN^- + Fe^{3+} \longrightarrow Fe(SCN)^{2+}$$

In the mercuric nitrate titration, chloride reacts with the mercury ion until all the available chloride is consumed, then the excess mercuric ion reacts with an organic ligand such as diphenylcarbazone to form a highly colored mercury complex. Although chloride can react with mercury (II) ion to form a number of soluble complexes the formation constants ($K[HgCl^+] = 5.5$ x 10^6, $K[HgCl_2] = 3.0$ x 10^6, $K[HgCl_3^-] = 7.1$, and $K[HgCl_4^{2-}] = 10$) are rapid for formation of the neutral $HgCl_2$, while further formation constants are very slow and faster competing organic ligand reactions allow visual indication at the end of the stoichiometric titration. The complex with diphenylcarbazone has a very narrow optimum pH range (3.2-3.3) and an indicator is added (Bromophenol blue) for visual adjustment with nitric acid or sodium hydroxide to the optimum pH. Xylene cyanole FF dye is added in the case of colored interferents to sharpen the end-point color change.

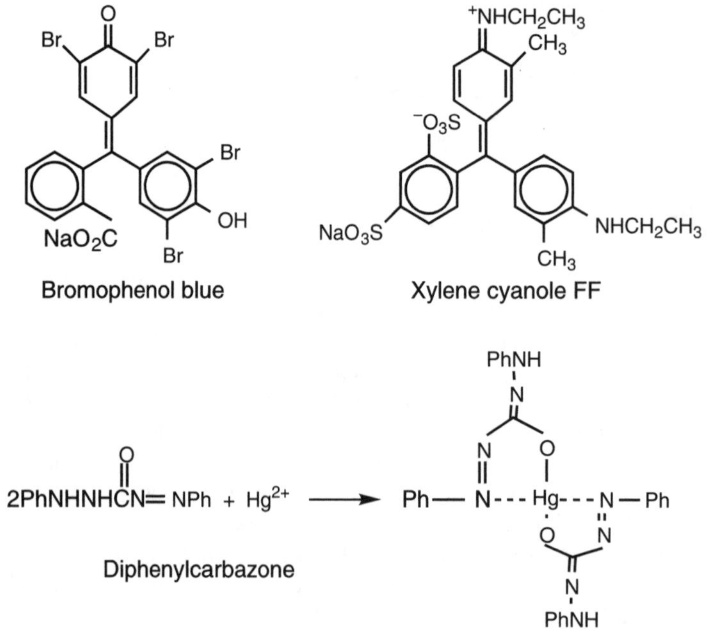

Bromophenol blue   Xylene cyanole FF

Diphenylcarbazone

Figure 2-51. Chemistry of the diphenyl carbazone indication of the mercuric nitrate titration end-point.

EPA method 9253 and SM_{20} 4500-Cl⁻ B are the classic Mohr Agentometric titration of chloride with silver nitrate to form the white insoluble silver chloride. The endpoint of the titration is determined by addition of chromate ion, which reacts with excess silver ion to form the insoluble red-orange silver chromate. Phenolphthalein indicator is used to allow adjustment of the solution pH to the optimum of 8.3. Sulfite ion can interfere with the titration, and if its presence is suspected, it can be removed by addition of hydrogen peroxide to oxidize the sulfite to sulfate. SM_{20} 4500-Cl⁻ D, uses a chloride-selective electrode for potentiometric determination of the endpoint of the Mohr titration.

$$Cl^- + Ag^+ \longrightarrow AgCl$$
$$2Ag^+ + CrO_4^{2-} \longrightarrow Ag_2CrO_4$$

Z. Ion Chromatography (EPA 300.0; EPA 9056; SM_{18} 4110)

Ion chromatography[92] is an instrumental technique that can be performed in either a cationic or anionic mode. In the anion mode it relies on sequential elution of anions in the sample from a strongly basic anionic exchange resin with a bicarbonate/carbonate buffer solution. Most of the systems use conductivity detectors. The detection is made simpler by exchanging the anions into the strong acid forms after elution from the analytical column but prior to the detector module. The sample is directly injected into the instrument after filtering, and concentration of the sample is not normally performed. If the sample and the eluting liquid phase are not of the same ionic strength, a water peak appears as the first signal. The water peak often masks the eluting signal of fluoride ion and so it is not on the target analyte list. Fluoride can be determined if the sample is diluted with the elution solvent prior to injection.

Interferences that can occur are anions, other than those on the target analyte list, which can co-elute or overlap calibrated anions. Another problem is that high concentrations of an anion can shift the retention of other target analytes. This is normally corrected by diluting and re-injecting the sample.

The halides and simple oxygenated anions (nitrate, nitrite, phosphate and sulfate) are analyzed in a single injection. The inorganic disinfection by-products (chlorate, chlorite and bromate) require a different strength of bicarbonate/carbonate eluant and are analyzed on a separate column.

Table 2-33. Target analytes of anion chromatography

Target analyte	MDL (mg/L)	Target analyte	MDL (mg/L)
Chloride	0.02	Bromide	0.01
Nitrate-N	0.002	Nitrite-N	0.004
Sulfate	0.02	ortho-Phosphate-P	0.003
Chlorate	0.003	Chlorite	0.01
Bromate	0.02		

[92] Mulik, J., and E. Sawicki. 1978-79. *Ion Chromatographic Analysis of Environmental Pollutants*, Vol. I and II, Ann Arbor Science Publishers, Ann Arbor, MI; "Application Reviews for Environmental Analysis, Water Analysis, Air Pollution and Industrial Hygiene." *Analytical Chemistry*. 1993. 65(12); Bahowick, T.J., V. Murugaiah, A.W. Sulya, D.B. Taylor, R.E. Synovec, R.J. Berman, C.N. Renn, and E.L. Johnson. "Column Liquid Chromatography: Equipment and Instrumentation," *Analytical Chemistry*. 1992. 64(12). pp. 255R-270R.

AA. Ion Selective Electrodes

A number of target analytes can be determined by ion selective electrodes (ISE) as discussed at various points in this Section. Examples include fluoride, chloride and hydrogen ion (pH). Some of the myriad procedures may entail direct determination of the concentration of the analyte in solution while others may use the ISE as an end-point indicator for a titration. An excellent reference on ISE has been published[93]. Other good reference materials are provided by the manufacturers of the devices.

ISE consist of four basic types. They are described below, along with their strengths and weaknesses:

1) Glass body - a thin glass bulb separates the working part of the electrode from the sample. The internal part of the electrode is filled with a buffered solution matched to the working electrode element, such as AgCl for a Ag wire element. The bulb must always be kept wet, generally stored in the lowest concentration standard of the target analyte. Frequently available as a combination electrode, i.e. the reference is attached to the electrode as a separate compartment. Examples are the pH and sodium ISE.

2) Solid state (crystal membrane) - a sealed electrode with a crystal membrane over the tip separating the sample from the sensing element. The inside of the electrode is filled with a liquid, which if gone indicates the electrode is ruined. Generally used with a separate reference electrode, although some combination electrodes are available. Can be stored dry or in a weak solution of the target analyte. The crystal should be kept polished with a soft cloth or fine abrasive. Examples are the fluoride and silver ISE.

3) Polymer membrane (liquid ion exchange) - a replaceable polymer membrane impregnated with an ion exchange resin, generally used with a separate reference electode. The electrode is filled with a solution specific to the target analyte. The electrode can be stored dry or in a weak solution of the target analyte. Exposure to organic solutions or high concentrations of organics in an aqueous sample will irreversibly damage the membrane. Examples are the calcium and nitrate sensing ISE.

4) Gas sensing - A replaceable gas permeable membrane is filled with a buffer solution that is in contact with a glass membrane pH sensor that has its own specific fill solution. Generally used with a separate reference electrode. Gaseous analytes diffuse from the sample across the membrane into the fill solution, that responds by changing pH. The pH change is sensed by the glass membrane electrode. The prototypical example is the ammonia electrode. The ammonia electrode should be stored by immersion in a 0.05 M solution of NH_4Cl. Frequent replacement of the gas permeable membrane and the fill solution are necessary.

The operation of the ISE is based upon potential difference (E) measured between the ISE and a reference electrode. The absolute value of the potential will depend on which reference electrode is used in the measurement. The potential is described by the Nernst equation:

$$E = E° + 2.3 \frac{RT}{nF} \log [\text{analyte ion}]$$

[93] Pungor, E. *Ion-Selective Electrodes*, Akademiai Kiado, Budapest, 1989.

where:
- $E°$ is the standard potential for the analyte and the cell conditions
- R is the gas constant
- T is the temperature in Kelvin
- n is the ionic charge on the analyte ions
- F is the Faraday constant

The ratio $\dfrac{RT}{nF}$ is termed the "Slope Factor" and it can be used as a preventative maintenance check on the condition of the ISE. These slope factors represent the change in measured potential in millivolts (mV) as the concentration of the target ion changes by factors of ten. The ideal slope values at 25 °C for a number of common ions are presented in Table 2-28. Determining and recording the slope value when the ISE is new and in perfect working condition serves as a set-point for future evaluations of performance.

Table 2-34. Ideal ISE slope values for common ions at 25 °C

Slope value (mV)	Ion charge	Examples
29.58	+2	Ca^{2+}, Ba^{2+}
59.16	+1	Na^+, H^+
-59.16	-1	Cl^-, F^-, Br^-
-29.58	-2	S^{2-}

Some of the many available ISE are listed in Table 2-35.

Table 2-35. Commonly available ISE

Ion	Electrode Type
Barium	Polymer membrane
Bromide	Solid state
Calcium	Polymer membrane
Chloride	Solid state
Copper	Solid state
Cyanide	Solid state
Fluoride	Solid state
Hydrogen	Glass
Iodide	Solid state
Nitrate	Polymer membrane
Potassium	Polymer membrane
Silver	Solid state
Sodium	Glass
Sulfide	Solid state
Thiocyanate	Solid state
Ammonia	Gas sensing

IV. APPLICATION TO SOLIDS AND OTHER MATRICES

Many of the methods discussed above in this Section are applicable only to aqueous samples, which is understandable since most of the procedures were developed within the context of the compliance monitoring requirements of drinking water, wastewater, and groundwater. However the need exists to determine many of these parameters in other matrices such as soil, sludge, sediment, chemical wastes, hazardous waste, and fuels.

Some methods, for example TKN, cyanide, fluoride, total metals and total phosphorus, that involve a sample pre-treatment step, can be readily modified for solid samples by simply weighing out a portion of the sample and then performing the sample digestion or distillation. On the other hand, for many common analyses, such as sulfate, chloride, and nitrate-nitrite, the target analyte must be extracted from the solid matix into an aqueous solution, then the determination can proceed as it would with water-based samples.

The environmental analytical field, in many respects is far behind other areas with respect to soil/solid analysis. The best information exists in methods developed in the agronomy and soil science areas for agricultural purposes. The standard texts and references are listed below with a general overview of the contents in Table 2-36. These methods were developed and are used to generate information related to agriculture, and the informational needs are not identical to those needed within the environmental industry.

Table 2-36. Overview of analytical methods for soil samples

Methods of Soil Analysis, Part 1: Physical and Mineralogical Methods Second Edition, 1986 American Society of Agronomy, Inc Soil Science Society of America, Inc, 677 South Segoe Rd., Madison WI 53711	
1. Errors and variability of observations	15. Particle-size analysis
2. Sampling	16. Specific surface
3. Geostatistical methods applied to soil science	17. Aggregate stability and size distribution
4. Extraneous values	18. Porosity
5. Pretreatment for mineralogical analysis	19. Penetrability
6. Oxides, hydroxides and aluminosilicates	20. Compressibility
7. Thermal analysis techniques	21. Water content
8. Petrographic microscope techniques	22. Water potential: Piezometry
9. Magnetic methods	23. Water potential: Tensiometry
10. Electron microprobe analysis	24. Water potential: Thermocouple Psychrometry
11. Infrared spectrometry	25. Water potential: Miscellaneous methods
12. X-ray diffraction techniques	26. Water retention: Laboratory methods
13. Bulk density	27. Water retention: Field methods
14. Particle density	28. Hydraulic conductivity and diffusion: Laboratory methods

Continued on next page.

Table 2-36. Overview of analytical methods for soil samples, *continued*

Methods of Soil Analysis, Part 1: Physical and Mineralogical Methods Second Edition, 1986, *continued* American Society of Agronomy, Inc Soil Science Society of America, Inc, 677 South Segoe Rd., Madison WI 53711	
29. Hydraulic conductivity and diffusion: Field methods	40. Heat flux
30. Hydraulic conductivity, diffusivity, and sorptivity of unsaturated soils: Field methods	41. Heat of immersion
31. Hydraulic conductivity of unsaturated soils: Prediction and formulas	42. Solute content
32. Intake rate: Cylinder infiltrometer	43. Solute diffusivity
33. Intake rate: Sprinkler infiltrometer	44. Solute dispersion coefficients and retardation factors
34. Intake rate: Border and furrow	45. Water and solute flux
35. Evaporation from bare soil measured with high spatial resolution	46. Gas diffusivity
36. Field capacity and available water capacity	47. Gas flux
37. Temperature	48. Air permeability
38. Heat capacity and specific heat	49. Oxygen electrode measurement
39. Thermal conductivity and diffusivity	50. Air pressure measurement

Methods of Soil Analysis, Part 2: Chemical and Microbiological Properties Second Edition, 1982 American Society of Agronomy, Inc Soil Science Society of America, Inc, 677 South Segoe Rd., Madison WI 53711	
1. Dissolution for total elemental analysis	21. Lead
2. Atomic absorption and flame emission spectrometry	22. Mercury
3. Optical emission spectrometry	23. Arsenic
4. Neutron activation analysis	24. Phosphorus
5. X-ray fluorescence spectrometry	25. Boron
6. High-pressure liquid chromatography	26. Bromine, chlorine and fluorine
7. Anodic stripping voltametry and differential pulse polarography	27. Cobalt, molybdenum and selenium
8. Cation exchange capacity	28. Sulfur
9. Exchangeable cations	29. Total carbon, organic carbon and organic matter
10. Soluble salts	30. Organic matter characterization
11. Carbonate and gypsum	31. Nitrogen - total
12. Soil pH and lime requirement	32. Nitrogen - organic forms
13. Lithium, sodium and potassium	33. Nitrogen - inorganic forms
14. Magnesium, calcium, strontium and barium	34. Nitrogen - urea
15. Silicon	35. Nitrogen - availability indices
16. Aluminum	36. Nitrogen - isotope-ratio analysis
17. Iron	37. Cultural methods for soil microorganisms
18. Manganese	38. Microscopic methods for soil microorganisms
19. Nickel, copper, zinc and cadmium	39. Most probable number method for microbial populations
20. Chromium	40. Microbial biomass

Continued on next page.

Table 2-36. Overview of analytical methods for soil samples, *continued*

Methods of Soil Analysis, Part 2: **Chemical and Microbiological Properties Second Edition, 1982,** *continued* **American Society of Agronomy, Inc** Soil Science Society of America, Inc, 677 South Segoe Rd., Madison WI 53711	
41. Soil respiration	48. Nitrifying bacteria
42. Composition of soil atmospheres	49. Rhizobium
43. Soil enzymes	50. Free-living dinitrogen-fixing bacteria
44. Filamentous fungi	51. Algae
45. Actinomycetes	52. Protozoa
46. Anaerobic bateria and processes	53. Nematodes
47. Denitrification	54. Mites and other soil microarthropods

Soil Sampling and Methods of Analysis, 1993, Lewis Publishers, Boca Raton FL **Canadian Society of Soil Science** 907-151 Slater St., Ottawa, Ontario K1P5H4 Canada	
1. Site description	30. Root nodule bacteria and nitrogen fixation
2. Soil sampling for environmental assessment	31. Microarthropods in soil and litter
3. Soil handling and preparation	32. Nematodes
4. Nitrate and exchangeable ammonium Nitrogen	33. Nitrogen mineralization potential in soils
5. Ammonium acetate-extractable elements	34. Denitrification
6. Mihlich III-extractable elements	35. Earthworms
7. Sodium bicarbonate-extractable P, K, and N	36. Total and labile polysaccharides
8. Available potassium	37. Organic forms of nitrogen
9. Extraction of available sulfur	38. Soil humus fractions
10. Available P	39. Light fraction and macroorganic matter
11. DTPA-extractable Fe, Mn, Cu and Zn	40. Water-soluble phenolic materials
12. Boron, molybdenum and selenium	41. Soil lipids
13. Cd, Cr, Pb and Ni	42. Sampling organic soils
14. Lime requirement	43. Physical properties of organic soils
15. Chemical characterization of plant tissue	44. Chemical properties of organic soils
16. Soil reaction and exchangeable acidity	45. Micromorphological methodology
17. Soil solution	46. Palynological assessments
18. Soluble salts	47. Particle size distribution
19. Ion exchange and exchangeable cations	48. Soil shrinkage
20. Carbonates	49. Soil consistency limits
21. Total and organic carbon	50. Density and compressibility
22. Total nitrogen	51. Soil water content
23. Total and organic phosphorus	52. Soil water potential
24. Total and fractions of sulfur	53. Soil water desorption curves
25. Extractable Al, Fe, Mn and Si	54. Soil porosity
26. Reference materials for data quality	55. Saturated hydraulic conductivity: Laboratory measurement
27. Cultural methods for soil microorganisms	56. Saturated hydraulic conductivity: Field measurement
28. Soil microbial biomass C and N	57. Unsaturated hydraulic conductivity and sorptivity: Laboratory measurement
29. Vesicular-arbuscular mycorrhiza	58. Unsaturated hydraulic conductivity: Estimation from desorption curves

Continued on next page.

Table 2-36. Overview of analytical methods for soil samples, *continued*

Soil Sampling and Methods of Analysis, 1993, Lewis Publishers, Boca Raton FL **Canadian Society of Soil Science** 907-151 Slater St., Ottawa, Ontario K1P5H4 Canada	
59. Unsaturated hydraulic conductivity: Field measurement	68. Sand analysis
60. Air permeability	69. Identification and measurement of carbonates
61. Aggregate stability to water	70. Chemical methods in mineralogy
62. Dry aggregate distribution	71. Sampling frozen soils
63. Soil air	72. Hydrological properties of frozen soils
64. Soil temperature	73. Thermal properties of frozen soils
65. Micromorphological methodology for inorganic soils	74. Frost heave potential
66. Soil separation for mineralogical analysis	75. Depth of frost penetration
67. Clay and silt analysis	

Handbook on Reference Methods for Soil Analysis, 3rd Edition, 1992 **Council on Soil Testing and Plant Analysis** Georgia University Station P.O. Box 2007, Athens, GA 30612-0007	
1. Soil water pH	17. Phosphorus by Mehlich No. 3 extraction
2. Soil pH in 0.01M $CaCl_2$	18. Ca, K, Mg and Na by Mehlich No. 3 extraction
3. Soil-paste pH and conductivity of saturated extract	19. Mn, Zn and Cu by Mehlich No. 3 extraction
4. Specific conductance in 1:2 soil:water solution	20. Boron by hot water extraction
5. Soil buffer pH by Adams-Evans lime buffer	21. Zn by 0.1 N HCl extraction
6. Soil buffer pH by SMP lime buffer	22. Acid-extractable Cu by Mehlich-Bowling
7. Exchangeable acidity and lime requirement	23. Ammonium bicarbonate-DTPA soil test for K, P, Zn, Fe, Mn, Cu and nitrate
8. Phosphorus by Bray P1 extraction	24. Zn, Mn, Fe and Cu by DTPA extraction
9. Phosphorus by Olsen's sodium bicarbonate extraction	25. Cd, Cu, Ni and Zn by DTPA extraction for sludge-amended soils
10. K, Mg, Ca and Na by ammonium acetate extraction	26. Nitrate-nitrite by ISE
11. Phosphorus by Mehlich No. 1 extraction	27. K, Ca, Mg and Na by water extraction
12. K, Mg, Ca and Na by Mehlich No. 1 extraction	28. Organic matter by wet digestion
13. Zn by Mehlich No. 1 extraction	29. Organic matter by loss-on-ignition
14. Phosphorus by Morgan extraction	30. Humic matter by NaOH extraction
15. K, Ca and Mg by Morgan extraction	31. Relative availabilities by small-exchange
16. pH, soluble salts, nitrate, P, Ca, Mg, Na, and Cl in greenhouse growth media (soil less mixes)	

The analysis of inorganic anions in solid phase samples has been addressed in the US Environmental Protection Agency's National Sewage Sludge Survey[94] and in the context of analysis of agricultural soils. The EPA testing needs were addressed as one line sample preparation modifications to already existing traditional wet chemical

---

[94] Analytical Methods for the National Sewage Sludge Survey, USEPA WH-585, September 1990; POTW Sludge Sampling and Analysis Guidance Document, USEPA August, 1989.

methods for determination of the specific anions total phosphate, chloride, sulfate, nitrite and nitrate. These, for the most part, involve mixing a portion of the solid with reagent grade water, agitating on a wrist-shaker or stirring for up to 24 hours, then filtering and treating the filtrate as a normal aqueous sample.

A number of procedures are available in methods manuals[95] (Table 2-36) used by agricultural soils testing laboratories. These involve extraction of the sample with either reagent grade water alone or reagent grade water with various additives. The results from the plain water extractions are most frequently regarded by agronomists, botanists, environmental assessors and other ecology related professionals as the "bio-available" fraction of the total analyte presence in the soil, although experimental justification for such a classification is lacking. The use of water fortified with a variety of additives, such as calcium sulfate, ammonia, ethylenediamine tetraacetic acid (EDTA), and diethylenetriamine pentaacetic acid (DTPA), for the isolation of anions, generates concentration estimates that are assumed to represent "total" content. These recipes were developed with the objective of the analysis of a single anion (such as sulfate), and in many cases they only work for that select anion.

Anions exist in soil samples in a variety of micro-environments[96]. The pore water of the sample can and does contain a number of dissolved components. As long as the samples can be finely divided, providing intimate interaction and dilution of the pore water with the bulk of the extraction mixture, anions contained in this micro-environment can be easily recovered. However, when the pore water is saturated with respect to any specific anion-cation combination, the excess analyte will precipitate as either a particle suspended in the pore water or as a solid upon the surface of the soil matrix, largely an alumino-silicate substrate. Another micro-environment consists of select cations partially incorporated into the alumino-silicate matrix and strongly binding anions to the matrix.

Soils can contain varying amounts of organic material. Most of the organic content is humus derived, which exhibits largely anionic character. Inorganic anions are not expected to be strongly associated with this soil fraction.

Three techniques have been used to recover analyte from these micro-environments. The first is a simple dilution of the pore water with the extraction solution, decreasing the saturation concentration of the solid which may allow more to re-dissolve. Kinetically this is frequently a slow process, and varying recoveries can be obtained depending on the length of contact time with the solid and extracting solvent. Increasing the temperature of the extraction can serve to hasten the process. The second technique is a displacement or exchange process where the solid is suspended in a solution containing an excess of an anion that, when combined with the cation, forms a more insoluble material. For example, sulfate can be solubilized from solid calcium sulfate when the extraction solution contains an excess of carbonate. The more insoluble calcium carbonate is precipitated.

---

[95] *Handbook on Reference Methods for Soil Analysis*, Soil and Plant Analysis Council, Inc. 1992. *Wisconsin Procedures for Soil Testing, Plant Analysis and Feed & Forage Analysis,* Department of Soil Science, College of Agricultural and Life Sciences, University of Wisconsin-Extension-Madison. 1987; *Soil Sampling and Methods of Analysis*, M.R. Carter (Ed), Canadian Society of Soil Science. 1993, CRC Press, Boca Raton FL; *Methods of Soil Analysis: Part 2 - Chemical and Microbiological Properties*, 2nd Edition, American Society of Agronomy Soil Science Society of America, Madison, WI. 1982.

[96] D.L. Winegardner *Introduction to Soils for Environmental Professionals. CRC Press.* 1996. Boca Raton, FL.

The third technique is directed toward the cation and uses active solubilizing agents such as EDTA, DTPA, cryptands or crown ethers. These agents form very strong complexes with the cation and release the associated anion to the solution. A brief examination of the suitability of various extraction mixtures (water, EDTA, DTPA, and, ammonia) for multi-anion analysis using capillary electrophoresis has been published.[97]

A potential approach, that has not been employed in anion analysis, would be to solubilize the soil matrix, such as is done in digestions with hydrofluoric acid for recovery of total metals.

---

[97] Smith, R.-K., J. Romano, J. Kruz, and D. Roth. Extraction of anious from Solid-Phase Samples for Capillary ion Electrophoresis. Proceeding of the Twelfth Annual Quality Assurance and Waste Testing Symposium, USEPA/ACS. Washington, D.C. 23-26 July, 1996. pp 128-138.

Organic Parameters

An analytical process generally first determines what is present (qualitative analysis) and then determines how much (quantitative analysis). Most of the methods discussed in the previous section are highly specific for the target parameter and have relatively few interferences. Thus the qualitative and quantitative analyses are performed simultaneously. The analysis of organic parameters is much more complex than the determination of the inorganics. To a large part the complexity of the analysis is due to the small range of physical and chemical properties the different organic target analytes exhibit. Any procedure used for organic pollutant analysis will almost always result in determination of a large number of compounds. The qualitative aspects of the analysis become of foremost importance before the determination of how much is present. Most methods for organic analysis embody some sort of separation technique (GC or HPLC) for isolating target analytes and then characterize the isolates with a detector.

Once compounds are separated by some means it is necessary to translate the chemical information of the separation to some usable data form, generally electrical. There are many types of detection, based on a variety of physical properties of the target compounds. In general the explanation of the technique is much more involved than the hardware and software required to put the technique in practice.

1. Conductivity - Conductivity is the inverse of resistance, which is actually what is measured. A potential is applied across a flow of solvent and the decrease in resistance is measured as a positive signal. This can be directly applied to the eluting solvent in HPLC. In GC this technique is used in the Hall (Electrolytic Conductivity) Detector. A selective detector for halogenated compounds is made by mixing the carrier gas stream from the GC column with hydrogen and passing it through a 800 - 900 °C nickel tube. The halogens are reduced to hydrogen halides such as HCl and HBr. The gas flow is then bubbled into a non-conductive yet polar solvent such as propanol. The fluid stream then passes through the conductivity cell, and the decrease in resistance of the flow measured as an electrical signal. Appropriate modifications allow selective detection of nitrogen and sulfur compounds.

2. Spectroscopy - Electromagnetic radiation interacts with compounds in a number of ways. These techniques are often used both as qualitative and quantitative tools. The quantitative aspect is embodied in Lambert-Beers Law (A = abc), which states that absorption is equal to the product of the absorption coefficient (a), the pathlength of the sample (b) and the molar concentration (c) of the analyte. For most procedures this is a linear relationship for at least some range of concentration.

decreasing energy, increasing wavelength, decreasing frequency

X-rays	Vacuum UV	Ultraviolet	Visible	Infrared	Microwave	Radiowave
<10 nm	10-20 nm	200-400 nm	400-800 nm	2-150 um	50 um - 30 cm	>30 cm

Figure 3-1. Energy spectrum.

Quite common detectors use the X-ray, UV-Visible and the IR parts of the spectrum. The X-ray and UV-Visible end of the spectrum correspond to allowed energy transitions of electrons within the atom or molecule. The IR area of the spectrum corresponds to bond vibrations and molecular rotations. Any photon of energy emitted or absorbed by a molecule will equate to a) an exactly allowed energy transition by an electron in an atom or molecule; or b) the frequency of a periodic atomic motion.

3. UV-Visible interactions - These can be either absorption or emission events. These always involve allowed electron transitions in either atoms or molecules. The molecular electronic transitions are most often absorption events that correspond to allowed jumps of an electron from a ground or low state to a higher energy level, tested on solutions of the target analytes at room temperature. The energy of the absorbed photon ($E = h\nu$) is always equal to the energy of the electron jump, and since most electrons are jumping from a ground state to an allowed excited state, the spectrum is simple with few signals. Solvation of the molecule tends to broaden the absorption bands, and changing the solvent can often affect the wavelength of maximum absorption. The detection can either be conducted in a scanning mode or as a fixed wavelength detector (common in HPLC). The diode array detector allows simultaneous acquisition of the entire spectrum.

Atoms can also participate in absorption events. A common procedure is to put the atoms into a gaseous state by burning the compound in a hydrogen or acetylene flame, then pass light of a particular frequency through the flame to see if the intensity of the light is decreased through absorption due to the presence of a particular element. These signals are quite sharp. The experiment is most often conducted in the set wavelength mode. The flame photometric detector (FPD) for phosphorus and sulfur in GC and the atomic absorption (FLAA and GFAA) metals analyzers operate on this principle.

Emission events are normally limited to atoms, because molecules do not tend to remain intact under the excitation conditions. Some elements are easily excited and exhibit lines in the visible range. This is the basis of the flame test where some of the sample is burned in a bunsen burner. A magenta-violet color indicates the presence of potassium, crimson - lithium or strontium, yellow - sodium, green - barium or copper, and blue - calcium. Altogether these explain why driftwood from the sea coast has such appeal as a fuel in fireplaces. In the more general case analytes are introduced into an atomic plasma created from either helium or argon, which has temperatures of 8000 - 10,000 °C. Molecules are instantly destroyed, and the resultant atoms are thermally excited to very high energy levels. As the atoms cool in the outer portions of the plasma the excited electrons drop down to lower energy levels, and the excess energy is given off as photons. The emitted light from the plasma is directed onto a diffraction grating to separate the light by wavelength, which hits a photodetector and registers as an electronic signal. Emission spectra are quite complex, being composed of many lines as a large number of different excited states are populated.

Another application of UV photons is the photoionization detector. The lamps are rated in electron volts (eV). An electron volt is the amount of energy gained by an electron when passed through a one volt potential. It is equal to 1.60×10^{-12} ergs or 1.60×10^{-19} joules. Lamps of a variety of power outputs are available, but the most useful generate photons of 9 to 10.5 eV.

Table 3-1.   Correlation of photon wavelength to energy content

nm	eV
130.0	9.5
129.0	9.6
123.6	10.0
121.6	10.2
116.5	10.6
105.0	11.8

These are sufficiently strong photons to completely remove an electron from a double or triple bond or an aromatic system in a molecule and create a cation from the molecule. The ionization is performed in a chamber with an applied potential, and the cations neutralize themselves on the negative electrode, registering as a current. The method is non-destructive and the neutralized molecules can be subjected to other detection systems - ELCD (Hall) is a common second detector in the series.

4. IR interactions - IR interactions with molecules exist in the context of heat and temperature. The terms temperature and heat are not synonymous. Temperature refers to the motion of a molecule. The more vigorous the motion, the higher the temperature. Molecules move in three different modes, vibrational, rotational and translational.

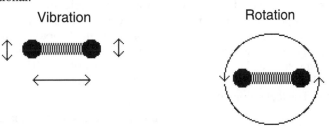

Vibration   Rotation

Figure 3-2.   Molecular bond motions.

The atomic bonds that hold molecules together can be pictured as springs that vibrate back and forth and flex from side to side. The movement of the centers of the atoms with respect to each other constitutes the vibrational mode. Molecules exposed to energy at the same level as the frequency of vibration ($E = h\nu$) can absorb the energy, and the vibration becomes more vigorous. This is the idea behind infrared spectroscopy (IR). Infrared radiation (longer wavelength than visible light) has energy content in the same range as molecular bond vibrations and rotations. Mono-atomic substances such as the rare gases have no vibrational energy levels. The rotational modes of movement result from the molecule spinning around its center of mass. The translational mode of motion is when the molecule is moving through space from one location to another. Heat is the transfer of energy from one molecule to another. It is always a collisional process. It is very possible to have molecules at very high temperatures but there be no heat to speak of. One such area is in the thermosphere; 80 km up in the atmosphere where the average temperature is about 2000 °C, but there are so few molecules that there is essentially no heat.

The IR experiment is most often conducted in the scanning mode as the IR spectrum is extremely useful in the qualitative analysis of unknowns. Many frequency-specific absorptions have been related to particular bondings in molecules. Over 1000 specific interactions have been described in the literature.

Table 3-2. Representative IR frequencies

Wavenumber cm^{-1}	Functional group	Wavenumber cm^{-1}	Functional group
3700-3100 (broad)	O—H	1800	-C-C(=O)OC-
3049	C=C—H	1710	C-C(=O)-C
2941-2857	C—H (saturated)	1690	H$_2$N(C=O)C
2273-2000	-C≡N	3310	-C≡C—H
2119	-C≡C-	1650	C=C

5. Fluorescence spectroscopy - This is a very simple method of analysis that entails a very complicated explanation. Essentially a molecule or atom is excited with a high energy source, either X-ray or UV photons, and an electron is bumped to a high energy state. The electron migrates to a slightly lower state with a simultaneous release of energy, generally as temperature (rotational, vibrational, or translational energy). After a period of time the electron relaxes to a significantly lower energy level with simultaneous release of a photon of light. Keys to this process are the time delay between excitation and the emission of fluorescence and the lower energy level of the emitted photon *vs.* the excitation photon. This allows a specific detector to be used that is non-responsive to the excitation source and the subsequent increase in sensitivity. The penultimate application of this method is to use an X-ray excitation source and a specific UV detector. The technology obeys Beers Law.

6. Mass spectrometry - The mass spectrometer consists of three major parts. They are the *ionization source* where analyte molecules are converted by either laser photoionization, collision, or thermal processes into ions. In some systems the ions will further fragment into smaller mass ions, the fragmentation pattern and abundance distribution being a constant phenomenon under the same experimental conditions. The ions and daughter ions are filtered through a variety of different types of *mass filters*, generally operating on the radius of curved movement of the charged ion (smaller radius for lighter ions) in a magnetic field. The ions are then directed onto a *ion detector* to generate an electric signal. Mass spectrometers often are used to generate a mass spectrum of the unknown analyte for identification.

Mass spectrometers have been coupled with a number of separatory and ionization sources including, GC, capillary electrophoresis, ion chromatographs, HPLC and plasma sources.

Table 3-3.   Commonly used detectors for gas chromatography

Equipment	Operation
Flame ionization detector (FID)	Burns eluting compounds to form positively charged ions detected as a current flow between the burner and a collector, which are held at a high potential. Most sensitive to C-H containing analytes.
Electrolytic conductivity detector (ELCD) or Hall detector	Converts organohalogen compounds into the halogen acid, then measures the increase in conductivity of the halogen acid dissolved in a flowing solvent stream.
Electron capture detector (ECD)	Functional groups capture electrons from a ^{63}Ni source and change the ionization level in the detector chamber. Halogen and nitro functions are detected among others.
Flame photometric detector (FPD)	Eluting compounds burned in a hydrogen-rich flame, phosphorus and sulfur atoms emit light, which passes through a narrow band pass filter to a photodetector.
Nitrogen-phosphorous detector (NPD)	Similar in construction to a FID, but a heated rubidium salt-covered bead serves as the ionization element rather than a flame. Nitrogen and phosphorous compounds are selectively ionized and detected as current as in the FID.
Photo-ionization detector (PID)	A 10.2 eV lamp serves to ionize substances that contain double bonds. An electric potential exists across the ionization cell. The flow of current indicates the presence of ionized molecules.
Mass selective detector (MS)	Fragments eluting compounds into ions that are detected by mass/charge as a spectrum. A three-dimensional detector.
Infrared detector (IRD)	Absorbed frequencies of IR light are diagnostic for functional group bonds and generate a spectrum. A three-dimensional detector.
Atomic emission detector (AED)	Eluting compounds enter a helium plasma and the emitted photons sorted by a diffraction grating and are collected by a photodetector

Two cases for identification of organic analytes exist. The first is a situation where an analytical standard of the target analyte is available. The second is when a standard is not available. The criteria for claiming an identification are different for the two situations.

When a standard is present the generally accepted identification criteria are that both the standard and the unknown exhibit the exact same properties under two different and independent test conditions. In so far as organic pollutant identifications are concerned, these criteria can be met by the unknown and the standard having the same retention time on two GC columns with different coatings, as embodied in EPA methods 601 and 602. It is incorrect to use identical behavior of the standard and unknown in two dimensional detectors as sufficient criteria for detection.

An example of this misuse is a lab performing 601/602 on a single GC capillary column with the PID and Hall detectors in series. An eluting compound matched the retention time for 1,2-dichlorobenzene, gave responses on both the PID and the Hall, and the lab reported 1,2-dichlorobenzene as present, which was a violation of the client's NPDES permit. The client spent large sums of money trying to track the contamination, but to no avail and the fines kept mounting. Subsequent reanalysis of the discharge water by another laboratory using an analytical GC capillary column and a different polarity confirmation capillary column, as specified in the method, showed the compound to not be 1,2-dichlorobenzene. Further work with GC/MS tentatively identified the compound as 2-chlorotoluene, which was then confirmed by comparison with a standard. The correct compound, 2-chlorotoluene, was not listed on the client's NPDES permit.

A better version of retention time comparison is co-injection of the standard and the unknown, resulting in only one peak on two GC columns with different polarity coatings. However, even this particular test fails for one pair of compounds, piperonyl butoxide and resmethrin, common insecticide ingredients. A more sure identification could depend on identical retention times for the standard and the unknown on a GC column and identical results from a spectral analysis (UV-vis, mass spectra, or IR spectra) for the two compounds. These data are the information obtained from a HPLC-DAD, HPLC/MS, GC/MS or GC/FTIR. These types of instruments provide what is called three dimensional information, i.e. retention time of the eluting compound and a spectrum (response *vs.* mass/charge or frequency) of the compound. The former pair of insecticide ingredients can be correctly identified with any of the four combination instruments.

When a standard is not present, any identification must be regarded as tentative. To claim an absolute identification, overwhelming evidence must be presented that leaves no possibility of misidentification. Suitable evidence would include NMR spectra, IR spectra, mass spectra, elemental analysis, etc. and chemical/physical properties, such as melting point, boiling point, chromatographic behavior, and diagnostic reaction results. These tests are well beyond the capabilities of most environmental laboratories. A mass spectral match out of one of the larger libraries such as the NIST or Wiley compilation is insufficient to claim an identification. Compounds identified on the basis of a spectral match alone are termed tentatively identified compounds (TIC).

There are three common methods of organic analysis used in the EPA protocols[1], with some examples of target analytes performed by the different techniques presented in Appendix A, List of Analytes. The first general method is based on the compounds having a low solubility in the water matrix and a vapor pressure at 20 °C of greater than 1 mm Hg. Compounds having these properties can be stripped from a water solution by purging the sample with helium gas. These compounds are termed "volatile" or "volatile organic compounds (VOC)" and are determined by a purge and trap concentrator attached to either a gas chromatograph (GC) or a gas chromatograph/mass spectrometer

---

[1] A complete listing of target analytes by the EPA is available in *Environmental Methods Monitoring Index* (EMMI), a software program available from NTIS PB95-502399, which cross-references methods and analytes between EPA, NIOSH, FDA, DOE, USGS, ASTM and Standard Methods.

(GC/MS) by "volatile organic analysis (VOA)." A reverse application of the purge and trap approach is spray extraction[2].

The second group of general methods is based on the compounds being insoluble in the water matrix, but soluble in a non-polar organic solvent such as methylene chloride or hexane. The extraction is refined by taking advantage of the acidic or basic nature of the target analytes and adjusting the pH of the water sample accordingly. Further, these compounds must be thermally stable to the conditions encountered in the heated injector and oven (above 270 °C) of the GC and exhibit an appreciable vapor pressure below 270 °C, i.e. $>10^{-7}$ mm Hg at 25 °C. Compounds that meet these criteria are termed semivolatile and are determined by extraction from the water matrix with a non-polar solvent (generally methylene chloride), concentrated and assayed by GC, GC/MS, or GC/FTIR (gas chromatograph/Fourier Transform Infrared). Compounds extracted from the sample when the pH is greater than 12 are called base-neutral extractables (BN). Compounds that are extracted from the sample when acidified to less than pH 2 are termed acid extractables. The combined analysis of base-neutral and acid extractables is termed BNA analysis.

The third general group of target analytes is assayed by high performance liquid chromatography (HPLC). These compounds exhibit a variety of properties such as water solubility, thermal unstability, or extremely low vapor pressure, which make them difficult to assay by GC. Samples are either solvent extracted similar to the semivolatiles preparation, or, in some cases, directly injected into the HPLC as a water solution. A variety of detectors are used with HPLC, both two- and three- dimensional. Techniques particular to HPLC are reversed-phase columns that allow chromatography of very polar analytes, ion-pairing chromatography, size-exclusion chromatography, and the related ion chromatography. Ion chromatography is finding many additional applications in the analysis of inorganic anions and cations.

The organic analytical methods are numbered in the 500s for drinking water, 600s and 1600s for surface and wastewaters, and 8000s for groundwater, landfill leachate, hazardous waste characterization, and solids. Other organic methods are found in the Contract Laboratory Program Statement of Work (CLP SOW). None of these methods are identical, although they are very similar. A number of publications have been written comparing and contrasting the methods. One is a special issue of *The Bench Sheet*, Spring, 1992, by Ann Rosencrance, published by the Water Environment Federation. Another is a series of articles by Zoe Grosser titled "EPA Methods Overview" beginning with the September/October 1992 issue of *Environmental Testing & Analysis*. Also available is the *Guide to Environmental Analytical Methods* and *Lectures in Wastewater Analysis and Interpretation* from Genium Publishing Company, One Genium Plaza, Schenectady, NY 12304-4690. These four are fairly inexpensive and a useful accessory to the printed methods. Lewis Publishers has a book titled *Compilation of EPAs Sampling and Analysis Methods* by W. Mueller, D.L. Smith, and L. Keith, which is available as either hardcopy or as a computer database, for a stiff fee. None of these materials replace having the methods on hand. They can only give guidance in picking out a method or adjusting a currently used method to another related method.

---

2   Baykut, G., and A. Voigt. "Spray Extraction of Volatile Organic Compounds from Aqueous Systems into the Gas Phase for Gas Chromatography/Mass Spectrometry." *Anal. Chem.* 64(6). 1992. pp. 677-681.

I. VOLATILES

A. Instrumentation

The basic instrument for volatile organic analysis (VOA) is a gas chromatograph equipped with a purge and trap injector[3] and a variety of detector options. The purge is accomplished by placing the sample in the sparge tube, then passing an inert gas through the sample. The purge can be performed at ambient or elevated temperatures. Purged compounds are retained on the trap, which is filled with one or more absorbents such as Tenax[4], silica gel, activated carbon, or molecular sieves. Purge gas can be passed through the trap after the completion of the sample purging cycle to remove water. The trap is heated to over 200 °C and the valve switched to route the trapped compounds to the gas chromatograph. As gas flows through the chromatographic column, and the oven temperature is raised, the target analytes are transported down the column at a rate depending on their vapor pressure and specific absorption characteristics. The compounds that exit the column (eluants) pass into a detector that tests some chemical or physical characteristic of the compound and sends the results as an electric signal (instrument response) to a processing device. The specific detector used most often constitutes the major hardware difference between the methods.

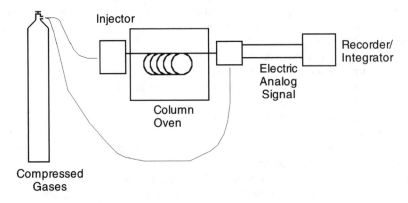

Figure 3-3. Diagram of a gas chromatograph.

---

[3] Headspace sampling with GC analysis is a viable technique that has received little EPA attention. For a comparison of headspace to purge and trap see Hewitt *et al., Environ. Sci. Technol.* 1992. 26(10). pp. 1932-1938.

[4] Tradename for a porous polymer made from 2,6-diphenyl-p-phenylene oxide.

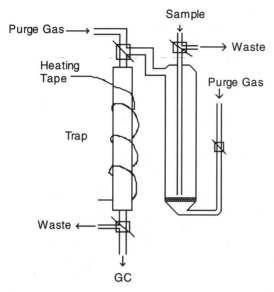

Figure 3-4.   Diagram of a purge and trap for GC.

The time required for the target analyte to transit the chromatographic column under a set of specified conditions is called the retention time. Known standards of target analytes are subjected to the GC conditions to determine the retention time, which serves as a characteristic piece of information toward establishing the identity of unknowns.

Quantitative analysis of organics is achieved by subjecting aliquots of known concentration standards to the analytical procedure and then preparing a plot of instrument response *vs.* concentration (calibration curve). Depending on the method protocol, a minimum of 3 to 5 different concentration levels of the standard must be analyzed to prepare the calibration curve. Many EPA methods require the addition of a known amount of a known compound as either a check on the efficiency of the sample preparation (surrogate) or as a means of internally calibrating the level of instrument response (internal standard). On rare occasion an added compound can serve both functions.

A key quality control for VOA requires the use of analyte-free water for blanks. This water is generated by obtaining deionized water, then boiling it for at least an hour, finally allowing it to cool while vigorously purging the water with analyte free helium or nitrogen. The water is stoppered with glass or Teflon and is generally good for 24 to 48 hours.

B. Methods

501 Trihalomethanes by GC-ECD or ELCD*

Method 501.1 requires a purge and trap injection system and a packed-column GC with a halogen specific detector to assay the four trihalomethanes. A second column is required for confirmation. Results are reported as total trihalomethanes (TTHM). Method 501.2 is a variation on TTHM determination using a 2.0 mL solvent extraction of a 10.0 mL sample, then direct injection of 3.0 μL of the solvent on the same GC-ECD or

---

* Sources of this and other cited methods can be found in the Tables in Section 1.II.

ELCD system. The recommended solvent is pentane, however hexane, methylcyclohexane or 2,2,4-trimethyl pentane (isooctane) may be substituted.

Table 3-4. Target Analytes and MDLs for Method 501

Target Analyte	MDL µg/L	Target Analyte	MDL µg/L
Trichloromethane	0.5	Dichlorobromomethane	0.5
Chlorodibromomethane	0.5	Tribromomethane	0.5

502.1 Volatile halogenated organics in drinking water by purge and trap GC-ECD or ELCD

This method uses a purge and trap with packed column GC and Hall electrolytic conductivity to determine halogenated organic target analytes. Five mL sample volumes are purged. Confirmation of identification is required using a second packed column of differing polarity. Calibration by the external standard method requires three-point calibration for a 20-fold concentration range, four-point for a 50-fold range and five-points for a 100-fold range. Internal standard calibration can be performed with either 2-bromo-1-chloropropane or 1,4-dichlorobutane as the internal standard. Daily checking of the calibration curve is required with a laboratory water spike. Further QC measures are daily analysis of a reagent blank and analysis of a laboratory water spike on each work shift.

Table 3-5. Target Analytes and MDLs for Method 502.1

Target Analyte	MDL µg/L	Target Analyte	MDL µg/L
Bromobenzene	-	1,2-Dichloroethane	0.002
Bromochloromethane	-	1,1-Dichloroethene	0.003
Bromodichloromethane	0.003	cis-1,2-Dichloroethene	0.002
Bromoform	0.05	trans-1,2-Dichloroethene	0.002
Carbon tetrachloride	0.003	1,2-Dichloropropane	-
Chlorobenzene	0.005	1,3-Dichloropropane	-
Chlorocyclohexane	-	2,2-Dichloropropane	-
1-Chlorocyclohexene	-	1,1-Dichloropropene	-
Chloroethane	0.008	cis-1,3-Dichloropropene	-
Chloroform	-	trans-1,3-Dichloropropene	-
Chloromethane	0.01	Methylene chloride	-
2-Chlorotoluene	-	1,1,1,2-Tetrachloroethane	-
4-Chlorotoluene	-	1,1,2,2-Tetrachloroethane	0.01
Dibromochloromethane	0.008	Tetrachloroethene	0.001
1,2-Dibromoethane	0.04	1,1,1-Trichloroethane	0.003
Dibromomethane	-	1,1,2-Trichloroethane	0.007
1,2-Dichlorobenzene	-	Trichloroethene	0.001
1,3-Dichlorobenzene	-	Trichlorofluoromethane	-
1,4-Dichlorobenzene	-	1,2,3-Trichloropropane	-
Dichlorodifluoromethane	-	Vinyl chloride	0.01
1,1-Dichloroethane	0.003		

502.2 Volatile organics by purge and trap capillary column GC in series with PID and ELCD

This method uses a purge and trap system to remove volatile organics from a 5.0 mL sample of water. The analysis is performed on a capillary column GC with PID and Hall detectors in series. The recommended operation of the GC is to begin the run at < -10 °C, thus requiring a cryogenically cooled oven. Liquid nitrogen is the most commonly used coolant. Tentative identification of target analytes is performed by matching retention time and by comparing response on the two detectors. GC/MS is recommended as the confirmatory technique. External or internal calibration may be performed. Suggested internal standards are either 1-chloro-2-fluorobenzene or fluorobenzene and 2-bromo-1-chloropropane. A minimum of a three-point calibration is required for a 20-fold calibration range, four-point for a 50-fold range, and five-point for a 100-fold range. Daily checking of the calibration curve is required by analysis of a calibration check standard. During each work shift a water blank and a water blank spike must be analyzed.

Table 3-6.   Target Analytes and MDLs for Method 502.2

Target Analyte	MDL μg/L	Target Analyte	MDL μg/L
Bromobenzene	0.01	Benzene	0.01
Bromochloromethane	0.01	n-Butylbenzene	0.02
Bromodichloromethane	0.02	sec-Butylbenzene	0.02
Bromoform	1.6	tert-Butylbenzene	0.06
Bromomethane	1.1	Ethylbenzene	0.01
Carbon tetrachloride	0.01	Hexachlorobutadiene	0.02
Chlorobenzene	0.01	Isopropylbenzene	0.05
Chloroethane	0.1	4-Isopropyltoluene	0.01
Chloroform	0.02	Naphthalene	0.06
Chloromethane	0.03	n-Propylbenzene	0.01
2-Chlorotoluene	0.01	Styrene	0.01
4-Chlorotoluene	0.01	Toluene	0.01
Dibromochloromethane	0.3	1,2,3-Trichlorobenzene	0.03
1,2-Dibromo-3-chloropropane	3.0	1,2,4-Trichlorobenzene	0.02
1,2-Dibromoethane	0.8	1,2,4-Trimethylbenzene	0.05
Dibromomethane	2.2	1,3,5-Trimethylbenzene	0.01
1,2-Dichlorobenzene	0.02	o-Xylene	0.02
1,3-Dichlorobenzene	0.02	m-Xylene	0.01
1,4-Dichlorobenzene	0.01	p-Xylene	0.01
Dichlorodifluoromethane	0.05	Methylene chloride	0.02
1,1-Dichloroethane	0.07	1,1,1,2-Tetrachloroethane	0.01
1,2-Dichloroethane	0.03	1,1,2,2-Tetrachloroethane	0.01
1,1-Dichloroethene	0.07	Tetrachloroethene	0.04
cis-1,2-Dichloroethene	0.01	1,1,1-Trichloroethane	0.03
trans-1,2-Dichloroethene	0.06	1,1,2-Trichloroethane	nd
1,2-Dichloropropane	0.01	Trichloroethene	0.01
1,3-Dichloropropane	0.03	Trichlorofluoromethane	0.03
2,2-Dichloropropane	0.05	1,2,3-Trichloropropane	0.4
1,1-Dichloropropene	0.02	Vinyl chloride	0.02

503.1 Volatile aromatic/unsaturated organics by purge and trap GC-PID

This is a purge and trap method with analysis of target compounds by packed column (5% SP-1200 and 1.75% Bentone 34 on Supelcoport) GC with PID. Compounds are identified by retention time and confirmed by retention times on a second packed column with a different polarity packing (5% 1,2,3-tris(2-cyanoethoxy)propane on Chromosorb W). External standard calibration may be used, however the internal standard method with α,α,α-trifluorotoluene as the internal standard is preferred. The calibration curve must be verified on each working day by analysis of a calibration check standard. Other QC measures include analysis on each work shift of laboratory reagent blanks and laboratory water spiked with the target analytes.

Table 3-7. Target Analytes and MDLs for Method 503.1

Target Analyte	MDL µg/L	Target Analyte	MDL µg/L
Benzene	0.02	4-Isopropyltoluene	0.009
Bromobenzene	0.002	Naphthalene	0.04
n-Butylbenzene	0.02	n-Propylbenzene	0.009
s-Butylbenzene	0.02	Styrene	0.008
t-Butylbenzene	0.006	Tetrachloroethene	0.01
Chlorobenzene	0.004	Toluene	0.02
2-Chlorotoluene	0.008	1,2,3-Trichlorobenzene	0.03
4-Chlorotoluene	nd	1,2,4-Trichlorobenzene	0.03
1,2-Dichlorobenzene	0.02	Trichloroethene	0.01
1,3-Dichlorobenzene	0.006	1,2,4-Trimethylbenzene	0.006
1,4-Dichlorobenzene	0.006	1,3,5-Trimethylbenzene	0.003
Ethylbenzene	0.002	o-Xylene	0.004
Hexachlorobutadiene	0.02	m-Xylene	0.004
Isopropylbenzene	0.005	p-Xylene	0.002

504.1 1,2-Dibromoethane (EDB) and 1,2-Dibromo-3-chloropropane (DBCP) by GC-ECD

This method depends on a 2.0 mL hexane extract of 35 mL of sample followed by direct injection of 2 µL of the extract onto a capillary column GC with ECD. A confirmation column is required along with normal quality control. MDL for the two compounds is 0.01 µg/L.

524.2 Capillary column GC/MS purgeable organics

The BFB tuning requirements are presented in Table 3-8.

Table 3-8. Daily BFB MS tuning criteria for Method 524.2

Mass M/z	BFB Relative Abundance Criteria
50	15 to 40% of mass 95
75	30 to 80% of mass 95
95	Base peak, 100% relative abundance
96	5 to 9% of mass 95
173	<2% of mass 174
174	>50% of mass 95
175	5 to 9% of mass 174
176	>95% but <101% of mass 174
177	5 to 9% of mass 176

The method uses an internal standard (fluorobenzene) for calibration. A minimum of three calibration standards are used for a 20-fold concentration range, four for a 50-fold range and five for a 100-fold range. Calibration may be performed by average response factors (RF), however for each calibrated analyte all individual RFs must be within 20% of the mean for the compound. The other alternative is a second- or third-order regression calibration. The calibrations must be checked at the beginning of each 12-hour shift. Surrogates, BFB and 1,2-dichlorobenzene-d_4, are also required. A 25 mL sample, spiked with the surrogates and internal standard, is purged to give the expected MDLs. The following MDLs were obtained from a wide-bore capillary (60 m x 0.75 mm VOCOL, 1.5 μm film). Use of a narrow-bore capillary (0.32 mm) gives generally better MDLs. The drinking water regulations (40 CFR 141) require a reporting limit of 0.5 μg/L for all primary volatile contaminants.

Table 3-9. Target Analytes and MDLs for Method 524.2

Target Analyte	MDL μg/L	Target Analyte	MDL μg/L
Benzene	0.04	1,3-Dichloropropane	0.04
Bromobenzene	0.03	2,2-Dichloropropane	0.35
Bromochloromethane	0.04	1,1-Dichloropropene	0.10
Bromodichloromethane	0.08	cis-1,2-Dichloropropene	-
Bromoform	0.12	trans-1,2-Dichloropropene	-
Bromomethane	0.11	Ethylbenzene	0.06
n-Butylbenzene	0.11	Hexachlorobutadiene	0.11
Benzene	0.04	1,3-Dichloropropane	0.04
tert-Butylbenzene	0.14	4-Isopropyltoluene	0.12
Carbon tetrachloride	0.21	Methylene chloride	0.03
Chlorobenzene	0.04	Naphthalene	0.04
Chloroethane	0.10	n-Propylbenzene	0.04
Chloroform	0.03	Styrene	0.04
Chloromethane	0.13	1,1,1,2-Tetrachloroethane	0.05
2-Chlorotoluene	0.04	1,1,2,2-Tetrachloroethane	0.04
4-Chlorotoluene	0.06	Tetrachloroethene	0.14
Dibromochloromethane	0.05	Toluene	0.11
DBCP	0.26	1,2,3-Trichlorobenzene	0.03
EDB	0.06	1,2,4-Trichlorobenzene	0.04
Dibromomethane	0.24	1,1,1-Trichloroethane	0.08

Continued on next page.

Table 3-9. Target Analytes and MDLs for Method 524.2, *continued*

Target Analyte	MDL µg/L	Target Analyte	MDL µg/L
1,2-Dichlorobenzene	0.03	1,1,2-Trichloroethane	0.10
1,3-Dichlorobenzene	0.12	Trichloroethene	0.19
1,4-Dichlorobenzene	0.03	Trichlorofluoromethane	0.08
Dichlorodifluoromethane	0.10	1,2,3-Trichloropropane	0.32
1,1-Dichloroethane	0.04	1,2,4-Trimethylbenzene	0.13
1,2-Dichloroethane	0.06	1,3,5-Trimethylbenzene	0.05
1,1-Dichloroethene	0.12	Vinyl chloride	0.17
cis-1,2-Dichloroethene	0.12	*o*-Xylene	0.11
trans-1,2-Dichloroethene	0.06	*m*-Xylene	0.05
1,2-Dichloropropane	0.04	*p*-Xylene	0.13

Table 3-10. Version 4.0 of 524.2 adds the following analytes

Target Analyte	MDL µg/L	Target Analyte	MDL µg/L
Acetone	0.28	Acrylonitrile	0.22
Allyl chloride	0.13	2-Butanone	0.48
Carbon disulfide	0.093	Chloroacetonitrile	0.12
1-Chlorobutane	0.18	*trans*-1,2-Dichloro-2-butene	0.36
1,1-Dichloropropanone	1.0	Diethyl ether	0.28
Ethyl methacrylate	0.028	Hexachloroethane	0.057
2-Hexanone	0.39	Methacrylonitrile	0.12
Methylacrylate	0.45	Methyl iodide	0.019
Methyl methacrylate	0.43	4-Methyl-2-pentanone	0.17
Methyl-*tert*-butyl ether	0.090	Nitrobenzene	1.2
2-Nitropropane	0.16	Pentachloroethane	0.14
Proprionitrile	0.14	Tetrahydrofuran	1.6

601 Purgeable halocarbons by GC-ELCD

The trap is at least 25 cm long and is packed from inlet to exit with 1.0 cm of methyl silicone coated packing (3% OV-1), 7.7 cm of 2,6-diphenylene oxide polymer (Tenax), 7.7 cm of silica gel, and 7.7 cm of coconut charcoal. An analysis column and confirmation column with Hall electrolytic conductivity detectors are used. The listed MDLs were obtained by EPA on 5.00 mL samples while using a 8-ft x 0.1-in ID GC column packed with 1% SP-1000 on Carbopack B (60-80 mesh). A confirmation column is required, and the suggested column is a 6-ft x 0.1-in ID column packed with chemically bonded *n*-octane on Porasil-C (100-120 mesh). All samples are required to be spiked with surrogates and recoveries calculated and maintained. Suggested surrogates are bromochloromethane, 2-bromo-1-chloropropane and 1,4-dichlorobutane. These can also be used as internal standards. Samples must be spiked with the target analytes at a minimum rate of 10% of the samples from each sampling site. Quality control check samples must be analyzed and passed on each working day prior to sample analysis. Acceptance criteria are included in the method. Target analytes that fail the daily acceptance criteria must be recalibrated. This method is most often used in series with method 602 by placing the PID detector first followed by the ELCD.

Table 3-11. Target Analytes and MDLs for Method 601

Target Analyte	MDL ppb	Target Analyte	MDL ppb
Bromodichloromethane	0.10	1,2-Dichloroethane	0.03
Bromoform	0.20	1,1-Dichloroethene	0.13
Bromomethane	1.18	*trans*-1,2-Dichloroethene	0.10
Carbon tetrachloride	0.12	1,2-Dichloropropane	0.04
Chlorobenzene	0.25	*cis*-1,3-Dichloropropene	0.34
Chloroethane	0.52	*trans*-1,3-Dichloropropene	0.20
2-Chloroethylvinyl ether	0.13	Methylene chloride	0.25
Chloroform	0.05	1,1,2,2-Tetrachloroethane	0.03
Chloromethane	0.08	Tetrachloroethene	0.03
Dibromochloromethane	0.09	1,1,1-Trichloroethane	0.03
1,2-Dichlorobenzene	0.15	1,1,2-Trichloroethane	0.02
1,3-Dichlorobenzene	0.32	Trichloroethene	0.12
1,4-Dichlorobenzene	0.24	Trichlorofluoromethane	nd
Dichlorodifluoromethane	1.81	Vinyl chloride	0.18
1,1-Dichloroethane	0.07		

602 Purgeable aromatics by GC-PID

This method is often run simultaneously with 601 by placing the PID detector in series before the Hall detector. If the method is run as a standalone, the trap is packed with 1.0 cm methyl silicone coated support (3% OV-1 on Chromosorb W) and 23 cm of 2,6-diphenylene oxide polymer (Tenax). The listed MDLs were obtained by EPA on 5.00 mL samples with a 6-ft x 0.082- in ID GC column packed with 5% SP-1200 and 1.75% Bentone-34 on Supelcoport (100-120 mesh). The confirmation column was an 8-ft x 0.1-in ID column packed with 5% 1,2,3-tris(2-cyanoethoxy)propane on Chromosorb W-AW (60-80 mesh). All samples are required to be spiked with a surrogate and recoveries calculated and maintained. The suggested surrogate is α,α,α-trifluorotoluene, which can also be used as an internal standard. Samples must be spiked with the target analytes at a minimum rate of 10% of the samples from each sampling site. Quality control check samples must be analyzed and passed on each working day prior to sample analysis. Acceptance criteria are included in the method. Target analytes that fail the daily acceptance criteria must be recalibrated.

Table 3-12. Target Analytes and MDLs for Method 602

Target Analyte	MDL µg/L	Target Analyte	MDL µg/L
Benzene	0.2	1,4-Dichlorobenzene	0.3
Toluene	0.2	1,3-Dichlorobenzene	0.4
Ethylbenzene	0.2	1,2-Dichlorobenzene	0.4
Chlorobenzene	0.2		

624 GC/MS purgeable organics

The specified trap is packed from the inlet to the exit with 1 cm 3% OV-1 on Chromosorb-W (60/80 mesh), 15 cm Tenax, and 8 cm Grade-15 silica gel (35/60 mesh). The listed MDLs were generated from 5.00 mL samples purged and the volatiles separated on a 6-ft x 0.1-in ID GC column packed with 1% SP-1000 on Carbopack B (60/80 mesh). A general variance has been granted from the EPA (Office of Science and Technology, Office of Water) for the use of capillary columns in place of the specified packed columns. The target analytes are identified by: 1) matching GC retention time *vs.* that of standards and, by 2) matching the primary peak and at least two secondary peaks in the electron impact mass spectrum obtained at 70 eV with that of the standard. The mass analyzer is tuned daily to meet relative mass abundance criteria for the tuning standard 4-bromo-1-fluorobenzene (BFB). Calibration is internal standard with a minimum of three points beginning at or slightly higher than the MDL. Individual RFs for each analyte must be within 35% RSD for use of an average RF. Otherwise a plot of RF *vs.* concentration is used. Identified compounds are quantified by the internal standard technique using the area of a key mass fragment in the mass spectrum. Internal standards and surrogates from the suggested list are added to each sample analyzed.

Samples at a minimum rate of 5% from each sampling site per month are spiked with the target analytes, i.e. the analytes on the permit, at the regulatory limit (there are other options for the spike level). In addition to the use of the required surrogates and internal standards, this point about the monthly spiking with the regulated analytes is a common item of non-compliance of commercial laboratories with Method 624. As most clients only have a requirement for a single monthly sample this means that each sample must be analyzed with a matrix spike. Obviously compliance with this part of the method is going to increase the overhead of the analysis and the expense is normally passed onto the client. For laboratories trying to win a low-price based bid from a client, the matrix spike requirement is generally the first item of quality control to be eliminated. Recoveries are calculated and maintained (control charts) for each target analyte. The recoveries listed below, in the table of target analytes for this method, were generated using a the packed column technique on a 20 μg/L reagent water spike. Use of capillary columns will drastically improve the matrix spike recoveries into the 70-130% range for most analytes in real samples, and continued use of the targets in the table by laboratories is not justified.

Continuing calibration standards containing all target analytes are analyzed on a daily basis to verify the calibration of the instrument. Target analytes not meeting calibration criteria are recalibrated.

Table 3-13. Internal Standards and Surrogates for Method 624

Benzene-d_6	1,2-Dichloroethane-d_4
Bromochloromethane	Ethylbenzene-d_5
2-Bromo-1-chloropropane	Ethylbenzene-d_{10}
4-Bromofluorobenzene	Fluorobenzene
1,4-Difluorobenzene	Pentafluorobenzene
1,4-Dichlorobutane	

Table 3-14. Daily MS tuning requirements for BFB for Method 624

Mass M/z	BFB Relative Abundance Criteria
50	15 to 40% of mass 95
75	30 to 60% of mass 95
95	Base peak, 100% relative abundance
96	5 to 9% of mass 95
173	<2% of mass 174
174	>50% of mass 95

Continued on next page.

Table 3-14. Daily MS tuning requirements for BFB for Method 624, *continued*

Mass M/z	BFB Relative Abundance Criteria
175	5 to 9% of mass 174
176	>95% but <101% of mass 174
177	5 to 9% of mass 176

Table 3-15. Target Analytes, MDLs, Precision and Accuracy (20 µg/L spike) for Method 624

Target Analyte	MDL ppb	%R	RPD
Benzene	4.4	37-151	0-14
Bromodichloromethane	2.2	35-155	0-13
Bromoform	4.7	45-169	0-11
Bromomethane	nd	D-242	0-36
Carbon tetrachloride	2.8	70-140	0-10
Chlorobenzene	6.0	37-160	0-13
Chloroethane	nd	14-230	0-23
2-Chloroethylvinyl ether	nd	D-305	0-52
Chloroform	1.6	51-138	0-12
Chloromethane	nd	D-273	0-40
Dibromochloromethane	3.1	53-149	0-12
1,2-Dichlorobenzene	nd	18-190	0-14
1,3-Dichlorobenzene	nd	59-156	0-11
1,4-Dichlorobenzene	nd	18-190	0-14
1,1-Dichloroethane	4.7	59-155	0-10
1,2-Dichloroethane	2.8	49-155	0-12
1,1-Dichloroethene	2.8	D-234	0-18
trans-1,2-Dichloroethene	1.6	54-156	0-11
1,2-Dichloropropane	6.0	D-210	0-28
cis-1,3-Dichloropropene	5.0	D-227	0-32
trans-1,3-Dichloropropene	nd	17-183	0-21
Ethylbenzene	7.2	37-162	0-15
Methylene chloride	2.8	D-221	0-15
1,1,2,2-Tetrachloroethane	6.9	46-157	0-15
Tetrachloroethene	4.1	64-148	0-10
Toluene	6.0	47-150	0-10
1,1,1-Trichloroethane	3.8	52-162	0-9
1,1,2-Trichloroethane	5.0	52-150	0-11
Trichloroethene	1.9	71-157	0-13
Trichlorofluoromethane	nd	17-181	0-20
Vinyl chloride	nd	D-251	0-40

1624 Volatile organic compounds by isotope dilution GC/MS

This method uses either deuterium or ^{13}C labeled isotopes as surrogates/internal standards. Those compounds lacking a labeled standard are calibrated against bromochloromethane as internal standard. The method requires a five-point calibration either by average RF (individual RFs must deviate less than 35% from the average) or by construction of a calibration curve. Daily tuning requirements for the MS are as listed for a 50 ng sample of BFB.

Table 3-16. Target Analytes and MDLs for Method 1624

Target Analyte	MDL ppb	Target Analyte	MDL ppb
Acetone	50	trans-1,2-Dichloroethene	10
Acrolein	50	1,2-Dichloropropane	10
Acrylonitrile	50	cis-1,3-Dichloropropene	10
Benzene	10	trans-1,3-Dichloropropene	10
Bromodichloromethane	10	Diethyl ether	50
Bromoform	10	p-Dioxane	10
Bromomethane	50	Ethyl benzene	10
Carbon tetrachloride	10	Methylene chloride	10
Chlorobenzene	10	Methyl ethyl ketone	50
Chloroethane	50	1,1,2,2-Tetrachloroethane	10
2-Chloroethylvinylether	10	Tetrachloroethene	10
Chloroform	10	Toluene	10
Chloromethane	50	1,1,1-Trichloroethane	10
Dibromochloromethane	10	1,1,2-Trichloroethane	10
1,1-Dichloroethane	10	Trichloroethene	10
1,2-Dichloroethane	10	Vinyl chloride	10
1,1-Dichloroethene	10		

Table 3-17. Daily BFB MS tuning requirements for Method 1624

Mass M/z	BFB Relative Abundance Criteria
50	15 to 40% of mass 95
75	30 to 60% of mass 95
95	Base peak, 100% relative abundance
96	5 to 9% of mass 95
173	<2% of mass 174
174	>50% of mass 95
175	5 to 9% of mass 174
176	>95% but <101% of mass 174
177	5 to 9% of mass 176

C. Solid Waste Methods

Contrasted to the Office of Water compliance monitoring methods of analysis, the solid waste methods, from SW-846, are modular, rather than complete procedures. There are sample preparation methods for liquids (5030B), solids (5035) and chemical waste samples (3585). There are general guidances in Chapters 1, 2, and 4, and Methods 5000 and 8000B are considered to be part of the procedure and should be consulted.

5030B Purge-and-trap for aqueous samples

Earlier versions of this Method described procedures for both aqueous and solid samples. In Update III, Method 5030B was reduced in scope to only aqueous samples.

The generic purge-and-trap apparatus is illustrated in Figure 3-4. An aqueous sample is added to the sparge tube with a syringe, then internal standard and surrogate solution added. The sample is purged with inert gas and the analytes transferred to the absorbent trap over a period of 10-14 minutes. The flow of gas through the trap is reversed and the trap heated to around 200 °C to move the trapped analytes to the GC column. Cryogenic cooled is sometimes used to focus the analytes at the head of the GC column. After desorption from the trap, the analytes are determined by GC or GC-MS.

5035 Closed system purge-and-trap and extraction for volatile organics in soil and waste samples

The tradition technique of collecting a soil sample for VOA by filling a 4 oz. wide-mouthed glass jar with dirt and screwing on the cap, is known to have several deficiencies. The analytes in the sample are subject to decomposition by bacteria and physical losses through volatilization. These processes manifest themselves in poor reproducibility when analyzing aliquots from the same container and sequential sampling events from the same site. Method 5035 is new to Update III of SW-846, and attempts to correct these problems by preserving samples to halt bacterial processes and hermetrically sealing the sample to prevent loss through volatilization. The method has been adopted as mandatory throughout the 10 EPA Regions.

Method 5035 presents several options in sampling, depending on the expected concentration of volatiles. Low concentration is defined as less than 200 μg/kg individual compounds. In the first option for low concentration samples, the vials are prepared ahead of time in the lab with the preservative solution (5 mL of a 20% solution of sodium bisulfate) and magnetic stir bar, then a tare weight determined. In the field a portion of solid sample is added to the pre-weighed 40 mL VOA vial, the top screwed tightly down on the vial, then the amount of sample added is immediately determined by weighing on a balance. The pH of the preserved soil must be ≤ 2, which needs to be checked on a separate sample. Samples that are classified as high-concentration are collected in pre-weighed VOA vials that contain 10.0 mL of methanol.

The second option for samples uses a specially designed sampling device that provides air-tight sealing of the sample until it is preserved in the lab. One such device is the EnCore® sampler[5]. This device uses compressed O-rings to form a seal around the sample. Each device comes in an individual foil bag that allows re-sealing with a ZipLock®-type closure. The samples are collected by pushing the EnCore® sampler into the soil, then seating the cap of the device firmly upon the sampler so that the locking lugs are engaged. The sealed device is replaced into its shipping bag, cooled to 4 °C and sent to the lab. Once in the lab the samples are transferred to either sodium bisulfate-water preservative for the low concentration samples or methanol for the higher concentration. Sample weights are determined in the lab. This must be done within 48 hours of sample collection.

Multiple samples must be taken for each sampling site as each sample represents only a single analysis. Method 5035 recommends at least duplicate samples, however practice has demonstrated that at least triplicate samples are needed. Further, if the analyte concentration is unknown, at least one additional sample needs to be taken for the high concentration methanol extraction. If quality controls such as matrix spikes and

---

[5] En Novative Technologies, Inc., 1241 Bellevue Street, Green Bay, WI 54302, 1-888-411-0757.

matrix spike duplicates are intended on the sampling site, a least two more samples must be taken, for a total of six or more vials or sampling devices.

In Method 5035 the preserved soil samples in sealed VOA vials can be held for up to 14 days from the moment of sampling. This has proven to present some problems that need to be addressed. Most persons are familiar with the collection of water samples in 40 mL VOA glass vials. The vial is sealed with a Teflon®-faced silicone septa (Teflon® against the sample) and one of the sampling/preservation requirements is that there be no air bubbles in the sample (zero headspace). One of the reasons the Teflon®-sealed vial works is that the Teflon® layer is in direct contact with the water of the sample. Organic volatiles can pass through the Teflon®-faced silicone septa, however the further movement of the analyte molecules from the Teflon® into the water sample is highly unfavorable. The direct contact of the Teflon® with the water sample serves as an additional physical barrier to movement.

In the case of the preserved soil sample in the same type of vial, the Teflon® layer is not in contact with water, rather it is in contact with air. Organic molecules diffuse through the septa into the headspace of the vial with no difficulty and cross-contamination among samples stored in the same refrigerator becomes a considerable problem. As an example, we inadvertently placed a 4 oz wide-mouthed glass jar containing gasoline-contaminated soil (150 mg/kg) in a refrigerator that contained about 40 VOA vials of sodium bisulfate-water preserved EnCore® samples. Within 2 days, all the preserved vials in the refrigerator were exhibiting from 5 to 35 µg/kg of toluene, ethyl benzene, xylenes, and other gasoline aromatics.

The bottom line is that low concentration soil samples preserved in VOA vials, need to segregated from the high concentration samples in separate refrigerators. A further suggested precaution is to prepare and monitor refrigerator blanks (5 mL water-bisulfate in a VOA vial) on a frequent basis.

The method is designed to be used with automated equipment that has a fairly stiff price tag - on the order of $20,000 for each autosampler. The autosampler serves to introduce the surrogates and internal standards solution to the vial, and then perform the purge, without puncturing the septum more than once. It also activates the magnetic stir bar in the sample to agitate the sample during the purge. Most reputable commercial laboratories have acquired the needed equipment (Precept II by Tekmar Dohrmann, Inc. or ARCHON by Varian, Inc.). However some of the more marginal labs are attempting to perform the sample manipulations by hand, while others are simply ignoring the method and equipment.

8015B   Nonhalogenated volatile organics by direct injection or purge and trap GC-FID

The earlier packed column version of this method formed the basis for the GC petroleum hydrocarbon techniques, commonly referred to as the "California Method" or the GRO method (gasoline range organic) and the DRO method (diesel range organic). Identification of compounds was confirmed using a second column of different polarity.

The method is completely revised and upgraded in Update III of SW-846. It now allows use of either packed or capillary columns for the separation and adds many new analytes, including GRO and DRO. A number of sample preparation/introduction techniques are applicable to the method including purge-and-trap, and azeotropic microdistillation (Method 5031) or solvent extraction coupled with direct injection. Most of the performance data presented in the method is derived from the azeotropic microdistillation/direct injection technique. However the most common configurations are with a purge-and-trap for GRO and a solvent extraction/direct injection for DRO.

Suggested internal standards for the azeotropic distillation procedure are 2-chloroacrylonitrile, hexafluoro-2-propanol, hexafluoro-2-methyl-2-propanol. The use of at least one or two surrogates are suggested during the analysis, however no particular compounds are listed. *o*-Terphenyl is present in the example DRO chromatograms as a surrogate.

Initial calibrations consist of at least 5 concentrations that describe the upper and lower boundaries of the calibration range. Use of a calibration factor (CF) is allowed if the %RSD of the target analyte is ≤ 20%. Otherwise one of the other options in Method 8000B can be used. DRO and GRO are calibrated as total area under the envelope of the pattern. Column bleed profiles are allowed to be subtracted from the total area for quantitation of DRO. Continuing calibration verification must be evaluated every 12 hours, with a %D of ≤ 15%.

Retention time windows are developed for 2-methylpentane and 1,2,4-trimethylbenzene for identification of GRO, and n-decane (C_{10}) and n-octacosane (C_{28}) for DRO. These compounds are also used to define the boundaries of the elution pattern for quantitation.

Table 3-18. Target Analytes and MDLs[6] for Method 8015B

Target Analyte	MDL µg/L	Target Analyte	MDL µg/L
Acetone	48	Acetonitrile	15
Acrolein	13	Acrylonitrile	8
Allyl alcohol	nd	n-Butyl alcohol	14
t-Butyl alcohol	8	Crotonaldehyde	nd
Diethyl ether	nd	1,4-Dioxane	12
Ethanol	18	Ethyl acetate	9
Ethylene glycol	nd	Ethylene oxide	8
Isobutyl alcohol	11	Isopropyl alcohol	18
Methanol	21	Methyl ethyl ketone (MEK)	4
Methyl isobutyl ketone (MIBK)	4	N-Nitroso-di-n-butylamine	nd
Paraldehyde	nd	2-Pentanone	2
2-Picoline	nd	n-Propyl alcohol	nd
Propionitrile	10	Pyridine	11

8021B Halogenated and aromatic volatiles by direct injection or purge and trap capillary column GC with ELCD and PID detectors in series

Method 8021B is the most common method used by laboratories that lack GC-MS. This is a reliable method for obtaining information that the analyte is absent from the sample, however the presence of analyte must be confirmed by a definitive method. Identification in Method 8021B consists of matching the responses from the two detectors and the retention time with that of standards, which is unreliable. This method is only for use in RCRA programs and is not equivalent to a combined 601-602 method for NPDES support, which requires a second column or GC/MS for confirmation. Fluorobenzene

---

6   Azeotropic microdistillation with direct injection on reagent water matrix.

and 2-bromo-1-chloropropane are used as internal standards. The surrogates consist of 1,4-dichlorobutane and bromochlorobenzene. A minimum of five calibration levels are used.

There is a place for this method within RCRA analysis. After a site has been completely characterized, with all present analytes identified using the definitive methods of GC-MS, then as the site remediation progresses, Method 8021B can be used to monitor the removal of the analytes of interest.

The ELCD detector of Method 8021B can be replaced with an FID, and the resulting hybrid 8015B/8021B instrument used for BTEX and GRO, or PAH and DRO evaluations. Although the GRO and DRO identifications are acceptable based on pattern recognition, the individual BTEX and PAH identifications must be confirmed, generally by GC-MS.

8260B   Volatile organic compounds by capillary column GC/MS

Update III to the Third Edition of SW-846 deleted the packed column VOA GC-MS method, 8240, in favor of the capillary column method 8260B. Besides the packed column/capillary column differences between the techniques the analyte lists were significantly different. In revision B to Method 8260, the two analyte lists have been merged, and a number of new analytes added. The scope of Method 8260B now covers 121 analytes, only about 95 of which can be isolated from the sample using purge-and-trap.

Method 8260B only covers the GC and MS set-up and operation. The purge-and-trap (Methods 5030B or 5035), normally considered to be an integral part of the instrument, is just one of several sample preparation/introduction methods that can be used with Method 8260B. Others include waste dilution (Method 3585), headspace screening (Method 3810), hexadecane extraction (Method 3820), headspace analysis of soils (Method 5021), azeotropic distillation (Method 5031), vacuum distillation (Method 5032), and desorption of sorbent cartridges (Method 5041A). Performance data from these various techniques are presented at the end of the Method and should be consulted.

A variety of capillary columns/instrument configurations are suggested for use with 8260B, the 60 meter x 0.75 mm ID VOCOL megabore capillary column by Supelco with a temperature program from 10 °C to 160 °C being one of them. This configuration can accept all the input from the trap, however it would overload the mass spectrometer, and thus it requires a jet separator. The 25 meter x 0.20 mm ID 624 column from Hewlett-Packard is another good choice. It requires a split of the trap input, generally 50:1, however the column flow of 1 mL/min can be directly plumbed into the mass detector source. Use of either of these configurations, along with pressure-programming can allow analysis of over 80 analytes with 7 internal standards and surrogates, base-line separation being achieved with most of the calibrated analytes, and the runtime around 18 minutes. Table 3-24 presents a 85 target analyte list in elution order, along with reasonable reporting limits from a 5-mL purge that can be achieved under these conditions. This list covers the regulatory requirements of the Appendix I, II, and IX analytes, as well as the common drinking water and wastewater analytes.

Calibration of Method 8260B is in accordance with Method 8000B, and requires at least a 5-level calibration, the lowest point being at the reporting limit or MDL. Surrogates should be calibrated just like target analytes at five different concentrations. A linear calibration is achieved using the response factor approach, if the %RSD of the analyte's response factors is ≤ 15%. Another option is the linear regression approach where a regression coefficient (r) of ≥ 0.99 must be obtained. Non-linear calibrations are permitted, but require more than 5 calibration levels.

At the start of each 12 hour analytical period, the instrument is first tuned to 4-bromofluorobenzene (BFB) , using the criteria listed in Table 3-19. Then the calibration is verified by analysis of a mid-level calibration standard. Each analyte (including surrogates) must exhibit a %D $\leq 20\%$ to be considered still in calibration. The run additionally serves to update the user library of target analyte mass spectra, however quantitation remains based on the initial calibration results. The retention time of the internal standards must be within ± 30 seconds of the times in the initial calibration. System performance check compounds (SPCC) and calibration check compounds (CCC), Tables 3-20 and 3-21, are analyzed each 12 hours to evaluate and verify instrument performance, however they are not substitutes for calibration verification of each target analyte.

There is great variation in the definition of a batch as applied to volatiles analysis using Method 8260B. Some laboratories will define a batch based on sample preparation, while others use the concept of sample delivery group (SDG), an artifact from the CLP. With the purge-and-trap GC-MS, the operation of the GC-MS should be separated from the operation of the purge-and-trap. Thus the sample-related quality controls (batch blanks, matrix spikes, and laboratory control samples) need to be performed for every 20 analytical samples run through the purge-and-trap. The instrument quality controls (tuning, calibration verification, SPCC, and CCC) need to be performed every 12 hours. However, it is inappropriate to run some samples in the batch through one purge-and-trap and others through a different purge-and-trap.

Table 3-19. Daily MS BFB tuning requirements for Method 8260B

Mass M/z	BFB Relative Abundance Criteria
50	15 to 40% of mass 95
75	30 to 60% of mass 95
95	Base peak, 100% relative abundance
96	5 to 9% of mass 95
173	<2% of mass 174
174	>50% of mass 95
175	5 to 9% of mass 174
176	>95% but <101% of mass 174
177	5 to 9% of mass 176

Table 3-20. SPCC requirements for Method 8260B

SPCC	Minimum RF	SPCC	Minimum RF
Chloromethane	0.300	1,1-Dichloroethane	0.300
Bromoform	0.250	1,1,2,2-Tetrachloroethane	0.300
Chlorobenzene	0.300		

Table 3-21. CCC requirements for Method 8260B

CCC	% RSD	CCC	%RSD
1,1-Dichloroethene	<30	Chloroform	<30
1,2-Dichloropropane	<30	Toluene	<30
Ethylbenzene	<30	Vinyl chloride	<30

Table 3-22. Surrogates and Internal Standards for Method 8260B

4-Bromofluorobenzene (surr)
Chlorobenzene-d_5 (is)
Dibromofluoromethane (surr)
1,4-Dichlorobenzene-d_4 (is)
1,4-Difluorobenzene (is)
Toluene-d_8 (surr)
1,2-Dichloroethane-d_4 (surr)

Table 3-23. Minimum matrix spike compounds for Method 8260B

Benzene
Chlorobenzene
1,1-Dichloroethene
Toluene
Trichloroethene

Table 3-24. Target Analytes and PQL for Method 5030B or 5035 and 8260B, in elution time order[7]

Target Analyte	Retention Time min	PQL μg/L
Dichlorodifluoromethane	1.24	3
Chloromethane	1.39	2
Vinyl chloride	1.48	1
Bromomethane	1.75	10
Chloroethane	1.84	2
Trichlorofluoromethane	2.08	3
Ethanol	2.09	250
Diethyl ether	2.39	5
Acrolein	2.51	25
1,1-Dichloroethene	2.60	0.12
Acetone	2.68	25
Acetonitrile	2.69	50
Iodomethane	2.75	2
Carbon disulfide	2.81	10
Allyl chloride	3.03	5
Methylene chloride	3.19	2

Continued on next page.

---

[7] HP 624 column 25m x 0.20 mm id, 1.12 μm film thickness, 50:1 split, constant flow mode at 1.00 mL/min, temperature program 35 °C for 4 min, followed by 12.5°/min to 200 °C.

Table 3-24. Target Analytes and PQL for Method 5030B or 5035 and 8260B, in elution time order[8], *continued*

Target Analyte	Retention Time min	PQL µg/L
Acrylonitrile	3.54	20
trans-1,2-Dichloroethene	3.54	2
Methyl-*t*-butyl ether	3.58	5
1,1-Dichloroethane	4.18	2
Vinyl acetate	4.32	2
2,2-Dichloropropane	5.02	10
cis-1,2-Dichloroethene	5.05	2
2-Butanone	5.11	10
Propionitrile	5.19	50
Methyl acrylate	5.26	5
Bromochloromethane	5.37	2
Methacrylonitrile	5.37	50
Tetrahydrofuran	5.43	5
Chloroform	5.53	2
1,1,1-Trichloroethane	5.71	2
Dibromofluoromethane (Surr)	5.74	-
1-Chlorobutane	5.88	10
Isobutanol	5.90	250
Carbon tetrachloride	5.92	2
1,1-Dichloropropene	5.94	2
1,2-Dichloroethane-d$_4$ (Surr)	6.14	-
Benzene	6.20	1
1,2-Dichloroethane	6.24	2
Fluorobenzene (IS)	6.57	-
1,4-Difluorobenzene (IS)	6.74	-
Trichloroethene	7.03	2
1,4-Dioxane	7.15	100
1,2-Dichloropropane	7.30	2
Dibromomethane	7.44	2
Methylmethacrylate	7.52	10
Bromodichloromethane	7.66	10
2-Nitropropane	7.94	20
2-Chloroethylvinyl ether	8.06	2
cis-1,3-Dichloropropene	8.20	2
4-Methyl-2-pentanone	8.41	5
Toluene-d$_8$ (Surr)	8.49	-
Toluene	8.57	2
trans-1,3-Dichloropropene	8.86	2
Ethyl methacrylate	9.01	2
1,1,2-Trichloroethane	9.07	2

Continued on next page.

---

[8] HP 624 column 25m x 0.20 mm id, 1.12 µm film thickness, 50:1 split, constant flow mode at 1.00 mL/min, temperature program 35 °C for 4 min, followed by 12.5°/min to 200 °C.

Table 3-24. Target Analytes and PQL for Method 5030B or 5035 and 8260B, in elution time order[9], *continued*

Target Analyte	Retention Time min	PQL μg/L
Tetrachloroethene	9.20	2
1,3-Dichloropropane	9.25	2
2-Hexanone	9.39	10
Dibromochloromethane	9.51	1
1,2-Dibromoethane	9.61	5
Chlorobenzene-d_5 (IS)	10.17	-
Chlorobenzene	10.20	2
1,1,1,2-Tetrachloroethane	10.31	1
Ethylbenzene	10.35	2
p+m-Xylene	10.48	3
o-Xylene	10.94	2
Styrene	10.96	2
Bromoform	11.16	10
Isopropylbenzene	11.38	10
Bromofluorobenzene (Surr)	11.54	-
Bromobenzene	11.70	2
1,1,2,2-Tetrachloroethane	11.75	2
1,2,3-Trichloropropane	11.78	3
1,4-Dichloro-2-butene	11.81	5
n-Propylbenzene	11.86	2
2-Chlorotoluene	11.94	2
4-Chlorotoluene	12.07	2
1,3,5-Trimethylbenzene	12.07	2
p-Isopropyltoluene	12.45	2
Pentachloroethane	12.45	10
tert-Butylbenzene	12.45	2
1,2,4-Trimethylbenzene	12.50	2
sec-Butylbenzene	12.70	2
1,3-Dichlorobenzene	12.81	2
1,4-Dichlorobenzene-d_4 (IS)	12.89	-
1,4-Dichlorobenzene	12.92	2
1,2-Dichlorobenzene	13.35	2
n-Butylbenzene	13.36	2
Hexachloroethane	13.64	5
1,2-Dibromo-3-chloropropane	14.27	10
Nitrobenzene	14.27	20
1,2,4-Trichlorobenzene	15.24	2
Hexachlorobutadiene	15.46	2
Naphthalene	15.52	5
1,2,3-Trichlorobenzene	15.81	2

[9] HP 624 column 25m x 0.20 mm id, 1.12 μm film thickness, 50:1 split, constant flow mode at 1.00 mL/min, temperature program 35 °C for 4 min, followed by 12.5°/min to 200 °C.

II. SEMIVOLATILES

A. Instrumentation

The instruments used in semivolatiles analysis are primarily GC and HPLC for separation and a wide variety of general and selective detectors for analysis. In general-purpose production-oriented labs the instruments on-site will be dual capillary column-dual injector GC with dual ECD, single injector capillary column quadrupole GC/MS for semivolatiles, purge-and-trap equipped single capillary column quadrupole GC/MS for volatiles, and HPLC with post-column derivatization-fluorescence detector and DAD. There may be GC-FID instruments as screening tools or if a lot of petroleum hydrocarbon analysis is being performed.

The quadrupole GC/MS is the workhorse of the lab. Most samples in the volatiles and semivolatiles labs are analyzed by GC/MS. The only reason for having the GC-ECD is because the detection limits required for chlorinated pesticides under the various regulatory programs are so low that the quadrupole GC/MS can't see them. Otherwise the GC-ECD wouldn't be there either. Recent advances by GC/MS manufacturers may bring this about. The quadrupole MS is the preferred instrument because it has the ruggedness to handle the garbage overload present in environmental samples, which the ion trap MS doesn't. This is despite the fact that the ion trap is at least 10 times more sensitive than the quadrupole.

Another reason for the primacy of the GC/MS in the lab is that the MS is a three-dimensional detector and gives analyte identification and confirmation in one run. Most GC instruments have slots for two detectors. If the slots are occupied by a PID and ELCD for volatiles analysis, even though in series, there is room for only one column in the instrument. Thus, to perform 601-602 in compliance with the method, two instruments are required to provide the required confirmation. Most production labs like to operate with a primary instrument and a back-up for the times when the primary is down due to maintenance or repair. This means four GCs are required for the 601-602 samples. On the semivolatiles side, performance of methods 604, 606, 607, 609, 610, 611, 612, 614, 616, 619, 620, 622, and a slew of others would require duplicate GCs equipped with dual ECD, dual FPD, dual NPD, and dual FID; or a single GC/MS with back-up. These considerations plus gas consumption, service contracts, technician salaries, instrument flexibility and GC consumables, such as columns, lead to economics that suggest that the GC/MS is the way to go. Most profitable labs have gone this way.

Balanced against these considerations is the reality of "If I buy an instrument, can I get in enough work to pay for it and still make a profit?" This is the major reason that HPLC/MS has not prospered in the environmental laboratory industry. It's a marvelous instrument. However, until the government regulations are written to require it as a necessary tool to achieve industrial discharge regulatory compliance, there is no profit to be made by paying $200,000 and performing analyses that can be more cheaply performed by a $50,000 HPLC state-of-the-art system, which is itself still (1999) a marginal investment. The same can be said of capillary electrophoresis and ion chromatography - nice instruments, but can the laboratory make a profit?

A diagram of a generic gas chromatography for direct injection is presented in Figure 3-5. The dual column instruments operate with a single auto-sampler and dual auto-injectors that are attached to the columns. The auto-sampler will place sample X in the front injector turret and then place sample Y in the back turret. The auto-injectors process the samples at the same time and make simultaneous injections onto the columns. The oven program starts, and samples X and Y are analyzed on the two different columns.

At the completion of the run, the data for X and Y are processed and stored in the computer. The autosampler next places sample Y in the front turret and sample Z in the back turret. At the completion of the run chromatograms have been generated for sample Y on both the analytical and the confirmation columns.

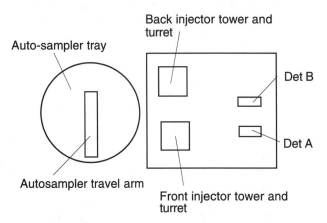

Figure 3-5.   Diagram of dual column GC.

B. Methods 500, 600, and 1600 Series

505   Organohalide pesticides & PCBs by GC-ECD

This is a micro-extraction method that uses 2.0 mL of hexane to extract chlorinated pesticides and PCBs from 35 mL of sample. Two µL of extract are assayed by capillary column (DB-1) GC equipped with an electron capture detector. Use of a confirmation capillary column (OV-17 or Durawax-DX3 are recommended) for identification verification is mandatory. Quantification is an external standard with a calibration curve (minimum three-point, recommended five-point). Daily analysis of reagent blanks, calibration check standards and laboratory water spikes are required. At least 10% of the samples must be analyzed as matrix spikes

Table 3-25. Target Analytes and MDLs for Method 505

Target Analyte	MDL µg/L	Target Analyte	MDL µg/L
Aldrin	0.075	*cis*-Nonachlor	0.027
Alachlor	0.225	*trans*-Nonachlor	0.011
Atrazine	2.4	Simazine	6.8
Chlordane	0.14	Toxaphene	1.0
Dieldrin	0.012	Aroclor 1016	0.08
Endrin	0.063	Aroclor 1221	15.0
Heptachlor	0.003	Aroclor 1232	0.48
Heptachlor epoxide	0.004	Aroclor 1242	0.31
Hexachlorobenzene	0.002	Aroclor 1248	0.102
Hexachlorocyclopentadiene	0.13	Aroclor 1254	0.102
Lindane	0.003	Aroclor 1260	0.189
Methoxychlor	0.96		

506 Phthalate and Adipate esters by GC-PID

Three isolation/concentration techniques are allowed to be used for sample preparation. The first is a liquid-liquid separatory funnel extraction using 1 L of sample with 50 g sodium chloride added and then extracted 3 x 60 mL CH_2Cl_2 and one time with 40 mL hexane. The combined organic layers are dried with sodium sulfate, and concentrated to 1.0 mL using a K-D and nitrogen blowdown. The second technique uses a reversed phase C-18 solid phase cartridge to isolate and concentrate the analytes, then they are eluted with 10 mL CH_2Cl_2 followed by drying (Na_2SO_4) and nitrogen blowdown to 1.0 mL. The third procedure uses 47 mm reversed-phase extraction disks to isolate the analytes that are eluted with acetonitrile and methylene chloride. Further cleanup of the sample extract is possible through florisil or alumina columns.

Calibration is external standard with a minimum of three-point calibration. The GC system is calibrated daily. Identification confirmation is required for this method. A GC/MS is the suggested confirmation instrument.

Table 3-26. Target Analytes and MDLs for Method 506

Target Analyte	MDL µg/L	Target Analyte	MDL µg/L
Dimethyl phthalate	1.14	Bis(2-ethylhexyl) adipate	11.82
Diethyl phthalate	0.84	Bis (2-ethylhexyl) phthalate	2.25
Di-n-butyl phthalate	1.23	Di-n-octyl phthalate	6.42
Butyl benzyl phthalate	2.67		

507 N & P pesticides by GC-NPD

Nitrogen- and phosphorus-containing pesticides are determined by addition of the surrogate (1,3-dimethyl-2-nitrobenzene) to 1.00 L of sample, buffering to pH 7 with phosphate buffer, extraction with methylene chloride, concentration in a K-D apparatus, solvent transfer to methyl-t-butylether (MTBE) and volume adjustment to 5.0 mL. Internal standard is added (triphenylphosphine) and the sample analyzed by capillary column (DB-5) GC with a Nitrogen Phosphorous detector. Identification is confirmed on a second column (DB-1701). Target analytes are quantified by response factors obtained from calibration curves (three-point minimum, five-point recommended). The calibration curves are checked on each working shift by analysis of a calibration check standard. [Alternately an external standard calibration is allowed.] Matrix spikes are required at a rate of 5% of the samples analyzed. A daily system performance check must be made for sensitivity (vernolate), chromatographic performance (bromacil) and column performance (prometon and atrazine). Daily analysis of reagent blanks and laboratory water spikes are required.

Table 3-27. Target Analytes and MDLs for Method 507

Target Analyte	MDL µg/L	Target Analyte	MDL µg/L
Alachlor	0.38	Methyl paraoxon	2.5
Ametryn	2	Metolachlor	0.75
Ametraton	0.6	Metribuzin	0.15

Continued on next page.

Table 3-27. Target Analytes and MDLs for Method 507, *continued*

Target Analyte	MDL µg/L	Target Analyte	MDL µg/L
Atrazine	0.13	Mevinphos	5
Bromacil	2.5	MGK 264	0.5
Butachlor	0.38	Molinate	0.15
Butylate	0.15	Napropamide	0.25
Carboxin	0.6	Norflurazon	0.5
Chlorpropham	0.5	Pebulate	0.13
Cycloate	0.25	Prometon	0.3
Diazinon	0.25	Prometryn	0.19
Dichlorvos	2.5	Pronamide	0.76
Diphenamid	0.6	Propazine	0.13
Disulfoton	0.3	Simazine	0.075
Disulfoton sulfone	3.8	Simetryn	0.25
Disulfoton sulfoxide	0.38	Stirofos	0.76
EPTC	0.25	Tebuthiuron	1.3
Ethoprop	0.19	Terbacil	4.5
Fenamiphos	1	Terbufos	0.5
Fenarimol	0.38	Terbutryn	0.25
Fluridone	3.8	Triademefon	0.65
Hexazinone	0.76	Tricyclazole	1
Merphos	0.25	Vernolate	0.13

508 Chlorinated pesticides by GC-ECD

Chlorinated pesticides are determined by addition of the surrogate (4,4'-Dichloro-biphenyl) to 1.00 L of sample, buffering to pH 7 with phosphate buffer, extraction with methylene chloride, concentration in a K-D apparatus, solvent transfer to methyl *t*-butyl ether (MTBE) and volume adjustment to 5.0 mL. Internal standard is added (Penta-chloronitrobenzene) and the sample analyzed by capillary column (DB-5) GC with an electron capture detector. Identification is confirmed on a second capillary column (DB-1701). Target analytes are quantified by response factors obtained from calibration curves (three-point minimum, five-point recommended). The calibration curve is veri-fied on each work shift by analysis of a calibration check standard. Daily (or 5% of samples performed daily) analysis of a laboratory water spike is required. System per-formance is checked daily by analysis of a laboratory performance check sample for sensitivity (chloropyrifos), chromatographic performance (DCPA) and column perfor-mance (chlorothalonil and δ-BHC).

Table 3-28. Target Analytes and MDLs for Method 508

Target Analyte	MDL µg/L	Target Analyte	MDL µg/L
Aldrin	0.075	Endrin aldehyde	0.025
Chlorneb	0.5	Etridiazole	0.025
Chlorobenzilate	5	α-BHC	0.025
Chlordane	0.0015	β-BHC	0.01

Continued on next page.

Table 3-28. Target Analytes and MDLs for Method 508, *continued*

Target Analyte	MDL µg/L	Target Analyte	MDL µg/L
Chlorthalonil	0.025	δ-BHC	0.01
DCPA	0.025	γ-BHC	0.015
4,4'-DDD	0.0025	Heptachlor	0.01
4,4'-DDE	0.01	Heptachlor epoxide	0.015
4,4'-DDT	0.06	Hexachlorobenzene	0.0077
Dieldrin	0.02	Methoxychlor	0.05
Endosulfan I	0.015	*cis*-Permethrin	0.5
Endosulfan II	0.024	*trans*-Permethrin	0.5
Endosulfan sulfate	0.015	Propachlor	0.5
Endrin	0.015	Trifluralin	0.025

508A   PCBs by derivatization and GC-ECD

This method serves as a pass/fail screening method for detection of PCBs in water with a MDL of 0.5 ppb. The sample (1.0 L) is extracted with methylene chloride; the extract is concentrated in a K-D apparatus; and the solvent exchanged to chloroform. The PCBs are transformed to decachlorobiphenyl by the reaction in Figure 3-6. Antimony pentachloride reacts with the biphenyl in the presence of the iron powder catalyst to perchlorinate the biphenyl in a sealed tube at 205 °C. After cooling the reaction to room temperature 1:1 hydrochloric acid and water destroy the excess $SbCl_5$. The decachlorobiphenyl is extracted into exactly 5.0 mL hexane, and the excess acid is neutralized with sodium bicarbonate followed by analysis on either a packed or capillary column GC with electron capture detector. A five-point calibration curve is required with daily analysis of reagent blanks and analysis of calibration check standards each working shift. Additional QC measures are analysis of laboratory water spikes and matrix spikes at a rate of 5% of the samples determined or at least daily.

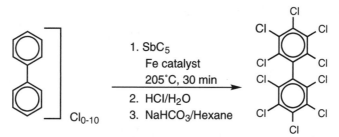

Figure 3-6.   Derivatization of biphenyls to decachlorobiphenyl.

513   2,3,7,8-TCDD by GC-High Resolution MS

This is an isotopic dilution method using $^{37}Cl_4$-TCDD as the surrogate compound and $^{13}C_{12}$-TCDD as the internal standard. One L of sample is extracted with CH_2Cl_2, dried and concentrated to 10 µL. (Disk extraction is allowed as an alternate). Further sample cleanup is performed with sequential silica gel and alumina columns. Aliquots of 2.0 µL injections into the GC High Res. MS are made. Calibration is five-point, checked every 12-hours. RFs are allowed to vary to 20% RSD from the average.

515.1 Chlorinated acid herbicides by GC-ECD; 515.2 Chlorinated acid herbicides by solid disk extraction and GC-ECD; and 515.3 Chlorinated acid herbicides by liquid-liquid extraction, derivatization and GC-ECD

The surrogate compound (2,4-dichlorophenylacetic acid, DCAA) is added to 200 mL to 1.0 L of the sample, the solution made strongly basic (pH 12) with sodium hydroxide and then periodically shaken over 1 hr. This serves to convert any esters or amine salts into the water soluble sodium salt of the acid.

$$RCO_2CH_3 \text{ or } RCO_2^-NR'_4^+ \text{ --- } NaOH \longrightarrow RCO_2Na$$

The sample is washed three times with methylene chloride to remove any base/neutral interferences. The sample is strongly acidified (pH < 2) with sulfuric acid to form the water insoluble free acids.

$$RCO_2Na \text{ --- } H_2SO_4 \longrightarrow RCO_2H$$

In 515.1 and 515.3 the acidified sample is next extracted with ethyl ether ($CH_3CH_2OCH_2CH_3$) and concentrated in a K-D apparatus with solvent exchange to methyl *tert*-butyl ether (MTBE). Methanol is added, and the sample esterified with diazomethane.

$$RCO_2H \text{ --- } CH_2N_2 \longrightarrow RCO_2CH_3$$

In Method 515.2 isolation of the target analytes from the acidified solution is achieved with a polystyrenedivinylbenzene 47 mm disk. The analytes are eluted from the disk with a methanol:MTBE (10:90) solution.

Two methods for generation of diazomethane are presented in the methods, both beginning with Diazald® (*N*-methyl-*N*-nitroso-*p*-toluenesulfonamide):

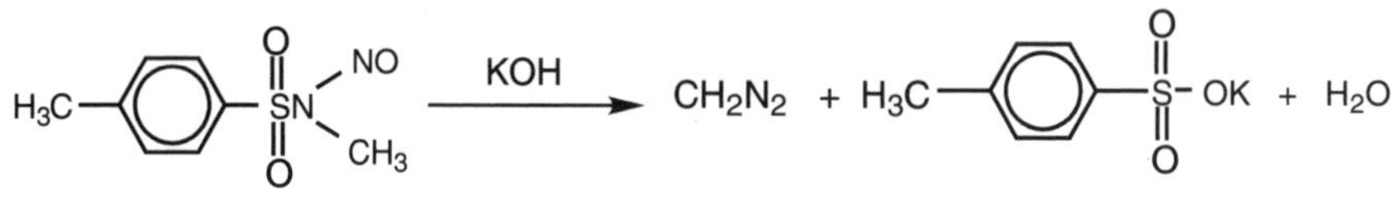

Figure 3-7. Generation of diazomethane from Diazald®.

The Diazald reaction can either be performed in bulk with distillation or in a 2-tube microgenerator. The latter procedure can be employed for methylation of up to 30 samples by addition of successive portions of Diazald to the reaction tube. An ether-saturated nitrogen stream is used to sweep the diazomethane from the reaction tube into the sample. Two points of contamination exist in the device: the connectors used to form the joints between the glass tubes and the delivery tube. The EPA methods suggest using rubber tubing for the connections, however a 1/4:1/4 screw fit Teflon® union is a suitable substitution with reduced chance of sample contamination. Use of disposable pipets for the delivery tube, which is changed with every sample, also reduces carryover. The biggest drawback to this procedure is the continuous venting of diazomethane into the air. Placing the apparatus in a hood with at least 100 cfs draw can lessen the hazard to the operator, however the diazomethane is still around.

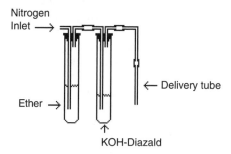

Figure 3-8. Diazald® microgenerator for diazomethane.

A simpler means of generating diazomethane, and potentially less of an explosion hazard, begins with 1-methyl-3-nitro-1-nitrosoguanidine, which is unfortunately a potent mutagen, teratogen, and carcinogen. **DO NOT USE GROUND GLASS VESSELS OR SCRATCHED GLASSWARE WITH ANY DIAZOMETHANE METHOD DUE TO THE VIOLENT EXPLOSIONS THAT ARE TRIGGERED BY CONTACT OF DIAZOMETHANE WITH ROUGH SURFACES.** Dissolve 2.3 g potassium hydroxide (KOH) in 2.3 mL of laboratory water in a 125 Erlenmeyer flask. Add 25 mL of ethyl ether and cool in the freezer. Perform the rest of the steps in a hood. Add 1.5 g 1-methyl-3-nitro-1-nitrosoguanidine in small portions over a period of several minutes to the cold mixture, and agitate the mixture well between additions. A white solid forms with a yellow ether layer. The ether layer contains the diazomethane. Decant the ether into a 40 mL glass vial with a Teflon® faced septum seal. Store in a < 0 °F freezer. Diazomethane can be added to desired reactions by disposable pipet. (Fire polish the end of the pipet first.)

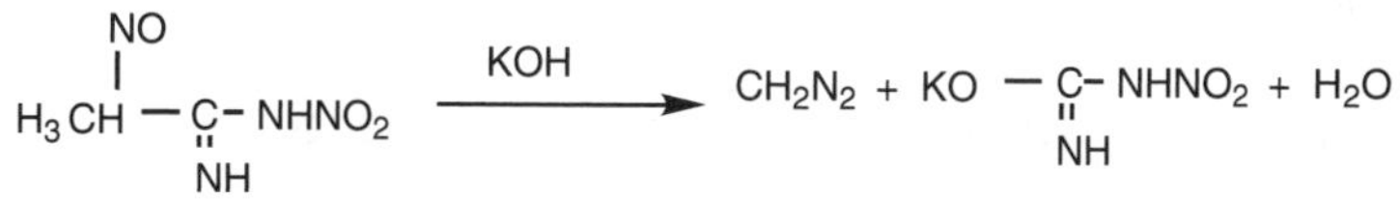

$$
\underset{\substack{| \\ NH}}{H_3CH - \overset{NO}{\overset{|}{\underset{\|}{C}}} - NHNO_2} \xrightarrow{\ KOH\ } CH_2N_2 + KO - \underset{\substack{\| \\ NH}}{C} - NHNO_2 + H_2O
$$

**Figure 3-9. Generation of diazomethane from 1-methyl-3-nitro-1-
              nitrosoguanidine.**

For the true acids, the reaction with diazomethane is almost instantaneous, even at 0 °C. Phenols and other compounds take longer to react.

An interesting development in the derivatization of organic acids to methyl esters is the use of trimethylsilyldiazomethane (*Yuki Gosei Kagaku Kyokaishi*. 44(2). 1986. pp. 149-159; *Chem Pharm. Bull.* 1981. 29. p. 3249). The material is safe and stable, available commercially as a 2.0 *M* solution in hexanes. It is reported to react instantly with organic acids at room temperature in methanol to give the methyl esters. However the directions in Method 515.2 call for heating the sample at 50 ˚C for 1 hour. Derivatization of phenols requires methanol/acetonitrile solvent, addition of ethyldiisopropyl amine as a base and heating at 50 ˚C.

Method 515.3 also presents a base-catalyzed esterification process using tetramethylammonium hydroxide and methyl iodide, with heating at 50 °C for 1.5 hours.

The sample after esterification is chromatographed on Florisil®. Internal standard (4,4'-dibromooctafluorobiphenyl, DBOB) is added and the solution analyzed by capillary column (DB-5) GC with electron capture detector. The method requires use of a capillary confirmation column (DB-1701) for identification verification. A minimum of a three-point calibration curve is prepared (five-point is recommended) with procedural calibration standards (each standard is taken through the entire sample preparation process) and checked at least once during every work shift by analysis of a calibration check standard. [An external standard calibration is allowed with a minimum of a three-point calibration curve, which must be verified during each work shift through analysis of at least two different calibration check standards.] Required quality control procedures include daily analysis of a laboratory reagent blank, analysis of a laboratory water spike daily or every 20 samples, and analysis of a sample matrix spike daily or every 10 samples. In addition the instrument system must be checked on a daily basis with a laboratory performance check sample for sensitivity (Dinoseb), chromatographic performance (4-nitrophenol) and column performance (3,5-dichlorobenzoic acid and 4-nitrophenol).

Table 3-29. Target Analytes and MDLs for Methods 515

Target Analyte	MDL µg/L	Target Analyte	MDL µg/L
Aciflourfen	0.096	Dichlorprop	0.26
Bentazon	0.2	Dinoseb	0.19
Chloramben	0.093	5-Hydroxydicamba	0.04
2,4-D	0.2	4-Nitrophenol	0.13
Dalapon	1.3	Pentachlorophenol	0.076
2,4-DB	0.8	Picloram	0.14
DCPA acid metabolites	0.02	2,4,5-T	0.08
Dicamba	0.081	2,4,5-TP	0.075
3,5-Dichlorobenzoic acid	0.061		

525.2 Semivolatile organics in drinking water by GC-MS

A 1.0 L sample is acidified to pH 2.0, and internal standards (acenaphthalene-d_{10}, phenanthrene-d_{10}, and chrysene-d_{12}) and surrogate (perylene-d_{12}) added. Analytes are isolated on a C-18 reversed-phase cartridge and eluted with 10 mL CH_2Cl_2 followed by sodium sulfate drying and nitrogen blowdown to 1.0 mL. Recovery standard (terphenyl-d_{14}) is added and 1-2 µL aliquots assayed by GC-MS (ion trap suggested). The MS must be tuned to DFTPP requirements at the start of each 8-hour shift. Calibration is a 6-point calibration. If performed by RF, each RF for an individual compound must be within 30% RSD from the average RF for that compound. A linear, second-, or third-degree regression calibration curve may be prepared and used as an alternative. The calibration is checked at the beginning of each work shift. EPA has published a revision of this method, 525.2 (February, 1994, available from EMSL, Cincinnati) that includes analyte isolation on extraction disks. It also has an interferences note concerning loss of PAH analytes in samples which are not dechlorinated at the time of collection.

Table 3-30. Target Analytes and MDLs for Method 525.2

Target Analyte	MDL µg/L	Target Analyte	MDL µg/L
Acenaphthalene	0.1	Endrin	0.5
Aldrin	0.1	Fluorene	0.2
Anthracene	0.04	Heptachlor	0.04
Atrazine	0.1	Heptachlor epoxide	0.2
Benzo(a)anthracene	0.04	2,2',3,3',4,4',6-Heptachlorobiphenyl	0.1
Benzo(b)fluoranthene	-	Hexachlorobenzene	0.1
Benzo(k)fluoranthene	0.2	2,2',4,4',5,6'-Hexachlorobiphenyl	0.1
Benzo(a)pyrene	0.04	Hexachlorocyclopentadiene	0.03
Benzo(ghi)perylene	0.1	Indeno(123cd)pyrene	0.1
Butylbenzylphthalate	0.3	Lindane	0.1
a-Chlordane	0.2	Methoxychlor	0.04
g-Chlordane	0.1	2,2',3,3',4,5',6,6'-Octachlorobiphenyl	0.2
trans-Nonachlor	0.3	2,2',3',4,6-Pentachlorobiphenyl	0.1
2-Chlorobiphenyl	0.1	Pentachlorophenol	0.3
Chrysene	0.04	Phenanthrene	0.01
Dibenzo(ah)anthracene	0.1	Pyrene	0.02
Di-n-butylphthalate	0.3	Simazine	0.2
2,3-Dichlorobiphenyl	0.1	2,2',4,4'-Tetrachlorobiphenyl	0.1
Diethylphthalate	0.8	Toxaphene	-
Bis(2-ethylhexyl)phthalate	0.6	2,4,5-Trichlorobiphenyl	0.06
Bis(2-ethylhexyl)adipate	0.6	Alachlor	1.0
Dimethylphthalate	0.04		

Table 3-31. Daily MS DFTPP Tune Requirements for Method 525.2

Mass M/z	DFTPP Relative Abundance Criteria
51	10-80% of base peak
68	<2% of mass 69
70	<2% of mass 69
127	10-80% of base peak
197	<2% of mass 198
198	base peak or >50% of 442
199	5-9% of mass 198
275	10-60% of base peak
365	>1% of base peak
441	present and < mass 443
442	base peak or >50% of 198
443	15-24% of mass 442

531.1 Measurement of *N*-Methyl carbamates and *N*-Methylcarbamoyl-oximates by direct injection HPLC with post column derivatization

The HPLC is calibrated using the internal standard procedure (4-bromo-3,5-dimethyl-phenyl-*N*-methylcarbamate [BDMC]), with a minimum of a three-point curve. The average RF can be used if the individual RFs for the analyte have <20% RSD, otherwise a calibration curve is prepared. CCV is performed each working shift.

The sample is buffered to pH 3 ± 0.2 units with monchloroacetic acid buffer, then filtered through a 0.2 µm pore polyester filter. A 0.400 mL sample is injected on the HPLC reverse phase column and chromatographed using a methanol:water linear gradient. The effluent is post-column derivatized (see Method 8318) by hydrolysis and reaction with ortho-phthalaldehyde (OPA). The fluorescent excitation is at 230 nm with detection at >418 nm. Analyte identification requires a confirmation column of different polarity.

Table 3-32. Target Analytes and MDLs for Method 531.1

Target Analyte	MDL µg/L	Target Analyte	MDL µg/L
Aldicarb	1.0	Carbofuran	1.5
Aldicarb sulfone	2.0	3-Hydroxycarbofuran	2.0
Aldicarb sulfoxide	2.0	Methiocarb	4.0
Baygon	1.0	Methomyl	0.5
Carbaryl	2.0	Oxamyl	2.0

547 Glyphosate by direct injection HPLC with post-column derivatization and fluorescence detection

Sample preparation consists of filtration through a 0.45 µm Acrodisc microfilter. A quantity of 0.200 mL of the sample is directly injected on a cation exchange HPLC column at 65 °C with an isocratic mobile phase composed of KH_2PO_4 : water : methanol. The eluting material passes through a hypochlorite oxidizing loop followed by reaction with OPA/2-mercaptoethanol in a post-column reactor. The derivatized material is detected by fluorescent excitation at 340 nm and emission detection at >455 nm. Calibration is external standard performed daily with a three-point curve. MDL for the technique runs from 6 to 9 ppb on a 0.200 mL injection. Glyphosate is quite unstable in chlorinated drinking water, which modifies demand for this method.

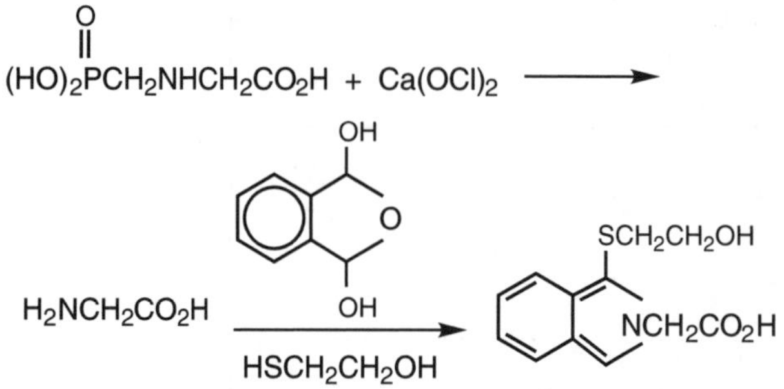

Figure 3-10. Post-column derivatization of glyphosate.

548 Endothall by derivatization and GC-ECD

A 5.0 mL sample is reduced in volume to less than 0.5 mL, then the endothall derivatized with pentafluorophenylhydrazine in glacial acetic acid with sodium acetate for 90 minutes at 150 °C. The derivative is isolated on a C-18 reversed-phase cartridge then eluted with 5.0 mL *tert*-butyl methyl ether. Endosulfan I is used as the internal standard. A four-point calibration curve is prepared and verified daily. Analysis is performed on a capillary column GC with ECD. Confirmation on a column of different polarity is required. Directions for preparation and purification of the endothall-PFPH derivative as a standard are included with the method as an appendix. The MDL is 11.5 µg/L beginning with the 5.0 mL sample.

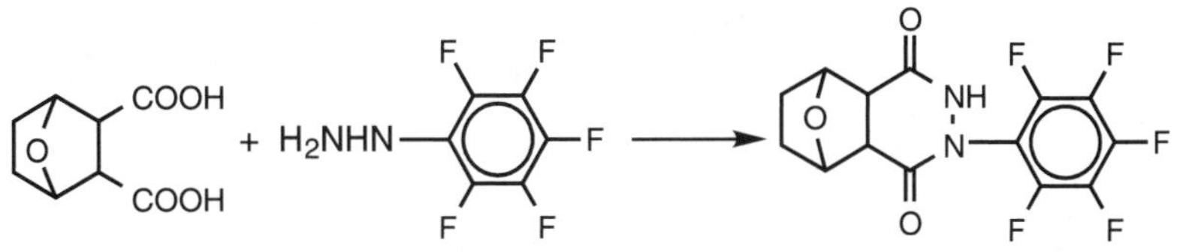

Figure 3-11. Derivatization of endothall.

548.1 Endothall by ion-exchange extraction, derivatization and GC-MS

Endothall is isolated on a tertiary amine anion exchange cartridge, then derivatized with acidic methanol at 50 °C in 30 minutes to the dimethyl ester. Analysis is by either GC-MS or GC-FID with confirmation column.

549 Diquat and paraquat by HPLC with UV detection

A 250 mL sample is acidified to pH 10.5 ± 0.2 then a C-8 reversed-phase cartridge is used to isolate the analytes based on an ion-pair mechanism. The analytes are isolated by elution with phosphoric acid-diethylamine solution. 1-Hexanesulfonic acid solution is added as an ion-pairing reagent, then the solution assayed by reversed phase HPLC with phosphoric acid : diethylamine : 1-hexanesulfonic acid eluent with detection at 308 nm (diquat) and 257 nm (paraquat) using a UV diode array detector. UV spectra are generated by the UV DAD for identification confirmation. Further identification is achieved by use of 1-heptanesulfonic acid as the ion-pairing reagent and re-running the analysis. Calibration is three-point external standard with daily checking with two different level calibration standards. MDL is 0.44 µg/L for diquat and 0.80 for paraquat based on the 250 mL sample processed.

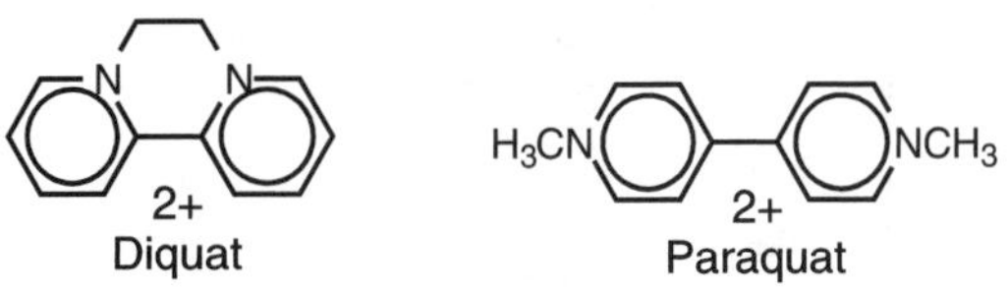

Figure 3-12. Diquat and paraquat.

549.1 Diquat and paraquat by ion-pair disk or cartridge and HPLC with DAD

The methodology of method 549 is extended to include the use of 47mm C-8 reversed-phase extraction disks.

550 PAHs by HPLC with UV and fluorescence detection

A 1.0 L sample is extracted with CH_2Cl_2. The extract is dried with sodium sulfate then concentrated and solvent exchanged to acetonitrile. The HPLC is configured for 5 to 100 μL injections with a reversed-phase column and a linear gradient with water : acetonitrile. Detectors are a UV at 254 nm and a fluorescent detector with excitation at 280 nm and detection at >389 nm. Calibration is external standard with a minimum of three-point (recommended five-point) curve, calibrated daily.

Method 550.1 uses a C-18 solid phase disk or cartridge for the analyte isolation with the rest of the method being almost exactly the same. MDLs are slightly lower.

Table 3-33. Target Analytes and MDLs for Method 550

Target Analyte	MDL μg/L	Target Analyte	MDL μg/L
Naphthalene	3.3 (UV)	Benzo(a)anthracene	0.002
Acenaphthalene	2.3 (UV)	Chrysene	0.063
Acenaphthene	3.0 (UV)	Benzo(b)fluoranthene	0.003
Fluorene	0.25 (UV)	Benzo(k)fluoranthene	0.002
Phenanthrene	0.162	Benzo(a)pyrene	0.029
Anthracene	0.079	Dibenzo(ah)anthracene	0.019
Fluoranthene	0.026	Benzo(ghi)perylene	0.014
Pyrene	0.126	Indeno(123-cd)pyrene	0.011

551 Chlorination disinfection by-products by GC-ECD

A 35 mL sample is mixed with 8 g NaCl and extracted with 2 mL of *tert*-butyl methyl ether in a 40 mL VOA vial, then directly injected on a GC with ECD. Calibration is three-point external standard. Identification is confirmed by re-analysis on a GC column of different polarity. This method and method 552 feature prominently in the Information Collection Rule - Disinfection Byproduct (ICR-DBP) program[10] for drinking water systems serving over 100,000 persons, originally set to go into effect October, 1994, but finalized by EPA in 1997.

Table 3-34. Target Analytes and MDLs for Method 551

Target Analyte	MDL μg/L	Target Analyte	MDL μg/L
Bromochloroacetonitrile	0.011	1,2-Dibromoethane	0.006
Bromodichloromethane	0.006	1,2-Dibromo-3-chloropropane	0.009
Bromoform	0.012	Dichloroacetonitrile	0.019
Carbon tetrachloride	0.004	1,1-Dichloropropanone	0.005
Chloral hydrate	0.026	Tetrachloroethene	0.004
Chloroform	0.002	Trichloroacetonitrile	0.092
Chloropicrin	0.012	1,1,1-Trichloroethane	0.008
Dibromoacetonitrile	0.034	Trichloroethene	0.002
Dibromochloromethane	0.012	1,1,1-Trichloropropanone	0.012

---

[10] *Federal Register*, Vol 59., No. 28, Thursday, 10 February, 1994.

552 Haloacetic acids by GC-ECD

Three versions of this method exist: 552, 552.1, and 552.2. In Method 552 a 100 mL sample is adjusted to a pH of 11.5 and washed with methyl *tert*-butyl ether (MTBE). After acidification to pH 0.5, the analytes are extracted with MTBE, dried over acidified sodium sulfate and concentrated. Derivatization to the methyl ester is performed with diazomethane (See Method 515.1.). 3,5-Dichlorobenzoic acid or 2,3-dichloropropionic acid is used as a surrogate, and 1,2,3-trichloropropane as the internal standard. A minimum of a three-point calibration curve (five recommended) is prepared. Confirmation on a second column is mandatory.

Method 552.1 uses a miniature anion exchange column to isolate the haloacetic acids from 100 mL of sample, then the analytes are eluted with acidified methanol and esterified with the acidified methanol prior to extraction into MTBE and analysis. Trichloropropane is used as the internal standard and 2-bromopropionic acid as the surrogate. Laboratory control samples and surrogates must be recovered in the 70-130% range to be acceptable.

Method 552.2 extracts the haloacetic acids from a 40 mL sample into 4.0 mL of MTBE, then forms the methyl esters prior to analysis by GC-ECD. The internal standard is again trichloropropane, but the surrogate changes to 2,3-dibromopropionic acid. The 70-130% recovery of surrogate and laboratory control samples remains as in 552.1

Table 3-35. Target Analytes and MDLs for Method 552.2

Target Analyte	MDL μg/L	Target Analyte	MDL μg/L
Monochloroacetic acid	0.052	Dibromoacetic acid	0.015
Monobromoacetic acid	0.0074	2-Chlorophenol	0.14
Dichloroacetic acid	0.015	2,4-Dichlorophenol	0.32
Trichloroacetic acid	0.085	2,4,6-Trichlorophenol	0.022
Bromochloroacetic acid	0.14		

604 Phenols by GC-FID and derivatization GC-ECD

A 1 L sample is pH adjusted with NaOH to pH > 12, then washed with CH_2Cl_2. The pH is then adjusted with H_2SO_4 to 1 to 2 and the analytes extracted three times with CH_2Cl_2. The extracts are dried with sodium sulfate and concentrated with solvent exchange to isopropanol to a volume of 1.0 mL. Calibration of the GC-FID is external standard with a minimum of a three-point calibration. If the RF technique is used each RF must be <10% RSD from the average to assume linearity. Otherwise a calibration curve can be prepared. It is of note that a Hewlett-Packard 5890A GC-FID used by the author resulted in linear calibrations for all the analytes over a 10^4 calibration range; however, use of another manufacturer's GC-FID system gave calibrations with a pronounced curve for some of the target analytes. Confirmation of identity is by derivatization with pentafluorobenzyl bromide and GC-ECD. (See Method 8040 for derivatization reaction.) The listed MDLs are for the GC-FID method.

Table 3-36. Target Analytes and MDLs for Method 604

Target Analyte	MDL µg/L	Target Analyte	MDL µg/L
2-Chlorophenol	0.31	4-Chloro-3-methylphenol	0.36
2-Nitrophenol	0.45	2,4-Dinitrophenol	13.0
Phenol	0.14	2-Methyl-4,6-dinitrophenol	16.0
2,4-Dimethylphenol	0.32	Pentachlorophenol	7.4
2,4-Dichlorophenol	0.39	4-Nitrophenol	2.8
2,4,6-Trichlorophenol	0.64		

604.1 Hexachlorophene and dichlorophen by HPLC with UV detection

A 1 L sample is pH adjusted to 4.0 - 4.5 by addition of 50 g NaH_2PO_4, then extracted three times with CH_2Cl_2. The combined extracts are dried over sodium sulfate and concentrated with solvent exchange to methanol to 2.5 mL. The extract is diluted to 5 mL with water. The HPLC analysis is performed on a reversed-phase column with isocratic acidified acetonitrile : water eluant. The UV detection is at 245 nm. Calibration of the GC-FID is external standard with a minimum of a three-point calibration. If the RF technique is used, each RF must be <10% RSD from the average to assume linearity. Otherwise a calibration curve can be prepared. Daily checking of the calibration curve is required with results within 10% RSD of the curve, otherwise the instrument is recalibrated. Identification is confirmed on a second column. MDLs are 1.0 µg/L for dichlorophen and 1.2 µg/L for hexachlorophene.

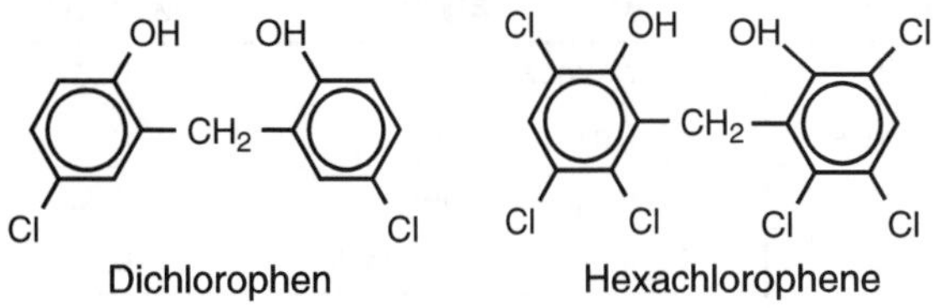

Dichlorophen   Hexachlorophene

Figure 3-13. Dichlorophen and hexachlorophene.

605 Benzidines by HPLC with electrochemical detection

A 1 L sample is pH adjusted to 6.5 - 7.5, then extracted three times with $CHCl_3$. The combined $CHCl_3$ extracts are extracted three times with 25 mL of 1.0 M H_2SO_4. Na_3PO_4 is added to the aqueous acid extracts followed by neutralization to pH 6 to 7 with 5 N NaOH. The neutralized solution is extracted three times with $CHCl_3$ and the combined extracts washed once with water. Methanol is added, and the solution concentrated with a vacuum rotary evaporator. Nitrogen blowdown to 1.0 mL is followed by dilution to 5.0 mL with acetate buffer. The HPLC column is reversed phase with a 1:1 acetonitrile/0.1 M pH 4.7 acetate buffer. Calibration is external standard with a minimum of three points by either RF or calibration curve. The electrochemical detector is run with a potential of +0.8 V; however, if significant interferences are present in the sample, the voltage can be reduced to +0.5 V. The MDLs are 0.08 µg/L for benzidine and 0.13 for 3,3'-dichlorobenzidine at +0.8 V.

606 Phthalates by GC-ECD

A 1 L sample is extracted three times with CH_2Cl_2, and the extracts dried over sodium sulfate and concentrated with solvent exchange to hexane to 1.0 mL. Further clean-up with Florisil or alumina is advised in the method. Calibration of the GC-ECD is three-point external standard by either RF (<10% RSD required for linearity) or calibration curve. The calibration curve is verified daily by analysis of one or more calibration standards with a <15% variation in results allowed. Identification is confirmed on a second column of different polarity than the analytical column or GC-MS.

Table 3-37. Target Analytes and MDLs for Method 606

Target Analyte	MDL µg/L	Target Analyte	MDL µg/L
Dimethyl phthalate	0.29	Butyl benzyl phthalate	0.34
Diethyl phthalate	0.49	Bis(2-ethylhexyl) phthalate	2.0
Di-*n*-butyl phthalate	0.36	Di-*n*-octyl phthalate	3.0

607 Nitrosamines by GC-NPD

A 1 L sample is pH adjusted to 5 to 9 with either NaOH or H_2SO_4 as required, then extracted three times with CH_2Cl_2. The combined extracts are washed with HCl, then dried with sodium sulfate and concentrated. Clean-up is performed on either Florisil or alumina. Calibration is external standard with a minimum of three standards by either RF (<10% RSD on individual RFs to assume linearity) or calibration curve. The calibration curve is checked daily by analysis of one or more calibration standards. All responses must be <15% from the expected, or the system must be recalibrated. Identification is confirmed on a second column of different polarity than the analytical column. Under the injection port heated conditions, *N*-nitrosodiphenylamine always degrades to diphenylamine, which is measured.

Table 3-38. Target Analytes and MDLs for Method 607

Target Analyte	MDL µg/L	Target Analyte	MDL µg/L
N-Nitrosodimethylamine	0.15	*N*-Nitrosodiphenylamine	0.81
N-Nitrosodi-*n*-propylamine	0.46		

608 Organochlorine pesticides and PCBs by GC-ECD

A 1 L sample is extracted three times with CH_2Cl_2, then the combined extracts dried over sodium sulfate and concentrated with solvent exchange to hexane. Clean-up is on Florisil. Sulfur sometimes interferes and is removed by treatment with either elemental mercury or activated copper powder. Calibration is an external standard with a minimum of three standards by either RF (<10% RSD to assume linearity) or calibration curve. The calibration is checked daily with one or more calibration standards. Acceptance criteria is <15% variation from the original calibration, otherwise the system gets recalibrated. Identification must be confirmed on either a second column of differing polarity from the analytical column or GC-MS.

Table 3-39. Target Analytes, MDLs, Precision and Accuracy for Method 608

Target Analyte	MDL µg/L	Spike Amt	%R	RPD
Aldrin	0.009	2.0	42-122	0-42
α-BHC	0.003	2.0	37-134	0-48
β-BHC	0.006	2.0	17-147	0-64
δ-BHC	0.009	2.0	19-140	0-72
γ-BHC	0.004	2.0	32-127	0-46
Chlordane	0.014	50	45-119	0-40
4,4'-DDD	0.011	10	31-141	0-56
4,4'-DDE	0.004	2.0	30-145	0-55
4,4'-DDT	0.012	10	25-160	0-72
Dieldrin	0.002	2.0	36-146	0-76
Endosulfan I	0.014	2.0	45-153	0-49
Endosulfan II	0.004	10	D-202	0-122
Endrin aldehyde	0.023	-	-	-
Endosulfan sulfate	0.066	10	26-144	0-54
Endrin	0.006	10	30-147	0-74
Heptachlor	0.003	2.0	34-111	0-40
Heptachlor epoxide	0.083	2.0	37-142	0-41
Toxaphene	0.24	50	41-126	0-51
PCB-1016	nd	50	50-114	0-40
PCB-1221	nd	50	15-178	0-99
PCB-1232	nd	50	10-215	0-71
PCB-1242	0.065	50	39-150	0-49
PCB-1248	nd	50	38-158	0-64
PCB-1254	nd	50	29-131	0-55
PCB-1260	nd	50	8-127	0-42

608.1   Organochlorine pesticides by GC-ECD

This method was prepared as an addendum to method 608 and adds a number of target analytes. The sample extraction and clean-up are essentially the same. A confirmation column is required for identification, although the method also recommends GC/MS as an alternative.

Table 3-40. Target Analytes and MDLs for Method 608.1

Target Analyte	MDL µg/L	Target Analyte	MDL µg/L
Dibromochloropropane	0.04	PCNB	0.06
Etridiazole	0.04	Chloropropylate	0.2
Chloroneb	0.04	Chlorobenzilate	0.2
Propachlor	1.0		

608.2   Organochlorine pesticides by GC-ECD

Adds several target analytes to the method 608 list without a significant change in the procedure. A silica gel column clean-up is included in addition to the Florisil column.

GC/MS is suggested for confirmation of analyte identification, or, alternatively, a confirmation column can be used.

Table 3-41. Target Analytes and MDLs for Method 608.2

Target Analyte	MDL µg/L	Target Analyte	MDL µg/L
Chlorothalonil	0.001	Methoxychlor	0.04
DCPA	0.003	*cis*-Permethrin	0.2
Dicloran	0.002	*trans*-Permethrin	0.2

609   Nitroaromatics and isophorone by GC-FID and GC-ECD

A 1 L sample is pH adjusted to 5 to 9 with either NaOH or H_2SO_4 as required, then extracted three times with CH_2Cl_2. The combined extracts are dried over sodium sulfate and concentrated with solvent exchange to hexane. Florisil is used for cleanup. Calibration is external standard with a minimum of three standards by either RF (<10% RSD to assume linearity) or calibration curve. The calibration is checked daily with one or more calibration standards. Acceptance criteria is <15% variation from the original calibration, otherwise the system gets recalibrated. Identification must be confirmed on either a second column of differing polarity from the analytical column or GC-MS. Isophorone and nitrobenzene are analyzed by FID, while the dinitrobenzenes are assayed by ECD.

Table 3-42. Target Analytes and MDLs for Method 609

Target Analyte	MDL µg/L	Target Analyte	MDL µg/L
Isophorone	5.7	2,4-Dinitrobenzene	0.02
Nitrobenzene	3.6	2,6-Dinitrobenzene	0.01

610   PAHs by GC-FID or HPLC with UV and fluorescence detectors

A 1 L sample is extracted three times with CH_2Cl_2, and the combined extracts dried with sodium sulfate and concentrated with solvent exchange to cyclohexane. Clean-up is on silica gel. Analysis by HPLC is on a reversed-phase column with a linear gradient of water/acetonitrile. UV is the preferred detector for naphthalene, acenaphthalene, acenaphthene and fluorene, while fluorescence is used for the rest of the PAHs. HPLC has the advantage over GC as all the PAHs are separated using the technique. GC is complicated by the pairs of compounds anthracene-phenanthrene, chrysene-benzo(a)anthracene, benzo(b)fluoranthene-benzo(k)fluoranthene, and dibenzo(a,h)anthracene-indeno(1,2,3-cd)pyrene being very difficult to separate. Although still not easy, all of these pairs can be successfully resolved on a capillary column if proper attention is paid to GC operating parameters. Calibration is external standard with a minimum of three standards by either RF (<10% RSD to assume linearity) or calibration curve. The calibration is checked daily with one or more calibration standards. Acceptance criteria is <15% variation from the original calibration, otherwise the system gets recalibrated. Identification must be confirmed on either a second column of differing polarity from the analytical column or GC-MS. The following MDLs are from HPLC with the appropriate detectors.

Table 3-43. Target Analytes and MDLs for Method 610

Target Analyte	MDL µg/L	Target Analyte	MDL µg/L
Naphthalene	1.8 (UV)	Benzo(a)anthracene	0.013
Acenaphthalene	2.3 (UV)	Chrysene	0.15
Acenaphthene	1.8 (UV)	Benzo(b)fluoranthene	0.018
Fluorene	0.21 (UV)	Benzo(k)fluoranthene	0.017
Phenanthrene	0.64	Benzo(a)pyrene	0.023
Anthracene	0.66	Dibenzo(a,h)anthracene	0.030
Fluoranthene	0.21	Benzo(ghi)perylene	0.076
Pyrene	0.27	Indeno(1,2,3-cd)pyrene	0.043

611   Haloethers by GC-ECD or GC-ELCD

A 1 L sample is extracted three times with CH_2Cl_2, the combined extracts dried with sodium sulfate and then concentrated with solvent exchange to hexane. An optional clean-up with Florisil is included in the method. Calibration is external standard with a minimum of three standards by either RF (<10% RSD to assume linearity) or calibration curve. The calibration is checked daily with one or more calibration standards. Acceptance criteria is <15% variation from the original calibration, otherwise the system gets recalibrated. Identification must be confirmed on either a second column of differing polarity from the analytical column or GC-MS.

Table 3-44. Target Analytes and MDLs for Method 611

Target Analyte	MDL µg/L	Target Analyte	MDL µg/L
Bis(2-chloroisopropyl) ether	0.8	4-Chlorophenyl phenyl ether	3.9
Bis(2-chloroethyl) ether	0.3	4-Bromophenyl phenyl ether	2.3
Bis(2-chloroethoxy) methane	0.5		

612   Chlorinated hydrocarbons by GC-ECD

A 1 L sample is extracted three times with CH_2Cl_2, the combined extracts dried with sodium sulfate and then concentrated with solvent exchange to hexane. An optional clean-up with Florisil is included in the method. Calibration is external standard with a minimum of three standards by either RF (<10% RSD to assume linearity) or calibration curve. The calibration is checked daily with one or more calibration standards. Acceptance criteria is <15% variation from the original calibration, otherwise the system gets recalibrated. Identification must be confirmed on either a second column of differing polarity from the analytical column or GC-MS.

Table 3-45. Target Analytes and MDLs for Method 612

Target Analyte	MDL µg/L	Target Analyte	MDL µg/L
1,3-Dichlorobenzene	1.19	1,2,4-Trichlorobenzene	0.05
Hexachloroethane	0.03	Hexachlorocyclopentadiene	0.40
1,4-Dichlorobenzene	1.34	2-Chloronaphthalene	0.94
1,2-Dichlorobenzene	1.14	Hexachlorobenzene	0.05
Hexachlorobutadiene	0.34		

613 2,3,7,8-TCDD by capillary column GC-MS

This is an internal standard method using either $^{13}C_{12}$ or $^{37}Cl_4$ 2,3,7,8-TCDD. A 1 L sample with internal standard is extracted three times with CH_2Cl_2, and the combined extracts concentrated with solvent exchange to hexane. The hexane solution is washed first with NaOH solution, then with water, at least twice with H_2SO_4 solution, and finally twice with water. The extracts are dried with sodium sulfate. Optional clean-ups with either silica gel or alumina are included in the method. Calibration is internal standard with a minimum of three standards by either RF (<10% RSD to assume linearity) or calibration curve. The calibration is checked daily with one or more calibration standards. Acceptance criteria is <15% variation from the original calibration, otherwise the system gets recalibrated. MDL for dioxin is 0.002 µg/L.

614 and 614.1 Organophosphorous pesticides by GC-FPD (614) or NPD (614.1)

A 1 L sample is extracted three times with 15% CH_2Cl_2 - hexane, dried with sodium sulfate and concentrated to 10 mL. An acetonitrile partition is described for fat and oil removal from the sample. A Florisil column clean-up is described in addition to an alumina microcolumn for selective sulfur removal. A silica gel column is used for clean-up of the 614.1 analytes. Calibration is minimum three-point external standard. If the RSD of the calibration factor is <10% over the entire working range, the average calibration factor may be used; otherwise a calibration curve is used. GC/MS or a second confirmation column are required for verification of analyte identification.

Table 3-46. Target Analytes and MDLs for Methods 614 and 614.1

Target Analyte	MDL µg/L	Target Analyte	MDL µg/L
Diazinon	0.012	Ethyl parathion	0.012
Disulfoton	-	Ethion (614.1)	0.1
Demeton	-	Malathion	-
Methyl parathion	0.012	Azinphos methyl	-
Terbuphos (614.1)	0.004	Dioxathion (614.1)	0.01
EPN (614.1)	0.2		

615 Chlorinated herbicides by GC-ECD

Although an EPA Method 615 does exist, the approved method for analysis of chlorinated herbicides in wastewater is SM_{18} 6640B. This is one of those instances where the analyst and data reviewer must pay special attention to the correct edition of *Standard Methods*, as 6640B presented in the 19th and later editions uses a micro-scale extraction and is completely oriented toward drinking water rather than wastewater.

In the correct version, a 1 L sample is acidified to pH < 2 with sulfuric acid (1:1) and extracted three times with diethyl ether. The ether extracts are combined in a 250 mL Erlenmeyer flask with a ground glass joint (24/40), 15 mL water and 2 mL 37% KOH added, a Snyder column attached, and the flask heated in a 60-65 °C water bath in the hood for 60 minutes. This hydrolyzes any herbicide esters in the original sample. After cooling the contents of the flask are extracted twice with diethyl ether, and the ether discarded. The aqueous layer is acidified to pH < 2 with sulfuric acid and the free herbicide acids extracted with three portions of ether. The ether extract is dried over acidified sodium sulfate with minimum contact time of 2 hours. After concentration to 0.5 mL, 0.1 mL methanol is added and the acids esterified with diazomethane (see Method 515.1). Silica gel is added (0.1-0.2 g) to destroy excess diazomethane. Calibration is a minimum of three-point external standard. Confirmation of analyte identification is achieved by analysis on a second column or GC/MS.

Table 3-47. Target Analytes and MDLs for Method 615

Target Analyte	MDL µg/L	Target Analyte	MDL µg/L
Dicamba	0.27	Dalapon	5.80
2,4-D	1.20	MCPP	192
2,4,5-TP	0.17	MCPA	249
2,4,5-T	0.20	Dichlorprop	0.65
2,4-DB	0.91	Dinoseb	0.07

616   Certain C, H, O pesticides by GC-FID

A 1 L sample is pH adjusted to 6.8 by the addition of 2 g each of NaH_2PO_4 and Na_2HPO_4, then solvent extracted three times with methylene chloride. The combined extracts are dried with sodium sulfate and concentrated to about 1-2 mL then solvent exchanged to tert-butyl methyl ether. Sample clean-up is accomplished with deactivated silica gel. Calibration is minimum three-point by the external standard procedure. Analyte identification is confirmed by either a second column or GC/MS.

Table 3-48. Target Analytes and MDLs for Method 616

Target Analyte	MDL µg/L	Target Analyte	MDL µg/L
Cycloprate	21	Methoprene	22
Kinoprene	18	Resmethrin	36

617   Organochlorine pesticides and PCBs by GC-ECD

A 1 L sample is extracted three times with 15% methylene chloride:hexane, then concentrated to 1.0 mL and diluted to the final volume of 10 mL. Clean-up is accomplished with acetonitrile partition for removal of fats and oils, Florisil column and mercury removal of sulfur. Calibration is minimum three-point external standard. A second column or GC/MS is required for confirmation of analyte identification.

Table 3-49. Target Analytes and MDLs for Method 617

Target Analyte	MDL µg/L	Target Analyte	MDL µg/L
Aldrin	0.009	Endosulfan II	0.17
α-BHC	0.004	Endosulfan sulfate	-
β-BHC	-	Endrin	-
δ-BHC	-	Endrin aldehyde	-
γ-BHC	0.002	Heptachlor	0.004
Captan	-	Heptachlor epoxide	0.003
Carbophenothion	-	Isodrin	-
Chlordane	-	Methoxychlor	0.176
4,4'-DDD	0.012	Mirex	0.015

Continued on next page.

Table 3-49. Target Analytes and MDLs for Method 617, *continued*

Target Analyte	MDL µg/L	Target Analyte	MDL µg/L
4,4'-DDE	0.004	PCNB	0.002
4,4'-DDT	0.032	Perthane	-
Dichloran	-	Strobane	-
Dicofol	-	Toxaphene	-
Dieldrin	0.011	Trifluralin	0.013
Endosulfan I	0.11	PCBs	-

618   Volatile pesticides by microextraction and GC-ECD

A 20 mL portion of sample is pH adjusted to the 6 to 8 range, then microextracted with 4 mL cyclohexane. Calibration is by either a minimum three-point external standard or a three-point internal standard with bromoform. Analyte confirmation required by either a second column or GC/MS.

Table 3-50. Target Analytes and MDLs for Method 618

Target Analyte	MDL µg/L	Target Analyte	MDL µg/L
Chloropicrin	0.8	EDB	0.2

619   Triazine pesticides by GC-NPD

A 1 L sample is extracted three times with 15% methylene chloride:hexane. The combined extract is dried with sodium sulfate and concentrated with solvent exchange to hexane to 10 mL. A Florisil column clean-up is described. Certain triazines will precipitate from hexane solution. If this occurs the sample is redissolved in methylene chloride and the extract analyzed by FID. Otherwise calibration is a minimum three-point external standard with confirmation required by either a second column or GC/MS.

Table 3-51. Target Analytes and MDLs for Method 619

Target Analyte	MDL µg/L	Target Analyte	MDL µg/L
Prometon	0.03	Prometryn	0.06
Atraton	-	Terbutryn	0.05
Propazine	0.03	Simazine	0.06
Terbuthylazine	0.03	Ametryn	0.06
Secbumeton	-	Simetryn	0.07
Atrazine	0.05		

622   Organophosphorous pesticides by GC-NPD or FPD

A 1 L sample is extracted three times with methylene chloride, the combined extracts are concentrated with solvent exchange to hexane to a final volume of 10 mL. Calibration is by a minimum three-point external standard. Analyte identification is confirmed by use of a second column or by GC/MS.

Table 3-52. Target Analytes and MDLs for Method 622

Target Analyte	MDL µg/L	Target Analyte	MDL µg/L
Demeton	0.25	Mevinphos	0.3
Phorate	0.15	Stirophos	5.0
Disulfonton	0.20	Ethoprop	0.25
Trichloronate	0.15	Parathion methyl	0.3
Fenthion	0.10	Ronnel	0.3
Tokuthion	0.5	Chlorpyrifos methyl	0.3
Bolstar	0.15	Chlorpyrifos	0.3
Fensulfothion	1.5	Merphos	0.25
Azinphos methyl	1.5	Diazinon	0.6
Coumaphos	1.5	Naled	0.1
Dichlorvos	0.1		

622.1 Thiophosphate pesticides by GC-NPD

A 1 L sample is pH adjusted to the range 6 to 8, then extracted with three portions of methylene chloride. The combined extracts are dried with sodium sulfate and concentrated to 1.0 mL. An optional Florisil column clean-up is described. Calibration is by a minimum three-point external standard.

Table 3-53. Target Analytes and MDLs for Method 622.1

Target Analyte	MDL µg/L	Target Analyte	MDL µg/L
Thionazin	1	Fennitrothion	2
Fonophos	0.7	Famphur	19
Dichlofenthion	0.7	Phosmet	1
Aspon	0.6		

625 GC/MS Base/neutral and acid extractables (BNA)

Method 625 requires extraction of the target analytes and acid and base/neutral surrogates from the wastewater with methylene chloride under first basic conditions to isolate the base/neutral fraction, and then acid conditions to remove the acidic fraction. The B/N and A extracts are not combined and through subsequent manipulations and analysis they are kept separate. After concentration, the internal standard(s) are added and the solutions analyzed by GC/MS. Retention time match and three peak MS matching is considered to be sufficient evidence for detection of a target analyte. The mass analyzer is operated at 70 eV in the electron impact mode with daily tuning to decafluorotriphenylphosphine (DFTPP) standards (Table 3-54). A minimum of 5% of samples from each sampling site are spiked with the entire complement of target analytes. Spikes that fail the acceptance criteria must immediately be followed with an analysis of a quality control check standard. Quality control check standards with all target analytes are analyzed on a daily basis, with failures being immediately recalibrated. See Method 610 for difficult resolution of PAH pairs. For many wastewater samples there exist significant levels of extractible chromatographic interferences that make this analysis difficult. EPA has published the "pumpkin" manual[5] (so called due to the color of the cover), which gives guidance on resolving analytical problems.

Without any doubt, Method 625 is most abused method in the entire realm of environmental analytical methods. The major reason for the abuse lies in the fact that this method was not developed for use by commercial laboratories. The intended user was the municipal laboratory that analyses the effluent from a single wastewater treatment plant. Thus the method was written to provide the best analytical data possible each month for the single effluent point.

There are a number of normal areas of departure from Method 625. Some are allowed such as the use of capillary columns instead of the method specified packed columns. Upon request, The Office of Science and Technology in the EPA Office of Water will supply a letter detailing the allowed modifications and how to obtain approval for proposed modifications. The guiding principle is that the modification must not degrade method performance. A number of modifications are possible that do not degrade method performance including the use of alternate quantitation ions, use of alternate surrogates or internal standards, use of alternate DFTPP tune criteria, and use of SPCC criteria instead of tailing factors to evaluate system inertness. Each of these modifications, if used, must be specifically allowed by letter from EPA. However there are four common unauthorized modifications that severely degrade method performance that will not be allowed by EPA. They are the use of CCC to verify daily continuing calibration requirements, the matrix spike requirement, the separate analysis of the acid and base/neutral fractions, and the detection/reporting limits.

Method 8270 presents a set of 13 compounds that are analyzed each day of operation to verify that the instrument remains in calibration. These compounds are called the Calibration Check Compounds (CCC). If they meet the method requirements (See Method 8270 discussion.) then the assumption is that all calibrated compounds are within control. The Method 625 requirement is that the calibration of each and every target analyte must be checked each day of operation prior to analysis of samples.

A matrix spike containing all of the regulated compounds at or below the permitted regulatory limit for the effluent is a monthly requirement for each sample point. Because each permit generally is different, in order to comply precisely with this method requirement, a commercial lab would need to spike each sample with different concentrations of different components. Compliance would necessitate maintaining individual stock solutions of each of the 54 base/neutral and 11 acidic target analytes of the method, in order to tailor the spike solution for each client. An alternate allowable strategy is to spike the sample with all 65 analytes at a level slightly above the reporting limit. Many commercial laboratories will simply substitute the 11 component matrix spike solution that is suggested for use in SW-846 Method 8270 at the standard concentration of 100 µg/L for the B/N components and 200 µg/L for the acid components..

Method 625 specifies separation and individual analysis of the acid and base/neutral extractable fractions. Most commercial laboratories and many regulators are under the illusion that the use of the believed all-powerful capillary column for GC-MS renders this requirement outdated and useless. Nothing could be further from the truth.

There are two technical problems that occur in gas chromatography-mass spectrometry (GC-MS) analysis of wastewater extracts. The first is the correct

---

[5]   Guidance on Evaluation, Resolution and Documentation of Analytical Problems Associated with Compliance Monitoring. USEPA, Office of Water, Engineering and Analysis Division, Washington DC 20460, EPA 821-B-93-001, June 1993.

identification of the target analytes. The second is the achievement of the lowest possible detection limits. Both of these objectives are directly affected by the laboratory's practice with regards to the separate analysis of the acid and base/neutral fractions.

Correct identification of the target analyte is an absolute requirement in compliance monitoring. GC-MS is one of the preferred analysis techniques because two independent measures of identification are produced. The first is the retention time. If the unknown peak is within ± 30 seconds of the retention time of the standard (± 0.06 relative retention time to the nearest internal standard), the measure is met. The second measure is the proper set of three ions (Tables 4 and 5, EPA Method 625, Appendix A, 40 CFR 136) from the mass spectrum must maximize within one scan of each other. Further the three ions must be within ± 20% relative intensity as compared to the reference spectrum.

The three characteristic ions of the target analyte are not unique to that compound. Each compound normally generates dozens of ions under the conditions of MS, and many compounds exhibit the same masses. There are many examples where isomeric compounds display very similar retention times and characteristic masses, the premier example being benzo(b)fluoranthene and benzo(k)fluoranthene. Most aliphatic hydrocarbons above C_{10} chain length display an exponential decay pattern of mass clusters centered on 43, 57, 71, 85, 99, etc. that renders identification of the exact compound difficult.

One well-known example of confused identification occurs between α-pinene and phenol[6]. These two compounds co-elute on capillary columns under most standard operating conditions used for analysis. The characteristic masses for phenol are 94, 65, and 66. These ions are also present in the mass spectrum of α-pinene as isotopic peaks of the main ions 93 and 64, and by coincidence happen to meet the relative abundance criteria for phenol. Anytime α-pinene is present in an extract, it will generate a false positive for phenol. Fortunately α-pinene is in the base/neutral fraction and phenol is in the acid extraction and the two are easy to isolate.

An example of wastewater effluent analyzed by EPA Method 625 is presented in Figures 3-14 and 3-15 to illustrate the problem. The sample was analyzed by two different laboratories. One followed the directions in EPA Method 625, while the other used EPA Method 3510/8270, a method combination not approved for wastewater monitoring. The lab using 3510/8270 reported hits for phenol, pentachlorophenol, 2-methyl phenol, 2-nitrophenol, 2,4-dimethyl phenol, 4-nitrophenol, 4-chloro-3-methyl phenol, and several other compounds, all in amounts which exceeded the permit limits. The lab using 625, separated the fractions and analyzed them individually. Comparison of the chromatograms of the two separated fractions (Figures 3-14 and 3-15) illustrates the ability of the acid-base isolation to separate the matrix co-extractables into two manageable portions. Phenol, 2-nitrophenol, pentachlorophenol, and 4-methylphenol were found to be present in the acid fraction, but in amounts under the permit limit. The peak tentatively identified as 4-chloro-3-methyl phenol did not meet the relative abundance criteria for the three masses. A close examination of the mass spectrum revealed that it bore no relationship to the target analyte. Combining the extractable fractions for analysis in this example generates false positives.

---

6   Smith, R.-K., 1999. *Lectures in Wastewater Analysis and Interpretation*, Genium Publishing, Schenectady, NY.

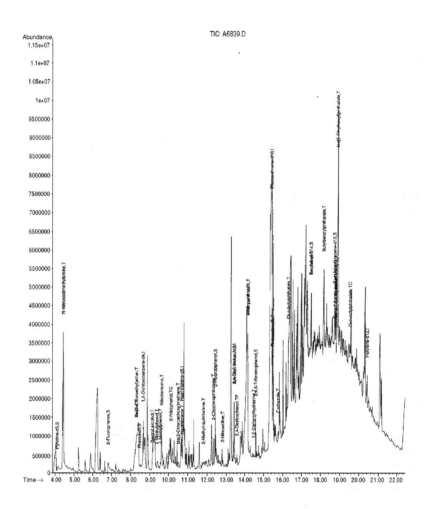

Figure 3-14. GC-MS chromatogram of the base/neutral extractables from a wastewater effluent.

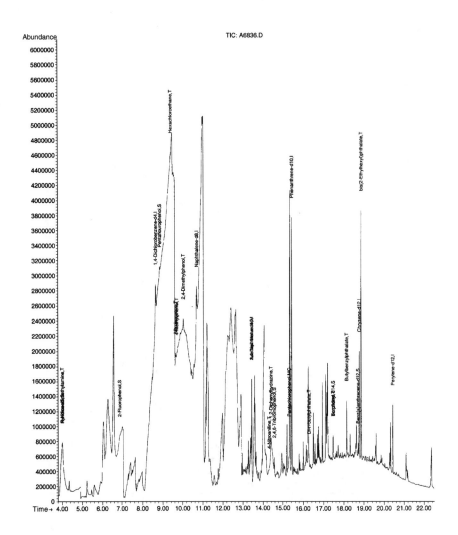

Figure 3-15. GC-MS chromatogram of the acid extractables from the same wastewater effluent as Figure 3-14.

The second technical issue is the analysis of the sample to achieve the lowest detection limits. In many wastewaters the majority of the matrix co-extractables can be isolated into one of the two extractable fractions. This allows uncomplicated analysis of the extract where the matrix co-extractables are minimized with the attending low detection limits for the analytes in the fraction. The common commercial laboratory practice of increasing detection limits for all compounds in the analysis, when only an acid fraction interference is present, is unconscionable and results in drastically lower data quality and reliability.

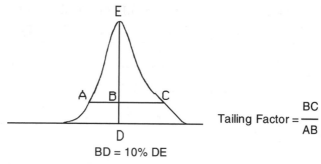

Figure 3-16. Structure of decafluorotriphenylphosphine (DFTPP).

Table 3-54. Daily MS Tune Criteria for DFTPP

Mass M/z	DFTPP Relative Abundance Criteria
51	30-60% of base peak
68	<2% of mass 69
70	<2% of mass 69
127	40-60% of mass 198
197	<1% of mass 198
198	base peak 100% relative abundance
199	5-9% of mass 198
275	10-30% of mass 198
365	>1% of mass 198
441	present and < mass 443
442	>40% of mass 198
443	17-23% of mass 442

Each operator must demonstrate proficiency in the method by four-fold analysis of a 100 ppb check standard containing each target analyte. The means and standard deviations of the results must meet the published acceptance criteria.

An additional QC procedure involves a daily check of the column performance for benzidine and acids and calculation of the tailing factor. The compound(s) is injected and the resulting peak analyzed. The tailing factor for benzidine must be less than 3.0 and for pentachlorophenol less than 5.0.

$$\text{Tailing Factor} = \frac{BC}{AB}$$

BD = 10% DE

Figure 3-17. Tailing factor calculation.

Table 3-55. Base/neutral Extractable Target Analytes and MDLs for Method 625

Target Analyte	MDL ppb	Target Analyte	MDL ppb
Acenaphthene	1.9	Dimethyl phthalate	1.6
Acenaphthylene	3.5	2,4-Dinitrotoluene	5.7
Anthracene	1.9	2,6-Dinitrotoluene	1.9
Aldrin	1.9	Di-*n*-octylphthalate	2.5
Benzo(a)anthracene	7.8	Endosulfan sulfate	5.6
Benzo(b)fluoranthene	4.8	Endrin aldehyde	nd
Benzo(k)fluoranthene	2.5	Fluoranthene	2.2
Benzo(a)pyrene	2.5	Fluorene	1.9
Benzo(ghi)perylene	4.1	Heptachlor	1.9
b-BHC	4.2	Heptachlor epoxide	2.2
d-BHC	3.1	Hexachlorobenzene	1.9
Bis(2-chloroethyl) ether	5.7	Hexachlorobutadiene	0.9
Bis(2-chloroethoxy) methane	5.3	Hexachloroethane	1.6
Bis(2-ethylhexyl) phthalate	2.5	Indeno(1,2,3-cd)pyrene	3.7
Bis(2-chloroisopropyl) ether	5.7	Isophorone	2.2
4-Bromophenyl phenyl ether	1.9	Naphthalene	1.6
Chlordane	nd	Nitrobenzene	1.9
2-Chloronaphthalene	1.9	N-Nitrosodi-*n*-propylamine	nd
4-Chlorophenyl phenyl ether	4.2	PCB-1016	nd
Chrysene	2.5	PCB-1221	30
4,4'-DDD	2.8	PCB-1232	nd
4,4'-DDE	5.6	PCB-1242	nd
4,4'-DDT	4.7	PCB-1248	nd
Dibenzo(ah)anthracene	2.5	PCB-1254	36
Di-*n*-butylphthalate	2.5	PCB-1260	nd
1,2-Dichlorobenzene	1.9	Phenanthrene	5.4
1,3-Dichlorobenzene	1.9	Pyrene	1.9
1,4-Dichlorobenzene	4.4	Toxaphene	nd
3,3'-Dichlorobenzidine	16.5	1,2,4-Trichlorobenzene	1.9
Dieldrin	2.5	Benzyl butyl phthalate	2.5
Diethyl phthalate	1.9		

Table 3-56. Acid Extractable Target Analytes and MDLs for Method 625

Target Analyte	MDL ppb	Target Analyte	MDL ppb
4-Chloro-3-methylphenol	3.0	2-Nitrophenol	3.6
2-Chlorophenol	3.3	4-Nitrophenol	2.4
2,4-Dichlorophenol	2.7	Pentachlorophenol	3.6
2,4-Dimethylphenol	2.7	Phenol	1.5
2,4-Dinitrophenol	42	2,4,6-Trichlorophenol	2.7
2-Methyl-4,6-dinitrophenol	24		

Table 3-57. Suggested Internal and Surrogate Standards for Method 625

Base/Neutral Extractables		
Aniline-d$_5$	Anthracene-d$_{10}$	1-Fluoronaphthalene
Benzo(a)anthracene-d$_{12}$	4,4'-Dibromobiphenyl	2-Fluoronaphthalene
Decafluorobiphenyl	4,4'-Dibromooctafluorobiphenyl	Naphthalene-d$_8$
2,2'-Difluorobiphenyl	4-Fluoroaniline	Nitrobenzene-d$_5$
Phenanthrene-d$_{10}$	Pyridine-d$_5$	2,3,4,5,6-Pentafluorobiphenyl
Acid Extractables		
2-Fluorophenol	Pentafluorophenol	
Phenol-d$_5$	2-Perfluoromethyl phenol	

627 Dinitroaniline pesticides by GC-ECD

A 1 L sample is extracted with three portions of methylene chloride. The combined extracts are dried with sodium sulfate and concentrated with solvent exchange to hexane to a final volume of 10 mL. Calibration is by a minimum three-point external standard procedure. A second column or GC/MS is required for analyte confirmation. The suggested packed columns are stated to not resolve benfluralin, ethalfluralin and trifluralin, and they are reported together as trifluralin. This resolution problem is not expected to exist if capillary columns are used.

Table 3-58. Target Analytes and MDLs for Method 627

Target Analyte	MDL µg/L
Benfluralin	-
Ethalfluralin	-
Isopropalin	0.02

Target Analyte	MDL µg/L
Profluralin	0.14
Trifluralin	0.03

629 Cyanazine by HPLC with UV detector

A 1 L sample is extracted three times with CH_2Cl_2. The combined extracts are dried with sodium sulfate and concentrated with solvent exchange to methanol. An optional activated Florisil cleanup is described. Analysis is by HPLC with reversed phase column and linear methanol : water gradient. Detection is UV at 245 nm. Calibration is external standard with a minimum of three standards by either RF (<10% RSD to assume linearity) or calibration curve. The calibration is checked daily with one or more calibration standards. Acceptance criteria is <15% variation from the original calibration, otherwise the system gets recalibrated. Identification must be confirmed on a second column of differing polarity from the analytical column. MDL is 6 mg/L.

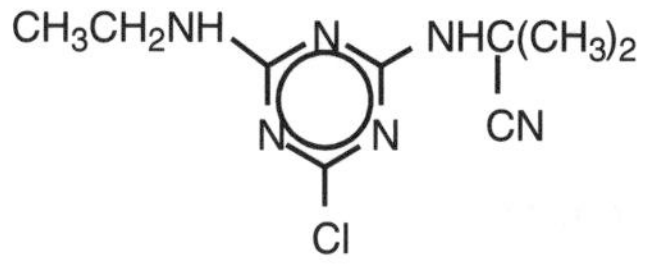

Figure 3-18. Cyanazine.

630 and 630.1   Dithiocarbamate pesticides by CS$_2$ evolution and UV-Vis colorimetry (630) or GC-ELCD (630.1)

Dithiocarbamates are hydrolyzed with acid to CS$_2$, which is then measured by either colorimetry or GC-ELCD in the sulfur mode. Both methods are non-discriminate, and results are reported as the analyte Ziram.

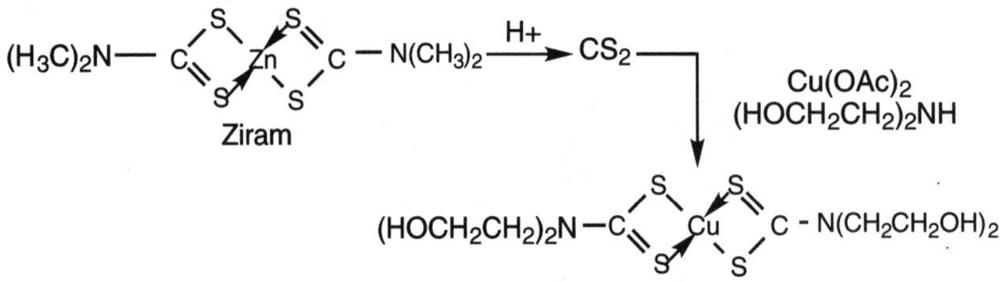

Figure 3-19. Colorimetric determination of CS$_2$ in Method 630.

Table 3-59. Target Analytes and MDLs for Methods 630 and 630.1

Target Analyte	MDL µg/L	Target Analyte	MDL µg/L
Amoban	-	Nabam	-
AOP	-	Niacide	-
Busan 40	-	Polyram	-
Busan 85	-	Sodium dimethyldithiocarbamate	-
Ferbam	-	Thiram	-
KN methyl	-	ZAC	-
Mancozeb	-	Zineb	-
Maneb	15.3	Ziram	1.9
Metham	3.7		

631   Benomyl and carbendazim by HPLC with UV detector

A 150 mL sample is stirred with 2 mL 50% H$_2$SO$_4$ for 16 to 24 hours to hydrolyze benomyl to carbendazim. The pH is then adjusted to 6 to 8 and the sample extracted three times with CH$_2$Cl$_2$. The combined extracts are dried with sodium sulfate and concentrated with solvent exchange to methanol. The HPLC is performed on a reversed phase column with a 1:1 methanol : water isocratic elution. Detection is UV at 254 nm. Calibration is external standard with a minimum of three standards. Confirmation on a second column is required. MDL is 25.0 µg/L for benomyl (as carbendazim) and 8.7 for carbendazim.

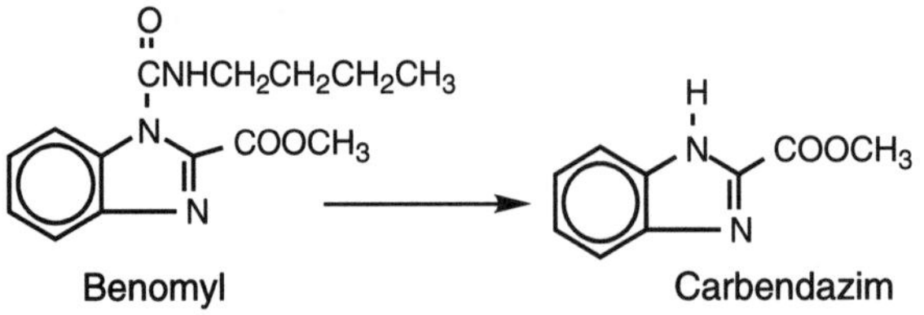

Figure 3-20. Hydrolysis of benomyl to carbendazim in Method 631.

632 Carbamate and urea pesticides by HPLC with UV detector

A 1 L sample is extracted three times with CH_2Cl_2. The combined extracts are dried with sodium sulfate and concentrated with solvent exchange to methanol or acetonitrile. An optional Florisil cleanup is described. Analysis is by HPLC with reversed-phase column and a variety of solvent systems. Detection is UV at 245 and 280 nm. Calibration is external standard with a minimum of three standards by either RF (<10% RSD to assume linearity) or calibration curve. The calibration is checked daily with one or more calibration standards. Acceptance criteria is <15% variation from the original calibration, otherwise the system gets recalibrated. Identification must be confirmed on a second column of differing polarity from the analytical column.

Table 3-60. Target Analytes and MDLs for Method 632

Target Analyte	MDL µg/L	Target Analyte	MDL µg/L
Mexacarbate	0.52	Neburon	0.012
Propoxur	0.11	Methomyl	8.9
Monuron	0.003	Carbofuran	3.2
Carbaryl	0.02	Fluorometuron	11.1
Propham	0.07	Oxamyl	9.2
Diuron	0.009	Chloropropham	0.03
Linuron	0.009	Barban	0.05
Methiocarb	0.02		

632.1 Carbamate and amide pesticides by HPLC with UV detection

A 1 L sample is neutralized to 6.5 to 7.5 pH, 200 g NaCl added and then extracted three times with CH_2Cl_2. The combined extracts are dried with sodium sulfate and concentrated with solvent exchange to acetonitrile. An optional Florisil cleanup is described. Analysis is by HPLC with reversed phase column and linear acetonitrile : water gradient. Detection is UV at 245 nm. Calibration is external standard with a minimum of three standards by either RF (<10% RSD to assume linearity) or calibration curve. The calibration is checked daily with one or more calibration standards. Acceptance criteria is <15% variation from the original calibration, otherwise the system gets recalibrated. Identification must be confirmed on a second column of differing polarity from the analytical column.

Table 3-61. Target Analytes and MDLs for Method 632.1

Target Analyte	MDL µg/L	Target Analyte	MDL µg/L
Napropamide	0.31	Propanil	0.85
Vacor	0.20		

633 and 633.1 Organonitrogen pesticides by GC-NPD

A 1 L sample is extracted three times with CH_2Cl_2. The combined extracts are dried with sodium sulfate and concentrated with solvent exchange to acetone. Calibration is external standard with a minimum of three standards by either RF (<10% RSD to assume linearity) or calibration curve. The calibration is checked daily with one or more calibration standards. Acceptance criteria is <15% variation from the original calibration, otherwise the system gets recalibrated. Identification must be confirmed on a second column of differing polarity from the analytical column.

Table 3-62. Target Analytes and MDLs for Methods 633 and 633.1

Target Analyte	MDL µg/L	Target Analyte	MDL µg/L
Terbacil	-	DEET	3.39
Bromacil	2.38	Pronamide (633.1)	4
Hexazinone	0.72	MGK 264 (633.1)	2
Tricyclazole	-	MGK 326 (633.1)	6
Metribuzin	0.46	Fenarimol	4
Triadimefon	0.78		

634 Thiocarbamate pesticides by GC-NPD

A 1 L sample is pH adjusted to the 6 to 8 range with either sodium hydroxide or sulfuric acid then extracted with methylene chloride for 18-24 hours using a continuous liquid-liquid extractor. The extract is dried with sodium sulfate and concentrated to 5.0 mL with solvent exchange to toluene. An optional silica gel clean-up is described. Calibration is either minimum three-point external standard or internal standard using carbazole.

Table 3-63. Target Analytes and MDLs for Method 634

Target Analyte	MDL µg/L	Target Analyte	MDL µg/L
EPTC	0.9	Butylate	0.6
Vernolate	1.1	Pebulate	0.8
Molinate	0.6	Cycloate	1.6

635 Rotenone by HPLC with UV detector

A 1 L sample is neutralized to pH 7 then extracted three times with CH_2Cl_2. The combined extracts are dried with sodium sulfate and concentrated with solvent exchange to acetonitrile. An optional silica gel cleanup is described. Analysis is by HPLC with reversed phase column and isocratic 60 : 40 acetonitrile : water. Detection is UV at 245 nm. Calibration is external standard with a minimum of three standards by either RF (<10% RSD to assume linearity) or calibration curve. The calibration is checked daily with one or more calibration standards. Acceptance criteria is <15% variation from the original calibration, otherwise the system gets recalibrated. Identification must be confirmed on a second column of differing polarity from the analytical column. MDL is 1.6 ug/L.

636 Bensulide by HPLC with UV detector

A 1 L sample is pH adjusted to 7 then extracted three times with CH_2Cl_2. The combined extracts are dried with sodium sulfate and concentrated with solvent exchange to acetonitrile. An optional Florisil cleanup is described. Analysis is by HPLC with reversed-phase column and isocratic 60 : 40 acetonitrile : water elution. Detection is UV at 270 nm. Calibration is external standard with a minimum of three standards by either RF (<10% RSD to assume linearity) or calibration curve. The calibration is checked daily with one or more calibration standards. Acceptance criteria is <15% variation from the original calibration, otherwise the system gets recalibrated. Identification must be confirmed on a second column of differing polarity from the analytical column. MDL is 1.6 µg/L.

641   Thiabendazole by direct injection HPLC with fluorescence detector

The HPLC system is reversed-phase column with 70:30 methanol : buffer (triethanol-amine : acetic acid : water) isocratic eluant. The fluorescent detector has excitation at 300 nm and detection at 360 nm. The sample is acidified to pH 1 to 3 and filtered, then 100 µL is injected into the HPLC. Calibration is external standard with a minimum of three standards by either RF (<10% RSD to assume linearity) or calibration curve. The calibration is checked daily with one or more calibration standards. Acceptance criteria is <15% variation from the original calibration, otherwise the system gets recalibrated. Identification must be confirmed on a second column of differing polarity from the analytical column. MDL is 1.7 µg/L.

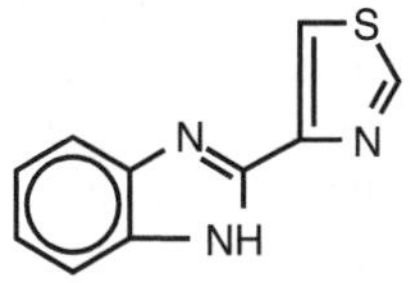

Figure 3-21. Structure of thiabendazole.

645   Certain amine pesticides and lethane by GC-NPD

A 1 L sample is pH adjusted to the 5 to 9 range, then extracted three times with methylene chloride. The extracts are dried over sodium sulfate and concentrated to 10 mL with solvent exchange to hexane. An optional clean-up with deactivated Florisil is described. Calibration is minimum three-point external standard. Analyte confirmation is required by re-analysis on a second column or by GC/MS.

Table 3-64. Target Analytes and MDLs for Method 645

Target Analyte	MDL µg/L	Target Analyte	MDL µg/L
Alachlor	0.2	Fluridone	0.5
Butachlor	0.3	Lethane	0.1
Diphenamide	0.2	Norflurazon	0.02

646   Dinitro aromatic pesticides by GC-ECD

A 1 L sample is pH adjusted to the 5 to 9 range then extracted three times with 15% methylene chloride : hexane. The combined extracts are dried with sodium sulfate and concentrated to 10 mL with solvent exchange to hexane. An optional Florisil clean-up is described. Analyte identification is verified on a second column or by GC/MS. CDN is 1-chloro-2,4-dinitrobenzene.

Table 3-65. Target Analytes and MDLs for Method 646

Target Analyte	MDL µg/L
CDN	0.0005
Dinocap	0.1
Basalin	0.0005

1625 Semivolatile organic compounds by isotope dilution GC/MS

Isotopically labeled analytes are added to a 1 L sample in a glass beaker and stirred for 1-2 hours. The solution is quantitatively transferred to a continuous liquid-liquid extractor. The sample is pH adjusted to >12 and extracted for 18-24 hours. The extraction solvent is removed, and the pH is adjusted to < 2 after cooling. More methylene chloride is added, and the extraction continued for 18-24 hours. The BN and acid extractables are maintained as separate extracts rather than combining them as in Method 8270. The extracts are dried with sodium sulfate and concentrated to 1.0 mL. Internal standard (2,2'-difluorobiphenyl) is added immediately before GC/MS analysis. Most of the isotopically labeled compounds are perdeuterated; however, a few contain limited numbers of deuterium or are labeled with ^{13}C. Calibration is either against the labeled analyte or the internal standard with a minimum of a five-point concentration range. The average RF can be used for a compound if each individual value in the calibration is within 10% of the average; otherwise a calibration curve is prepared. At the beginning of each 8-hour shift a calibration standard containing all components at the 100 µg/mL must meet the listed performance criteria in addition to the passing of DFTPP tune criteria. Most of the analytes are the same as those listed in method 625. Of note is the addition of a number of straight-chain saturated hydrocarbons.

Table 3-66. Daily MS Tune Criteria for DFTPP

Mass M/z	DFTPP Relative Abundance Criteria
51	30-60% of base peak
68	<2% of mass 69
70	<2% of mass 69
127	40-60% of mass 198
197	<1% of mass 198
198	base peak 100% relative abundance
199	5-9% of mass 198
275	10-30% of mass 198
365	>1% of mass 198
441	present and < mass 443
442	>40% of mass 198
443	17-23% of mass 442

1656 Organohalide pesticides by GC-ECD or ELCD

This is the first of the combined methodologies that attempts to meet drinking water, wastewater, RCRA, and CLP protocols. It covers a large number of analytes as shown in Table 3-67. The method describes a number of extraction procedures that are used depending on the solids content of the sample. This is determined by overnight drying of a 5 to 10 g subsample. If the sample is <1% solids, a 1.00 L sample is pH adjusted to 5-9 and continuously extracted with CH_2Cl_2 for 18-24 hours. If the sample is 1% to 30% solids, a portion is sonicated with CH_2Cl_2 : acetone (1:1), then diluted with water to 1% solids and extracted with CH_2Cl_2 in a continuous extractor for 18-24 hours. Samples containing >30% solids are mixed with powdered anhydrous sodium sulfate and sonicated three times with 1:1 CH_2Cl_2 : acetone. Municipal sludges with >30% solids are sonicated two times with acetonitrile and 1 time with CH_2Cl_2. The filtered combined extracts are washed three times with 2% sodium sulfate solution. Optional clean-ups include gel permeation chromatography, C_{18} reversed phase extraction cartridge, Florisil column, alumina column, and sulfur removal. The sample extracts are dried over sodium sulfate and concentrated with solvent exchange to hexane. Calibration is an external standard with a minimum of three standards by either RF (< 20% coefficient of variation to assume linearity) or calibration curve. The calibration is checked daily with one or more calibration standards. Acceptance criteria is compound specific and must be met, otherwise the system gets recalibrated. Identification must be confirmed on a second column of differing polarity from the analytical column. Surrogate (dibutyl-chlorendate suggested, tetrachloro-*m*-xylene or decachlorobiphenyl are possible if DBC is not available) is added to each sample, and recoveries must be 40-120%.

Table 3-67. Target Analytes and MDLs for Method 1656

Target Analyte	MDL µg/L	Target Analyte	MDL µg/L
Acephate	2000	δ-Chlordane	9
Trifluralin	50	Butachlor	30
Ethalfluralin	5	α-Chlordane	8
Benfluralin	20	Endosulfan I	11
Diallate-A	45	4,4'-DDE	10
Diallate-B	32	Dieldrin	6
α-BHC	6	Captan	100
PCNB	6	Chlorobenzilate	25
Simazine	400	Endrin	4
Atrazine	500	Nitrofen (TOK)	13
Terbutylazine	300	Kepone	100
δ-BHC	11	4,4'-DDD	5
β-BHC	7	Endosulfan II	8
Heptachlor	5	Bromoxynil octanoate	30
Chlorothalonil	15	4,4'-DDT	12
Dichlone	4	Carbophenothion	50
Terbacil	200	Endrin aldehyde	11
γ-BHC	5	Endosulfan sulfate	7
Alachlor	20	Captafol	100
Propanil	-	Norfluorazon	50
Aldrin	8	Mirex	4
DCPA	3	Methoxychlor	30
Metribuzin	5	Endrin ketone	8
Triadimefon	50	Fenarimol	20
Isopropalin	20	*cis*-Permethrin	200
Isodrin	13	*trans*-Permethrin	200
Heptachlor epoxide	12	PCBs	150
Pendamethalin	30	Toxaphene	910
Bromacil	70		

1657 Organophosphorous pesticides by GC-FPD

This is another of the combined methodologies that attempts to meet drinking water, wastewater, RCRA, and CLP protocols. It covers a large number of analytes as indicated in Table 3-68. The method describes a number of extraction procedures that are used depending on the solids content of the sample, which is determined by overnight drying of a 5 to 10 g subsample. If the sample is <1% solids, a 1.00 L sample is pH adjusted to 5-9 and continuously extracted with CH_2Cl_2 for 18-24 hours. If the sample is 1% to 30% solids, a portion is sonicated with CH_2Cl_2 : acetone (1:1), then diluted with water to 1% solids and extracted with CH_2Cl_2 in a continuous extractor for 18-24 hours. Samples containing >30% solids are mixed with powdered anhydrous sodium sulfate and sonicated three times with 1:1 CH_2Cl_2 : acetone. Municipal sludges with >30% solids are sonicated two times with acetonitrile and one time with CH_2Cl_2. The filtered combined extracts are washed three times with 2% sodium sulfate solution. There is a procedure for extraction and isolation of water soluble pesticides such as methamidophos. Optional clean-ups include gel permeation chromatography and C_{18} reversed-phase extraction cartridge. The sample extracts are dried over sodium sulfate and concentrated with solvent exchange to hexane. Calibration is external standard with a minimum of three standards by either RF (< 20% coefficient of variation to assume linearity) or calibration curve. The calibration is checked daily with one or more calibration standards. Acceptance criteria is compound-specific and must be met, otherwise the system gets recalibrated. Identification must be confirmed on a second column of differing polarity from the analytical column. Surrogate (tributyl phosphate and triphenylphosphate) is added to each sample, and recoveries must be 40-120%.

Table 3-68. Target Analytes and MDLs for Method 1657

Target Analyte	MDL µg/L	Target Analyte	MDL µg/L
Dichlorvos	4	Ronnel	11
Mevinphos	74	Malathion	11
Acephate	500	Fenthion	22
Trichlorofon	150	Parathion	10
Methamidophos	100	Chlorpyrifos	4
Demeton-A	19	Trichloronate	14
Ethoprop	7	Chlorfevinphos	2
Naled	18	Crotoxyphos	81
Dicrotophos	81	Tokuthion	2
Monocrotophos	85	Tetrachlorvinphos	12
Sulfotepp	6	DEF	50
Phorate	10	Merphos-B	18
Dimethoate	27	Fensulfothion	104
Demeton-B	21	Methyl trithion	10
Dioxathion	121	Ethion	13
Terbufos	26	Sulprofos	6
Phosphamidon-E	28	Famphur	27
Disulfoton	32	Phosmet	14
Diazinon	38	EPN	9
Phosphamidon-Z	116	Azinphos methyl	9
Methyl parathion	18	Leptophos	14
Dichlorofenthion	6	Azinphos ethyl	22
Methylchlorpyrifos	13	Coumaphos	24

1658 Phenoxy-acid herbicides by derivatization and GC-ECD or ELCD

This is another of the combined methodologies that attempts to meet drinking water, wastewater, RCRA, and CLP protocols. It covers analytes as indicated in Table 3-69. The method describes a number of extraction procedures used depending on the solids content of the sample, which is determined by overnight drying of a 5 to 10 g subsample. If the sample is <1% solids, a 1.00 L sample is pH adjusted to >12 to hydrolyze compounds, then adjusted to < 2 and continuously extracted with CH_2Cl_2 for 18-24 hours. If the sample is 1% to 30% solids, a portion is sonicated with CH_2Cl_2 : acetone (1:1), then diluted with water to 1% solids and extracted with CH_2Cl_2 in a continuous extractor for 18-24 hours. Samples containing >30% solids are mixed with powdered anhydrous sodium sulfate and sonicated three times with 1:1 CH_2Cl_2 : acetone. Municipal sludges with >30% solids sonicated two times with acetonitrile and one time with CH_2Cl_2. The filtered combined extracts are washed three times with 2% sodium sulfate solution. Optional clean-ups include gel permeation chromatography, C_{18} reversed-phase extraction cartridge, and Florisil column. The sample extracts are dried over sodium sulfate and concentrated with solvent exchange to hexane, then esterified with diazomethane. Calibration is an external standard with a minimum of three standards by either RF (< 20% coefficient of variation to assume linearity) or calibration curve. The calibration is checked daily with one or more calibration standards. Acceptance criteria is compound- specific and must be met, otherwise the system gets recalibrated. Identification must be confirmed on a second column of differing polarity from the analytical column or GC-MS. Surrogate (2,4-DCPA) is added to each sample, and recoveries must be 40-120%.

Table 3-69. Target Analytes and MDLs for Method 1658

Target Analyte	MDL µg/L	Target Analyte	MDL µg/L
2,4-D	100	Dicamba	110
Dinoseb	50	Dichlorprop	40
2,4,5-T	50	MCPA	90
2,4,5-TP	40	MCPP	56
Dalapon	100	2,4-DB	50

1659 Dazomet by hydrolysis to methyl isothiocyanate and GC-NPD

A 50 mL sample is pH adjusted to 10 to 12 and allowed to sit for 3 hours at room temperature. This hydrolyzes the dazomet to methyl isothiocyanate, which is extracted with ethyl acetate and analyzed by GC with an NPD. Calibration is an external standard with a minimum of three standards by either RF (<10% RSD to assume linearity) or calibration curve. The calibration is checked daily with one or more calibration standards. Acceptance criteria is < 15% variation from the original calibration, otherwise the system gets recalibrated. Identification must be confirmed on a second column of differing polarity from the analytical column. MDL is 3 µg/L.

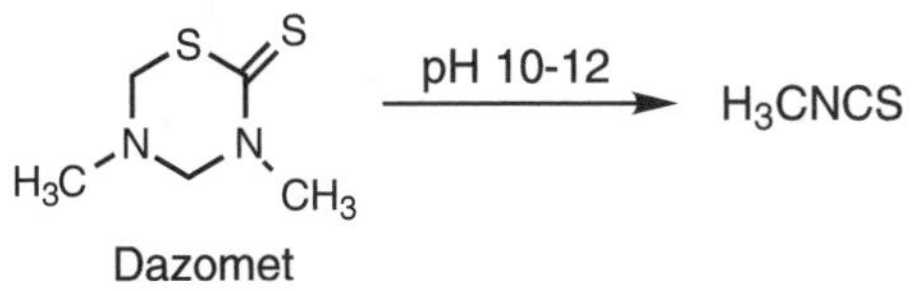

Figure 3-22. Hydrolysis reaction of dazomet.

1660 Pyrethrins and pyrethroids by HPLC with UV detector

A 750 mL sample is placed in a 1 L volumetric flask, then 230 g NaCl and 160 mL acetonitrile added. The flask is stirred with a magnetic stir bar for 5 minutes then allowed to sit for 5 minutes. The top layer of acetonitrile is withdrawn (2-5 mL) and 5 mL added. The flask is again stirred. The combined extracts from three extractions are concentrated to 7.5 mL and analyzed by HPLC on a dual-coupled C_{18} reversed-phase columns with a linear gradient elution of 70:30 acetonitrile : water to 100% acetonitrile. Detection is by UV at 235 and 245 nm. Identification is assumed if the response of the eluting compound is the same as that of the standard with the same retention time at the two analytical wavelengths. Calibration is multi-point with daily checking of the curve.

Table 3-70. Target Analytes and MDLs for Method 1660

Target Analyte	MDL µg/L	Target Analyte	MDL µg/L
Pyrethrin II	19	Resmethrin	22
Tetramethrin	16	Fenvalerate	10
Allethrin	16	c/t-Permethrin	20
Pyrethrin I	22	Sumithrin	25
Cyfluthrin	22	t/c-Permethrin	20

1661 Bromoxynil by direct injection HPLC with UV detector

The sample is pH adjusted to 3 to 7 and 40 µL injected on a HPLC with reversed-phase column and detection by UV at 255 and 280 nm. Mobile phase is 50 : 50 methanol : water. The multi-point external standard calibration is checked daily. Identification is assumed if the eluting compound has the same retention time as the standard and equivalent response at the two wavelengths. Bromoxynil is 3,5-dibromo-4-hydroxybenzonitrile, and the MDL is 20 µg/L.

C. Extraction Techniques

All of the 500, 600, and 1600 series methods are self-contained, covering sample collection, handling, preservation, extraction, clean-up, analysis, and quality control. Only a few of the 8000 series methods (SW-846) are similar in this respect. Most refer the analyst to sections on quality control (Chapter 1 and Method 8000B), extraction (3500 series methods) and clean-up (3600 series methods). Detailed information on surrogate and matrix spike solutions and use are found in 3500B, the introduction section to the extraction methods.

3510C Separatory funnel liquid-liquid extraction

This is a method that relies upon partitioning the analytes between the water matrix and an organic phase, most commonly CH_2Cl_2. A separatory funnel of 2 L capacity is normally used. Processing of a large number of samples is very labor intensive. In general a fast method, it can become time consuming when emulsion layers form. A BNA extraction may use 300-500 mL of solvent. See method 3650 for information on pH adjustment during the extraction process.

3520C Continuous liquid-liquid extraction

This is a method that avoids the problem of emulsions; however, continuous liquid-liquid extraction requires a 18-24 hour extraction period. It is not as labor intensive as separatory funnel extractions. A single technician can set-up and process a very large number of samples on a regular basis. Solvent usage is around 300-500 mL, and either lighter-than-water or heavier-than-water solvents can be used, depending on the exact extractor design. A solvent pool sits at the bottom of the extracting chamber when heavier-than-water solvents such as CH_2Cl_2 are used. Extracted analytes are diluted into this solvent pool, then slowly removed by siphon. Modern designs add a stopcock to the siphon tube and a K-D (Kuderna-Danish) Snyder column to the device for extraction, followed by concentration without transferring the sample extract to another set of glassware. The use of the siphon tube allows water to become entrained in the extracting solvent. On solvent removal the major part of the resulting concentrate can be water. A recent technology advance adds a hydrophobic membrane to the bottom of the sample chamber, which allows rapid and efficient separation of the extraction solvent from the water sample and immediate return of the solvent to the concentrator reservoir[7]. The elimination of the solvent pool shortens the extraction time to 4-6 hours, reduces solvent usage to less than 100 mL and makes the technique more time efficient and competitive with separatory funnel methods. A further advantage is elimination of water from the sample concentrate without further sample manipulation. See Appendix C for examples of continuous extractors. If pH adjustment is required during the sample extraction, as in BNA sample preparation, normally the sample is first acidified and then basified. The reason behind this reversal in the procedure is that basic pH conditions for prolonged periods of time can irreversibly change the analytes through hydrolysis reactions. For example any phthalate esters in the sample are hydrolyzed to the respective alcohols and phthalic acid. This also results in all the surrogates being isolated in the first extraction.

3535 Solid phase extraction of liquids

This method uses a C_{18} or other chain-length reversed-phase cartridge or disk for isolation and concentration of non-polar organic analytes from water, then elutes the absorbed compounds with an organic solvent, ready for analysis. Recent introduction of the styrene-divinylbenzene copolymer disks solve many of the breakthrough problems seen with the reversed-phase disks. SPE is also available with ion exchange resins and size-exclusion gels. Current problems include clogging of the disk or cartridge with particulate matter, and incomplete retention of all compounds. The process can be fine tuned for a particular matrix and analysis with superb results. Many of the newer drinking water and wastewater semivolatiles methods are oriented toward SPE.

3540C Soxhlet extraction of solids

This method is considered by EPA to be the exhaustive extraction procedure for solids. It is always the benchmark procedure for comparison when proposed extraction methods are being validated. The solid material is mixed with anhydrous sodium sulfate, then subjected to soxhlet extraction for 16-24 hrs. The method uses up to 300 mL of solvent for the extraction. It can use either lighter-than-water solvents, heavier-than-water solvents or mixtures of the two without modification. When used with heavier-than-

---

[7] Accelerated One-Step™ Extractor-Concentrator, Corning Glassworks, Corning, NY. One-Step is a registered trademark of Corning Glassworks.

water solvents such as Freon or methylene chloride, a glass wool plug is added on top of the sample to avoid particles floating up in the sample cup. A soxhlet extractor is pictured in Appendix C.

3541 Automated soxhlet extraction

The sample is dried, powdered, and loaded into an extractor cup, then submersed into 50 mL of the extraction solvent (1:1 acetone : hexane) and boiled for 1 hour. Afterwards the sample cup is raised to the rinse position, and the solvent is allowed to drain through the cup for an hour. The solvent is then removed by concentration by diverting the solvent return from the condenser. The method is used primarily for PCBs in solids, and a solvent exchange into pure hexane is required prior to analysis.

3550B Sonication extraction

A sample is mixed with anhydrous sodium sulfate then extracted three times with one of a variety of solvent mixtures (1:1 acetone : CH_2Cl_2). The extraction uses an ultrasonic disrupter horn of at least 300 watts power for agitation of the mixture. See the reference in footnote 9 for an examination of some problems associated with this method. Application of this technique to novel matrices or new analytes (organophosphorus pesticides) should be validated against the soxhlet extraction to verify the sonication is not biasing the preparation through destruction of target analytes.

3560 Supercritical fluid extraction

Supercritical fluid extraction (SFE) is a technique that extracts a solid sample under high pressure and elevated temperatures with carbon dioxide (340 atm., 80 °C, 500-1000 mL/min flow). Supercritical fluids exist at any combination of temperature and pressure above the critical point. The supercritical fluid is an excellent solvent for non-polar analytes with the solubilizing ability increasing with increasing density, a function of the pressure. For extraction of more polar analytes, the fluid is modified by addition of methanol, acetonitrile, or a number of other common solvents. Once the pressure is released, the carbon dioxide vaporizes, leaving the concentrated analyte in an appropriate solvent. The instrument has been directly interfaced to both GC and HPLC for automated extraction and analysis. Draft method 3561, SFE of polyaromatic hydrocarbons from soils, is under consideration for inclusion in SW-846. A comparison of SFE and sonication for the removal of amines from soils has been published[8].

---

[8] Oostdyk, T.S., R.L. Grob, J.L. Snyder and M.E. McNally. "Study of Sonication and Supercritical Fluid Extraction of Primary Aromatic Amines." *Anal. Chem.* 1993. 65(5). pp. 596-600.

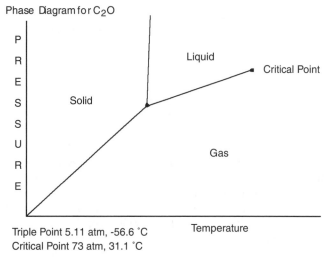

Phase Diagram for C$_2$O

Triple Point 5.11 atm, -56.6 °C
Critical Point 73 atm, 31.1 °C

Figure 3-23. Phase diagram for supercritical carbon dioxide.

A recent article reports use of supercritical water for selective extractions of organic analytes[9]. A remarkable selectivity for polar and non-polar target analytes is detailed, which could find extensive use in remediation monitoring.

3580 Waste dilution

In this preparation method the non-aqueous sample is diluted with an appropriate organic solvent, often in the ratio of 1 gm sample to 10.0 mL solution.

D. Other extraction techniques

1. Liquid-membrane-liquid extraction[10]

These techniques try to perform a simultaneous analyte isolation and introduction of the sample to an analytical instrument similar in idea to the purge and trap - GC interface used in VOC analysis. A relatively large volume (20-100 mL) of the aqueous sample is separated from a small volume (< 5 mL) of an organic solvent by a polymer membrane. The organic analytes diffuse across the membrane, become concentrated in the organic solvent, and, after a suitable contact time, are introduced into the GC or HPLC for analysis.

2. Microwave-assisted liquid extraction from soils

In addition to the metals digestion area, the microwave oven can be used to assist liquid extraction of organic analytes from solid matrices[11]. The extraction was tested in the

---

9   Hawthorne, S.B., Y. Yang, and D.J. Miller. "Extraction of Organic Pollutants from Environmental Solids with Sub- and Supercritical Water." *Analytical Chemistry.* 1994. 66(18). pp. 2912-2920.

10 Melcher, R.G., D.W. Bakke, and G.H. Hughes. "On-line Membrane/Liquid Chromatographic Analyzer for Pentachlorophenol and Other Trace Phenols in Wastewater." *Anal. Chem.* 1992. 64(19). pp. 2258-2262.

11 Lopez-Avila, V., R. Young and W.F. Beckert "Microwave-assisted Extraction of Organic Compounds from Standard Reference Soils and Sediments." *Analytical Chemistry* 1994. 66(7). pp. 1097-1106.

screw cap sealed Teflon® bomb discussed in the metals digestions in Section 2. The extraction solvent tested was hexane : acetone (1:1) and the optimum time was found to be 10 minutes.

E. Clean-up

Clean-up methods are directed toward reducing interfering materials in analyte extracts prior to instrument analysis. Environmental samples are unbelievably complex matrices. To achieve the MDLs demanded by government regulators, the samples have to be processed to remove as much garbage as possible. Most MDLs were derived from matrix spikes into purified water, or, in the case of solid samples, the matrix spikes were into purified sand. Sand and DI water are not anything like wastewater from a pulp plant, Georgia red clay, or other real-life samples. A practical reason for clean-up procedures is to extend the useful life of GC and HPLC columns. A five-dollar clean-up often allows use of a $400 column on another day. Method 3600C gives an overview of clean-up methods and a guide to applications.

3610B Alumina column

This cleanup method describes various activity grades and pHs of alumina (Al_2O_3). Alumina is prepared from $Al(OH)_3$, which is dehydrated and calcined at 900 °C in a carbon dioxide atmosphere. The resulting aluminum oxide particles are coated with a layer of aluminum oxycarbonate $[Al_2(OH)_5]_2CO_3$. This allows for pH adjustment to the acidic, neutral, and basic grades for particular applications. Addition of known quantities of water are used to deactivate the alumina, as it serves as a very active catalytic substance for compound decomposition when anhydrous. Uses are for phthalate esters and nitrosamines.

3611B Alumina column clean-up and separation of petroleum wastes

This method is specifically tailored for clean-ups of petroleum wastes and separation into aliphatic, aromatic, and polar fractions for analysis.

3620B Florisil column clean-up

Florisil is an activated form of magnesium silicate. It has more acidic character than alumina or silica gel but is still classified as amphoteric. Commonly used as a clean-up material in pesticide residue analysis, it is considered to be a much milder absorbent than silica gel or alumina with regard to compound decomposition. Specific procedures are given for application to phthalate ester, nitrosamine, nitroaromatic, and chlorinated hydrocarbon target analytes. Florisil is variable in its adsorptive capacity from batch to batch. Determination of the lauric acid value allows Florisil standardization, which is used to calculate the amount of Florisil needed to perform a desired separation. The lauric acid value is determined by measuring the amount of lauric acid adsorbed in milligrams per gram of Florisil from a hexane solution[12]. A standard column for clean-up is determined by dividing the lauric acid value by 110 and multiplying by 20 g (See methods 614 and 617.).

---

[12] "Standardization of Florisil Column by Weight Adjustment Based on Adsorption of Lauric Acid." *ASTM Annual Book of Standards.* 1980. Part 31, D3086, Appendix X3, p. 765.

3630C Silica gel column clean-up

Silica gel is a precipitated form of silicic acid (H_2SiO_3), formed from addition of sulfuric acid to sodium silicate. It forms very strong hydrogen bonds to polar materials and can lead to analyte decomposition. It is somewhat soluble in methanol, which should never be used as an elution solvent. Silica gel will quantitatively remove even slightly polar substances from hexane solutions and serves to isolate the strictly petroleum hydrocarbon analytes from interferences in the DRO and IR-TPH procedures. This procedure presents applications to PCB, PAH and derivatized phenol target analytes.

3640A Gel permeation column clean-up

A cross-linked divinylbenzene-styrene copolymer (hydrophobic gel) and organic solvents are used to selectively pass large macromolecules such as proteins, phospholipids, resins, lignins, fulvic and humic acids, etc. from sample extracts while retaining the smaller target analyte molecules in the pores of the gel. The desired analytes are displaced from the gel with a smaller-sized organic solvent, methylene chloride. After preparation the column must be calibrated with a mixture of corn oil, bis(2-ethylhexyl) phthalate, methoxychlor, perylene, and sulfur. Eluants are detected by monitoring flow through a UV detector. Exactly half the sample is lost due to loading the column through an automated injection loop, therefore if GPC is used, the matrix spike and surrogate compounds are added at twice their normal concentration. This problem of losing half the sample can be eliminated by performing a direct injection onto the GPC through a 4-way valve by syringe, or by using an auto-sampler without an injection loop.

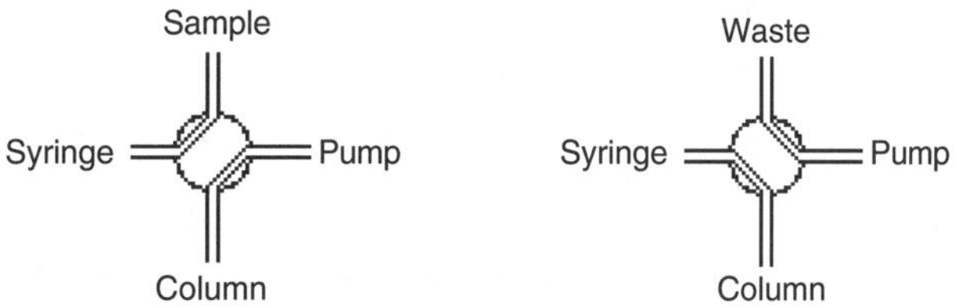

Figure 3-24. 4-way valve configuration used for manual GPC. The position on the left is for syringe filling and column elution, the position on the right is for injection of sample on the column.

The styrene-divinyl benzene polymeric packing of the column is not inert toward surface adsorption of organic molecules, particularly those with aromatic rings or electron rich substituents. The effect is not very pronounced with eluting solvents such as methylene chloride or toluene due to the high partition ratio in favor of the solvent. However when less interactive solvents are used such as cyclohexane or ethyl acetate, substantial increases in retention times of PAH and PCB analytes have been noted. This effect has been demonstrated[13] to be a useful tool for clean-up when the target analytes are in a hydrocarbon oil matrix, a very common occurrence.

---

[13] Conrad, E.C., K.P. Kelly and N.L. Schwartz. "GPC and oily solvents." *Environmental Testing and Analysis*, 3(5). 1994. pp. 34-39.

3650B Acid-base partition clean-up

Normally considered a part of the separatory funnel or continuous liquid-liquid extraction, this technique calls for pH adjustment of the water sample with sodium hydroxide to >12 and extraction of all the basic and neutral organics with CH_2Cl_2, referred to as the base-neutral (BN) fraction. Then the pH is adjusted to < 2 with sulfuric acid and the sample again extracted to obtain the acid (A) fraction. When used with the continuous extractor, the solution is made acid first, extracted, then pH-adjusted for the base fraction extraction. Some problems in the procedure have been the subject of recent articles[14].

3660B Sulfur clean-up

The sample is agitated with either powdered copper, mercury metal, or tetrabutyl-ammonium sulfite to remove elemental sulfur interferences. The latter is the gentlest and suggested for use on organophosphorous and organochlorine pesticide extracts. Sulfur is a common contaminant, and since it is non-polar and easily chromatographs on a GC as a semivolatile, it can dominate an extract. Sulfur is also removed by the GPC.

3665A Sulfuric acid/permanganate clean-up

This is a very rigorous oxidative clean-up that will remove most interferents except PCBs, chlorinated benzenes and chlorinated naphthalenes (Halowaxes). A few organochlorine hydrocarbons will survive.

F. Methods 8000 Series

8000B Determinative Chromatographic Separations

Method 8000B gives general information about gas chromatographic (GC) and high pressure liquid chromatographic (HPLC) analysis of sample extracts. Operational guidelines and maintenance are discussed. However the real meat of the Method lies in the discussions of calibration, retention times, and quality control. With regards to calibration, the linearity of the calibration is evaluated, and then a variety of calibration options are described, such as average response or calibration factors, linear calibrations via least squares regression, and non-linear calibrations. Each of these options have required quantitative measures of successful calibration. Continuing calibration verification introduces the metric of percent drift (%D) and percent difference (%D) as a measure of calibration validity. The %D of each analyte must be within ±15%.

$$\%D = [\ \frac{\text{Daily CF}}{\text{Initial CF}_{ave}}\ \text{or}\ \frac{\text{Daily RF}}{\text{Initial RF}_{ave}}\ \text{or}\ \frac{\text{Daily concentration}}{\text{True concentration}}\ ]\ x\ 100$$

Initial demonstrations of proficiency are required quality controls for each analytical technique, and the procedure is described in detail.

Guidance is presented on performance of method blanks, matrix spikes, and laboratory controls. The blank acceptance criteria are:

---

[14] Chen, P. H., W. A. VanAusdale, and D. F. Roberts. "Oxidation of Phenolic Acid Surrogates and Target Analytes During Acid Extraction of Natural Water Samples for Analysis by GC/MS Using EPA Method 625." *Environmental Science and Technology.* 1991. 25(3). pp. 540-546.

- Less than the laboratory MDL
- Less than 5% of the regulatory limit
- Less than 5% of the sample analyte level

The laboratory is required to calculate acceptance limits for MS and LCS. In the absence of an historical acceptance limit the generic 70-130% LCS recovery is used as a guide to assessing data. The point is made (Section 8.5.5) that the average MS recovery (of the MS and MSD) is the appropriate control criteria, rather than the individual MS recoveries.

8032A Acrylamide by derivatization then GC-ECD

A 50 mL sample is mixed with 7.5 g KBr, then the solution is pH adjusted with HBr to 1 to 3, bromine water is added, followed by stoppering the flask and storing in the dark at 0 °C for at least an hour. The excess bromine is reduced with sodium thiosulfate. Then sodium sulfate is added, and the mixture extracted two times with ethyl acetate. The combined extracts are dried over sodium sulfate, then dimethyl phthalate internal standard is added, and the volume brought up to 25.0 mL in a low-actinic volumetric flask. An optional Florisil column clean-up is described. Analysis is by packed column GC (free fatty acid polyester FFAP) and ECD. Confirmation of identification is with a second column of differing polarity or GC-MS. Calibration is five-point by either RF or actual curve, checked daily. MDL is 0.032 µg/L of acrylamide monomer.

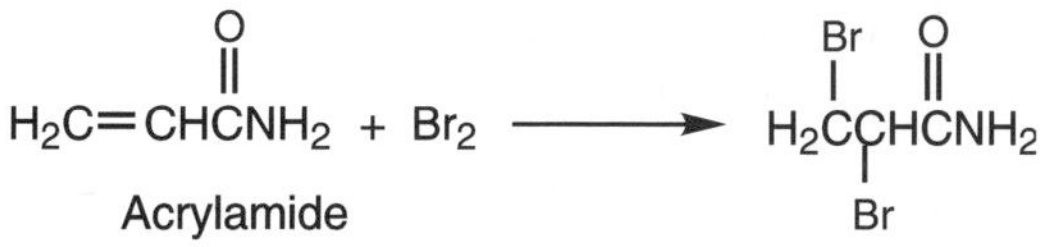

Figure 3-25. Derivatization reaction of acrylamide.

8041 Phenols by GC FID underivatized; ECD for pentafluorobenzyl-bromide derivatives

Methods 3510, 3520, 3540, 3550 and 3580 are used as appropriate for extraction followed by concentration with solvent exchange to 2-propanol. If the extraction procedure does not have pH adjustment to < 2, then acid-base clean-up (Method 3650) is performed prior to concentration. Use of either or both 2-fluorophenol and 2,4,6-tribromophenol as surrogate compounds is recommended. Calibration is an external standard with a five-point calibration and daily checking. Identification of compounds detected using the FID is confirmed by the derivatization GC-ECD procedure. MDLs are listed for the FID; generally higher MDLs are obtained for the derivatization ECD.

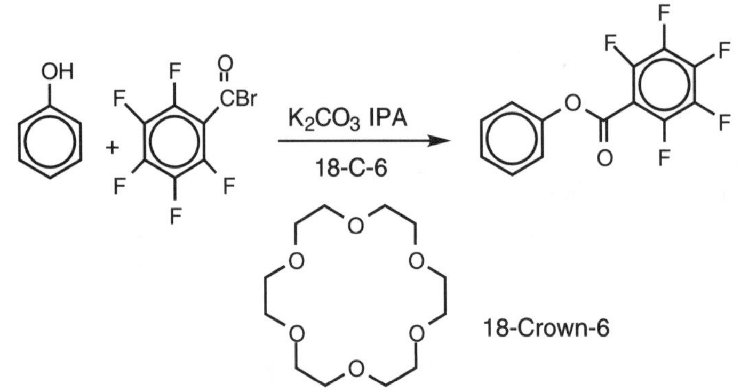

Figure 3-26. Derivatization reaction of phenols.

Table 3-71. Target Analytes and MDLs for Method 8041

Target Analyte	MDL µg/L	Target Analyte	MDL µg/L
2-sec-butyl-4,6-dinitrophenol	-	2-Methyl-4,6-dinitrophenol	16.0
4-Chloro-3-methylphenol	0.36	2-Nitrophenol	0.45
2-Chlorophenol	0.31	4-Nitrophenol	2.8
Cresols (methyl phenols)	-	Pentachlorophenol	7.4
2-Cyclohexyl-4,6-dinitrophenol	-	Phenol	0.14
2,4-Dichlorophenol	0.39	Tetrachlorophenols	-
2,6-Dichlorophenol	-	Trichlorophenols	-
2,4-Dimethylphenol	0.32	2,4,6-Trichlorophenol	0.64
2,4-Dinitrophenol	13.0		

8061A   Phthalate esters by capillary column GC-ECD

Samples (if liquid) are pH adjusted to 5 to 7 and extracted using methods 3510, 3540 or 3550. Method 3520 is not suggested due to loss of analytes by absorption on the glass-ware. The method includes a description of the use of C_{18} extraction disks for analyte isolation. Samples can be cleaned-up using methods 3610, 3620, 3640 and/or 3660. A modification describing the use of Florisil cartridges for clean-up is included in the method. Extracts are solvent exchanged to hexane or acetonitrile prior to GC analysis. The GC is configured with dual capillary columns and ECDs and a single injector with a Y-splitter. DB-5 and DB-1701 are suggested columns. Calibration is an internal standard (butyl benzoate) with a five-point curve either by RF or actual curve, with daily checking.

Table 3-72. Target Analytes and MDLs for Method 8061

Target Analyte	MDL µg/L	Target Analyte	MDL µg/L
Dimethyl phthalate	0.64	Butyl benzyl phthalate	0.042
Diethyl phthalate	0.25	Bis(2-n-butoxyethyl) phthalate	0.084
Diisobutyl phthalate	0.12	Bis(2-ethylhexyl) phthalate	0.27

Continued on next page.

Table 3-72. Target Analytes and MDLs for Method 8061, *continued*

Target Analyte	MDL µg/L		Target Analyte	MDL µg/L
Di-*n*-butyl phthalate	0.33		Dicyclohexyl phthalate	0.022
Bis(4-methyl-2-pentyl) phthalate	0.37		Di-*n*-octyl phthalate	0.049
Bis(2-methoxyethyl) phthalate	0.51		Dinonyl phthalate	0.022
Diamyl phthalate	0.11		Diphenyl phthalate (surrogate)	nd
Bis(2-ethoxyethyl) phthalate	0.27		Diphenyl isophthalate (surrogate)	nd
Hexyl-2-ethylhexyl phthalate	0.13		Dibenzyl phthalate (surrogate)	nd
Dihexyl phthalate	0.068		Benzyl benzoate (Internal Standard)	nd

8081A   Organochlorine pesticides by capillary column GC-ECD or ELCD

Update III of SW-846 split the PCBs analysis out of Method 8081 and created Method 8082 specifically for determination of PCBs. 8081A is an internal standard method using pentachloronitrobenzene (PCNB) as the internal standard, and decachlorobiphenyl (DCB)and 2,4,5,6-tetrachloro-*m*-xylene (TCMX) as the surrogates. Some laboratories use an additional surrogate, either dibutylchlorendate (DBC), a late-eluting chlorinated diester that is very sensitive to exposure to acids and bases, or 4-chloro-3-nitrobenzotrifluoride, an early-eluting sensitive compound. Each sample is spiked with surrogates, then extracted using Method 3510 or 3520 for liquids or Method 3540, 3541, or 3550 for solids. 1:1 hexane : acetone is recommended instead of methylene chloride : acetone in method 3550. When spiking solid samples, they must be mixed with the spike for one to two minutes then allowed to sit for one hour prior to extraction. A variety of clean-ups are suggested based on the exact set of analytes being determined. The pesticides and PCBs can be separated and determined through use of the silica gel fractionation (Method 3630).

DDT and endrin are particularly sensitive to the condition of the GC injector and column. Column condition must be monitored on a daily basis by injecting a mid-level calibration standard containing DDT and endrin. DDT degrades into DDD and DDE. Endrin degrades into endrin aldehyde and endrin ketone. If breakdown for either exceeds 15%, the system must be corrected. The calculations are shown. Control charts for column condition are a good way to visually monitor the system.

$$\% \text{ DDT breakdown} = \frac{\text{Peak area [DDD + DDE]}}{\text{Peak area [DDD + DDE + DDT]}}$$

$$\% \text{ Endrin breakdown} = \frac{\text{Peak area [aldehyde + ketone]}}{\text{Peak area [endrin + ketone + aldehyde]}}$$

Figure 3-27. Breakdown equations for monitoring column conditions.

Calibration is five-point by either RF or calibration curve, verified on a daily basis. Analyte identification is confirmed on a second column of differing polarity from the analytical column. This is most often accomplished by having parallel columns with auto-injectors and ECDs on a dedicated instrument.

Chlordane, strobane (chlorinated camphenes and pinenes) and toxaphene are subject to weathering, and measuring the total area of the elution envelope results in better quantitation for most samples. Some analytsts use specific peaks such as α-chlordane and γ-chlordane as the response for the entire technical chlordane analyte. This is a very useful technique when there is substantial non-target analyte co-extracted matrix background, such as petroleum fuels, in the sample

Table 3-73. Target Analytes and Retention times for Method 8081A in elution order

Target Analyte	RT DB 608	RT DB 1701
Trifluralin	3.49	6.24
TCMX (surr)	4.25	4.86
Hexachlorobenzene	5.73	6.55
α-BHC	6.14	7.50
γ-BHC	7.40	8.84
β-BHC	7.63	11.51
Heptachlor	8.51	9.58
δ-BHC	8.92	12.46
Aldrin	9.69	10.95
Isodrin	11.54	12.31
Heptachlor epoxide	11.84	13.14
γ-Chlordane	12.47	14.40
α-Chlordane	13.13	14.62
Endosulfan I	13.20	14.21
4,4'-DDE	14.21	15.00
Dieldrin	14.46	15.65
Endrin	15.95	16.46
Toxaphene (main peak)	16.29	17.34
4,4'-DDD	16.51	18.17
Endosulfan II	16.71	18.41
4,4'-DDT	17.75	18.84
Endrin aldehyde	18.10	20.11
Endosulfan sulfate	18.61	21.14
DCB (surr)	19.90	21.60
4,4'-Methoxychlor	21.49	21.35
Endrin ketone	21.81	23.10
Octachloronaphthalene	28.15	27.24
DBC (surr)	28.22	27.40

8082 Polychlorinated biphenyls (PCBs) by capillary column GC-ECD or ELCD

PCB is the abbreviation for a polychlorinated biphenyl. The abbreviation is used in both the singular and the plural sense, although some persons will indicate the plural as PCBs. There are 206 individual PCBs divided into homologues (sets of PCBs with the same number of chlorines, such as the hexachlorobiphenyls) and congeners (individual PCBs with the same number of chlorines). There is also division of the PCBs into the planar and non-planar groups. PCBs that can exist in the planar configuration have both rings in the same plane and are believed to be able to mimic the toxic effects of the dioxins. Planar PCBs are also referred to as toxic PCBs. The manufacturing of PCBs was achieved by treating biphenyl with chlorine gas and a catalyst to achieve a mixture of PCBs with an overall set percentage (by weight) of chlorine. When manufactured by Monsanto, these mixtures were called Arochlors and the individual mixture was designated by a code such as 1242. Although it is incorrect to speak of Monsanto's product as PCB 1242, this practice is widespread in the environmental industry.

Method 8082 is a specialized modification of the pesticide method 8081. The same surrogates and extraction procedure are followed until after the extract is solvent exchanged to hexane. Then there is an acid treatment of the extract to remove interferences from the PCB extract. Method 8082 has quality controls oriented specifically to PCB analysis. These include multi-point calibration of all the common PCB mixtures and calibration verification, laboratory control, and matrix spikes with a PCB 1016/1260 mixture.

Method 8082 identifies PCB as the respective Arochlor, and is calibrated with the various Arochlor mixtures. The GC separation and ECD in Method 8082 lack the resolution to specifically identify individual PCB congeners. Congener-specific analysis is detailed in EPA Method 1668 and requires a high-resolution mass spectrometer coupled with a specialized GC separation to unambiguously identify the 206 individual PCBs[15]. The required instrument is the same high resolution mass spectrometer used for dioxin analysis, and is beyond the means of the average environmental laboratory, although several less scrupulous commercial laboratories will report congener-specific results from use of Method 8082, particularly in support of Cluster-rule analysis for the paper and pulp industry.

Table 3-74. Target Analytes for Method 8082

Target Analyte	CAS No.	Target Analyte	CAS No.
Arochlor 1016	12674-11-2	Arochlor 1248	12672-29-6
Arochlor 1221	11104-28-2	Arochlor 1254	11097-69-1
Arochlor 1232	11141-16-5	Arochlor 1260	11096-82-5
Arochlor 1242	53469-21-9		

The identification of the multi-peaked analytes such as chlordane, toxaphene and the PCBs can be performed by a combination of pattern recognition and retention time. The different Arochlors are normally identified by retention time windows such as those illustrated. Quantitation is based upon indicator peaks that are generally present in more than one PCB mixture. Six peaks are chosen for each Arochlor and each peak is calibrated to represent the Arochlor, resulting in separate calibration files for PCB 1016, 1221, 1232, 1242, 1248, 1254 and 1260. The chromatogram of the sample is then processed against each calibration file. If the six peaks in the calibration file all give approximately the same value, then the Arochlor is fairly well assured of being a single mixture instead of a mixture of mixtures. This works in most cases for Arochlors because they were not subject to variation in the congener distribution in the manufacturing process (although there are two slightly different 1254 standards available[16]), not subject to substantial weathering, and the sulfuric acid/permanganate

---

[15] Frame, G., 1997. Congener-specific PCB analysis. *Anal. Chem.* 69(15):468A-475A.

[16] Dale Chappelow, Analytical Services, Atlanta; GA.

cleanup reduces interferences. This is not to say that biological modification of the PCB isomer distribution does not occur, because it does, and this quantitation method does not work as well for tissue samples.

Treatment of the hexane solution of the sample extract with concentrated sulfuric acid removes most or the chlorinated pesticides including chlordane and toxaphene. The polychlorinated naphthalenes (PCN) and terphenyls (PCT), and the bromine analogs of PCN and PCT will survive the sulfuric acid treatment and can cause substantial interference to PCB analysis.

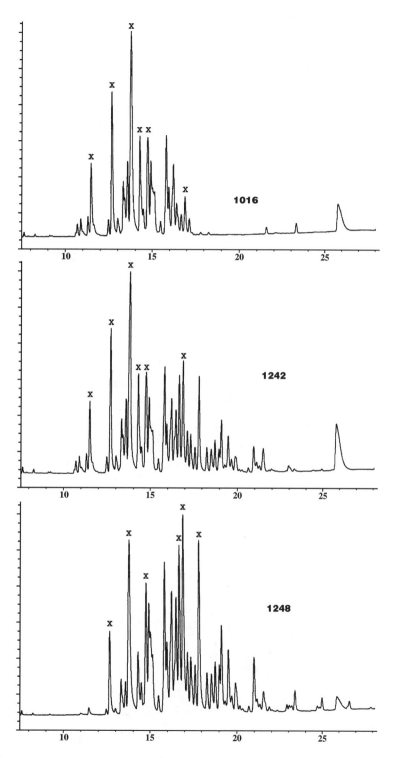

Figure 3-28. PCBs 1016, 1242 and 1248.

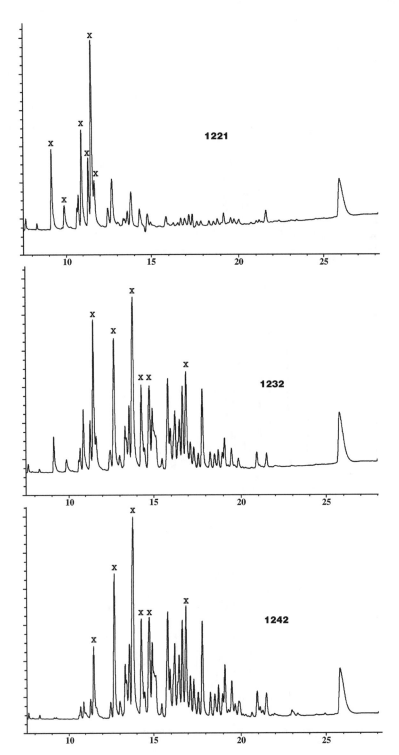

Figure 3-29. PCBs 1221, 1232 and 1242.

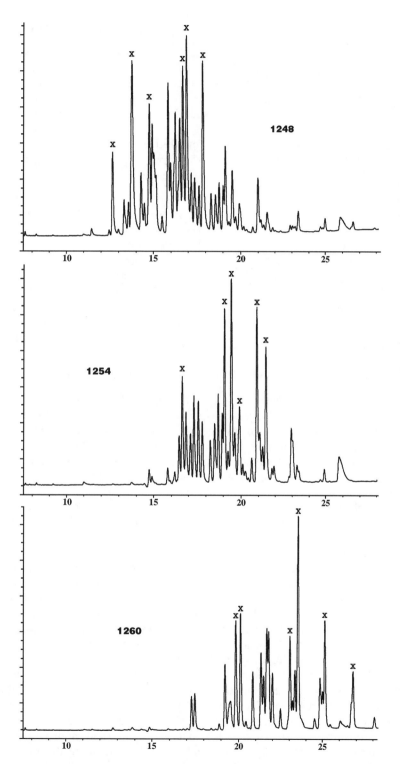

Figure 3-30. PCBs 1248, 1254 and 1260.

8121   Chlorinated hydrocarbons by capillary column GC-ECD

Suggested surrogates are α,2,6-Trichlorotoluene, 1,4-dichloronaphthalene and 2,3,4,5,6-pentachlorotoluene. Suggested internal standards are 2,5-dibromotoluene, 1,3,5-tribromobenzene, and α, α'-dibromo-m-xylene. Initial sample extraction is with methylene chloride, followed by drying with sodium sulfate and concentration with solvent exchange to hexane. Methods 3620, 3640, and 3660 are recommended clean-ups.

Table 3-75. Target Analytes and MDLs for Method 8121

Target Analyte	MDL µg/L	Target Analyte	MDL µg/L
Benzal chloride	2-5	γ-BHC	23
Benzotrichloride	6.0	δ-BHC	20
Benzyl chloride	180	Hexachlorocyclopentadiene	240
2-Chloronaphthalene	1300	Hexachloroethane	1.6
1,2-Dichlorobenzene	270	Pentachlorobenzene	38
1,3-Dichlorobenzene	250	1,2,3,4-Tetrachlorobenzene	11
1,4-Dichlorobenzene	890	1,2,4,5-Tetrachlorobenzene	9.5
Hexachlorobenzene	5.6	1,2,3,5-Tetrachlorobenzene	8.1
Hexachlorobutadiene	1.4	1,2,4-Trichlorobenzene	130
α-BHC	11	1,2,3-Trichlorobenzene	39
β-BHC	31	1,3,5-Trichlorobenzene	12

8141A Organophosphorus compounds by gas chromatography

This technique makes use of the specificity of the Flame Photometric detector (FPD) in the phosphorus mode or the Nitrogen-Phosphorus detector (NPD). The FPD contains a flame to burn the sample and ionize any phosphorus in the eluant. The ionized phosphorus is detected with a photodetector. The heart of the NPD is a heated ceramic bead coated with a salt of an easily ionizable material, rubidium being a common choice. The heating creates a surface plasma on the bead. Nitrogen or phosphorus compounds are ionized and create a current between charged poles of the device. Either detector gives a substantial selectivity for molecules that contain phosphorus and/or nitrogen. The most common target analytes of the method are organophosphorus pesticides, although a few industrially important phosphorus-containing solvents are mentioned as being within the scope of the procedure.

A big difference between the industrial analytes and the pesticide compounds is that the latter are very labile. The acutely lethal properties of these compounds that makes them useful as pesticides, are due to the chemical reactivity of the substances. Abuse of the sample during preparation such as exposure to extremes of acid or base, highly active absorbents in columns, or mechanical abuse such as sonication at high settings or heating will effectively destroy the analytes. Sonication extraction is possible using the milder settings of the probe for longer periods of time.

Most of the analytes are known by tradenames and one analyte may have several tradenames. A resource such as a dictionary of farm chemicals or the older catalog of the available compounds from the EPA repository of pesticides, is a very valuable reference material for wading through the maze of trade and formulation names.

A variety of surrogates are suggested. Tributyl phosphate and triphenyl phosphate are very stable compounds, and do not reflect any abusive conditions that may occur during sample preparation, however they are widely used.

Table 3-76. Target Analytes, retention times, and PQLs for Method 8141A

Target Analyte	RT 608	DB-5	PQL µg/L
Dichlorovos	4.76	4.54	1
1-Bromo-2-nitrobenzene (IS)	5.85	-	-
Mevinphos	6.98	7.76	1
Demeton-O	9.11	11.40	1
Ethoprop	9.36	11.84	1
Tributylphosphate (Surr)	9.40	11.90	-
Sulfotepp	9.88	12.89	1
Phorate	10.02	13.08	1
Naled	10.02	12.46	1
Demeton-S	10.36	13.70	1
Dimethoate	10.38	13.90	1
Diazinon	11.13	15.19	1
Disulfoton	11.20	15.35	1
Parathion Methyl	12.06	17.08	1
Ronnel	12.38	17.59	1
Merphos	13.01	21.37	1
Trichloronate	13.01	19.28	1
Parathion	13.01	18.86	1
Chlorpyrifos	13.29	18.81	1
Fenthion	14.32	18.81	1
Tokuthion	14.67	22.09	1
Stirophos	14.76	21.96	1
Bolstar	15.46	24.28	1
Fensulfothion	15.85	23.55	1
Famfur	15.96	24.67	1
Triphenylphosphate (Surr)	16.52	25.70	-
Azinphos Methyl	17.65	27.37	1
Coumaphos	18.74	28.95	1

8151A Chlorinated herbicides by capillary column GC (derivatization with diazomethane and ECD or Hall detection)

An internal standard (4,4'-dibromooctafluorobiphenyl) and surrogate (2,4-dichloro-phenylacetic acid) method that uses prior derivatization with either diazomethane (See method 515.1) or pentafluorobenzyl bromide before GC-ECD analysis. Calibration is five-point, checked daily. All detected compounds must be confirmed on a second column of different polarity. The method includes the extraction technique.

A 1 L sample is mixed with 250 g NaCl, then the pH is adjusted to >12 with 6 N NaOH and allowed to sit for one hour with occasional shaking. The solution is extracted three times with CH_2Cl_2, which is discarded. The pH is adjusted to < 2 with H_2SO_4 and extracted three times with diethyl ether. The combined extracts are dried over sodium sulfate for a minimum of two hours or better, overnight. The dried extracts are concentrated without allowing the extract to go dry. Isooctane and methanol are added if the sample is to be methylated; acetone if derivatized with pentafluorobenzylbromide.

Table 3-77. Target Analytes and PQLs for Method 8151A with retention times

Target Analyte	RT 608	RT 1701	PQL µg/L
Dalapon	3.76	4.29	25
DCAA (surr)	9.46	9.77	-
MCPP	9.68	10.28	1000
Dicamba	9.86	10.11	1
MCPA	10.20	10.69	1000
Dichloroprop	10.61	11.19	10
2,4-D	11.26	11.74	10
Pentachlorophenol	12.1	12.2	10
2,4,5-TP	12.28	12.93	1
2,4,5-T	13.09	13.63	1
Dinoseb	13.26	15.40	5
2,4-DB	13.75	14.32	10
Picloram	14.70	16.4	10

8270C Semivolatile organic compounds by capillary column GC/MS

The increased efficiency of the capillary column over that of the packed column allows
8270C to have a vastly increased target analyte list as compared to the technically-
obsolete 8250. Otherwise these are very similar methods as far as sample preparation
and clean-up, MS tuning, SPCC, CCC (one compound added), surrogates, internal
standards, and matrix spikes are concerned. Calibration is still five-point internal
standard by either average RF or by a regression on RF. Earlier versions of 8270 had
acceptance criteria for the average RF of less than 30% RSD, however in 8270B
(September 1994) the acceptance criteria dropped to 15% or less. The Estimated
Quantitation Limits (EQL) listed are for groundwater. Soil/sediment EQLs run 33 times
higher. A recent trend in state regulatory agencies has been to demand that groundwater
be analyzed by method 8270C with MDLs appropriate for drinking water.

Table 3-78. Daily MS DFTPP tune criteria for Method 8270C

Mass M/z	DFTPP Relative Abundance Criteria
51	30-60% of base peak
68	< 2% of mass 69
70	< 2% of mass 69
127	40-60% of mass 198
197	<1% of mass 198
198	base peak 100% relative abundance
199	5-9% of mass 198
275	10-30% of mass 198
365	>1% of mass 198
441	present and < mass 443
442	>40% of mass 198
443	17-23% of mass 442

Table 3-79. SPCC for Method 8270C

SPCC	Minimum RF
N-Nitroso-di-n-propylamine	0.050
2,4-Dinitrophenol	0.050

SPCC	Minimum RF
Hexachlorocyclopentadiene	0.050
4-Nitrophenol	0.050

Table 3-80. Calibration Check Compounds (CCC) for Method 8270C

Acenaphthene
4-Chloro-3-methylphenol
1,4-Dichlorobenzene
2,4-Dichlorophenol
Hexachlorobutadiene
2-Nitrophenol
Fluoranthene

N-Nitrosodiphenylamine
Phenol
Di-n-octyl phthalate
Pentachlorophenol
Benzo(a)pyrene
2,4,6-Trichlorophenol

Table 3-81. Internal standards and surrogates for Method 8270C

Internal Standards	Surrogates
1,4-Dichlorobenzene-d_4	Phenol-d_6
Acenaphthene-d_{10}	2,4,6-Tribromophenol
Chrysene-d_{12}	2-Fluorobiphenyl
Naphthalene-d_8	2-Fluorophenol
Phenanthrene-d_{10}	Nitrobenzene-d_5
Perylene-d_{12}	p-Terphenyl-d_{14}

Table 3-82. Minimum matrix spike compounds for Method 8270C

1,2,4-Trichlorobenzene
Pentachlorophenol
Acenaphthene
Phenol
2,4-Dinitrotoluene
2-Chlorophenol

Pyrene
4-Chloro-3-methylphenol
N-Nitroso-di-n-propylamine
4-Nitrophenol
1,4-Dichlorobenzene

Table 3-83. Appendix II and Appendix IX Target Analytes, Retention times,[17] and EQLs by Method 8270C

Target Analyte	Retention time	EQL μg/L
Pyridine	3.85	50
N-Nitrosodimethylamine	3.98	10
2-Picoline	5.41	10
N-Nitrosomethylethylamine	5.81	20
Methyl methanesulfonate	6.45	20
2-Fluorophenol (Surr)	6.63	-
N-Nitrosodiethylamine	7.09	10
Ethyl methanesulfonate	7.69	20
Aniline	8.31	10
Phenol-d5 (Surr)	8.32	-
Phenol	8.35	10
Bis(2-chloroethyl)ether	8.43	10
2-Chlorophenol	8.45	10
1,3-Dichlorobenzene	8.66	10
1,4-Dichlorobenzene-d4 (IS)	8.73	-
1,4-Dichlorobenzene	8.76	10
1,2-Dichlorobenzene	9.06	10
Benzyl alcohol	9.08	10
2-Methylphenol	9.30	10
Bis(2-chloroisopropyl)ether	9.31	10
Acetophenone	9.50	10
Hexachloroethane	9.55	10
Pentachloroethane	9.55	10
3-Methylphenol + 4-Methylphenol	9.57	10
N-Nitrosopyrrolidine	9.58	20
o-Toluidine	9.58	20
N-Nitroso-di-n-propylamine	9.60	10
N-Nitrosomorpholine	9.61	10
Nitrobenzene-d5 (Surr)	9.76	-
Nitrobenzene	9.79	10
N-Nitrosopiperidine	10.05	20
Isophorone	10.16	10
2-Nitrophenol	10.30	10
2,4-Dimethylphenol	10.41	10
Bis(2-chloroethoxy)methane	10.56	10
O,O,O-Triethylphosphorothioate	10.57	20
2,4-Dichlorophenol	10.67	10
1,2,4-Trichlorobenzene	10.79	10
Naphthalene-d8 (IS)	10.86	-
Benzoic acid	10.86	50

Continued on next page.

[17] 30 m x 0.25 mm id Restek RTX-5, 1 mL/min constant flow, 40 °C for 4 min, followed by 15 °C/min to 160 °C, then 20 °C/min to 310 °C for 6.5 min; total run time 26.5 min.

Table 3-83. Appendix II and Appendix IX Target Analytes, Retention times,[18] and EQLs by Method 8270C, *continued*

Target Analyte	Retention time	EQL µg/L
Naphthalene	10.90	10
a,a-Dimethylphenethylamine	10.93	30
2,6-Dichlorophenol	11.05	10
4-Chloroaniline	11.07	10
Hexachloropropene	11.08	30
Hexachlorobutadiene	11.19	10
N-Nitrosodibutylamine	11.66	10
1,4-Phenylenediamine	11.68	10
4-Chloro-3-methylphenol	11.87	20
Isosafrole	11.93	10
2-Methylnaphthalene	12.03	10
1,2,4,5-Tetrachlorobenzene	12.37	10
Hexachlorocyclopentadiene	12.38	20
2,4,6-Trichlorophenol	12.54	10
2,4,5-Trichlorophenol	12.60	10
2-Fluorobiphenyl (Surr)	12.67	-
Safrole	12.74	50
2-Chloronaphthalene	12.80	10
2-Nitroaniline	13.07	50
1,4-Naphthoquinone	13.12	10
Dimethyl phthalate	13.40	10
Acenaphthylene	13.44	10
2,6-Dinitrotoluene	13.50	20
Acenaphthene-d10 (IS)	13.66	-
3-Nitroaniline	13.70	50
Acenaphthene	13.72	10
2,4-Dinitrophenol	13.82	50
4-Nitrophenol	13.94	50
Dibenzofuran	13.95	10
1,3-Dinitrobenzene	13.95	10
4-Bromophenyl phenyl ether	13.98	10
Pentachlorobenzene	13.98	10
2,4-Dinitrotoluene	14.07	20
2-Naphthylamine	14.07	10
1-Naphthylamine	14.09	10
4-Nitroquinoline-1-oxide	14.11	10
2,3,4,6-Tetrachlorophenol	14.19	10

Continued on next page.

---

[18] 30 m x 0.25 mm id Restek RTX-5, 1 mL/min constant flow, 40 °C for 4 min, followed by 15 °C/min to 160 °C, then 20 °C/min to 310 °C for 6.5 min; total run time 26.5 min.

Table 3-83. Appendix II and Appendix IX Target Analytes, Retention times,[19] and EQLs by Method 8270C, *continued*

Target Analyte	Retention time	EQL µg/L
Diethyl phthalate	14.40	10
Fluorene	14.43	10
4-Chlorophenyl phenyl ether	14.44	10
Thionazine	14.50	20
4,6-Dinitro-2-methylphenol	14.59	50
4-Nitroaniline	14.60	50
Diphenylamine	14.64	10
5-Nitro-*o*-toluidine	14.64	10
N-Nitrosodiphenylamine	14.64	10
Diphenyl hydrazine	14.65	10
2,4,6-Tribromophenol (Surr)	14.79	-
Sulfotepp	14.99	20
Phorate	15.08	20
Diallate, total	15.15	10
1,3,5-Trinitrobenzene	15.15	10
Phenacetin	15.17	100
Hexachlorobenzene	15.29	10
Dimethoate	15.36	20
4-Aminobiphenyl	15.48	10
Pentachlorophenol	15.53	50
Pronamide	15.61	10
Pentachloronitrobenzene	15.65	10
Phenanthrene-d10 (IS)	15.69	-
Phenanthrene	15.73	10
Disulfoton	15.76	10
Dinoseb	15.78	20
Anthracene	15.79	10
Methyl parathion	16.26	10
Di-*n*-butyl phthalate	16.51	10
Parathion	16.75	10
Methapyrilene	16.88	10
Isodrin	17.06	20
Fluoranthene	17.25	10
Benzidine	17.40	80
Pyrene	17.53	10
Terphenyl-d14 (Surr)	17.73	-
Aramite	17.83	20
Dimethylaminoazobenzene	17.93	10
Chlorobenzilate	18.00	50

Continued on next page.

[19] 30 m x 0.25 mm id Restek RTX-5, 1 mL/min constant flow, 40 °C for 4 min, followed by 15 °C/min to 160 °C, then 20 °C/min to 310 °C for 6.5 min; total run time 26.5 min.

Table 3-83. Appendix II and Appendix IX Target Analytes, Retention times,[20] and EQLs by Method 8270C, *continued*

Target Analyte	Retention time	EQL µg/L
Kepone	18.35	20
3,3'-Dimethylbenzidine	18.35	10
Famphur	18.36	20
Butyl benzyl phthalate	18.38	10
2-Acetylaminofluorene	18.71	10
Methoxychlor	18.97	10
Benz(a)anthracene	19.02	10
3,3'-Dichlorobenzidine	19.03	10
Chrysene-d12 (IS)	19.05	-
Bis(2-ethylhexyl)phthalate	19.08	10
Chrysene	19.09	10
Di-*n*-octyl phthalate	19.80	10
Benzo(b)fluoranthene	20.38	10
7,12-Dimethylbenz(a)anthracene	20.39	10
Benzo(k)fluoranthene	20.41	10
Hexachlorophene	20.65	100
Benzo(a)pyrene	20.81	10
Perylene-d12 (IS)	20.88	-
3-Methylcholanthrene	21.36	10
Indeno(1,2,3-cd)pyrene	22.70	10
Dibenz(a,h)anthracene	22.72	10
Benzo(g,h,i)perylene	23.22	10

[20] 30 m x 0.25 mm id Restek RTX-5, 1 mL/min constant flow, 40 °C for 4 min, followed by 15 °C/min to 160 °C, then 20 °C/min to 310 °C for 6.5 min; total run time 26.5 min.

8275A Semivolatile organic compounds by thermal chromatography/MS

This is a fast screening method for solid or waste samples using a pyrolysis cell temperature-programmed to 260 °C for sample introduction. Direct interface to an FID is used to obtain a rough idea of the amount of analyte in the sample, then the test is repeated with a capillary column and MS for quantitation and identification. Calibration is five-point internal standard with 1,4-dichlorobenzene-d_4, naphthalene-d_8, acenaphthene-d_{10}, phenanthrene-d_{10}, chrysene-d_{12}, and perylene-d_{12}. Sample size is limited to about 0.10 g, which implies that sample representativeness may be a problem and multiple assays of a solid may be warranted.

Table 3-84. Target Analytes and % Recovery for Method 8275A

Target Analyte	% Recovery	Target Analyte	% Recovery
2-Chlorophenol	18	Hexachlorobenzene	71
4-Methylphenol	31	Dibenzothiophene	35
2,4-Dichlorophenol	23	Phenanthrene	24
Naphthalene	87	Carbazole	7
4-Chloro-3-methylphenol	10	Aldrin	12
1-Chloronaphthalene	90	Pyrene	15
2,4-Dinitrotoluene	9	Benzo(k)fluoranthene	8
Fluorene	18	Benzo(a)pyrene	8
Diphenylamine	6		

8290 Polychlorinated dibenzodioxins (PCDDs) and polychlorinated dibenzofurans (PCDFs) by high-resolution gas chromatography/ high-resolution mass spectrometry (HRGC/HRMS)

This method requires use of a high resolution magnetic sector MS for the analysis. The sample is spiked with the labeled internal standards in Table 3-85, then extracted and cleaned-up. The extraction is with toluene in a Soxhlet-Dean Starke for solids and methylene chloride separatory funnel for liquids. Clean-up consists of acid-base washing followed by Biosil, alumina and a mixed Celite 545/AX-21 carbon column fractionations. Recovery standards ($^{13}C_{12}$-1,2,3,4-TCDD and $^{13}C_{12}$-1,2,3,7,8,9-HxCDD) are added immediately prior to GC/MS analysis.

Table 3-85. Internal standards of Method 8290

$^{13}C_{12}$-2,3,7,8-TCDD	$^{13}C_{12}$-2,3,7,8-TCDF	$^{13}C_{12}$-1,2,3,7,8-PeCDD
$^{13}C_{12}$-1,2,3,7,8-PeCDF	$^{13}C_{12}$-1,2,3,6,7,8-HxCDD	$^{13}C_{12}$-1,2,3,4,7,8-HxCDF
$^{13}C_{12}$-1,2,3,4,6,7,8-HpCDD	$^{13}C_{12}$-1,2,3,4,6,7,8-HpCDF	$^{13}C_{12}$-OCDD

Surrogate and alternate standards can be added to the sample extract prior to any clean-up and fractionation. Good recovery of these compounds indicates that there was no problem with the sample processing and that any poor internal standard recoveries are strictly due to matrix effects of the original sample. Poor recovery of surrogate/alternate standards indicates problems with the extraction/clean-up.

Table 3-86. Surrogate and alternate standards of Method 8290

$^{37}Cl_4$-2,3,7,8-TCDD	$^{13}C_{12}$-2,3,4,7,8-PeCDF	$^{13}C_{12}$-1,2,3,4,7,8-HxCDD
$^{13}C_{12}$-1,2,3,4,7,8-HxCDF	$^{13}C_{12}$-1,2,3,4,7,8,9-HpCDF	$^{13}C_{12}$-1,2,3,7,8,9-HxCDF
$^{13}C_{12}$-2,3,4,6,7,8-HxCDF		

The guidelines for acceptable internal, surrogate and alternate[1] standard recoveries is 40-135% for the tetra- through hexa-substituted compounds and 25-135% for the higher hepta- and octa- homologues. Mass tuning of the mass spectrometer is achieved by leak of perfluoro kerosene into the ionization chamber during analysis of each sample. Mass lock is achieved at 354.9792 for C_9F_{13}, 430.9728 for C_9F_{17} and 442.9278 for $C_{10}F_{17}$.

Compound identification for the dioxins is based on analysis on the DB-5 column with exact retention time within 0.005 units from the calibration if a labeled analog is used as a standard and the simultaneous detection of the two most abundant ions in the molecular ion area in the correct ratio. Furans are not adequately resolved on DB-5 and if detected are re-analyzed on a DB-225 column for identification and quantitation.

Table 3-87 Target analytes and minimum calibration levels of Method 8290

Target analytes	Water ppq	Solids ppt
2,3,7,8-TCDD	10	1
1,2,3,7,8-PeCDD	50	5
1,2,3,4,7,8-HxCDD	50	5
1,2,3,6,7,8-HxCDD	50	5
1,2,3,7,8,9-HxCDD	50	5
1,2,3,4,7,8,9-HpCDD	50	5
1,2,3,4,6,7,8,9-OCDD	100	10
2,3,7,8-TCDF	10	1
1,2,3,7,8-PeCDF	50	5
2,3,4,7,8-PeCDF	50	5
1,2,3,4,7,8-HxCDF	50	5
1,2,3,6,7,8-HxCDF	50	5
2,3,4,6,7,8-HxCDF	50	5
1,2,3,7,8,9-HxCDF	50	5
1,2,3,4,6,7,8-HpCDF	50	5
1,2,3,4,7,8,9-HpCDF	50	5
1,2,3,4,6,7,8,9-OCDF	100	10
Total TCDD	10	1
Total PeCDD	50	5
Total HxCDD	50	5
Total HpCDD	50	5
Total TCDF	10	1
Total PeCDF	50	5
Total HxCDF	50	5
Total HpCDF	50	5

---

[1] Alternate and surrogate standards are used for the same purpose in analysis of water and solid samples. The distinction lies in analysis of PUF samples of air. These surrogate standards are added to the PUF prior to air sampling. Internal standards are added to the PUF prior to extraction and alternate standards are added to the sample extract prior to clean-up and fractionation.

The minimum calibration levels are listed in Table 3-88. Detection limits are variable for each sample depending on the complexity of the background, the initial size of the sample, the solids content of the sample and the judgment of the operator. Many times they are reported as less than the lowest calibration standard. Partly due to the very complex nature of the mixture of dioxins present in a sample and co-occurring PCBs, many interferences are frequently present in the chromatogram from overlapping signals with the analyte peaks. Quantitation of the target analyte is often reported as the Estimated Maximum Possible Concentration (EMPC) when interferences are suspected.

The distinction between surrogate and alternate standards is noticeable when air samples are analyzed. Alternate standards are added to the air sampler media prior to any sampling, while surrogate standards are added during the normal initiation of the clean-up process.

Table 3-88. Acceptance ranges for molecular ion ratios

Number of Cl atoms	Ion type	Acceptance range
4	M/M+2	0.65-0.89
5	M+2/M+4	1.32-1.78
6	M+2/M+4	1.05-1.43
6^2	M/M+2	0.43-0.59
7	M+2/M+4	0.88-1.20
7^3	M/M+2	0.37-0.51
8	M+2/M+4	0.76-1.02

Methods 513 and 1613 are similar to 8290 in requiring use of a HRMS. Although the CLP-SOW for dioxins does not specify a HRMS, the SOW is almost identical to method 8290. Other dioxin methods are based upon GC-MS using a low resolution mass spectrometer. The mass spectrometer is tuned to DFTPP standards as in 8270 and 625. These methods include 8280, 40 CFR 261 Appendix X, 40 CFR 60 Appendix A Method 23, method 613, and in the BIF methods manual (40 CFR 266 Appendix IX) method 3.4.

8310 Polynuclear aromatic hydrocarbons (PAH) by HPLC with UV and fluorescence detection

This is very similar to Method 610 (same target analytes and HPLC instrument and operation) with the additional requirements for five-point external standard calibration and decafluorobiphenyl as surrogate. Sample extraction is by Methods 3510 or 3520 at pH 7 for liquids and either 3540 or 3550 for solids. Clean-up by silica gel column (Method 3630) is an option.

8315A Formaldehyde and acetaldehyde by HPLC UV detection

---

2 $^{13}C_{12}$-HxCDF only

3 $^{13}C_{12}$-HpCDF only

Formaldehyde and/or acetaldehyde are isolated by toxic characteristic leaching procedure or TCLP extraction (Method 1311) from solids. The leachate or aqueous sample is buffered to pH 5.0 ± 0.5 with acetate buffer and derivatized with 2,4-dinitrophenylhydrazine. The hydrazone derivative is isolated by either solid phase extraction using a C_{18} cartridge or CH_2Cl_2 liquid-liquid extraction. Analysis is by isocratic HPLC (3:1 methanol : water) on a reversed-phase column with UV detection at 360 nm. Calibration is external standard with a minimum five-point curve. MDL is 7.2 µg/L for formaldehyde and 171 µg/L for acetaldehyde. Confirmation of identity can be by GC-MS or use of another analytical column of different polarity. (The author has performed many of these analyses for aldehydes and found that the hydrazones are GC stable. Preparation of the hydrazone from any of a variety of aldehydes leads to a suitable internal standard; pivalaldehyde has been used with success.)

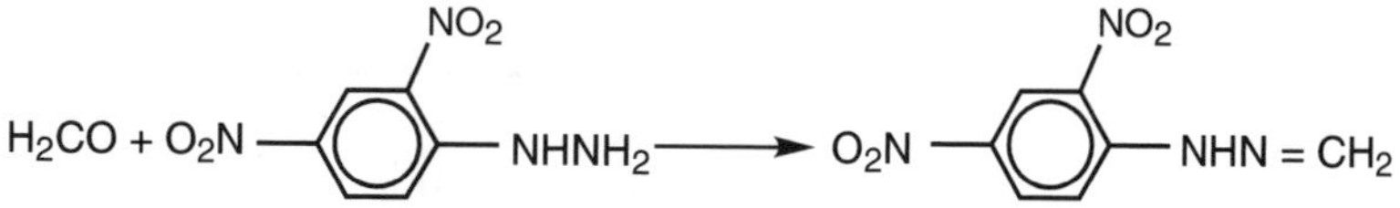

Figure 3-31. Reaction of formaldehyde with 2,4-DNP.

8316 Acrylamide, acrylonitrile, and acrolein by HPLC

This is a direct injection technique into the HPLC with a C_{18} reversed-phase column and water-mobile phase with UV detection at 195 nm. Calibration is five-point external standard. MDLs are 10 µg/L for acrylamide, 20 for acrylonitrile and 30 for acrolein.

8318 *N*-Methyl carbamates by HPLC

Aqueous samples are extracted with CH_2Cl_2 and solid samples with acetonitrile. The extract is then concentrated with solvent exchange to ethylene glycol. The concentrated extracts are diluted with methanol followed by clean-up with a C_{18} reversed-phase cartridge. Calibration is five-point external standard. The HPLC is equipped with a post-column derivatization unit with excitation at 340 nm and emission detection at >418 nm. The separation is performed on a reversed-phased column with a binary non-linear gradient formed from acidified water and 1:1 methanol : acetonitrile.

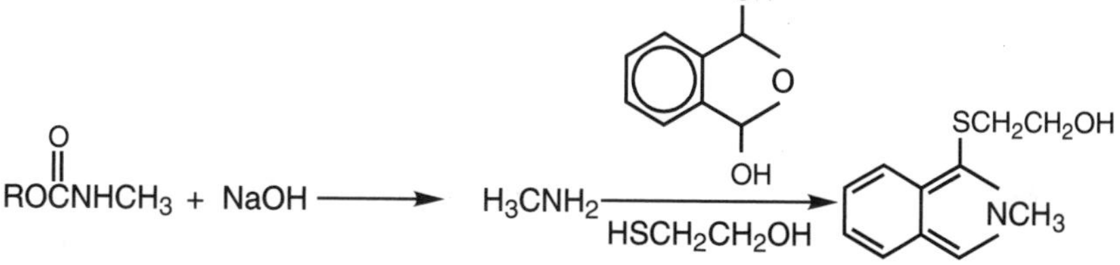

Figure 3-32. Post-column derivatization/fluorescence detection of *N*-methyl carbamates.

Thiofluor, the reagent combination used by Pickering Labs replaces the mercaptoethanol with $(CH_3)_2NCH_2CH_2SH$ HCl.

Table 3-89. Target Analytes and MDLs for Method 8318

Target Analyte	MDL aqueous µg/L	MDL soil µg/Kg
Aldicarb sulfone	1.9	44
Methomyl	1.7	12
3-Hydroxycarbofuran	2.6	10
Dioxacarb	2.2	>50
Aldicarb	9.4	12
Propoxur	2.4	17
Carbofuran	2.0	22
Carbaryl	1.7	31
Methiocarb	3.1	32
Promecarb	2.5	17

8321A   Non-volatile solvent extractable compounds by HPLC/Thermospray MS

Samples are extracted using 3510 or 3520 for aqueous matrices and 3540 or 3550 for solids. The calibration is five-point external standard. Surrogates are suggested, but none are listed. MS tuning is with polyethylene glycol (PEG-400, 600 or 800).

Table 3-90. MS Tune Criteria Using PEG 400 for Method 8321A

Calibration Mass PEG 400	% Relative Abundance
18.0	32.3
35.06	13.5
36.04	40.5
50.06	94.6
77.04	27.0
168.12	5.5
212.14	10.3
256.17	17.6
300.20	27.0
344.22	45.9
388.25	64.9
432.28	100.0
476.30	94.6
520.33	81.1
564.35	67.6
608.38	32.4
652.41	16.2
653.41	4.1
696.43	8.1
697.44	2.7

Compound classes that have been analyzed by HPLC-MS include disperse azo dyes, methine dyes, arylmethane dyes, coumarin dyes, anthraquinone dyes, xanthene dyes, flame retardants, alkaloids, aromatic ureas, amides, amino acids, organophosphorous compounds, and chlorinated phenoxyacid herbicides.

III. MISCELLANEOUS ORGANIC INFORMATION

A. Mass Spectrometer Tuning

EPA mass analyzer tuning standards 4-bromofluorobenzene (BFB) and decafluorotri-phenylphosphine (DFTPP) are required to be met on every 12-hour working shift. Quadrupole electron impact mass analyzers (Hewlett-Packard 5970 and 5971), which autotune results from perfluorotributylamine (PFTBA, FC-43) are generally insufficient to meet the tuning requirements. Recent tuning software updates allow user-defined target abundance ranges for PFTBA. The PFTBA target ranges[4] are listed in Table 3-91 with peak widths at half height 0.48 ± 0.02 for hitting DFTPP.

Table 3-91. PFTBA Target Tune for DFTPP

Mass M/z	Target Relative Abundance
50	1.5 ± 0.5
69	100
131	40 ± 15
219	40 ± 15
414	1.5 ± 0.5
502	1.0 ± 0.5

Table 3-92. Ideal Results for PFTBA with Peak Widths of 0.50

Mass M/z	Ideal Relative Abundance
50	1-2
69	100
131	35
219	30
414	1-2
502	0.8

General guidelines from the PFTBA autotune results for other models of mass analyzers are:

BFB - mass 69 (100%), 131 (25%), 219 (20%)

DFTPP - mass 131 = mass 219

---

[4]   Neal, Barney. Hewlett-Packard Analytical Education Center. Atlanta, GA. 1992.

B. Freons

Freon nomenclature[5]

E   D   X   Y   Z   iiiii

E   indicates the molecule is an ether

D   indicates the number of multiple bonds in the molecule (a 2 in this position can indicate either a triple bond or two double bonds)

X   is one less than the number of carbons in the molecule

Y   is one more than the number of hydrogens in the molecule

Z   is the number of fluorines in the molecule

iiiii   represents isomeric structures when small case letters; when capital B followed by digits, i represents the number of bromines in the molecule

Frequently the code numbers will be prefixed with an "R." This stands for "refrigerant." A prefix of "C" indicates the molecule is cyclic.

Add "90" to the code number. That gives as the first digit the number of carbons, the second digit, the number of hydrogens and the last digit the number of fluorines[6].

---

[5] Number Designation and Safety Classification of Refrigerants, ASHRAE standard, ANSI/ASHRAE 34-1992, American Society of Heating, Refrigerating, and Air-Conditioning Engineers, 1791 Tullie Circle, Atlanta, GA 30329, 1992.

[6] Bruno, T.J. *Handbook for the Analysis and Identification of Alternate Refrigerants*. CRC Press, Boca Raton, FL. ISBN 0-8493-3926-X. 1995.

Table 3-93. Freons

Freon ID[22]	+ 90	Formula	CAS	Structure
11	101	$CFCl_3$	75-69-4	$CFCl_3$
12	102	CF_2Cl_2	75-71-8	CF_2Cl_2
12B2	102	CF_2Br_2	75-61-6	CF_2Br_2
13	103	CF_3Cl	75-72-9	CF_3Cl
13B1	103	CF_3Br	75-63-8	CF_3Br
13I1	103	CF_3I	2314-97-8	CF_3I
14	104	CF_4	75-73-0	CF_4
21	111	$CHFCl_2$	75-43-4	$CHFCl_2$
22	112	CHF_2Cl	75-45-6	CHF_2Cl
22B1	112	CHF_2Br	1511-62-2	CHF_2Br
23	113	CHF_3	75-46-7	CHF_3
31	121	CH_2ClF	593-70-4	CH_2ClF
31B1	121	CH_2BrF	373-52-4	CH_2BrF
32	122	CH_2F_2	75-10-5	CH_2F_2
40	130	$ClCH_3$	74-87-3	$ClCH_3$
41	131	CH_3F	593-53-3	CH_3F
112	202	$C_2Cl_4F_2$	76-12-0	CCl_2FCCl_2F
112a	202	$C_2Cl_4F_2$	76-11-9	$CClF_2CCl_4$
113	203	$C_2F_3Cl_3$	76-13-1	$CF_2ClCFCl_2$
113a	203	$C_2F_3Cl_3$	354-58-5	CCl_3CF_3
114	204	$C_2F_4Cl_2$	76-14-2	CF_2ClCF_2Cl
114a	204	$C_2F_4Cl_2$	374-07-2	CCl_2FCF_3
115	205	C_2ClF_5	76-15-3	$CClF_2CF_3$
115I1	205	C_2F_5I	–	C_2F_5I
116	206	C_2F_6	76-16-4	CF_3CF_3
121	211	C_2Cl_4FH	354-14-3	CCl_2FCCl_2H
122	212	$C_2Cl_3F_2H$	354-21-2	$CClF_2CCl_2H$
123	213	$C_2HF_3Cl_2$	306-83-2	CF_3CHCl_2
123a	213	$C_2HF_3Cl_2$	354-23-4	$CClF_2CClFH$
124	214	C_2HF_4Cl	2837-89-0	CF_3CHFCl
124a	214	C_2HF_4Cl	354-25-6	CF_2ClCHF_2
125	215	C_2HF_5	354-33-6	CF_3CHF_2
131	221	$C_2Cl_3FH_2$	359-28-4	$CCl_2HCClFH$
131a	221	$C_2Cl_3FH_2$	811-95-0	CCl_2FCClH_2
132b	222	$C_2Cl_2F_2H_2$	1649-08-7	$CClF_2CClH_2$
133a	223	$C_2ClF_3H_2$	75-88-7	CF_3CClH_2
134	224	$C_2H_2F_4$	359-35-3	CF_2HCF_2H
134a	224	$C_2H_2F_4$	811-97-2	CF_3CH_2F
141	231	$C_2Cl_2FH_3$	25167-88-8	$CClFHCClH_2$
141b	231	$C_2H_3FCl_2$	1717-00-6	$CFCl_2CH_3$
142b	232	$C_2H_3F_2Cl$	75-68-3	$CClF_2CH_3$

Continued on next page.

---

[22] These freon numbers are frequently preceeded by CFC, HCF, or HCFC, however it is the number that identifies the compound. For example Freon-32, HCF-32, and CFC-32 describe exactly the same compound.

Table 3-93. Freons, *continued*

Freon ID	+ 90	Formula	CAS	Structure
143	233	$C_2H_3F_3$	430-66-0	CF_2HCFH_2
143a	233	$C_2H_3F_3$	420-46-2	CF_3CH_3
150	240	$C_2H_4Cl_2$	107-06-2	$CClH_2CClH_2$
150a	240	$C_2H_4Cl_2$	75-34-3	$CHCl_2CH_3$
151a	241	C_2H_4ClF	1615-75-4	$CHClFCH_3$
152	242	$C_2H_4F_2$	624-72-6	CFH_2CFH_2
152a	242	$C_2H_4F_2$	75-37-6	CH_3CHF_2
160	250	C_2H_5Cl	75-00-3	CH_3CH_2Cl
161	251	C_2H_5F	353-36-6	CFH_2CH_3
113B2ab	203	$C_2Br_2ClF_3$	354-51-8	$CBrF_2CBrClF$
113B2	203	$C_2Br_2ClF_3$	754-17-6	CBr_2ClCF_3
114B1	204	C_2BrClF_4	354-53-0	$CBrF_2CClF_2$
114B2	204	C_2BrClF_4	25497-30-7	$CBrF_2CBrF_2$
123B1	213	$C_2HBrClF_3$	151-67-7	$CF_3CBrClH$
123B2	213	$C_2HBr_2F_3$	354-04-1	$CBrF_2CBrFH$
123aB1a	213	$C_2HBrClF_3$	354-06-3	$CBrF_2CClFH$
132bB2	222	$C_2H_2Br_2F_2$	75-82-1	$CBrF_2CBrH_2$
133aB1	223	$C_2H_2BrF_3$	421-06-7	$CBrH_2CF_3$
142B1	232	$C_2H_3BrF_2$	359-07-9	CF_2HCBrH_2
151B1	241	C_2H_4BrF	762-49-2	$CBrH_2CFH_2$
160B1	250	C_2H_5Br	74-96-4	CH_3CH_2Br
1110	1200	C_2Cl_4	127-18-4	$Cl_2C=CCl_2$
1111	1201	C_2Cl_3F	359-29-5	$Cl_2C=CClF$
1112	1202	$C_2Cl_2F_2$	27156-03-2	$ClFC=CClF$
1112a	1202	$C_2Cl_2F_2$	79-35-6	$Cl_2C=CF_2$
1112c	1202	$C_2Cl_2F_2$	–	*cis* $ClFC=CFCl$
1112t	1202	$C_2Cl_2F_2$	598-88-9	*trans* $ClFC=CFCl$
1113	1203	C_2ClF_3	79-38-9	$ClFC=CF_2$
1114	1204	C_2F_4	116-14-3	$F_2C=CF_2$
1120	1210	C_2HCl_3	79-01-6	$Cl_2C=CClH$
1121c	1211	C_2HCl_2F	430-58-0	*cis* $ClFC=CClH$
1121t	1211	C_2HCl_2F	–	*trans* $ClFC=CClH$
1122	1212	C_2HClF_2	359-10-4	$F_2C=CClH$
1123	1213	C_2HF_3	359-11-5	$F_2C=CFH$
1130	1220	$C_2H_2Cl_2$	540-59-0	$ClHC=CClH$
1130a	1220	$C_2H_2Cl_2$	75-35-4	$Cl_2C=CH_2$
1131a	1221	C_2H_2ClF	2317-91-1	$ClFC=CH_2$
1132a	1222	$C_2H_2F_2$	75-38-7	$F_2C=CH_2$
1141	1231	C_2H_3F	75-02-5	$FHC=CH_2$
1112aB2	1202	$C_2Br_2F_2$	430-85-3	$Br_2C=CF_2$
1113B1	1203	C_2BrF_3	598-73-2	$BrFC=CF_2$
1122B1	1212	C_2HBrF_2	–	$BrHC=CF_2$
1140B1	1230	C_2H_3Br	593-60-2	$H_2C=CBrH$
215aa	305	$C_3Cl_3F_5$	1599-41-3	$CClF_2CCl_2CF_3$
215ba	305	$C_3Cl_3F_5$	76-17-5	$CClF_2CClFCClF_2$

Continued on next page.

Table 3-93. Freons, *continued*

Freon ID	+ 90	Formula	CAS	Structure
216ba	306	$C_3Cl_2F_6$	661-97-2	$CClF_2CClFCF_3$
217ba	307	C_3ClF_7	76-18-6	$CF_3CClFCF_3$
225ca	315	$C_3HCl_2F_5$	422-56-0	$CF_3CF_2CCl_2H$
225cb	315	$C_3HCl_2F_5$	507-55-1	$CClF_2CF_2CClFH$
227ca	317	C_3HF_7	–	$CF_3CF_2CHF_2$
227ea	317	C_3HF_7	431-89-0	CF_3CFHCF_3
236ea	326	$C_3H_2F_6$	431-63-0	CF_3CFHCF_2H
236fa	326	$C_3H_2F_6$	690-39-2	$CF_3CH_2CF_3$
243db	333	$C_3H_3Cl_2F_3$	338-75-0	$CF_3CClHCClH_2$
245ca	335	$C_3H_3F_5$	679-86-7	$CHF_2CF_2CH_2F$
245cb	335	$C_3H_3F_5$	–	$CF_3CF_2CH_3$
245eb	335	$C_3H_3F_5$	431-31-2	$CF_3CHFCFH_2$
245fa	335	$C_3H_3F_5$	690-39-1	$CF_3CH_2CHF_2$
253fb	343	$C_3H_4ClF_3$	460-35-5	$CF_3CH_2CClH_2$
254cb	344	$C_3H_4F_4$	40723-63-5	$CHF_2CF_2CH_3$
262da	352	$C_3H_5ClF_2$	–	$CFH_2CClHCFH_2$
263fb	353	$C_3H_5F_3$	421-07-8	$CF_3CH_2CH_3$
270aa	360	$C_3H_6Cl_2$	594-20-7	$CH_3CCl_2CH_3$
270fa	360	$C_3H_6Cl_2$	142-28-9	$CClH_2CH_2CClH_2$
270da	360	$C_3H_6Cl_2$	78-87-5	$CClH_2CClHCH_3$
270fb	360	$C_3H_6Cl_2$	78-99-9	$CCl_2HCH_2CH_3$
280da	370	C_3H_7Cl	75-29-6	$CH_3CClHCH_3$
280fa	370	C_3H_7Cl	540-54-5	$CH_3CH_2CH_2Cl$
216B2	306	$C_3Br_2F_6$	661-95-0	$CBrF_2CBrFCF_3$
217caB1	307	C_3BrF_7	422-85-5	$CF_3CF_2CF_2Br$
217I1	307	C_3IF_7	677-69-0	$CF_3CF_2CF_2I$
280B1a	370	C_3H_7Br	106-94-5	$CH_3CH_2CH_2Br$
280B1	370	C_3H_7Br	75-26-3	$CH_3CBrHCH_3$
365mfc	455	$C_4H_5F_5$	406-58-6	$CF_3CH_2CH_2CHF_2$
1243b	1333	$C_3H_3F_3$	677-21-4	$H_2C=CHCF_3$
1250	1340	$C_3H_4Cl_2$	542-75-6	$ClHC=CHCClH_2$
1250a	1340	$C_3H_4Cl_2$	78-88-6	$H_2C=CClCClH_2$
1250b	1340	$C_3H_4Cl_2$	563-58-6	$Cl_2C=CHCH_3$
1260	1350	C_3H_5Cl	107-05-1	$H_2C=CHCClH_2$
1260B1	1350	C_3H_5Cl	106-95-6	$H_2C=CHCBrH_2$
2240	2330	C_3H_3Cl	624-65-7	$HCCCClH_2$
C318	408	C_4F_8	115-25-3	Cyclo-C_4F_8
CE216	306	C_3F_6O	–	$\begin{array}{c} F_2C-CF_2 \\ \vert \quad\ \vert \\ F_2C-O \end{array}$
E125	215	C_2HF_5O	–	CF_3OCHF_2
E134	224	$C_2H_2F_4O$	1691-17-4	HF_2COCHF_2
E143a	233	$C_2H_3F_3O$	–	CH_3OCF_3
E150a	240	$C_2H_4Cl_2O$	4885-02-3	Cl_2HCOCH_3
E160	250	C_2H_5ClO	107-30-2	ClH_2COCH_3

Continued on next page.

Table 3-93. Freons, *continued*

Freon ID	+ 90	Formula	CAS	Structure
E235ca2	325	$C_3H_2F_5ClO$	–	$CHF_2CClFOCHF_2$
E235da1	325	$C_3H_2F_5ClO$	–	$CF_3CHClOCHF_2$
E236ea1	326	$C_3H_2F_6O$	–	$CF_3CHFOCF_2H$
E245fa1	335	$C_3H_3F_5O$	–	$CF_3CH_2OCHF_2$
E263fb1	353	$C_3H_5F_3O$	–	$CF_3CH_2OCH_3$
E270b	360	$C_3H_6Cl_2O$	34862-07-2	$CCl_2HCH_2OCH_3$
E280	370	C_3H_7ClO	627-42-9	$CClH_2CH_2OCH_3$
E280a	370	C_3H_7ClO	3188-13-4	$CClH_2OCH_2CH_3$
E347	437	$C_4H_3F_7O$	–	$CH_2FOC(CF_3)_2$

Analysis of freons is very similar if not exactly the same as analysis of most volatile halocarbons. Most of the compounds are either permanent gases or liquids with high vapor pressures[23]. The standard EPA methods using GC-MS (624 and 8260) can be used effectively for identification and quantitation. Specialized gas chromatographic columns such as PLOT columns[24] and graphitized carbon black[25] have been proven useful for separation of the many isomers of freons.

C. Dyes and Pigments

Dyes and pigments are named in the Colour Index (C.I.)[26] based on first, their chemical properties or preparation, and second, their use in the industry. Most of the C.I. named dyes also have traditional names in addition to the proper scientific name (Table 3-94).. Dyes are retained in the substrate material by a variety of mechanisms such as hydrogen-bonding, covalent-bonding, insolubility (precipitation), Van der Waals attraction, and electrostatic attractions[27]. Dye structures are generally complex unsaturated systems with many different conjugated structures represented (Table 3-97). Any single dye or pigment may contain more than one characteristic functionality and be listed in several fashions. For example Fluorescent Brightener 28 can be listed as both a stilbene and a triazine dye.

EPA reviewed dyes and pigments in a study in 1985[28] and concluded that the dye groups listed in Table 3-96 offered significant potential as health hazards. Most of the compounds are suspected mutagens or carcinogens and should be handled with due respect.

Dyes are mostly water insoluble and when introduced into water systems, accumulate in the bottom sediments where they may be found as either the original dye molecule or transformed to degradation products. The azo linkage is particularly prone

[23] Heiskel, E. *Aerosol Rep.* 1983. 22. pp. 403-415.

[24] de Zeeuw, J., D. Zwiep and J.W. Marinissen, "Separation of Chlorofluorocarbons Using High-Resolution PLOT Columns." *American Laboratory*, March, 1996. 24C-24H.

[25] Bruno, T.J., K.H. Wetz and M. Caciari, 1996. Kovats retention Indices of Halocarbons on a Hexafluoropropylene Epoxide-Modified Graphitized Carbon Black." *Anal. Chem.* 68(8). pp. 1347-1359.

[26] Society of Dyers and Colorists (SDC). Colour Index, Yorkshire, England; and other monograph and periodic publications of the Society.

[27] Shenai, V.A. 1973. *Chemistry of Dyes and Principles of Dyeing*. Bombay India, Skuak Publications.

[28] *Textile dyes and dyeing equipment classification, properties and environmental aspects*. EPA-600/2-85-010, February, 1995, PB85-173771.

to reductive cleavage in the anoxic sediments, releasing hazardous aromatic amines to the water[29]. Sodium dithionite ($Na_2S_2O_4$) in methanol was found to be a facile chemical way to reductively cleave the azo linkages in azo dyes, mimicking the environmental reduction of the compounds.

Table 3-94. Some common and cross-named dyes within the C.I.

Synonymous CI Names		Common name
Solvent yellow 77	Disperse yellow 3	-
Solvent orange 52	Disperse orange 13	-
Solvent orange 53	Disperse yellow 9	-
Solvent red 47	Acid red 93	-
Solvent red 48	Acid red 92	Phloxine B
Solvent red 43	Acid red 87	Eosin Y
Solvent red 49	Basic violet 10	Rhodamine B
Solvent red 111	Disperse red 9	-
Solvent violet 8	Basic violet 1	Methyl Violet B
Solvent violet 10	Acid violet 9	Violamine R
Solvent violet 26	Disperse red 1	-
Solvent blue 4	Basic blue 26	Victoria Blue B
Solvent blue 5	Basic blue 7	Victoria Pure Blue BO
Solvent blue 6	Basic blue 11	Victoria Blue R
Solvent blue 8	Basic blue 9	Methylene Blue
Solvent blue 68	Disperse blue 19	-
Solvent blue 69	Disperse blue 7	-
Solvent blue 36	Disperse blue 134	-
Solvent green 1	Basic green 4	Malachite Green
Solvent green 7	Acid green 9	-
Solvent green 15	Acid green 7	-
Developer 14	Oxidation Base 20	-

Table 3-95. Functional groups found in dyes and representative examples

Functional group	Examples
triarylmethane	Basic Violet 3, Solvent Blue 4
xanthene	Basic Red 1, Pigment Red 60, Solvent Red 43
anthraquinone	Acid Blue 40, Disperse Blue 3, Disperse Blue 14, Reactive Blue 4, Reactive Blue 19, Mordant Red 11, Vat Blue 6, Vat Brown 1
azo	Acid Orange 60, Acid Black 5
disazo	Direct Red 81, Mordant Orange 6
stilbene	Direct Yellow 4, Fluorescent Brightener 28
pyrazoline	Pigment Orange 34

Continued on next page.

29 Weber, E.J. and R.L. Adams, Chemical and Sediment Mediated Reduction of The Azo Dye Disperse Blue." 79, 1995. *Environ. Sci. Technol.* 29(5). pp. 1163-1170.

Table 3-95. Functional groups found in dyes and representative examples, *continued*

Functional group	Examples
coumarin	Fluorescent Brightener 61
triazine	Fluorescent Brightener 28, Reactive Yellow 2
phthalocyanine	Direct Blue 86, Pigment Blue 15
quinacridone	Pigment Violet 19
methine	Basic Yellow 2

Table 3-96. Classes of dyes that present potential environmental/health hazards

Dye type	Properties/Use
Acid	Water soluble dyes that are applied under acidic conditions. Further classified as to leveling dyes (uniformity of color coverage), milling dyes (water fast properties which hold in the fibers when wool is converted to felt), super milling dyes (applied from neutral solutions) and metal complex dyes (addition of metal ions forms an insoluble complex). Sulfonic acid groups generally present on the dye molecules
Direct (Substantive)	Water soluble ionic materials that are applied without any mordant pre-dyes. Bond through hydrogen bonding and electrostatic attraction to the surface of the textile fibers. Salt and heat are used to transfer dye from the solution to the fiber. Chemical structure is more linear when compared to the compact acid dyes
Azoic Diazo and Azoic Coupling Component	Two-component dyes that react in the fiber to form a high molecular weight insoluble colored molecule.
Disperse	Suspensions of low water soluble dyes that preferentially dissolve in hydrophobic fibers. Heat and pressure along with a number of chemical additives, such as anionic surfactants, organic solvent carriers and antifoaming agents, are used to enhance contact with the receiving fibers.
Sulfur	Poorly characterized dyes obtained from reaction of complex heterocyclic molecules with either molten sulfur or sodium polysulfide. Typical substrates have been amino and nitrobenzenes, nitro- and aminobiphenyls, phenols, naphthalenes, condensed aromatics, indophenols and various azine, oxazine and thiazone containing molecules. Generally applied by soaking dye recipient in a reduced water-soluble solution of the dye, then oxidizing the dye to an insoluble form.
Fiber reactive	Dye molecules with reactive groups attached for forming covalent bonds with nitrogen or oxygen atoms on the fiber. Common reactive groups are dichlorotriazine, dichloroquinoxaline, vinyl sulfone, monochlorotriazine, chloropyrimidine, sulfatoethyl sulfonamide, acrylamide, and *N*-methylol ureas.
Basic	Water soluble quarternary ammonium dyes that are basified to the free base form to precipitate inside the fibers.
Oxidation Base	Precursors are water soluble salts of small molecules such as aniline, phenylene diamines, *p*-aminophenyl sulfamic acid, aminophenols, *o*-toluidine, dianisidine, xylidene, *p*-amino-diphenylamine, and 1,4-naphthalenediamine After penetration of the fiber, treatment with inorganic oxidizers create reactive imines that couple and precipitate. Many oxidation bases are also developers.
Mordant (chrome)	Dye molecules that are complexed in the fiber to chromium or other metal ions to form large stable molecular groups.

Continued on next page.

Table 3-96. Classes of dyes that present potential environmental/health hazards, *continued*

Dye type	Properties/Use
Developed (developers)	Small molecular weight aromatic amines that are used to treat the fiber, followed by reaction with nitrite to form reactive diazo- groups that can couple with other added amines, phenols or naphthalenes to produce dye molecules similar to the direct dyes.
Vat	Dye is initially reduced to the hydroquinoid and solubilized in caustic to form the leuco vat dye. After the fiber is treated with the leuco vat dye, oxidation with air or inorganic chemicals is used to reform the quinoid dye and precipitate it in the fiber.
Pigment	High molecular weight insoluble inorganic and organic materials with no innate attraction for textile fibers. Must be compounded with natural or synthetic resins for application and retention.
Optical/Fluorescent brightners	Frequently referred to as fluorescent whitening agents (FWA) they are used to enhance the whiteness of fabrics. The intense blue fluorescence when bound to laundered fabrics offsets the slight yellow cast of the cotton. Common classes are anionic, cationic and nonionic materials of a variety of chemical forms.
Solvent	Oil-soluble dyes used for coloration of plastics and non-aqueous products such as brake fluid and gasoline.

Table 3-97. Structures of common dyes and pigments

C.I. name	CAS No.	Structure
Acid black 52 (Palatine Fast Black WAN)	5610-64-0	
Acid blue 40	6424-85-7	
Acid orange 60	–	
Acid red 266	–	

Continued on next page.

Table 3-97. Structures of common dyes and pigments, *continued*

C.I. name	CAS No.	Structure
Acid yellow 151	–	
Azoic diazo component 1 (Fast Bordeaux)	96-96-8	
Azoic diazo component 2 (Fast Orange GC)	108-42-9	
Azoic diazo component 10 (Fast Red RC)	95-03-4	
Azoic diazo component 13 (Fast Scarlet R)	99-59-2	
Azoic diazo component 28 (Fast Red PDC)	80-22-8	
Azoic diazo component 48 (Fast Blue B)	14263-94-6	
Basic orange 2 (Chrysoidin)	532-82-1	
Basic red 1 (Rhodamine 6G)	989-38-8	

Continued on next page.

Table 3-97. Structures of common dyes and pigments, *continued*

C.I. name	CAS No.	Structure
Basic violet 3 (Crystal Violet)	548-62-9	
Basic yellow 2 (Auramine O)	2465-27-2	
Basic yellow 11	4208-80-4	
Coupling component 2 (Naphtol AS)	92-77-3	
Coupling component 7 (Naphtol AS-SW)	135-64-8	
Coupling component 11 (Naphtol AS-RL)	–	
Coupling component 12 (Naphtol AS-ITR)	–	
Developer 1	–	
Developer 5	135-19-3	
Developer 8	92-70-6	

Continued on next page.

Table 3-97. Structures of common dyes and pigments, *continued*

C.I. name	CAS No.	Structure
Developer 13	106-50-3	
Developer 14 (Oxidation base 20)	95-80-7	
Developer 17	100-01-6	
Direct black 22	6473-13-8	
Direct blue 53 (Evans Blue)	314-13-6	
Direct blue 86	1330-38-7	

Continued on next page.

Table 3-97. Structures of common dyes and pigments, *continued*

C.I. name	CAS No.	Structure
Direct brown 154	–	
Direct red 81	2610-11-9	
Direct yellow 4 (Brilliant Yellow)	3051-11-4	
Disperse blue 3	2475-46-9	
Disperse blue 14	2475-44-7	

Continued on next page.

Table 3-97. Structures of common dyes and pigments, *continued*

C.I. name	CAS No.	Structure
Disperse brown 1	17464-91-4	
Disperse orange 3	730-40-5	
Disperse orange 30	5261-31-4	
Disperse red 1	2872-52-8	
Disperse red 13	2832-40-8	
Disperse yellow 3	2832-40-8	
Disperse yellow 5	6439-53-8	
Disperse yellow 54	–	
Fluorescent brightener 28	4404-43-7	

Continued on next page.

Table 3-97. Structures of common dyes and pigments, *continued*

C.I. name	CAS No.	Structure
Fluorescent brightener 61 (Coumarin 1)	91-44-1	
Mordant black 11 (Eriochrome Black T)	1787-61-7	
Mordant brown 1	3564-15-6	
Mordant orange 6	3564-27-0	
Mordant red 11 (Alizarin)	72-48-0	
Pigment blue 15 (Copper phthalocyanine)	147-14-8	
Pigment orange 34	–	

Continued on next page.

Table 3-97. Structures of common dyes and pigments, *continued*

C.I. name	CAS No.	Structure
Pigment red 90	–	
Pigment violet 19	–	
Pigment yellow 1 (Hansa Yellow)	–	
Reactive Blue 4	13324-20-4	
Reactive Blue 19 (Remazol Brilliant Blue R)	2580-78-1	

Continued on next page.

Table 3-97. Structures of common dyes and pigments, *continued*

C.I. name	CAS No.	Structure
Reactive Yellow 2 (Cibacron Brilliant Yellow 3G-P	50662-99-2	
Solvent blue 4	–	
Solvent blue 36	–	
Solvent green 3	128-80-3	
Solvent red 3 (Fat Brown B)	6535-42-8	
Solvent red 23 (Sudan III)	85-86-9	

Continued on next page.

Table 3-97. Structures of common dyes and pigments, *continued*

C.I. name	CAS No.	Structure
Solvent red 24 (Sudan IV)	85-83-6	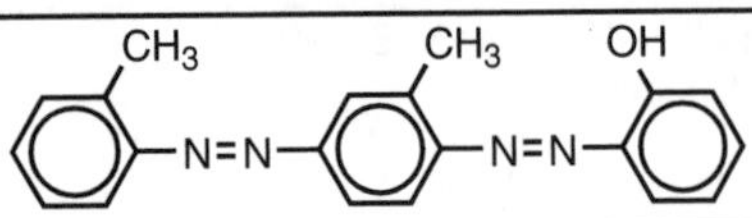
Solvent red 43 (Eosin Y)	15086-94-9	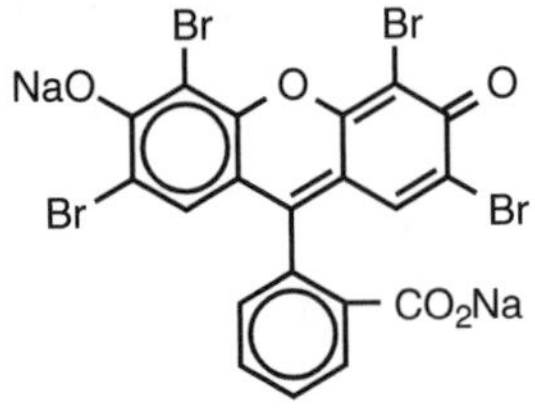
Vat blue 6	–	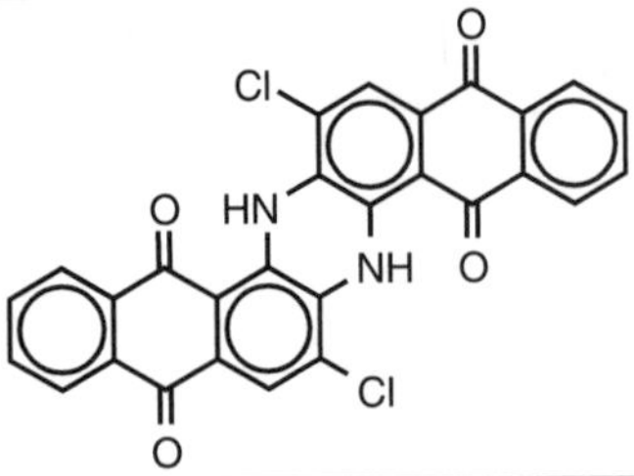
Vat brown 1	–	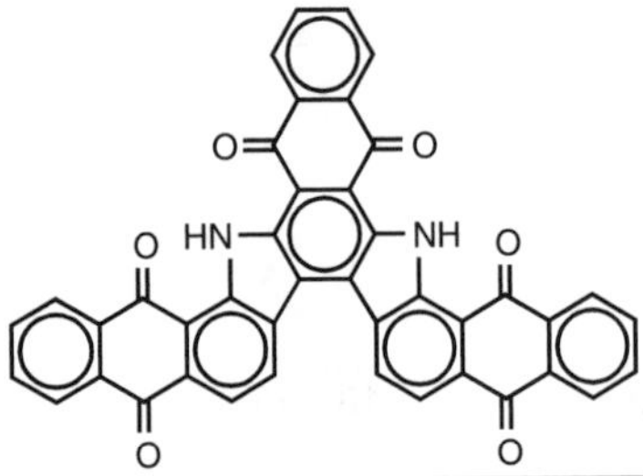
Vat red 1	–	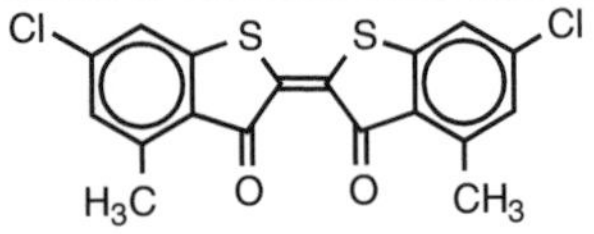

The analysis of environmental samples for residues of dyes, pigments and their degradation products can be quite challenging. Many papers have been published concerning analysis of dyes and pigments[30], and several books have included chapters on the subject[31]. Although thin layer chromatography can be used as a screening tool prior to analysis, instrumental methods are needed for accurate qualitative and quantitative determinations. Some of the materials, particularly the azoic diazo components and some of the developers are standard target analytes under the semivolatile GC-MS

---

[30] Poiger, T., J.A. Field, T.M. Field and W. Giger, 1996. "Occurrence of Fluorescent Whiting Agents in Sewage and River Water Determined by Solid-Phase Extraction and High-Performance Liquid Chromatography." *Environ. Sci. Technol.* 30(7). pp. 2220-2226; Kramer, J.B., S. Canonica, J. Hoigne, and J. Kaschig, 1996. "Degradation of Fluorescent Whiting Agents in Sunlit Natural Waters." *Environ. Sci. Technol.* 30(7). pp. 2227-2234.

[31] Reife, A. and H.S. Freeman, 1996. *Environmental Chemistry of Dyes and Pigments*. John Wiley & Sons, New York, NY.

---

procedures (EPA Methods 625 and 8270). Other dyes and pigments are specifically listed as target analytes by LC-MS (EPA Methods 8321 and 8325). Most of the potential targets are large molecules that are not amenable to gas chromatographic techniques and require HPLC for separation. Given the literally thousands of potential compounds to be identified, three dimensional detectors (FTIR, PDA-UV, or MS) are an absolute necessity.

D. Hydrocarbon Solvents and Fuels

Most hydrocarbon solvents and fuels are obtained from petroleum. Petroleum hydrocarbons are multi-component analytes consisting of four major structural types:

- straight and branched chain aliphatic hydrocarbons (parafins)
- straight and branched chain aliphatic hydrocarbons with various degrees of unsaturation (olefins)
- cyclic aliphatic hydrocarbons (termed naphthalenes in the petroleum industry)
- mono- and polycyclic aromatic hydrocarbons (termed aromatics).

Petroleum hydrocarbons are widely used as industrial solvents and fuels. Classification of petroleum hydrocarbons is by boiling point range and PONA (parafin, olefin, naphthalene, aromatic) content. For example aircraft turbine fuels are differentiated from fuel oils even though they have about the same distillation range, because the turbine fuels have essentially no aromatic compound content while the fuel oils can have substantial percentages (20-30%) of aromatics. Some commercial products are listed in Table 3-98. Greases and lubrication oils are not listed as they generally are above the temperature range analyzed by GC. Many of the solvents and fuels have common names, for example mineral spirits are frequently called Stoddard solvents.

Table 3-98. Common industrial hydrocarbon solvents and fuels encountered in GC analysis

Solvent/fuel	Standard	Boiling point range °C
Petroleum ether	ACS reagent	30-60
Petroleum benzin (naphtha)	-	35-80
Lacquer thinner	-	93-115
Hexanes	ASTM D1836	63-71
VM&P[32] naphtha (ligroin)	ASTM D3735	
Type I - regular		120-150
Type II - high flash		140-175
Type III - odorless		120-150
Mineral spirits	ASTM D235	
Type I - regular[33]		149-213
Type II - high flash point		177-213
Type III - odorless		149-213
Type IV - low dry point		149-185

Continued on next page.

[32] Varnish Makers' and Painters' naphtha
[33] Also called Stoddard solvent, Texsolve S, and Varsol 1.

Table 3-98. Common industrial hydrocarbon solvents and fuels encountered in GC analysis, *continued*

Solvent/fuel	Standard	Boiling point range °C
Kerosine	ASTM D3699	205-300
Kerosene	non-standard	175-325
Aromatic naphtha	ASTM D3734	
Type I - aromatic 100		150-175
Type II - aromatic 150		180-215
Fuel oils	ASTM D396	
Grade 1 - light distillate		215-288
Grade 2 - heavy distillate		up to 338
Grade 4 - residual/distillate mix		-
Grade 5 - residual		-
Grade 6 - residual (Bunker C)		-
Naval distillate fuel (military)	MIL-F-16884H	end point 385
Aviation gasolines	ASTM D910	75-170
Diesel fuel oils[34]	ASTM D975	
Low sulfur No. 1		up to 288
Low sulfur No. 2		282-338
Grade 1 - light distillate		up to 288
Grade 2 - heavier distillate		282-338
Grade 4 - distillate/residual mix		-
Diesel fuel oil (military)	VV-800-D	
DF-A - Arctic grade		up to 300
DF-1		up to 330
DF-2		up to 370
Aviation turbine fuels	ASTM D1655	
Jet A		205-300
Jet A-1 - low freezing point		205-300
Jet B - wide distillation range kerosine		<145 to >245
Aviation turbine fuels (military)	MIL-T-5624P	
JP-4		145-270
JP-5		205-300
JP-5/JP-8ST (worst case test mixture)		205-300
JP-8	MIL-T-83133D	205-300
High-boiling hydrocarbon solvent for wood preservative carrier	ASTM 2604	up to 307
Low-boiling hydrocarbon solvent for wood preservative carrier	ASTM 3225	up to 213

Continued on next page

.

---

[34] Grades 1, 2 and 4 are required to contain a visible amount of blue dye, 1,4-dialkylamino-anthraquinone.

Table 3-98. Common industrial hydrocarbon solvents and fuels encountered in GC analysis, *continued*

Solvent/fuel	Standard	Boiling point range °C
Gas turbine fuel oils	ASTM 2880	
Grade 0-GT - mixture of Jet B + naphtha		-
Grade 1-GT - distillate		up to 288
Grade 2-GT - distillate		up to 338
Grade 3-GT - distillate/residual mix		-
Grade 4-GT - residuals + topped crude		-

Many of the fuel blends also contain non-hydrocarbon additives. In domestic automobile gasoline a variety of oxygenate additives are found. Common oxygentates and other additives are listed in Table 3-99.

Table 3-99. Common additives in hydrocarbon fuels

Additive	Function
Ethanol	Gasoline oxygenate
Methyl *tert*-butyl ether (MTBE)	Gasoline oxygenate
Methyl *tert*-amyl ether (TAME)	Gasoline oxygenate
Ethyl *tert*-butyl ether (ETBE)	Gasoline oxygenate
Isopropyl alcohol	Fuel system icing inhibitor
Ethylene glycol monomethyl ether	Fuel system icing inhibitor
1,4-Dialkylamino-anthraquinone	Blue dye
p-Diethylaminoazobenzene	Yellow dye
2,4-bis(alkylphenylazo)-1,3-benzenediol	Yellow dye
Alkylazobenzene-4-azo-2-naphthol	Red dye
Tetraethyl lead - Ethylene dibromide	Anti-knock mixture
N,N'-diisopropyl-p-phenylenediamine	Antioxidant
N,N'-di-sec-butyl-p-phenylenediamine	Antioxidant
2,4-dimethyl-4-t-butylphenol	Antioxidant
2,6-di-t-butyl-4-methylphenol	Antioxidant
2,6-di-t-butylphenol	Antioxidant
Tri-t-butylphenols	Antioxidant
Di- and tri-isopropylphenols	Antioxidant
N,N'-disalicylidene-1,2-propanediamine	Metal deactivator
Amyl nitrate	Cetane improver
Isopropyl nitrate	Cetane improver
Hexyl nitrate	Cetane improver
Cyclohexyl nitrate	Cetane improver
2-Ethylhexyl nitrate	Cetane improver
Octyl nitrate	Cetane improver

In addition to the petroleum hydrocarbons as sources of hydrocarbon solvents, there is considerable use of terpene solvents in industry. These are loosely classified as turpentines of which there are several in general use.

- Gum turpentine or gum spirits consist of mainly α-pinene with some β-pinene and other hydrocabons, obtained from distillation of gum or resin from living pine trees, boiling point range 154-170 °C

- Steam distilled wood turpentine is mainly α-pinene with traces of dipentene and other hydrocarbon terpenes, obtained through steam distillation of pine chips, BP 150-170 °C

- Sulfate wood turpentine is recovered from the Kraft paper making procedure and is mainly α- and β-pinene

- Dipentene is obtained from continued distillation of the pine resin, BP 170-190 °C

- Pine oil is isolated during the processing of the turpentines and consists of terpene alcohols, BP 200-225° C.

A solvent of increasing industrial and domestic use is d-limonene, BP 176 °C which is refined from the oil of citrus.

Another commonly encountered material that contributes to co-extracted background in fuels analysis is called creosote. This oily material is used for wood preservation and is made from coal tar by distillation. It is characterized by very large amounts of 2- to 4- ring aromatic hydrocarbons (50%), tar acids (up to 5%) and tar bases (45%). Phenanthrene is typically very abundant, as well as carbazole, a nitrogen-containing 3-ring aromatic molecule (tar base). Other tar bases include quinoline, quinoline and acridine[34].

418.1 and 9073. Total Petroleum Hydrocarbons by IR

Method 9073 is a draft method that was eliminated from inclusion in SW-846 due to the reduction of Freon 113 usage and eventual discontinuation. However, the method, which is very similar to 418.1, has been specified by many states as the preferred method for TPH analysis. If the sample is aqueous, 1 L is acidified to pH <2 with HCl, and extracted three times with 30 mL portions of Freon 113. The solvent is drained through filter paper containing sodium sulfate into a 100 mL volumetric flask. The flask is brought to volume with Freon, then several mL discarded. Three grams silica gel is added, and the mixture stirred with a magnetic stir bar for several minutes. The silica gel removes the polar co-extractants such as fatty acids, although several portions of silica gel may be required for complete removal. The sample is read with an IR spectrophotometer at 2950 cm⁻¹ against a standard curve. Standards are prepared from an oil mixture consisting of 15.0 mL n-hexadecane, 15.0 mL isooctane and 10.0 mL chlorobenzene.

This standard mixture was chosen to approximate the number and type of carbon-hydrogen bonds found in petroleum products that are a mixture of straight and branched chain aliphatic hydrocarbons and aromatic hydrocarbons. The IR method effectively quantitates the number of C-H bonds in the sample. Falsely high values can

---

[34] Lantz, S.E., M.T. Montgomery, W.W. Schultz, P.H. Pritchard, B.J. Spargo, and J.G. Mueller, 1997. Constituents of an organic wood preservative that inhibit the fluoranthene-degrading activity of *Sphingomonas paucimobilis* strain EPA505. EST 31(12):3573-3580.

result when pure oils, such as hexadecane are analyzed. The number of C-H bonds in the standard is approximated by the percent mass of hydrogen in the calibration mix. It can be calculated as follows:

Compound	Hexadecane	Chlorobenzene	Isooctane	Total
Formula	$C_{16}H_{34}$	C_6H_5Cl	C_8H_{18}	
Molecular wt	226.43	112.55	114.22	
% Hydrogen	15.13	4.48	15.88	
Density	0.773	1.107	0.692	
mL	15.0	10.0	15.0	
Mass in Cal mix	11.595	11.070	10.380	33.045
Weight %	35.09	33.50	31.41	100
Weight %H	5.3091	1.5008	4.9882	11.7981

For a pure hydrocarbon sample such as hexadecane the weight % hydrogen is 15.13. Analysis of pure hexadecane using the above calibration solution would give:

$$\frac{15.13}{11.7981} = 1,280,000 \text{ mg/kg.}$$

Lighter hydrocarbons will give higher values, while heavier hydrocarbons will give lower maximum results.

Variations on the method use soxhlet extraction, ultrasonic horn extraction, sonication bath or a simple vigorous hand-shaking for two minutes with a Freon 113 extracting solvent for solids. The soxhlet procedure is generally regarded as the most rigorous; however, some clients insist on the open-beaker ultrasonic-horn extraction, which almost always results in lower values. Continuous liquid-liquid extraction with Freon 113 has been used. A novel procedure is required by Missouri where a weighed amount of solid is mixed with sodium sulfate to dry the sample, then packed into a chromatography column and extracted in one pass with 100 mL Freon 113. The eluted Freon 113 is then treated as above with silica gel.

As more and more surcharges and restrictions are placed by the government on Freon 113, these methods will disappear or be modified to use other solvents. Carbon disulfide is used as the solvent in a California method, however it presents its own problems of smell and toxicity. A SW-846 method for supercritical carbon dioxide extraction of solids (Method 3560) has been published. The extraction eluant is transferred to tetrachloroethene, then read by IR at 2950 cm^{-1} in Method 8440. Although tetrachloroethene possesses toxic properties, it is non-ozone depleting. See the discussion in Section 2 on Oil & Grease for information on draft Method 1664 and other performance-based modifications.

BTEX and GRO by GC

BTEX and GRO are determined by either headspace or purge & trap attached to a GC-FID-PID (modified Method 8021) or a GC/MS (Method 8260), or by methanol or hexadecane microextraction followed by purge & trap or direct injection into the GC or GC/MS. For BTEX the individual benzene, toluene, ethylbenzene and xylenes peaks are summed for the result. For GRO there are several approaches used by the various states. One is to sum the largest 10 peaks in the gasoline envelope. Another is to sum all peaks eluting in the same envelope as a standard gasoline (2-methyl pentane to 1,2,4-trimethyl-benzene). Tennessee suggests the gasoline standard as API PS-6 (American Petroleum Institute) or other appropriate certified standard. Calibration is most commonly five-point external standard.

DRO by GC

Diesel range organics are determined with a GC-FID. Diesel fuel is normally considered to consist of the hydrocarbon compounds that will elute between decane and pentacosane C_{10} - C_{25}. A variety of extraction methods and solvents are used. The California method calls for Freon 113. Other methods use methylene chloride, carbon disulfide, or hexane. Separatory funnels and continuous liquid-liquid extractors are common for water samples. Soxhlet extractors, ultrasonic cell disruptors, sonication baths and simple hand shaking are also used. Calibration and quantitation are variously based on the total envelope between decane to penta- or octacosane or on the ten indicator compounds which are the even straight chain saturated hydrocarbons from decane to octacosane, but generally require a five-point curve. Surrogates of pentacosane and o-terphenyl have been used and an internal standard, 5-α-androstane, is suggested in the Tennessee method.

A very utilitarian procedure is to add 1.00 mg/L (1.00 mL of a 1000 µg/mL solution of the surrogates in methanol) of the surrogates n-nonane and n-pentacosane to 1 L of aqueous sample in a hydrophobic membrane continuous liquid-liquid extractor/concentrator such as the Accelerated One-Step® by Corning, Incorporated. The sample is acidified to pH < 2 with 1:1 H_2SO_4 : water, extracted for 4 hrs (1 hr gives quantitative results) with 100 mL methylene chloride and concentrated to about 2 mL. After transfer to a 2.00 mL volumetric tube (which has been calibrated at 1.00 mL), the sample is reduced in volume to exactly 1.00 mL with a gentle nitrogen stream and mild heating in a 40 °C waterbath. Final transfer to an autosampler vial finishes the sample preparation for liquid samples. Surrogate recoveries from the Accelerated One-Step range from 60-80% for the nonane to 80-100% for the pentacosane, which are directly related to the DRO recovery.

Solid samples are processed in a soxhlet extraction apparatus using 30 g of sample well mixed with 30 g of anhydrous sodium sulfate (dried and baked in a 550 ± 50 °C furnace for 4 hours in a quartz pan) and glasswool plugs (solvent extracted with methylene chloride for 18 hrs in a continuous liquid-liquid extractor) at the top and bottom of the sample. 1.00 mL of the above surrogate solution is added and the sample extracted for 4 hours using methylene chloride (about 4-6 cycles per hour). The extract is dried over anhydrous sodium sulfate (furnace dried) and concentrated with either a K-D apparatus or a TurboVap® (Zymark) apparatus to no less than 2 mL. After transfer to a 2.00 mL volumetric tube (which has been calibrated at 1.00 mL), the sample is reduced in volume to exactly 1.00 mL with a gentle nitrogen stream and mild heating in a 40 °C waterbath. Final transfer to an autosampler vial finishes the sample preparation.

Analysis is performed by FID-GC with a 30m x 0.32mm id capillary column with a 95:5 methyl:phenyl silicone stationary phase. The position of the DRO envelope as compared to the surrogates serves to identify the analyte as kerosene, diesel #2, mineral spirits, JP-4, etc. Figures 3-33 through 3-38 illustrate chromatograms of a various fuel types.

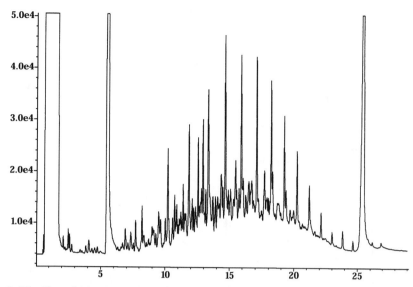

Figure 3-33. Gas chromatogram of diesel fuel bracketed by the surrogates *n*-nonane and *n*-pentacosane.

Quantitation of the target analyte is by area of the whole envelope above the baseline, against a 5-point calibration curve. QC is assessed by having minimum acceptable recoveries of the surrogates of 45% for nonane and 75% for the pentacosane. The analysis is critically sensitive to volume. Never allow the volume of the sample extract to fall below 1.00 mL, and the final volume of the extract for analysis must be 1.00 mL. Allowing the volume of the extract to fall to as little as 0.75 mL will result in 0-6% recovery of nonane and 10-30% recovery of pentacosane with comparable recoveries of the target analytes.

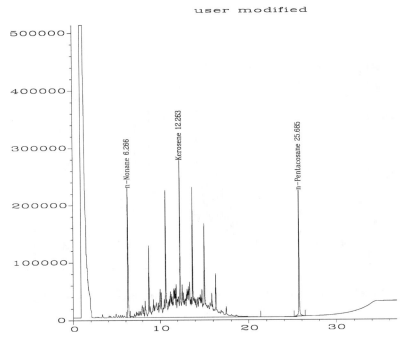

Figure 3-34. Kerosene by GC-FID.

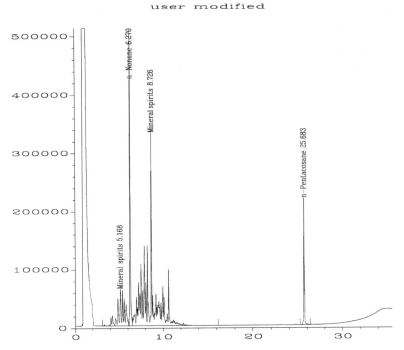

Figure 3-35. Mineral Spirits by GC-FID.

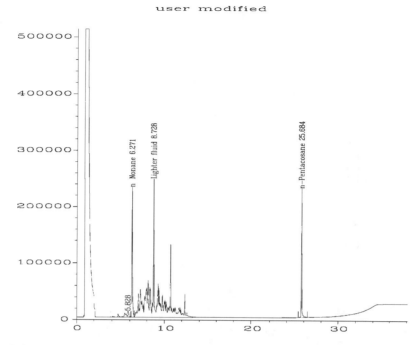

Figure 3-36. Charcoal lighter fluid by GC-FID.

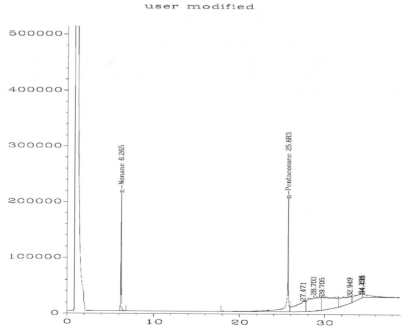

Figure 3-37. SAE 30 weight oil by GC-FID.

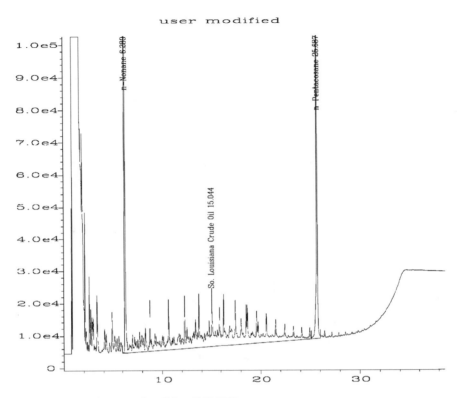

Figure 3-38. Louisiana crude oil by GC-FID.

Most petroleum based fuels, solvents and oils can be determined and identified by GC-FID. The key to the identification is frequently determining the boiling point or distillation range. The saturated straight chain hydrocarbons can serve as the calibration standard for boiling points. Table 3-100 lists the boiling points of most of the commonly available hydrocarbon standards.

Table 3-100. Boiling points of common hydrocarbon standards

Hydrocarbon	Carbon number	BP °C
Propane	3	-42.1
n-Butane	4	-0.5
n-Pentane	5	35-36
n-Hexane	6	69
Cyclohexane	6	80.7
Benzene	6	80
n-Heptane	7	98
Methylcyclohexane	7	101
Toluene	7	111
n-Octane	8	125-127
Ethylbenzene	8	136
p-Xylene	8	138
n-Nonane	9	151
n-Decane	10	174
Decalin (*c* + *t*)	10	189-193
Naphthalene	10	218
n-Undecane	11	196
n-Dodecane	12	216
n-Tridecane	13	234
n-Tetradecane	14	252-254
Anthracene	14	342
n-Pentadecane	15	270
n-Hexadecane	16	284
n-Heptadecane	17	302
n-Octadecane	18	317
n-Nonadecane	19	330
n-Eicosane	20	343
n-Heneicosane	21	356
n-Docosane	22	369
n-Tricosane	23	380
n-Tetracosane	24	391
n-Pentacosane	25	402
n-Hexacosane	26	412
n-Heptacosane	27	422
n-Octacosane	28	432
n-Nonacosane	29	441
n-Triacontane	30	450
n-Hentriacontane	31	458

E. Explosives and chemical warfare residues

In most contract work for the military, samples will eventually arrive that require analysis of explosives and/or chemical warfare residues. Methods for determination of these analytes generally were developed at the USACE Cold Regions Research and

Engineering Laboratory in New Hampshire, although there are other contributors. EPA has adopted many of these methods in either draft or finalized form into SW-846.

Although the standards may pose a small risk of explosion, in general this type of work is no more hazardous than other procedures performed in the semivolatile extractions laboratory. Most of the materials are now commercially available as solutions for calibration and check samples. There are many different types of explosives as illustrated in Table 3-101. Most residues determined in the laboratory are derived from highly nitrated organic structures.

Table 3-101. Common military explosives and residues

Name	CAS	Structure
246TNT 2,4,6-Trinitrotoluene	118-96-7	
RDX Research Dept. Explosive Royal Demolition Explosive Hexahydro-1,3,5-trinitro-1,3,5-triazine	121-82-4	
HMX High Melting Explosive Octahydro-1,3,5,7-tetranitro-1,3,5,7-tetrazocine	2691-41-0	
ADN Ammonium dinitramide	-	$NH_4N(NO_2)_2$
AP Ammonium perchlorate	7790-98-9	NH_4ClO_4
TNAZ Trinitroazetidine	-	
KDN-AN Potassium dinitramide - ammonium nitrate co-crystal	-	$KN(NO_2)_2$-NH_4NO_3
Tetryl N-Methyl-N,2,4,6-tetranitrobenzamine	479-45-8	
135TNB 1,3,5-Trinitrobenzene	99-35-4	

Continued on next page.

Table 3-101. Common military explosives and residues, *continued*

Name	CAS	Structure
13DNB 1,3-Dinitrobenzene	99-65-0	O_2N — NO_2 (benzene ring)
2-ADNT	35572-78-2	CH_3, O_2N, NH_2, NO_2 (benzene ring)
4-ADNT	1946-51-0	CH_3, O_2N, NO_2, NH_2 (benzene ring)
2,6-DNT	606-20-2	CH_3, O_2N, NO_2 (benzene ring)
2,4-DNT	121-14-2	CH_3, NO_2, NO_2 (benzene ring)
2NT	88-72-2	CH_3, NO_2 (benzene ring)
3NT	99-08-1	CH_3, NO_2 (benzene ring)
4NT	99-99-0	CH_3, NO_2 (benzene ring)
NG Nitroglycerine	55-63-0	CH_2ONO_2 $CHONO_2$ CH_2ONO_2

Continued on next page.

Genium Publishing Corporation

Table 3-101. Common military explosives and residues, *continued*

Name	CAS	Structure
Tetrazine	31330-63-9	(structure)

8330 Nitroaromatics and nitramines by HPLC[35]

Although it is possible to determine these analytes when they are present in high concentration by direct injection of the aqueous sample diluted 1:1 with acetonitrile, the normal procedure uses a salting-out process to isolate and concentrate the target analytes[36]. The sample is saturated with sodium sulfate, and acetonitrile is added. Most of the acetonitrile remains dissolved in the aqueous layer. However, a small portion separates as a layer, and the organic target analytes are concentrated in this layer, which is removed. After repeating the isolation, the combined acetonitrile extracts are back-extracted with a sodium chloride solution, then filtered and analyzed by reverse phase HPLC on a C-18 column with 1:1 methanol:water eluant. Confirmation is achieved on a CN reversed-phase column. Solid samples are prepared by extended sonication (18 hrs in an ultrasonic bath) of the solid with acetonitrile. The extract is treated with calcium chloride solution, then analyzed by reversed-phase HPLC as above.

Recent developments for sample preparation have used solid phase extraction disks and cartridges for isolation of the target analytes from aqueous solutions[37]. Both styrene- divinylbenzene and the more traditional C-18 disks were evaluated. Detection levels were 5 to 10 times lower than the values listed in Table 3-102. An Army publication compares the disk and cartridge solid-phase extractions to the salting-out procedure[38].

Table 3-102. Target Analytes of Method 8330

Target Analyte	CAS Number	Water EQL µg/L	Soil EQL mg/kg
HMX	2691-41-0	-	2.2
RDX	121-82-4	0.84	1.0
1,3,5-Trinitrobenzene	99-35-4	0.26	0.25
1,3-Dinitrobenzene	99-65-0	0.11	0.25

Continued on next page.

---

35 Developed from U.S. Army methods SM01 and SM02.

36 Leggett, D.C, T.F. Jenkins and P.H. Miyares, "Salting-Out Solvent Extraction for Preconcentration of Neutral Polar Organic Solutes from Water." *Analytical Chemistry.* 1990. 62(13). pp. 1355-1356; T.F. Jenkins, and P.H. Miyares, "Nonevaporative Preconcentration Technique for Volatile and Semi-volatile Solutes in Certain Polar Solvents." *Analytical Chemistry.* 1991. 63(13). pp. 1341-1343.

37 Le Brun, G., "A Solid-Phase Extraction Disk Method for the Extraction of Explosives from Water." *Proceedings of the Fifteenth Annual EPA Conference on Analysis of Pollutants in the Environment.* 1992. pp. 143-175.

38 Jenkins, T.F., P.H. Miyares, K.F. Myers, E.F. McCormick, and A.B. Strong. "Comparison of Cartridge and Membrane Solid-Phase Extraction with Salting-Out Solvent Extraction for Preconcentration of Nitroaromatic and Nitramine Explosives from Water." U.S. Army CRREL Special Report 92-25. 1992.

Table 3-102. Target Analytes of Method 8330, *continued*

Target Analyte	CAS Number	Water EQL μg/L	Soil EQL mg/kg
Tetryl	479-45-8	-	0.65
Nitrobenzene	98-95-3	-	0.26
TNT	118-96-7	0.11	0.25
4-Amino-2,6-dinitrotoluene	1946-51-0	0.060	-
2-Amino-4,6-dinitrotoluene	35572-78-2	0.035	-
2,4-Dinitrotoluene	121-14-2	0.31	0.26
2,6-Dinitrotoluene	606-20-2	0.020	0.25
2-Nitrotoluene	88-72-2	-	0.25
3-Nitrotoluene	99-08-1	-	0.25
4-Nitrotoluene	99-99-0	-	0.25

8331 Tetrazene by RP-HPLC

This is a direct injection technique that uses ion pair C-18 reversed phase HPLC for analysis. The ion pairing reagent is 1-decanesulfonic acid, and the eluent is 2:3 methanol : water with acetic acid. Solids are shaken for 5 hrs at 2000 rpm on a platform shaker with a 0.1M solution of 1-decanesulfonic acid in 55:45 methanol : water. Then, the extract is filtered and analyzed. The EPA method is based on research at the USACE Cold Regions Research and Engineering Laboratory[39].

8332 Nitroglycerine by HPLC

The presence of nitroglycerine in the sample is determined by thin layer chromatography on silica gel with 20% dichloroethane in carbon tetrachloride as the developing solvent. The spots are visualized with either a 5% diphenylamine in ethanol spray followed by UV light exposure or an alternate Greiss reagent (sulfanilic acid and alpha-naphthylamine in an acetic acid alcoholic KOH mixture) spray followed by heating. Quantitation is by CN reversed-phase HPLC with 60:40 acetonitrile : water mobile phase.

USATHAMA Method (KN01) for White Phosphorus in Soil or Sediment

This method has been adopted by the EPA for inclusion in SW-846 as Method 7580. White phosphorus is the tetrahedral form of elemental phosphorus. It is highly combustible in the presence of oxygen and used by the military in incendiary devices, where it is referred to by the slang term "willy pete." The material is stored under water and can safely be manipulated under a pure nitrogen atmosphere in either a glove bag or box. The analyte is extracted from soil by mixing with isooctane and degassed water for 18 hrs on a platform shaker. Aliquots of the isooctane extract are injected into a GC equipped with a 15 m x 0.53 mm DB-1 capillary column and nitrogen-phosphorous detector. Quantitation is by external standard calibration.

---

[39] Walsh, M.E, and T.F. Jenkins. *Analytical Method for Determining Tetrazine in Water*, Special Report 87-25, 1987, USATHAMA AMXTH-TE-CR-87139; *Analytical Method for Determining Tetrazine in Soil*, 1988. Special Report 88-15, USATHAMA AMXTH-TE--CR-88019.

Chemical warfare residues

Nerve gases (various organophosphates) and blister agents (nitrogen-or sulfur-based mustards) are the more common chemical warfare compounds that result in requests for residue analysis inside the US. The various residues arise during both the manufacturing process and during decontamination procedures. The residue analytes are listed in Table 3-103 along with the referenced USATHAMA methodology. Possible routes to the residues from the materials used by the US military in munitions are indicated in Figure 3-39.

Table 3-103. Chemical warfare agent residues

Residue	Abbreviation	Method Number	CAS Number
Isopropylmethylphosphonic acid	IMPA	UT03 (aqueous), LT03 (soils)	–
Methylphosphonic acid	MPA	UT03 (aqueous) LT03 (soils)	993-13-5
Fluoroacetic acid	FC2A	UT03 (aqueous) LT03 (soils)	62-74-8
Chloroacetic acid	ClC2A	UT03 (aqueous), LT03 (soils) LW18(soil)	79-11-8
Ethylmethylphosphonic acid[40]	EMPA	UT03 (aqueous), LT03 (soils)	–
Thiodiglycol	TDGCL	LW18 (soil), UW22 (aqueous)	111-48-8
Thiodiglycolic acid	TDGCLA	UW22 (aqueous)	123-93-3
Diisopropylmethylphosphonate	DIMP	UK08 (aqueous), TT9 (soils)	1445-75-6
Dimethylmethylphosphonate	DMMP	UK08 (aqueous), TT9 (soils)	756-79-6

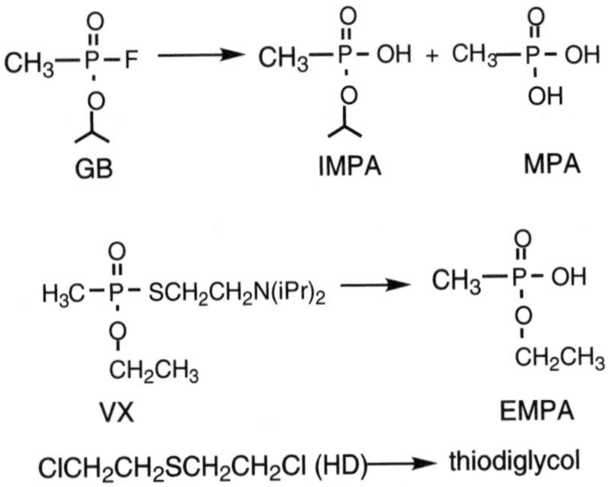

Figure 3-39. Breakdown products from common military chemical agents.

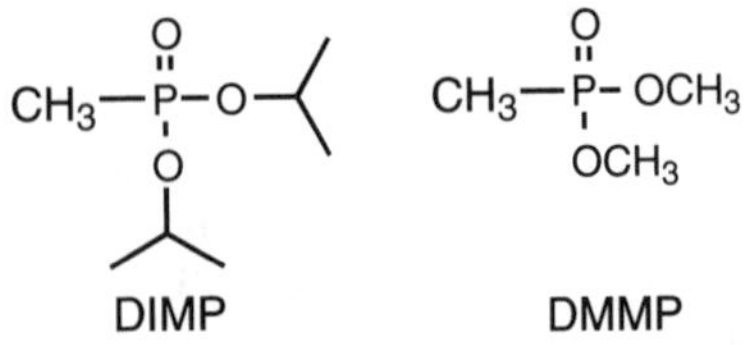

Figure 3-40. Alkaline/alcohol decontamination products from common military nerve agents.

[40] Due to co-elution, quantitated as MPA.

Table 3-104. Holding times, preservatives and sample containers for chemical warfare residue samples

Method	Container and sample size	Preservative	Holding time
UT03	Amber glass jar with Teflon lid liner 60 mL	4 °C, minimum headspace	40 days
LT03	Amber glass with Teflon lid liner, 100 g	4 °C, minimum headspace	7 days to extraction, 40 days to analysis
LW18	Amber glass jars with Teflon lid liner, 1.2 L capacity or polybutyrate core tubes	4 °C	7 days to extraction, 40 days to analysis
UW22	Amber glass jar with Teflon lid liner, 1.2 L	4 °C	7 days to extraction, 40 days to analysis
UK08	Amber glass jar with Teflon lid liner, 1L	4 °C	7 days to extraction, 40 days to analysis
TT9	Glass with Teflon lid liner,	4 °C	7 days to extraction, 40 days to analysis

Method UT03 uses a gradient elution ion chromatograph with a conductivity detector for direct analysis of filtered samples. A silver-form cation exchange resin is used to reduce chloride interference. Method LT03 requires a DI water extraction of the soil, then is similar to UT03.

Method LW18 requires extraction of the target analytes from soil in alkaline methanol, filtration and concentration, then dilution with acidification and water. Analysis is performed by HPLC with a reversed-phase C18 column and a buffered phosphate eluant. Detection is by UV at 215 nm. Method UW22 concentrates a 500 mL aliquot to 50 mL by boiling, purifies the concentrate by passage through a XAD-7 resin column, further reduces the volume to 5 mL, then dilutes the sample to 10 mL with buffered water. Analysis is identical to LW18.

Method UK08 uses a continuous liquid-liquid extractor to isolate the target analytes from 1 L of sample with methylene chloride. The extract is concentrated to 5 mL and analyzed on a FPD-GC with a 5% SP-1000 on Supelcoport 100/120 2 mm glass column. Method TT9 extracts the soil with DI water then directly injects the water solution on the FID-GC specified in method UK08.

F. Plasticizers, anti-oxidants and other additives

Plasticizers, anti-oxidants, UV-inhibitors and flame retardants are frequent contaminants found during forward library searches for non-target compounds (TICs) in GC-MS analyses. Although these can be environmental pollutants, they may also be present as laboratory contamination. Anti-oxidants are added to plastic formulations to trap or destroy radicals and peroxides that occur during the initiation of polymer breakdown through oxidation. Radical traps are commonly hindered phenols and secondary arylamines. A frequently encountered anti-oxidant of this type is BHT, used to protect processed or preserved foods from oxidation/discoloration. Compounds used to destroy radicals are phosphites, esters of thiodipropionic acid and other sulfur-containing materials such as thioureas. Both anti-oxidant functions can be designed into the same compound, for example thiobis (di-sec-amylphenol).

Organic flame retardants commonly contain chlorine, bromine or phosphorus and may be mixed with metal species such as antimony trioxide, antimony pentoxide or sodium antimonate. Examples of organic flame retardants include deca- and octa-bromodiphenyloxide, tetrabromo phthalic anhydride and phthalate esters, tris (2,3-dibromopropyl) phosphate, tris (2-chloroethyl) phosphate, tetrabromobisphenol-A, and dibromoneopentyl glycol. The compounds may simply be mixed into the bulk plastic or fiber or they may be incorporated as monomers in the polymerization reaction to form the plastic.

Lubricants are used in the plastics industry to ease handling of the materials during molding and fabrication. These additives include many fatty acids and esters, fatty alcohols, and bis-amides. Examples are glycerol monostearate, olelyl alchol, and ethylene bis-stearamide, to name just a very few.

When the base polymer is pure polyvinyl chloride, a very rigid, hard plastic results. To make the formulation flexible and more useable, many different classes of compounds are added to the material as plasticizers. Included as part of this group are the lubricants, although the compounds may serve more important functions than simply lubrication. Tygon tubing is an excellent example. It contains up to 40% by weight bis-(2-ethylhexyl) phthalate as a plasticizer. Compounds frequently found in these applications include monoesters (abietates, lactates, myristates, palmitates, ricinoleates, stearates and tallates), diesters (adipates, azelates, itacontates, maleates, phthalates, terephthalates, sebacates, succinates, and tartrates), triesters (citrates, glycolate-phthalates, phosphates, and trimellitates), glycol esters, glycerol esters, amides, toluenesulfonamides, and tin diesters.

A final group of chemical additives are the UV-stabilizers. These additives are termed hindered amine light stabilizers (HALS). They function by trapping free-radicals, generated in the polymer by UV-light, forming nitroxyl groups that are efficient traps for other radicals. The UV-stabilizers are particularly useful in protecting pigment molecules from UV light bleaching. The HALS are known by tradenames such as Tinuvin, Chimassorb, Maxxim, Cyasorb, Good-rite, Topanex, Lupersol and Sanduvor.

Sometimes the chemical names for these compounds are quite long and the compound is listed in the mass spectral library by a tradename. An example is "octicizer", found in the Wiley MS collection. Some materials are listed in Table 3-105. The research literature contains some reports of analysis of environmental samples for these compounds as target analytes[41], however there have been no regulatory methods written specifically for them.

Table 3-105. Plasticizers, anti-oxidants, flame retardants and other additives

Name	CAS	Structure
2.6-Bis(1,1-dimethylethyl)-4-methyl phenol; butylated hydroxytoluene (BHT)	38222-83-2	H₃C─⬡─OH with C(CH₃)₃ groups at top and bottom
Butlyated hydroxyanisole (BHA)	489-01-0	H₃CO─⬡─OH with C(CH₃)₃ groups at top and bottom

Continued on next page.

---

[41] Wright, S.J., M.J. Dale, P.R.R. Langridge-Smith, Q. Zhan, and R. Zenobi. "Selective in Situ Detection of Polymer Additives Using Laser Mass Spectrometry." *Anal. Chem.* 1996. 68(20). pp. 3585-3594.

Table 3-105. Plasticizers, anti-oxidants, flame retardants and other additives, *continued*

Name	CAS	Structure
Trioctyl trimellitate	3319-31-1	$CO_2CH_2CHC_4H_9$ with C_2H_5 groups (three substituents on benzene ring)
Tris(2-chloroethyl) phosphate	115-96-8	$OP(OCH_2CH_2Cl)_3$
Dimethylitacontate	617-52-7	$CH_3O_2CCH_2C(=CH)_2CO_2CH_3$
Octicizer	1241-94-7	
Irganox 1076	—	$H_{37}C_{18}OCCH_2CH_2O$ — with $C(CH_3)_3$, OH, $C(CH_3)_3$ substituents
Irgafos 168	—	$[(CH_3)_3C$ — O$]_3$P with $C(CH_3)_3$
Santo White	—	
Tinuvin 327	—	

G. Endocrine disruptors

A recent book[42] has brought to public attention the potential environmental role of compounds that either mimic the action or block the synthesis/action of hormones within the endocrine systems of such diverse creatures as alligators, frogs, birds, seals, otters, and possibly humans. These compounds act as endocrine disruptors in nature at substantially lower concentrations than any toxicity-derived safe exposure limit. Many of the endocrine disruptors are suspected to be synergistic with each other. Certain combinations of compounds can result in highly active materials at levels where the individual compounds exhibit little to no effects.

Some of the compounds identified as endocrine disruptors have a long history as regulated environmental pollutants. These include many of the chlorinated hydrocarbon pesticides (chlordane, toxaphene, lindane, kepone, methoxychlor, kelthane, dieldrin, and the DDT family), triazine herbicides (atrazine, prometon, propazine, simazine, etc.), diethylstilbesrol, and some industrial chemicals and by-products (PCBs, dioxins, furans, bis(2-ethylhexyl) phthalate). Other compounds singled out as presenting significant problems, that have not attracted very much regulatory attention to date, include octachlorostyrene, synthetic pyrethroids, nonyl phenol and bisphenol-A. The last two materials are common substances arising from the surfactant (non-ionic surfactants) and plastics (epoxy resins) industries, respectively.

Table 3-106. Some endocrine disruptors

Name	CAS	Structure
Dicofol (kelthane)	115-32-2	
Chlordecone (kepone)	143-50-0	
4,4'-DDT	50-29-3	
4-Nonylphenol	104-40-5	
Bisphenol-A	80-05-7	
Diethylstilbestrol (DES)	6898-97-1	

Regardless of the socio-political implications and predictions presented in the book, analytically speaking, determination of these compounds in environmental samples

---

[42] Colborn, T., D. Dumanoski and J.P. Myers. *Our Stolen Future*. 1996. Penguin Books, New York, NY.

offers a substantial challenge. Although methods are available for analysis of all these materials, the detection capabilities of the techniques are at levels considerably higher than estimated requirements. These needed "safe" levels may range from the sub-part per trillion to sub-part per billion (fg/L to ng/L), over a thousand-fold more sensitivity than is commonly reported from environmental laboratories.

See Section 2.II.F for other information about endocrine disruptors.

Hazardous Waste and Remediation Analysis

I. HAZARDOUS WASTE CHARACTERIZATION

Chemical hazards are everywhere there is industry, and most chemicals present health and environmental dangers. EPA is not overly concerned with the responsible use of chemicals for manufacturing. A 55 gallon steel drum of 50% sodium cyanide in water solution is not a EPA hazard if it is intended to be used. However once the decision is made by the owner that the drum is not to be used, and he will dispose of it, then EPA becomes involved. The legislated responsibility of EPA is to oversee proper disposal of wastes to insure protection of human health and the environment.

Hazardous wastes can be identified by one of two general processes. The first is a list of specific wastes from industrial sources that are designated as hazardous. EPA has four lists that cover these classifications of wastes, the F, K, P and U lists.

Hazardous wastes in the F- series are from generic industrial sources. An example is F007 - Spent cyanide plating bath solutions from electroplating operations.

Hazardous wastes in the K-series are from specific sources. An example is K024 - Distillation bottoms from the production of phthalic anhydride from naphthalene.

Hazardous wastes from commercial chemical products, intermediates and residues are listed in the P-series (acute hazard) and U-series (general hazard). Examples are P057 - 2-Fluoro acetamide (CAS No. 640-19-7) and U202 - Saccharin and salts (CAS No. 81-07-2).

These regulations and lists are presented in 40 CFR 261 through 264. Part 261 contains Appendix VII, the basis for listing chemical wastes. In chemical terms this is a list of what hazardous compounds are contained in the waste that causes it to be the F list or the K list. Also in Part 261 is the Appendix VIII list of hazardous constituents. Appendix VIII is nothing more than the alphabetical listing of the P-series and U-series substances. A number of persons in the environmental industry are under the misconception that Appendix VIII is a list of analytical targets for laboratory testing. In reality performing an "Appendix VIII" analysis is impossible - many of the compounds (137) are either not available as standards on a routine basis or the appropriate technique for unambiguous analysis is well beyond the means of the average environmental laboratory. Examples are A2213 (CAS 30558-43-1, U394), aluminum phosphide (CAS 20859-73-8, P006), mercury fulminate (CAS 628-86-4, P065), and mitomycin C (CAS 50-07-7, U010). Instead the intention of the list is so that if the generator of the waste, through knowledge of the history and source of the waste, knows that the waste consists of one or more of the listed compounds, the waste is hazardous by definition.

On the other hand, the Appendix IX list from 40 CFR Part 264 was originally intended as an analytical list for monitoring the groundwater around hazardous waste landfills to detect leachate intrusion from the landfill into the subsurface aquifers. All the analytes on the list have validated detection methods and well-characterized detection levels. The utility of the Appendix IX analyte list has been expanded substantially beyond the original intention, and is now used as a general analytical scheme for evaluating both water and soil contamination from suspected sites. The Appendix IX list (presented in Table 4-1) contains a considerably greater number of analytes than the comparable CLP target compound and target analyte lists.

Table 4-1. Appendix IX to 40 CFR 264 - Groundwater monitoring list (1 July 1998)

Analyte	CAS Number	PQL µg/L[1]
Acenaphthene	83-32-9	10
Acenaphthylene	208-96-8	10
Acetone	67-64-1	100
Acetophenone	98-86-2	10
Acetonitrile	75-05-8	100
2-Acetylaminofluorene	53-96-3	10
Acrolein	107-02-8	5
Acrylonitrile	107-13-1	5
Aldrin	309-00-2	0.05
Allyl chloride	107-05-1	100
4-Aminobiphenyl	92-67-1	10
Aniline	62-53-3	10
Anthracene	120-12-7	10
Antimony	total	300
Aramite	140-57-8	10
Arsenic	total	20
Barium	total	20
Benzene	71-43-2	5
Benzo(a)anthracene	56-55-3	10
Benzo(b)fluoranthene	205-99-2	10
Benzo(k)fluoranthene	207-08-9	10
Benzo(ghi)perylene	191-24-2	10
Benzo(a)pyrene	50-32-8	10
Benzyl alcohol	100-51-6	20
Beryllium	total	3
α-BHC	319-84-6	0.05
β-BHC	319-85-7	0.05
δ-BHC	319-86-8	0.1
γ-BHC (Lindane)	58-89-9	0.05
Bis(2-chloroethoxy)methane	111-91-1	10
Bis(2-chloroethyl)ether	111-44-4	10

Continued on next page.

[1] By the relevant SW-846 preferred method, 6010, 8081, 8082, 8151, 8260, 8270, etc.

Table 4-1. **Appendix IX to 40 CFR 264 - Groundwater monitoring list (1 July 1998),** *continued*

Analyte	CAS Number	PQL µg/L[2]
Bis(2-chloro-1-methylethyl)ether (2,2'-dichloroisopropyl ether)	108-60-1	10
Bis(2-ethylhexyl)phthalate	117-81-7	10
Bromodichloromethane	75-27-4	5
Bromoform	75-25-2	5
4-Bromophenyl phenyl ether	101-55-3	10
Butyl benzyl phthalate	85-68-7	10
Cadmium	total	40
Carbon disulfide	75-15-0	5
Carbon tetrachloride	56-23-5	5
Chlordane	57-74-9	0.1
p-Chloroaniline	106-47-8	20
Chlorobenzene	108-90-7	5
Chlorobenzilate	510-15-6	10
p-Chloro-m-cresol (4-Chloro-3-methylphenol)	59-50-7	20
Chloroethane	75-00-3	10
Chloroform	67-66-3	5
2-Chloronaphthalene	91-58-7	10
2-Chlorophenol	95-57-8	10
4-Chlorophenyl phenyl ether	7005-72-3	10
Chloroprene	126-99-8	5
Chromium	total	70
Chrysene	218-01-9	10
Cobalt	total	70
Copper	total	60
m-Cresol	108-39-4	10
o-Cresol	95-48-7	10
p-Cresol	106-44-5	10
Cyanide	57-12-5	40
2,4-D	94-75-7	10
4,4'-DDD	72-54-8	0.1
4,4'-DDE	72-55-9	0.05
4,4'-DDT	50-29-3	0.1
Diallate	2303-16-4	10
Dibenz(a,h)anthracene	53-70-3	10
Dibenzofuran	132-64-9	10
Dibromochloromethane	124-48-1	5
1,2-Dibromo-3-chloropropane (DBCP)	96-12-8	5
1,2-Dibromoethane (EDB)	106-93-4	5

Continued on next page.

---

[2] By the relevant SW-846 preferred method, 6010, 8081, 8082, 8151, 8260, 8270, etc.

Table 4-1. **Appendix IX to 40 CFR 264 - Groundwater monitoring list (1 July 1998),** *continued*

Analyte	CAS Number	PQL µg/L[3]
Di-n-butylphthalate	84-74-2	10
1,2-Dichlorobenzene	95-50-1	10
1,3-Dichlrobenzene	541-73-1	10
1,4-Dichlorobenzene	106-46-7	110
3,3'-Dichlorobenzidine	91-94-1	10
trans-1,4-dichloro-2-butene	110-57-6	5
Dichlorodifluoromethane	75-71-8	5
1,1-Dichloroethane	75-34-3	5
1,2-Dichloroethane	107-06-2	5
1,1-Dichloroethene	75-34-4	5
trans-1,2-Dichloroethene	156-60-5	5
2,4-Dichlorophenol	120-83-2	10
2,6-Dichlorophenol	87-65-0	10
1,2-Dichloropropane	78-87-5	5
cis-1,3-Dichloropropene	10061-01-5	5
trans-1,3-Dichloropropene	10061-02-6	5
Dieldrin	60-57-1	0.05
Diethylphthalate	84-66-2	10
Thionazin	297-97-2	10
Dimethoate	60-51-5	10
p-(Dimethylamino)azobenzene	60-11-7	10
7,12-Dimethylbenz(a)anthracene	57-97-6	10
3,3'-Dimethylbenzidine	119-93-7	10
α, α-Dimethylphenethylamine	122-09-8	10
2,4-Dimethylphenol	105-67-9	10
Dimethylphthalate	131-11-3	10
1,3-Dinitrobenzene	99-65-0	10
4,6-Dinitro-o-cresol	534-52-1	50
2,4-Dinitrophenol	51-28-5	50
2,4-Dinitrotoluene	121-14-2	10
2,6-Dinitrotoluene	606-20-2	10
Dinoseb (DNBP)	88-85-7	10
Di-n-octylphthalate	117-84-0	10
1,4-Dioxane	123-91-1	150
Diphenylamine	122-39-4	10
Disulfoton	298-04-4	2
Endosulfan I	959-98-8	0.1
Endosulfan II	33213-65-9	0.05

Continued on next page.

---

[3] By the relevant SW-846 preferred method, 6010, 8081, 8082, 8151, 8260, 8270, etc.

Table 4-1. **Appendix IX to 40 CFR 264 - Groundwater monitoring list (1 July 1998),** *continued*

Analyte	CAS Number	PQL µg/L[4]
Endosulfan sulfate	1031-07-8	0.5
Endrin	72-20-8	0.1
Endrin aldehyde	7421-93-4	0.2
Ethylbenzene	100-41-4	5
Ethylmethacrylate	97-63-2	5
Ethyl methanesulfonate	62-50-0	10
Famphur	52-85-7	10
Fluoranthene	206-44-0	10
Fluorene	86-73-7	10
Heptachlor	76-44-8	0.05
Heptachlor epoxide	1024-57-3	1
Hexachlorobenzene	118-74-1	10
Hexachlorobutadiene	87-68-3	10
Hexachlorocyclopentadiene	77-47-4	10
Hexachloroethane	67-72-1	10
Hexachlorophene	70-30-4	10
Hexachloropropene	1888-71-7	10
2-Hexanone	591-78-6	50
Indeno(1,2,3-cd)pyrene	193-39-5	10
Isobutyl alcohol	78-83-1	50
Isodrin	465-73-6	10
Isophorone	78-59-1	10
Isosafrole	120-58-1	10
Kepone	143-50-0	10
Lead	total	40
Mercury	total	2
Methacrylonitrile	126-98-7	5
Methapyrilene	91-80-5	10
Methoxychlor	72-43-5	2
Methyl bromide	74-83-9	10
Methyl chloride	74-87-3	10
3-Methylcholanthrene	56-49-5	10
Methylene bromide	74-95-3	5
Methylene chloride	75-09-2	5
Methyl ethyl ketone (MEK, 2-butanone)	78-93-3	100
Methyl iodide	74-88-4	5
Methyl methacrylate	80-62-6	5
Methyl methanesulfonate	66-27-3	10

Continued on next page.

---

[4]   By the relevant SW-846 preferred method, 6010, 8081, 8082, 8151, 8260, 8270, etc.

Table 4-1. **Appendix IX to 40 CFR 264 - Groundwater monitoring list (1 July 1998),** *continued*

Analyte	CAS Number	PQL μg/L[5]
2-Methylnaphthalene	91-57-6	10
Methyl parathion	298-00-0	0.5
4-Methyl-2-pentanone (MIBK)	108-10-1	50
Naphthalene	91-20-3	10
1,4-Naphthoquinone	130-15-4	10
1-Naphthylamine	134-32-7	10
2-Naphthylamine	91-59-8	10
Nickel	total	50
2-Nitroaniline	88-74-4	50
3-Nitroaniline	99-09-2	50
4-Nitroaniline	100-01-6	50
Nitrobenzene	98-95-3	10
2-Nitrophenol	88-75-5	10
4-Nitrophenol	100-02-7	10
4-Nitroquinoline-1-oxide	56-57-5	10
N-Nitrosodi-n-butylamine	924-16-3	10
N-Nitrosodiethylamine	55-18-5	10
N-Nitrosodimethylamine	62-75-9	10
N-Nitrosodiphenylamine	86-30-6	10
N-Nitrosodi-n-propylamine	621-64-7	10
N-Nitrosomethylethylamine	10595-95-6	10
N-Nitrosomorpholine	59-89-2	10
N-Nitrosopiperidine	100-75-4	10
N-Nitrosopyrrolidine	930-55-2	10
5-Nitro-o-toluidine	99-55-8	10
Parathion	56-38-2	10
PCB	arochlors	50
Polychlorinated dibenzo-p-dioxins	-	0.01
Polychlorinated dibenzofurans	-	0.01
Pentachlorobenzene	608-93-5	10
Pentachloroethane	76-01-7	10
Pentachloronitrobenzene	82-68-8	10
Pentachlorophenol	87-86-5	50
Phenacetin	62-44-2	10
Phenanthrene	85-01-8	10
Phenol	108-95-2	10
p-Phenylenediamine	106-50-3	10
Phorate	298-02-2	10

Continued on next page.

[5] By the relevant SW-846 preferred method, 6010, 8081, 8082, 8151, 8260, 8270, etc.

Table 4-1. **Appendix IX to 40 CFR 264 - Groundwater monitoring list (1 July 1998),** *continued*

Analyte	CAS Number	PQL µg/L[6]
2-Picoline	109-06-8	10
Pronamide	23950-58-5	10
Propionitrile	107-12-0	5
Pyrene	129-00-0	10
Pyridine	110-86-1	10
Safrole	94-59-7	10
Selenium	total	20
Silver	total	70
Silvex (2,4,5-TP)	93-72-1	2
Styrene	100-42-5	5
Sulfide	18496-25-8	10,000
2,4,5-T	93-76-5	2
2,3,7,8-TCDD	1746-01-6	0.005
1,2,4,5-Tetrachlorobenzene	95-94-3	10
1,1,1,2-Tetrachloroethane	630-20-6	5
1,1,2,2-Tetrachloroethane	79-34-5	5
Tetrachloroethene	127-18-4	5
2,3,4,6-Tetrachlorophenol	58-90-2	10
Sulfotepp	3689-24-5	10
Thallium	total	10
Tin	total	8000
Toluene	108-88-3	5
o-Toluidine	95-53-4	10
Toxaphene	8001-35-2	2
1,2,4-Trichlorobenzene	120-82-1	10
1,1,1-Trichloroethane	71-55-6	5
1,1,2-Trichloroethane	79-00-5	5
Trichloroethene	79-01-6	5
Trichlorofluoromethane	75-69-4	5
2,4,5-Trichlorophenol	95-95-4	10
2,4,6-Trichlorophenol	88-06-2	10
1,2,3-Trichloropropane	96-18-4	5
O,O,O-Triethylphosphorothiolate	126-68-1	10
Trinitrobenzene	99-35-4	10
Vanadium	total	80
Vinyl acetate	108-05-4	5
Vinyl chloride	75-01-4	10
Xylene (total)	1330-20-7	5
Zinc	total	20

[6]   By the relevant SW-846 preferred method, 6010, 8081, 8082, 8151, 8260, 8270, etc.

The other method for identifying hazardous wastes is to describe chemical properties or characteristics that the waste will exhibit if it is hazardous, and not be concerned with where the waste came from. Four characteristics of hazardous waste are recognized with specific test methods being listed for each characteristic in Chapter 7, SW-846 (EPA's methods manual for analysis of solid wastes).

A. Ignitability Characteristic (D001)

A hazardous waste exhibits the characteristic of ignitability if a representative sample of the waste has any of the following properties.

1. The material is a liquid, other than an aqueous solution, containing less than 24% alcohol by volume and exhibits a Flash point <60 °C in a Pensky-Martens closed cup flash tester under ASTM D-93-79 or D-93-80 (Methods 1010 or 1020).

2. The material is not a liquid and is capable under standard temperature and pressure conditions of causing a fire through friction, absorption of moisture, or spontaneous chemical changes and, when ignited, burns so vigorously and persistently that it creates a hazard.

3. The material is an ignitable compressed gas as defined in 49 CFR 173.300. A compressed gas is defined as any substance that exhibits a pressure of >40 psi at 70 °F in a cylinder or an absolute pressure of >104 psi at 130 °F. The gas is flammable if a mixture of 13% or less with air is flammable at atmospheric pressure and temperature. A gas is also considered to be flammable if it is found to be so with the Bureau of Explosives Flame Projection Apparatus, the Open Drum Apparatus or the Closed Drum Apparatus.

4. The material is an oxidizer as defined in 49 CFR 173.151. An oxidizer is any material that yields oxygen readily to stimulate combustion. Examples are chlorates (ClO_3^-), perchlorates (ClO_4^-), permanganates (MnO_4^-), peroxides (such as H_2O_2 or Na_2O_2), and nitrates (NH_4NO_3).

B. Corrosivity Characteristic (D002)

A hazardous waste exhibits the characteristic of corrosivity if a representative sample of the waste has either of the following properties:

1. The material is aqueous and exhibits a pH >12.5 or <2 (Methods 9040 and 9041).

2. The material is a liquid and corrodes SAE 1020 steel at a rate >6.35 mm (0.250 inch) per year at a temperature of 55 °C (Method 1110).

A problem with the first laboratory test is that the pH of alkaline solutions changes drastically with temperature[7]. This is illustrated in Figure 4-1, where the inverse relationship of temperature to pH and pK_w is shown. Alkaline solutions which are considered hazardous under the corrosivity characteristic by virtue of a pH slightly greater than 12.5 at room temperature (20 °C) can pass the characteristic if stored above room temperature (25 °C). This is completely converse to physical reality where

---

[7]   Meiggs, T.O. "pH in Alkaline Solutions." *Environmental Testing & Analysis.* 1994. 3(1). pp. 58-61.

increasing the temperature of a solution will always make it more corrosive, as demonstrated in the second test for the characteristic, where an elevated temperature is used to complete the test in a shorter period of time. A standard temperature of 25 °C should always be used for corrosivity characterization by pH; however, this is not expressly included in the test description.

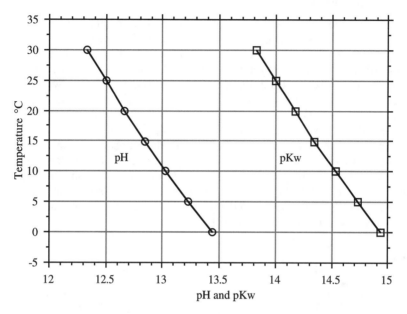

Figure 4-1. Relationship of temperature to pK_w and pH for constant strength alkaline solution.

C. Reactivity Characteristic (D003)

A hazardous waste exhibits the characteristic of reactivity if a representative sample of the waste has any of the following properties:

1. The material is normally unstable and readily undergoes violent change without detonating.

2. The material reacts violently with water.

3. The material forms potentially explosive mixtures with water.

4. When mixed with water, the material generates toxic gases or fumes in a quantity hazardous to human health or the environment.

5. The material is a sulfide- or cyanide-containing substance, which, in the pH range 2 to 12.5, can generate H_2S or HCN in a quantity hazardous to human health or the environment. (In order to test for this characteristic use Method 7.3.3.2 and 7.3.4.2 for distillation of HCN and H_2S from acidified wastes, followed by analysis by Methods 9014 and 9034 respectively).

6. The material will detonate if subjected to a strong initiating source or is heated while confined.

7. The material is capable of detonation or explosive decomposition under standard temperature and pressure conditions.

8. The material is a Class A or Class B explosive as defined in 49 CFR 173.51, 49 CFR 173.53, or 49 CFR 173.88.

D. Toxicity Characteristic

The TCLP was formalized and revised from the previous EPA toxicity test in Federal Register Vol. 55, No. 61, 29 March, 1990, pages 11798-11877. Toxicity consists of a list of specific substances whose presence in a waste above a set level is considered to be toxic. These specific substances are given a D-series code, such as D012 for Endrin. However, the existence of these substances in the waste does not render the waste hazardous as long as they stay in the waste. Occasionally waste is placed in a municipal landfill when it properly belongs in a controlled hazardous waste facility. The biggest difference between the two types of waste facility is that the hazardous waste site is completely isolated from the surrounding environment, while most municipal landfills are in intimate contact with the ground[8]. As rainwater percolates down through the landfill and mixes with the acidic products of organic decomposition, many materials become solubilized and travel down toward the groundwater. The Toxic Characteristic Leaching Procedure (TCLP, Method 1311) is used to model the organic acid leaching of hazardous contaminants from municipal landfills.

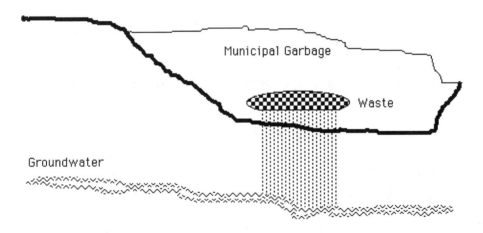

E. TCLP (Method 1311[*])

The TCLP is actually a sample processing procedure that precedes any analytical sample preparation. Table 4-2 lists the target analytes under the TCLP along with the original Federal regulatory limits. Several States have decided that TCLP extracts must be analyzed to the drinking water MCL level. These values have been included in Table 4-2 for comparison with the Federal level.

---

8 Newer municipal landfills must meet subtitle D regulations, which require liners and leachate collection and treatment capability.

* Sources of this and other methods can be found in Section 1.II.

TCLP consists of determination of the percent solids in the waste, determination of the pH, separation of solid from liquid phases, reduction of the particle size of the solid, extraction of the solid with agitation for 18 hours, filtration of the extract, combination of the extract with any original liquid phase, and preservation of the extract for analysis by the required methods (Table 4-3). These procedures are outlined in the flowchart in Figure 4-2. The pH of the sample will determine which of two extraction fluids will be used. For acidic or neutral samples an acetic acid-sodium acetate buffered fluid is used. For basic materials, an acetic acid solution is used. These fluids mimic the acidic "soup" generated in the municipal landfill from the decomposition of organic wastes. A number of the analytes are volatile, and a special extraction-filtration apparatus called a Zero Headspace Extractor (ZHE) is used to process these analytes. Reports of TCLP analyte determinations are based on the level of contaminants in the extraction fluid. They are not corrected to the original waste.

Table 4-2. Substances listed under TCLP Toxicity Characteristic

HW No.	Contaminant	DW MCL (mg/L)	Regulatory Level (mg/L)
D004	Arsenic	0.05	5.0
D005	Barium	2	100.0
D018	Benzene	0.005	0.5
D006	Cadmium	0.005	1.0
D019	Carbon tetrachloride	0.005	0.5
D020	Chlordane	0.002	0.03
D021	Chlorobenzene	0.1	100.0
D022	Chloroform	0.1 (TTHM)	6.0
D007	Chromium	0.1	5.0
D023	o-Cresol	-	200.0
D024	m-Cresol	-	200.0
D025	p-Cresol	-	200.0
D026	Cresol[9]	-	200.0
D016	2,4-D	0.07	10.0
D027	1,4-Dichlorobenzene	0.075	7.5
D028	1,2-Dichloroethane	0.005	0.5
D029	1,1-Dichloroethylene	0.007	0.7
D030	2,4-Dinitrotoluene	-	0.13
D012	Endrin	0.002	0.02
D031	Heptachlor + Heptachlor epoxide	0.0004 0.0002	0.008
D032	Hexachlorobenzene	0.001	0.13
D033	Hexachlorobutadiene	-	0.5
D034	Hexachloroethane	-	3.0

Continued on next page.

---

[9] Total cresol or the separate isomers may be determined. If total cresol is determined, the regulatory level is 200.0 mg/L, while if the individual isomers are determined, each has a regulatory level of 200.0 mg/L.

Table 4-2.   Substances listed under TCLP Toxicity Characteristic, *continued*

HW No.	Contaminant	DW MCL (mg/L)	Regulatory Level (mg/L)
D008	Lead	0.015	5.0
D013	Lindane	0.0002	0.4
D009	Mercury	0.002	0.2
D014	Methoxychlor	0.04	10.0
D035	Methyl ethyl ketone	-	200.0
D036	Nitrobenzene	-	2.0
D037	Pentachlorophenol	0.001	100.0
D038	Pyridine	-	5.0
D010	Selenium	0.05	1.0
D011	Silver	-	5.0
D039	Tetrachloroethylene	0.005	0.7
D015	Toxaphene	0.003	0.5
D040	Trichloroethylene	0.005	0.5
D041	2,4,5-Trichlorophenol	-	400.0
D042	2,4,6-Trichlorophenol	-	2.0
D017	2,4,5-TP (Silvex)	0.05	1.0
D043	Vinyl chloride	0.002	0.2

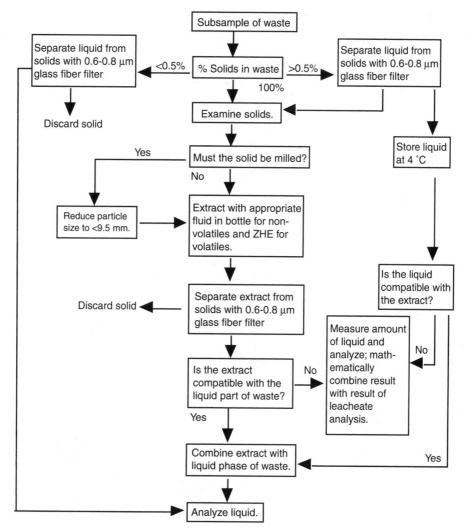

Figure 4-2.   Flowchart of TCLP.

Table 4-3.   Analytical Methods required under TCLP

Volatiles (8260B)
Benzene
Carbon tetrachloride
Chlorobenzene
Chloroform
1,2-Dichloroethane
1,1-Dichloroethylene
Methyl ethyl ketone
Tetrachloroethylene
Trichloroethylene
Vinyl chloride

Metals (6010A)
Arsenic
Barium
Cadmium
Chromium
Lead
Mercury (7471)
Selenium
Silver

Continued on next page.

Table 4-3. **Analytical Methods required under TCLP,** *continued*

Semivolatiles (8270C)
Cresols
1,4-Dichlorobenzene
2,4-Dinitrotoluene
Hexachlorobenzene
Hexachlorobutadiene
Hexachloroethane
Nitrobenzene
Pentachlorophenol
2,4,5-Trichlorophenol
2,4,6-Trichlorophenol
Pyridine

Herbicides (8151A)
2,4-D
2,4,5-TP (Silvex)

Pesticides (8081A)
Chlordane
Endrin
Heptachlor (and epoxide)
Lindane
Methoxychlor
Toxaphene

Method 1312: Synthetic Precipitation Leaching Procedure

This method is designed to mimic the effect of acidic rainfall on wastes and soils. Operationally it is very similar to TCLP except extraction fluid #1 is pH 4.20 H_2SO_4/HNO_3 (60/40) for soil samples east of the Mississippi River and all wastes and wastewaters, extraction fluid #2 is pH 5.00 H_2SO_4/HNO_3 (60/40) for testing the leachability of soils west of the Mississippi River, and extraction fluid #3 is reagent water for extraction of volatile organics and cyanide.

II. LANDFILL LEACHATE AND GROUNDWATER MONITORING

A topic of increased interest is the monitoring of surfacewater and groundwater contaminated by municipal landfill leachate. Landfill leachate is defined as water that leaves a landfill by either percolation through the underlying soil to the water table or by breaking the surface at a downgradient point (toe) of the landfill. Landfill leachate exhibits the typical characteristics listed in Table 4-4.

Table 4-4. **Typical characteristics of landfill leachate**

Parameter	Range mg/L	Typical mg/L
BOD_5	2000-30000	10000
TOC	1500-20000	6000
COD	3000-45000	18000
TSS	200-1000	500
Organic N	10-600	200
Ammonia N	10-800	200
Nitrate N	5-40	25
Total P	1-70	30
Ortho P	1-50	20
Alkalinity	1000-10000	3000

Continued on next page.

Table 4-4. Typical characteristics of landfill leachate, *continued*

Parameter	Range mg/L	Typical mg/L
pH	5.3-8.5	6
Total hardness	300-10000	3500
Calcium	200-3000	1000
Magnesium	50-1500	250
Potassium	200-2000	300
Sodium	200-2000	500
Chloride	100-3000	500
Sulfate	100-1500	300
Total iron	50-600	60

Table 4-5. Semiannual landfill surface water monitoring

Indicator Parameters	Inorganic Parameters
DO	Arsenic
Temperature	Barium
pH	Cadmium
Specific conductance	Chromium
Chloride	Cyanide
TOC	Lead
COD	Nickel
	Mercury
	Selenium
	Silver
	Zinc

Table 4-6. Landfill stormwater monitoring parameters

Ammonia	Magnesium (Total & dissolved)
Nitrate + Nitrite N	COD
TDS	TOC
Oil & Grease	pH
Arsenic	Barium
Cadmium	Chromium
Cyanide	Lead
Silver	Selenium
Mercury	

Most landfills collect the leachate and either discharge to a municipal POTW or treat the leachate and dispose of it appropriately (surface water discharge, land application, pass it on the POTW, etc.). EPA examined landfill leachate as a point source and has published draft effluent guidelines[10], for eventual inclusion in the CFR as Part 445. If the treated leachate is discharged to surface water the guidelines are those presented in Table 4-7. Discharge to a POTW or other disposal options were not given guidelines.

---

[10] *Federal Register*, 6 February, 1998, Vol 63, Number 25, p 6425-6463.

Table 4-7. **Non-hazardous landfill concentration limitations for discharges to surface water (draft 40 CFR 445).**

Parameter	Maximum for 1 day (mg/L)	Maximum monthly average (mg/L)
BOD_5	160	40
TSS	89	27
Ammonia	5.9	2.5
Zinc	0.20	0.11
Alpha Terpineol	0.059	0.029
Benzoic acid	0.23	0.13
p-Cresol	0.046	0.026
Phenol	0.045	0.026
Toluene	0.080	0.026
pH	in the range 6.0-9.0 pH units	

The EPA has instituted an extensive groundwater monitoring program based on downgradient monitoring wells as landfill checks. Rather than a specific regulatory limit for contaminants, the requirement is to detect a statistically significant increase of contaminants in the downgradient wells over those in the normal background, which is determined by simultaneous monitoring of upgradient wells. The statistically significant increase is determined through use of one of several approved spreadsheet/statistical programs[11]. The analytes are required to be checked on a regular basis - four times a year is recommended[12]. These are known as the Appendix I analytes (40 CFR Part 258, Appendix I). They were chosen to require only two analytical methods and thereby ease the cost burden on the regulated community. Several states have modified the original intent of the leacheate monitoring program by applying drinking water MCLs as minimum detection levels for the Appendix I analyses. This requires switching from ICP-AES to either GFAA or ICP-MS to meet the detection levels and results in a significant increase in the costs of the monitoring.

Table 4-8. **Appendix I Target Analytes for landfill leachate monitoring**

Inorganic Constituents (Method 6010)	
Antimony	Lead
Arsenic	Nickel
Barium	Selenium
Beryllium	Silver
Cadmium	Thallium
Chromium	Vanadium
Cobalt	Zinc
Copper	

Continued on next page.

---

[11] GSAS Intelligent Decision Technologies, Ltd, 3308 Fourth St., Boulder, CO 80304. GRITS and GRITSTAT version 4.14 USEPA Office of Solid Waste; SAGE PC Engineering Inc., PO Box 52712, Knoxville, TN 37950-2712. A spreadsheet program for data entry into GRITS.

[12] "Solid Waste Disposal Facility Criteria; Final Rule." *Federal Register*. October 9, 1991. pp. 50978-51119.

Table 4-8. **Appendix I Target Analytes for landfill leachate monitoring,** *continued*

Organic Constituents (Method 8260)	
Acetone	*trans*-1,3-Dichloropropene
Acrylonitrile	Ethylbenzene
Benzene	2-Hexanone
Bromodichloromethane	Methyl chloride
Bromoform	Methylene bromide
Carbon disulfide	Methylene chloride
Carbon tetrachloride	Methyl ethyl ketone
Chlorobenzene	Methyl iodide
Chloroethane	4-Methyl-2-pentanone
Chloroform	Styrene
Dibromochloromethane	1,1,1,2-Tetrachloroethane
1,2-Dibromo-3-chloropropane	1,1,2,2-Tetrachloroethane
1,2-Dibromoethane	Tetrachloroethene
1,2-Dichlorobenzene	Toluene
1,4-Dichlorobenzene	1,1,1-Trichloroethane
trans-1,4-Dichloro-2-butene	1,1,2-Trichloroethane
1,1-Dichloroethane	Trichloroethene
1,2-Dichloroethane	Trichlorofluoromethane
1,1-Dichloroethene	1,2,3-Trichloropropane
cis-1,2-Dichloroethene	Vinyl acetate
trans-1,2-Dichloroethene	Vinyl chloride
1,2-Dichloropropane	Xylenes
cis-1,3-Dichloropropene	

If any of the Appendix I analytes are detected during the periodic monitoring, assessment monitoring with the Appendix II analytes begins. Appendix II contains many target analytes, covering a number of methods, as illustrated in the Tables.

Table 4-9. **Analyte Groups in 40 CFR Part 258, Appendix II**

Analyte Group	Number of Analytes	Test Method
Chlorinated Acid Herbicides	4	8151
Chlorinated Pesticides	19	8081A
PCBs	6	8082
Semivolatile Organics	112	8270
Volatile Organics	61	8260
Metals	16	6010
Cyanide	1	9010/9014
Sulfide	1	9030/9034
Mercury	1	7470

Table 4-10. Semivolatile Organic Target Analytes from Appendix II by Method 8270

Target Analyte	PQL µg/L	Target Analyte	PQL µg/L
Acenaphthene	10	Acenaphthylene	10
Acetonphenone	10	2-Acetylaminofluorene	20
4-Aminobiphenyl	20	Anthracene	10
Benzo(a)anthracene	10	Benzo(b)fluoranthene	10
Benzo(k)fluoranthene	10	Benzo(ghi)perylene	10
Benzo(a)pyrene	10	Benzyl alcohol	20
Bis(2-chloroethoxy)methane	10	Bis(2-chloroethyl)ether	10
Bis(2-chloroisopropyl)ether	10	Bis(2-ethylhexyl)phthalate	20
4-Bromophenyl phenyl ether	10	Butyl benzyl phthalate	10
p-Chloroaniline	20	4-Chloro-3-methylphenol	20
Chlorobenzilate	10	2-Chloronaphthalene	10
2-Chlorophenol	10	4-Chlorophenyl phenyl ether	10
Chrysene	10	m-Cresol	10
o-Cresol	10	p-Cresol	10
Diallate	10	Dibenz(a,h)anthracene	10
Dibenzofuran	10	Di-n-butyl phthalate	10
1,2-Dichlorobenzene	10	1,3-Dichlorobenzene	10
1,4-Dichlorobenzene	10	3,3'-Dichlorobenzidine	20
2,4-Dichlorophenol	10	2,6-Dichlorophenol	10
Diethyl phthalate	10	Thionazin	20
Dimethoate	20	p-(Dimethylamino)azobenzene	10
7,12-Dimethylbenz(a)anthracene	10	3,3'-Dimethylbenzidine	10
2,4-Dimethylphenol	10	Dimethyl phthalate	10
m-Dinitrobenzene	20	4,6-Dinitro-2-methylphenol	50
2,4-Dinitrophenol	50	2,4-Dinitrotoluene	10
2,6-Dinitrotoluene	10	Di-n-octyl phthalate	10
Diphenylamine	10	Disulfoton	10
Ethyl methansulfonate	20	Famphur	20
Fluoranthene	10	Fluorene	10
Hexachlorobenzene	10	Hexachlorobutadiene	10
Hexachlorocyclopentadiene	10	Hexachloroethane	10
Hexachloropropene	10	Indeno(1,2,3-cd)pyrene	10
Isodrin	20	Isophorone	10
Isosafrole	10	Kepone	20
Methapyrilene	100	3-Methylcholanthrene	10
Methyl methanesulfonate	10	2-Methylnaphthalene	10
Methyl parathion	10	Naphthalene	10
1,4-Naphthoquinone	10	1-Naphthylamine	10
2-Naphthylamine	10	2-Nitroaniline	50
3-Nitroaniline	50	4-Nitroaniline	20
Nitrobenzene	10	2-Nitrophenol	10
4-Nitrophenol	50	N-Nitrosodi-n-butylamine	10
N-Nitrosodiethylamine	20	N-Nitrosodimethylamine	10
N-Nitrosodiphenylamine	10	N-Nitrosodipropylamine	10
N-Nitrosomethylethylamine	10	N-Nitrosopiperidine	20
N-Nitrosopyrrolidine	40	5-Nitro-o-toluidine	10
Parathion	10	Pentachlorobenzene	10
Pentachloronitrobenzene	20	Pentachlorophenol	50

Continued on next page.

Table 4-10. Semivolatile Organic Target Analytes from Appendix II by Method 8270, *continued*

Target Analyte	PQL µg/L
Phenacetin	20
Phenol	100
Phorate	10
Pyrene	10
1,2,4,5-Tetrachlorobenzene	10
o-Toluidine	10
2,4,5-Trichlorophenol	10
O,O,O-Triethyl phosphorothiolate	10

Target Analyte	PQL µg/L
Phenanthrene	10
p-Phenylenediamine	10
Pronamide	200
Safrole	10
2,3,4,6-Tetrachlorophenol	10
1,2,4-Trichlorobenzene	10
2,4,6-Trichlorophenol	10
1,3,5-Trinitrobenzene	10

Table 4-11. Volatile Organic Target Analytes from Appendix II by Method 8260

Target Analyte	PQL µg/L
Acetone	100
Acrolein	100
Allyl chloride	10
Bromochloromethane	5
Bromoform	5
Carbon tetrachloride	10
Chloroethane	10
Chloroprene	20
1,2-Dibromo-3-chloropropane	25
1,2-Dichlorobenzene	5
1,4-Dichlorobenzene	5
Dichlorodifluoromethane	5
1,2-Dichloroethane	5
cis-1,2-Dichloroethene	5
1,2-Dichloropropane	5
2,2-Dichloropropane	15
cis-1,3-Dichloropropene	10
Ethylbenzene	5
2-Hexanone	50
Methacrylonitrile	100
Chloromethane	10
Iodomethane	10
Methyl isobutyl ketone	100
Methylene chloride	10
Priopronitrile	150
1,1,1,2-Tetrachloroethane	5
Tetrachloroethene	5
1,1,1-Trichloroethane	5
Trichloroethene	5
Vinyl acetate	50
Xylene	5

Target Analyte	PQL µg/L
Acetonitrile	-
Acrylonitrile	200
Benzene	5
Bromodichloromethane	5
Carbon disulfide	100
Chlorobenzene	5
Chloroform	5
Dibromochloromethane	5
1,2-Dibromoethane	5
1,3-Dichlorobenzene	5
trans-1,4-Dichloro-2-butene	100
1,1-Dichloroethane	5
1,1-Dichloroethene	5
trans-1,2-Dichloroethene	5
1,3-Dichloropropane	5
1,1-Dichloropropene	5
trans-1,3-Dichloropropene	10
Ethyl methacrylate	10
iso-Butyl alcohol	100
Bromomethane	10
Methyl ethyl ketone	100
Methylmethacrylate	30
Methylene bromide	10
Naphthalene	5
Styrene	10
1,1,2,2-Tetrachloroethane	5
Toluene	5
1,1,2-Trichloroethane	5
Trichlorofluoromethane	5
Vinyl chloride	10

Table 4-12. Organochlorine Pesticide Target Analytes from Appendix II by Method 8081A and 8082

Target Analyte	PQL µg/L	Target Analyte	PQL µg/L
Aldrin	0.05	α-BHC	0.05
β-BHC	0.05	δ-BHC	0.1
γ-BHC	0.05	Chlordane	0.1
4,4'-DDD	0.1	4,4'-DDE	0.05
4,4'-DDT	0.1	Dieldrin	0.05
Endosulfan I	0.1	Endosulfan II	0.05
Endosulfan sulfate	0.5	Endrin	0.1
Endrin aldehyde	0.2	Heptachlor	0.05
Heptachlor epoxide	1	Methoxychlor	2
PCB	50	Toxaphene	2

Table 4-13. Metal Elements Target Analytes from Appendix II by Method 6010

Target Analyte	PQL µg/L	Target Analyte	PQL µg/L
Antimony	300	Arsenic	500
Barium	20	Beryllium	3
Cadmium	40	Chromium	70
Cobalt	70	Copper	60
Lead	400	Nickel	150
Selenium	750	Silver	70
Thalium	400	Tin	40
Vanadium	80	Zinc	20

Table 4-14. Chlorinated Acid Herbicide Target Analytes from Appendix II by Method 8151

Target Analyte	PQL µg/L	Target Analyte	PQL µg/L
2,4-D	10	Dinoseb	1
2,4,5-TP	2	2,4,5-T	2

Table 4-15. Miscellaneous Target Analytes from Appendix II

Target Analyte	PQL µg/L	Target Analyte	PQL µg/L
Cyanide	200	Mercury	2
Sulfide	4000		

III. UNDERGROUND STORAGE TANKS

There are a tremendous number of underground storage tanks (UST) used for a wide variety of purposes in the United States. The most common purpose is the storage of refined petroleum products for fuel at gas stations and other facilities. Many of these are leaking. The EPA oversees, and the states implement remediation of, the leaking underground storage tanks (LUST). There are a wide variety of analytical methods that are used to support these programs, almost as many as there are states.

The analytical challenge is two-fold. First, the petroleum analyte must be removed from the solid or water matrix and second, a qualitative and quantitative determination of the analyte is performed. Often the first is predetermined by the choice of the second.

The common methods for determination of the petroleum products are gas chromatography (GC) with a variety of detectors and infrared spectrophotometry (IR). Other far less common methods are gravimetric, immunoassay, and colorimetric. Traditional gas chromatographic analysis within the petroleum industry has concentrated upon characterization of the oil as to the boiling range (simulated distillation) and PONA (paraffins, olefins, naphthalenes and aromatics). Environmental qualitative determinations of petroleum range from characterization as oil & grease to geographic location of the origin of the petroleum. Total petroleum hydrocarbons (TPH), total benzene, toluene, ethylbenzene and xylene (BTEX), gasoline range organics; (GRO) and diesel range organics (DRO) are the most common requested determinations, although further classification as to gasoline, diesel, kerosene, aviation fuel, mineral spirits, etc. is sometimes requested. Additionally, the determination of oxygenates in the fuel is becoming more commonplace. These are ethanol, methyl *tert*-butyl ether (MTBE), methyl *tert*-amyl ether (TAME), or ethyl *tert*-butyl ether (ETBE). Other than ethanol, the oxygenates can be calibrated and run as target analytes using purge and trap GC or GC-MS. Ethanol is miscible with water and can most effectively be determined by direct injection into a GC-FID with either a Pora-Pac Q packed -column or a PLOT capillary column

The common extraction methods are liquid-liquid separatory funnel, continuous liquid-liquid extractor, soxhlet extractor, ultrasonic horn, ultrasonic bath, purge & trap, and headspace. Listed in Table 4-16 are some of the variety of analytical methods required for similar parameters from a random selection of State UST programs.

Table 4-16. Analytical Methods required for UST Characterizations from a random selection of State programs

State	Parameter	Approved Methods[13]
Missouri [14]	BTEX	8020 or 8240
	TRPH	418.1 modified to mix sample with anh. Na_2SO_4, pack into a column and elute in a single pass with 100 mL Freon-113
	Heavy metals	1311 (TCLP extraction)/6010
Mississippi[15]	BTEX	602, 624, 8020, 8240 or 8260
	TPH	418.1 or SM 503E
Texas[16]	BTEX + MTBE	5030/8020
	TPH (water)	418.1 or ASTM D-3328-78, method B (capillary column FID-GC) with samples and standard oil prepared as in 418.1
	TPH (soil)	Extraction by 3540 or 3550 with Freon, analysis as for water.
	TDS[17]	160.1

Continued on next page.

[13] All methods EPA unless otherwise indicated.

[14] Underground Storage Tank Closure Guidance Document, January 1992, Missouri Department of Natural Resources, Division of Environmental Quality, Water Pollution Control Program, P.O. Box 176 Jefferson City MO 65102.

[15] State of Mississippi Underground Storage Tank Program Sampling Policy for Petroleum Tank Closures, October, 1991, Mississippi Department of Environmental Quality, Office of Pollution Control P.O. Box 10385, Jackson, MS 39289-0385.

[16] *Guidance Manual for LPST Cleanups in Texas*, January 1990, Texas Water Commission, Petroleum Storage Tank Division, P.O. Box 13087, Austin, TX 78701.

[17] Remediation goal levels for benzene, BTEX and TPH depend on initial TDS values for the groundwater.

Table 4-16. Analytical Methods required for UST Characterizations from a random selection of State programs, *continued*

State	Parameter	Approved Methods[18]
Illinois[19]	BTEX	any appropriate method from SW-846
	PAH	any appropriate method from SW-846
	Metals	TCLP plus any appropriate method from SW-846
	BNA	any appropriate method from SW-846
	Pesticides	any appropriate method from SW-846
South Carolina[20,21]	BTEX + MTBE	602 or 5030/8020 for water, 5030/8020 for soil
	TPH gasoline	5030/FID-GC
	TPH diesel	3510/FID-GC for water, 3550/FID-GC for soil
	TPH waste oil	9070 with silica gel clean-up for water, 9071 with silica gel clean-up for soil.
	PAH (water)	610, 625, 3510/8100, 8270 or 8310
	PAH (soil)	3550/8100, 8270 or 8310
	Mercury (water)	245.1, 245.2, 7470 or 7471
	Mercury (soil)	7470 or 7471
	Metals	digestion followed by FLAA, GFAA or ICP
California[22]	TPH (TRPH)	SCL 418[23] for waters and 418 with Freon hand shake extraction of soil/sodium sulfate mixture
	TPH as gasoline (GRO) and BTEX	Headspace/FID-GC (SCL 818) or purge & trap/FID-GC (SCL 815) (methanol extraction of soils)
	TPH as diesel (DRO)	SCL 816, waters are extracted with Freon, soils are mixed with sodium sulfate and shaken with carbon disulfide, methylene choride or Freon, then analyzed by direct injection FID-GC
	Organolead	Extract with xylene then react with Aliquat336[24]/MIBK and I_2/benzene and analyze by FLAA for lead.

Continued on next page.

---

[18] All methods EPA unless otherwise indicated.

[19] *Leaking Underground Storage Tank Soil Sampling Requirements*, February 1993, Illinois Environmental Protection Agency, Bureau of Land, 2200 Churchill Road, Springfield, IL 62794-9276.

[20] *Petroleum Hydrocarbon Analytical Methology for Ground-water and Soil Assessment*, January, 21, 1992, South Carolina Department of Health and Environmental Control, Laboratory Certification Section, P.O. Box 72, State Park, SC 29147.

[21] "The laboratory may use an alternate analytical technique that has at least equivalent detection limits, precision, and accuracy as the referenced method, if approval is obtained from the GWPD prior to use. Use of alternate columns and gas chromatographic operating conditions is encouraged to obtain better sensitivity and quantitation of the contaminants of interest. Laboratories are also encouraged to develop new analytical techniques for identifying the type of contamination as well as the extent of contamination...EPA method 418.1 will not be used for TPH analyses conducted for groundwater and soil assessment."

[22] *Guidelines for Choosing the Proper Analytical Methods for TPH Analysis*, Rev. No. 1, February 3, 1992, State of California Department of Health Services, California Leaking Underground Fuel Tank Task Force, 2151 Berkeley Way, Berkeley, CA 94704-1011.

[23] Southern California Laboratory modification of EPA method 418.1.

[24] Tricapryl methyl ammonium chloride.

Table 4-16. Analytical Methods required for UST characterizations from a random selection of state programs, *continued*

State	Parameter	Approved Methods[25]
Tennessee[26]	GRO + BTEX	Purge & trap FID-GC or PID/FID-GC, high level soils extracted with methanol then a portion of the methanol is added to water and purged. Standards, calibration and surrogates are specific in the TN method.
	DRO	Waters are extracted by separatory funnel or continuous liquid-liquid extraction and soils by sonication, both with methylene chloride, analysis by FID-GC. Standards, calibration and surrogates are specific in the TN method.
Wisconsin[27]	GRO	Wisconsin modified GRO, all soils preserved in methanol, purge and trap FID-GC or PID/FID-GC
	DRO	Wisconsin modified DRO, soils extracted in VOA vial by sonication, waters extracted by 3010 or 3020, analysis by FID-GC
	VOC	5030/8021 or 8260
	PVOC	5030/8020, 8021 or 8260
	PAH	8310, 3540/8270, or 3550/8270
	PCB	3540 or 3550/8080 or 3510 or 3520/8080
	Lead	3020 or 3050/7420, 7421 or 6010
	Cadmium	3020 or 3050/7130, 7131 or 6010
	Cyanide	7.3.3.2 of SW-846
	Sulfide	7.3.4.2 of SW-846
	Free liquids	9095
	% moisture	7.3.3.1.5 of SW-846
	Oil & grease	413.1
	TSS	160.2
Florida[28]	BTEX	602, or 5030/8020
	1,2-Dichloroethane	601 or 5030/8010
	Total volatile aromatics	602 or 5030/8020
	Volatile halocarbons	601 or 5030/8010
	TPH	418.1 or 9073
	PAH	610, 625, 8100, 8250, 8270

Continued on next page.

---

[25] All methods EPA unless otherwise indicated.

[26] State of Tennessee Department of Environment and Conservation, Division of Underground Storage Tanks, 4th Floor L & C Tower, 401 Church St, Nashville, TN 37243-1541.

[27] *Leaking Underground Storage Tank (LUST) and Petroleum Analytical and Quality Assurance Guide*, July 1993, PUBL-SW-13093, Wisconsin Department of Natural Resources, P.O. Box 7921 Madison, WI 53707.

[28] Florida FAC Rule 17.770, 1993.

Table 4-16. Analytical Methods required for UST Characterizations from a random selection of State programs, *continued*

State	Parameter	Approved Methods[29]
New Mexico[30]	Gasoline	Field analysis of headspace in a 500 mL jar half full of soil with a PID or FID OVA.
		Laboratory analysis by 8240
	TPH	418.1 or prior approved equivalent method
Washington[31]	Identification	WTPH-HCID GC direct injection of methylene chloride extract of soils or water to identify petroleum fraction
	GRO	WTPH-G methanol extract of soil or direct water sample is purged into FID-GC. Trifluorotoluene and bromofluorobenzene surrogates, total envelope to dodecane quantitated
	DRO	WTPH-D 3510 for water and either 3540 or 3550 extraction for soils with methylene chloride followed by FID-GC. 2-Fluorobiphenyl and *o*- or *p*-terphenyl surrogates used and total envelope dodecane to tetracosane quantitated.
	TPH	WTPH-418.1 for heavy petroleum oils other than DRO or GRO. 3510 for water and either 3540 or 3550 with freon for soils
Arizona[32]	TPH-IR	Method BLS-181, 20 g soils are extracted by shaking 30 min with freon in a 40 mL VOA vial with sodium sulfate and silica gel. Aqueous samples are extracted with freon. 418.1 analysis at 2930 cm^{-1}.
	BTEX	Method BLS-191, 193, Soil is extracted with methanol (40 mL VOA vial), then extract or aqueous sample 5030/8015. Peak height quantitation. Surrogates are benzotrifluoride and bromochloropropane
	DRO	Method BLS-191, Freon or methylene chloride extraction of soil (40 mL VOA vial with sodium sulfate and silica gel) 10 mL extract conc. to 1.0 mL then 8015. All peaks C10 to C22 above baseline are integrated.
Alaska[33]	GRO	Method AK101.0 Purge and trap GC-FID or PID/FID or water samples or methanol extracts of soil samples, baseline integration of C6 to C10
	DRO	Method AK102.0 GC-FID analysis of methylene chloride extracts, baseline integration of C10 to C25
	Residual Range Organics RRO	Method AK103.0 GC-FID analysis of methylene chloride extracts, baseline integration from C25 to C45

IV. MONITORED NATURAL ATTENUATION

Natural attenuation is the stabilization/degradation/mineralization of environmental contaminants by natural processes, most commonly microbiologically mediated degradation. It has become a well recognized, and in some cases preferred, remediation process for certain restricted classes of contaminants. The lighter petroleum hydrocarbons such as benzene, toluene, ethyl benzene, and xylenes (BTEX), napthalene and the straight-chain hydrobarbons are easily degraded. The trimethyl benzenes (TMB),

---

[29] All methods EPA unless otherwise indicated.
[30] Underground Storage Tank Regulations, EIB/USTR State of New Mexico, amended 1990.
[31] Total Petroleum Hydrocarbons Analytical Methods for Soil and Water, Washington State Department of Ecology, April, 1992.
[32] Arizona Department of Health Services, State Laboratory Services.
[33] Alaska Department of Environmental Conservation, AS44.46.03.100(a)(17), December 1993.

heavier polycyclic aromatic hydrocarbons (PAH), branched alkanes, and cycloalkanes are recalcitrant. Some oxygenated materials such as methyl-*t*-butyl ether are easily degraded while 1,4-dioxane is inert. Attenuation of chlorinated solvents is compound and condition dependent.

Biologically mediated natural attenuation is essentially an reduction-oxidation reaction that has four requirements: an electron donor (reductant), a food (carbon) source, an electron acceptor (oxidant), and the microorganisms. Contaminants can be degraded as either electron donors or electron acceptors, depending on the compound and the conditions. Petroleum hydrocarbons are always degraded as electron donors and further serve as the food source. The most common electron acceptors, in order of oxidation-reduction potential (ORP) and efficiency are molecular oxygen (+820 mV), nitrate (+740 mV), iron +3 (-50 mV), sulfate (-220 mV), and carbon dioxide from the contaminant itself. The latter situation occurs with potentials less than -240 mV and the process is called methanogenesis, due to the production of methane as one of the final products. The dominant electron acceptor can be identified by the ORP reading.

Both aerobic and anaerobic processes have been well characterized. As the sub-surface contains only limited quantities of dissolved oxygen, aerobic degradation processes, although highly effective and efficient, are less important overall than the anaerobic processes.

Chlorinated solvents are more resistant to natural attenuation than the petroleum hydrocarbons. Perchloroethene (PCE), trichloroethene (TCE), dichloroethenes (DCE), chloroform, and carbon tetrachloride are degraded only under anaerobic, methanogenic conditions where they function as electron acceptors. This is called Type I attenuation. Vinyl chloride, a more toxic material, is the major end-product of the process. In certain cases gasoline or sugar solutions have been injected into the sub-surface environment to supply sufficient electron donors and food for satisfactory attenuation of PCE and TCE. Vinyl chloride, the chlorinated ethanes containing up to four chlorine atoms, and the mono-, di-, tri-, and tetrachlorobenzenes are resistant to methanogenic conditions, however are degraded as electron donors under aerobic conditions.

Remediations proposed and conducted under conditions of natural attenuation require substantial and continued analysis of the groundwater, both from within the contaminant plume and outside the plume as a background control. Some of the key references to natural attenuation are listed in Table 4-17, while Tables 4-18 and 4-19 present some of the analyses required and observed trends for different types of attenuation situations.

Table 4-17. References to Monitored Natural Attenuation

USAF, AFCEE, 1995	Technical protocol for implementing intrinsic remediation with long-term monitoring for natural attenuation of fuel contamination in groundwater
EPA, USAF, AFCEE, 1998	Technical protocol for evaluating natural attentuation of chlorinated solvents in ground water. EPA 600/R-98/128, September, 1998
USEPA, OSWER, 1997	Use of monitored natural attenuation at Superfund, RCRA Corrective Action, and UST sites. OSWER Directive 9200.4-17, 1 December, 1997
USEPA, 1997	Proceedings of the symposium on natural attenuation of chlorinated organics in ground water. EPA/540/R-97/504
USEPA, 1998	Seminars on monitored natural attenuation for ground water. EPA/625/K-98/001

Table 4-18. Analytical trends for petroleum hydrocarbon natural attentuation

Oxygen utilization	DO	decreases
	BTEX	decreases
	TMB (trimethylbenzene)	constant
	chloride	constant
	conductivity	constant or increase
	alkalinity	increases
Denitrification	nitrate	decreases
	BTEX	decreases
	TMB	constant
	chloride	constant
	conductivity	constant
	alkalinity	increases
Iron utilization	Fe(II)	increases
	BTEX	decreases
	TMB	constant
	conductivity	constant
	chloride	constant
	alkalinity	increases
Sulfate utilization	sulfate	decreases
	sulfide	increases
	BTEX	decreases
	TMB	constant
	conductivity	constant
	chloride	constant
	alkalinity	increases
Methanogenesis	(methane)	increases
	BTEX	decreases
	TBM	constant
	conductivity	constant
	chloride	constant
	alkalinity	constant

Table 4-19. Analytical trends for chlorinated solvent natural attenuation

Type 1	PCE, TCE	decreases
	Vinyl chloride	increases
	BTEX	decreases
	TMB	constant
	chloride	increases
	(methane)	increases
	alkalinity	increases
	(hydrogen)	increases, then constant
	ORP	< -240

Continued on next page.

Table 4-19. Analytical trends for chlorinated solvent natural attenuation, *continued*

Type 2	PCE, TCE	constant
	Vinyl chloride	decreases
	DCA, DCM	decreases
	DCB, TCB, TeCB	decreases
	BTEX	decreases
	TMB	constant
	chloride	increases
	(methane)	constant
	(hydrogen)	constant
	alkalinity	increases
	ORP	> +800
	DO	decreases

Consultants are under the impression, fostered by several seminars on Monitored Natural Attenuation presented by EPA during the Fall of 1998, that methane monitoring is a required analysis. As illustrated above, methane values can assist in making the decision whether or not methanogenesis is occurring, however they are not the sole indicator of the process. The more conclusive evidence is provided by the ORP reading and the reduction in concentrations of target analytes over time.

Another re-occurring observation from the laboratory point-of-view is that consultants engaged in a Natural Attenuation evaluation will take samples for all the parameters in jars and send them off to the lab for analysis. However there are several of the analytes that must be monitored on-site to provide reliable information. They include ORP, DO, conductivity, iron (II), pH, and methane. A flow-through sampling/analysis cell that provides for aeration-free monitoring is an absolute necessity. These are commercially available and come equipped with electrode probes for DO, conductivity, temperature, pH, and ORP. The methane must be immediately analyzed on-site with a field-portable GC. Iron (II) can be determined on-site with a simple colorimetric test and a battery powered colorimeter.

V. EPA CONTRACT LABORATORY PROGRAM

CLP and CLP deliverables are the magic buzz words among sales and promotion persons in the environmental business, despite there being very few CLP laboratories in the industry. The contract laboratory program exists so that the government and EPA will have sufficient laboratory capability to monitor the Superfund remediation projects authorized under CERCLA. The CLP is not a laboratory certification program. The only CLP laboratories are those holding current contracts with the EPA under the most recent bid and accepted Statement of Work (SOW). Copies of the most recent CLP SOW are available from NTIS. Contact with the program is through the CLP technical project officer (TPO) at each of the EPA regional headquarters. Having an EPA contract under the CLP is predicated upon having the required number and types of instruments and technicians to perform the work as specified in the SOW, passing a set of PE samples related to the SOW, passing an on-site audit by the EPA, being able to produce all the required forms and documents related to the analysis as specified in the SOW in both hardcopy and electronic media (the deliverables), and finally being one of the low bidders for the current contract period.

The Statements of Work are not so much written toward producing the best data possible, but rather producing comparable data from a variety of laboratories of known quality that is legally defensible. Further there is distinct slant in the methods toward identification of what is possibly on the site, rather than rigorous quantitation of a select set of regulated analytes. Work undertaken by the EPA under CERCLA and supported by CLP laboratories is totally oriented toward litigation against the offending parties, thus all laboratory results must be ready for court challenge.

Two general SOWs are bid – the organic and the inorganic – and both exist in low-concentration, multi-concentration, and high-concentration versions. A SOW for dioxins is available. A SOW for air analysis exists in draft form, as does a Quick Turnaround SOW. The organic SOW contains methods and specifications for volatiles, semivolatiles, and pesticides/aroclors modeled after methods 8260, 8270 and 8080 respectfully. The inorganic multi-concentration SOW covers specifications for 22 metals, mercury, and cyanide, while the high-concentration version adds pH and conductivity to the analytes. The organic analytes are specified in the Target Compound List (TCL), while the inorganic analytes are specified in the Target Analyte List (TAL).

In addition to the TCL compounds the organic SOW requires reporting of tentatively identified compounds (TIC). These are components that are at least 10% of the response of the nearest internal standard and are searched against the mass spectral library for possible matches. The contractor must examine the 30 largest peaks in the volatile run for TIC and the 30 largest peaks in each extractable run that fit the criteria. If no match is found in the library, the peak is reported as unknown.

Table 4-20. CLP[34] Inorganic Target Analyte List (TAL) for metals

Analyte	Method[35]	CRQL[36] µg/L
Aluminum	200.7	200
Antimony	200.7, 204.2	60
Arsenic	200.7, 206.2	10
Barium	200.7	200
Beryllium	200.7, 210.2	5
Cadmium	200.7, 213.2	5
Calcium	200.7, 215.1	5000
Chromium	200.7, 218.2	10
Cobalt	200.7	50
Copper	200.7	25

Continued on next page.

---

[34] CLP-SOW ILM03

[35] All of these methods are modified for the CLP-SOW and are found in Exhibit D, ILM03.0.

[36] The CRDLs are the instrument detection limits obtained in pure water that must be met using the procedure in Exhibit E, ILM03.0. The detection limits for samples may be considerably higher, depending on the sample matrix.

Table 4-20. CLP[37] Inorganic Target Analyte List (TAL) for metals, *continued*

Analyte	Method[38]	CRQL[39] µg/L
Iron	200.7	100
Lead	200.7, 239.2	3
Magnesium	200.7, 242.1	5000
Manganese	200.7	15
Mercury	245.1, 245.2, 245.5	0.2
Nickel	200.7	40
Potassium	200.7, 258.1	5000
Selenium	200.7, 270.2	5
Silver	200.7, 272.2	10
Sodium	200.7, 273.1	5000
Thallium	200.7, 279.2	10
Vanadium	200.7	50
Zinc	200.7	20
Cyanide	335.2	10

Table 4-21. CLP Forms included as deliverables with each sample for metals

Form	Title
I-IN	Inorganic Analysis Data Sheet
II(Part 1)-IN	Initial and Continuing Calibration Verification
II(Part 2)-IN	CRDL Standard for AA and ICP
III-IN	Blanks
IV-IN	ICP Interference Check Sample
V(Part 1)-IN	Spike Sample Recovery
V(Part 2)-IN	Post Digest Spike Sample Recovery
VI-IN	Duplicates
VII-IN	Laboratory Control Sample
VIII-IN	Standard Addition Results
IX-IN	ICP Serial Dilutions
X-IN	Instrument Detection Limits (Quarterly)
XI(Part 1)-IN	ICP Interelement Correction Factors (Annually)
XI(Part 2)-IN	ICP Interelement Correction Factors (Annually)
XII-IN	ICP Linear Ranges (Quarterly)
XIII-IN	Preparation Log
XIV-IN	Analysis Run Log

---

[37] CLP-SOW ILM03

[38] All of these methods are modified for the CLP-SOW and are found in Exhibit D, ILM03.0.

[39] The CRDLs are the instrument detection limits obtained in pure water that must be met using the procedure in Exhibit E, ILM03.0. The detection limits for samples may be considerably higher, depending on the sample matrix.

Table 4-22. CLP VOA Target Compound List (TCL)[40]

Analyte	CAS	CRQL Water μg/L	CRQL Soil μg/kg
Chloromethane	74-87-3	10	10
Bromomethane	74-83-9	10	10
Vinyl chloride	75-01-4	10	10
Chloroethane	75-00-3	10	10
Methylene chloride	75-09-2	10	10
Acetone	67-64-1	10	10
Carbon disulfide	75-15-0	10	10
1,1-Dichloroethene	75-35-4	10	10
1,1-Dichloroethane	75-34-3	10	10
1,2-Dichloroethene	540-59-0	10	10
Chloroform	67-66-3	10	10
1,2-Dichloroethane	107-06-2	10	10
2-Butanone	78-93-3	10	10
1,1,1-Trichloroethane	71-55-6	10	10
Carbon tetrachloride	56-23-5	10	10
Bromodichloromethane	75-27-4	10	10
1,2-Dichloropropane	78-87-5	10	10
cis-1,3-Dichloropropane	10061-01-5	10	10
Trichloroethene	79-01-6	10	10
Dibromochloromethane	124-48-1	10	10
1,1,2-Trichloroethane	79-00-5	10	10
Benzene	71-43-2	10	10
trans-1,3-Dichloropropene	10061-02-6	10	10
Bromoform	75-25-2	10	10
4-Methyl-2-pentanone	108-10-1	10	10
2-Hexanone	591-78-6	10	10
Tetrachloroethene	127-18-4	10	10
1,1,2,2-Tetrachloroethane	79-34-5	10	10
Toluene	108-88-3	10	10
Chlorobenzene	108-90-7	10	10
Ethylbenzene	100-41-4	10	10
Styrene	100-42-5	10	10
Xylenes (total)	1330-20-7	10	10

40 CLP-SOW OLM02.1, 1993.

Table 4-23. CLP Forms included as deliverables with each sample for VOA

Form	Title
I VOA	Volatile Organics Analysis Data Sheet
I VOA-TIC	Volatile Organics Analysis Data Sheet Tentatively Identified Compounds
II VOA-1	Water Volatile System Monitoring Compound Recovery
II VOA-2	Soil Volatile System Monitoring Compound Recovery
III VOA-1	Water Volatile Matrix Spike/Matrix Spike Duplicate Recovery
III VOA-2	Soil Volatile Matrix Spike/Matrix Spike Duplicate Recovery
IV VOA	Volatile Method Blank Summary
V VOA	Volatile Organic Instrument Performance Check Bromofluorobenzene (BFB)
VI VOA	Volatile Organics Initial Calibration Data
VII VOA	Volatile Continuing Calibration Check
VIII VOA	Volatile Internal Standard Area and RT Summary

Table 4-24. CLP Target Analyte List (TCL) for Semivolatile Organic Compounds[41]

Analyte	CAS	CRQL Water μg/L	CRQL Soil μg/kg
Phenol	108-95-2	10	330
Bis(2-Chloroethyl)ether	111-44-4	10	330
2-Chlorophenol	95-57-8	10	330
1,3-Dichlorobenzene	541-73-1	10	330
1,4-Dichlorobenzene	106-46-7	10	330
1,2-Dichlorobenzene	95-50-1	10	330
2-Methylphenol	95-48-7	10	330
2,2'-oxybis(1-Chloropropane)	108-60-1	10	330
4-Methylphenol	106-44-5	10	330
N-Nitroso-di-n-propylamine	621-64-7	10	330
Hexachloroethane	67-72-1	10	330
Nitrobenzene	98-95-3	10	330
Isophorone	78-59-1	10	330
2-Nitrophenol	88-75-5	10	330
2,4-Dimethylphenol	105-67-9	10	330
Bis(2-Chloroethoxy)methane	111-91-1	10	330
2,4-Dichlorophenol	120-83-2	10	330
1,2,4-Trichlorobenzene	120-82-1	10	330
Naphthalene	91-20-3	10	330
4-Chloroaniline	106-47-8	10	330
Hexachlorobutadiene	87-68-3	10	330
4-Chloro-3-methylphenol	59-50-7	10	330
2-Methylnaphthalene	91-57-6	10	330
Hexachlorocyclopentadiene	77-47-4	10	330
2,4,6-Trichlorophenol	88-06-2	10	330
2,4,5-Trichlorophenol	95-95-4	25	830

Continued on next page.

---

[41] CLP-SOW OLM02.1, 1993

Table 4-24. CLP Target Analyte List (TCL) for Semivolatile Organic Compounds[42], *continued*

Analyte	CAS	CRQL Water µg/L	CRQL Soil µg/kg
2-Chloronaphthalene	91-58-7	10	330
2-Nitroaniline	88-74-4	25	830
Dimethylphthalate	131-11-3	10	330
Acenaphthylene	208-96-8	10	330
2,6-Dinitrotoluene	606-20-2	10	330
3-Nitroaniline	99-09-2	25	830
Acenaphthene	83-32-9	10	330
2,4-Dinitrophenol	51-28-5	25	830
4-Nitrophenol	100-02-7	25	830
Dibenzofuran	132-64-9	10	330
2,4-Dinitrotoluene	121-14-2	10	330
Diethylphthalate	84-66-2	10	330
4-Chlorophenylphenylether	7005-72-3	10	330
Fluorene	86-73-7	10	330
4-Nitroaniline	100-01-6	25	830
4,6-Dinitro-2-methylphenol	534-52-1	25	830
N-Nitroso-diphenylamine	86-30-6	10	330
4-Bromophenylphenylether	101-55-3	10	330
Hexachlorobenzene	118-74-1	10	330
Pentachlorophenol	87-86-5	25	830
Phenanthrene	85-01-8	10	330
Anthracene	120-12-7	10	330
Carbazole	86-74-8	10	330
Di-n-butylphthalate	84-74-2	10	330
Fluoranthene	206-44-0	10	330
Pyrene	129-00-0	10	330
Butylbenzylphthalate	85-68-7	10	330
3,3'-Dichlorobenzidine	91-94-1	10	330
Benzo(a)anthracene	56-55-3	10	330
Chrysene	218-01-9	10	330
Bis(2-Ethylhexyl)phthalate	117-81-7	10	330
Di-n-octylphthalate	117-84-0	10	330
Benzo(b)fluoranthene	205-99-2	10	330
Benzo(k)fluoranthene	207-08-9	10	330
Benzo(a)pyrene	50-32-8	10	330
Indeno(1,2,3-cd)pyrene	193-39-5	10	330
Dibenzo(a,h)anthracene	53-70-3	10	330
Benzo(g,h,i)perylene	191-24-2	10	330

---

[42] CLP-SOW OLM02.1, 1993

Table 4-25. CLP Forms included as deliverables with each sample for Semivolatile Organic Compounds

Form	Title
I SV-1	Semivolatiles Organics Analysis Data Sheet
I SV-2	Semivolatiles Organics Analysis Data Sheet (page 2)
I SV-TIC	Semivolatile Organics Analysis Data Sheet Tentatively Identified Compounds
II SV-1	Water Semivolatile Surrogate Recovery
II SV-2	Soil Semivolatile Surrogate Recovery
III SV-1	Water Semivolatile Matrix Spike/Matrix Spike Duplicate Recovery
III SV-2	Soil Semivolatile Matrix Spike/Matrix Spike Duplicate Recovery
IV SV	Semivolatile Method Blank Summary
V SV	Semivolatile Organic Instrument Performance Check Decafluorotriphenylphosphine (DFTPP)
VI SV-1 & 2	Semivolatile Organics Initial Calibration Data
VII SV-1 & 2	Semivolatile Continuing Calibration Check
VIII SV-1 & 2	Semivolatile Internal Standard Area and RT Summary

Table 4-26. CLP Pesticide/Aroclor Target Compound List (TCL)[43]

Analyte	CAS	CRQL Water µg/L	CRQL Soil µg/kg
α-BHC	319-84-6	0.050	1.7
β-BHC	319-85-7	0.050	1.7
δ-BHC	319-86-8	0.050	1.7
γ-BHC (Lindane)	58-89-9	0.050	1.7
Heptachlor	76-44-8	0.050	1.7
Aldrin	309-00-2	0.050	1.7
Heptachlor epoxide	111024-57-3	0.050	1.7
Endosulfan I	959-98-8	0.050	1.7
Dieldrin	60-57-1	0.10	3.3
4,4'-DDE	72-55-9	0.10	3.3
Endrin	72-20-8	0.10	3.3
Endosulfan II	33213-65-9	0.10	3.3
4,4'-DDD	72-54-8	0.10	3.3
Endosulfan sulfate	1031-07-8	0.10	3.3
4,4'-DDT	50-29-3	0.10	3.3
Methoxychlor	72-43-5	0.50	17
Endrin ketone	53494-70-5	0.10	3.3
Endrin aldehyde	7421-93-4	0.10	3.3
α-Chlordane	5103-71-9	0.050	1.7
γ-Chlordane	5103-74-2	0.050	1.7
Toxaphene	8001-35-2	5.0	170
Aroclor-1016	12674-11-2	1.0	33

Continued on next page.

[43] CLP-SOW OLM02.1, 1993

Table 4-26. CLP Pesticide/Aroclor Target Compound List (TCL)[44] , *continued*

Analyte	CAS	CRQL Water µg/L	CRQL Soil µg/kg
Aroclor-1221	11104-28-2	2.0	67
Aroclor-1232	11141-16-5	1.0	33
Aroclor-1242	53469-21-9	1.0	33
Aroclor-1248	12672-29-6	1.0	33
Aroclor-1254	11097-69-1	1.0	33
Aroclor-1260	11096-82-5	1.0	33

Table 4-27. CLP Forms included as deliverables with each sample for Pesticide/Aroclor

Form	Title
I PEST	Pesticide Organics Analysis Data Sheet
II PEST-1	Water Pesticide Surrogate Recovery
II PEST-2	Soil Pesticide Surrogate Recovery
III PEST-1	Water Pesticide Matrix Spike/Matrix Spike Duplicate Recovery
III PEST-2	Soil Pesticide Matrix Spike/Matrix Spike Duplicate Recovery
IV PEST	Pesticide Method Blank Summary
VI PEST-1	Pesticide Initial Calibration of Single Component Analytes (RT Data)
VI PEST-2	Pesticide Initial Calibration of Single Component Analytes (Calibration Factor Data)
VI PEST-3	Pesticide Initial Calibration of Multicomponent Analytes
VI PEST-4	Pesticide Analyte Resolution Summary
VI PEST-5	Performance Evaluation Mixture
VI PEST-6	Individual Standard Mixture A
VI PEST-7	Individual Standard Mixture B
VII PEST-1	Pesticide Calibration Verification Summary (Breakdown Summary)
VII PEST-2	Pesticide Calibration Verification Summary (Mixtures A & B Summary)
VIII PEST	Pesticide Analytical Sequence
IX PEST-1	Pesticide Florisil Cartridge Check
IX PEST-2	Pesticide GPC Calibration
X PEST-1	Pesticide Identification Summary for Single Component Analytes
X PEST-2	Pesticide Identification Summary for Multicomponent Analytes

The CLP deliverables for each sample for organics analysis consist of CLP Form DC-1 (Sample Log-in Sheet), DC-2-1 through DC-2-5 (Organics Complete SDG File [CSF] Inventory Sheet), SDG Case Narrative, SDG Cover Sheet/Traffic Report and the specific forms in Tables 4-23, 4-25, and 4-27, depending on the type of sample and exact analysis required. Additional information in the deliverable package for VOA includes the reconstructed ion chromatogram (RIC) for the sample, raw spectra and background-subtracted mass spectra of target compounds identified, quantitation reports, mass spectra of all reported TICs with three best library matches, RICs and Quan reports for all standards for both initial and continuing calibrations, and finally raw QC data for BFB, blanks, and MS/MSD. Semivolatile data packages consist of the same material required for VOA samples with the substitution of DFTPP tune data for BFB tune data

[44] CLP-SOW OLM02.1, 1993

and the addition of GPC calibration data-UV detector traces, raw GPC data and GPC chromatograms. Pesticide analyses have copies of the chromatograms from the primary and secondary columns, GC integration report or data system printout, manual work sheets, calibration chromatograms and data system printouts, calibration printouts of retention times and corresponding peak areas or peak heights, GPC calibration data-UV detector traces, and raw QC data concerning blanks, MS/MSD, GPC and Florisil clean-up. If the pesticide/PCB is confirmed by GC/MS, copies of raw spectra and copies of background-subtracted mass spectra of target compounds (samples and standards) must be included. Miscellaneous data in the sample package include copies of preparation and analysis logbook pages, internal sample and sample extract transfer chain-of-custody records, screening records, all instrument output from screening activities, airbills, chain-of-custody records, sample tags, sample log-in sheet, other shipping/receiving records, internal lab sample transfer records and tracking sheets, and telephone communication log.

Data in the organic reports are qualified by data flags. These are commonly used throughout the remediation business and have the following meanings as described in Tables 4-28 through 4-31.

Table 4-28. Laboratory flags for organic data

Flag	Use
U	Compound was a target analyte but was not detected.
J	Reported value is estimated. This could arise because the compound is a TIC and was not calibrated or the compound was detected at a level less than the CRQL.
N	Applied to all TICs when a definitive compound is reported. Not used for generic descriptions of TICs such as "chlorinated hydrocarbon".
NJ	Applied to TICs when an estimated amount has been determined for a definitive compound.
P	Used for Pesticide/PCB target analytes when more than 25% difference in quantitation exists between the two columns. The lower of the 2 values is reported and flagged.
C	Used for Pesticide/PCB target analytes when the presence is confirmed by GC-MS.
B	Used when the reported target analyte or TIC is also found in the blank.
E	Used for target analytes when the reported value exceeds the upper limit of the calibration curve.
D	Used to indicate that the value for the analyte was obtained from a diluted re-analysis. Separate Form I are used for original analysis and diluted re-analysis. All results on the diluted Form I will be flagged with a D.
A	Used to indicate that the reported TIC is a suspected aldol condensation product.
X, Y, Z	Laboratory defined flags.

Table 4-29. Data Reviewer flags for organic data

Flag	Use
U	Compound was a target analyte but was not detected.
J	Reported value is estimated. This could arise because the compound is a TIC and was not calibrated or the compound was detected at a level less than the CRQL.
N	Applied to all TICs when a definitive compound is reported. Not used for generic descriptions of TICs such as "chlorinated hydrocarbon".
NJ	Applied to TICs when an estimated amount has been determined for a definitive compound.
R	Sample results are rejected due to a serious deficiency in the ability to analyze the sample and meet quality control criteria. The presence or absence of the target analyte can not be verified.
UJ	The analyte was not detected at the stated quantitation limit, however the value is an estimate and may be inaccurate or imprecise.

Table 4-30. Laboratory flags for inorganic data. The fields are Concentration(C), Qualifier(Q) and Method(M)

Field	Flag	Use
C	B	The reported value was obtained from a reading that was less than the CRDL but greater than or equal to the IDL.
	U	Target analyte was not detected.
Q	E	Estimated value
	M	Duplicate injection precision was not met.
	N	Spiked sample recovery was not within control limits.
	S	Reported value determined by method of standard additions (MSA).
	W	Post digestion spike for graphite furnace AA analysis is out of control limits and sample absorbance is less than 50% of spike absorbance.
	*	Duplicate analysis is not within control limits.
	+	Correlation coefficient for MSA is less than 0.995.
M	P	ICP-AES
	A	Flame AA
	F	Furnace AA
	M	Microwave digestion.
	CV	Manual cold vapor AA
	AV	Automated cold vapor AA
	CA	Midi-distillation spectrophotometric
	AS	Semi-automated spectrophotometric
	C	Manual spectrophotometric
	T	Titrimetric
	NR	Analyte is not required to be analyzed.

Table 4-31. Data Reviewer flags for inorganic data

Flag	Use
U	Compound was a target analyte but was not detected.
J	Reported value is estimated. This could arise because the compound was detected at a level less than the CRQL.
R	Sample results are rejected due to a serious deficiency in the ability to analyze the sample and meet quality control criteria. The presence or absence of the target analyte cannot be verified.
UJ	The analyte was not detected at the stated quantitation limit, however the value is an estimate and may be inaccurate or imprecise.

The CLP deliverables for inorganic sample analysis consist of Form DC-2 (Full Inorganics Complete SDG File [CSF] Inventory Sheet), a cover page and the complete set of Inorganics forms listed in Table 4-21. In addition, ICP raw data, GFAA raw data, mercury raw data, cyanide raw data, preparation logs raw data, percent solids determination log, traffic report, shipping/receiving documents (airbill, chain-of-custody records, sample tags, lab and DCI sample log-in sheets, and SDG cover sheet), internal lab sample transfer records and tracking sheets, internal original sample prep and analysis records (prep records, analysis records, and others), telephone communication log, and any other miscellaneous documents must be included.

Evaluation of the data provided by the contract laboratory is guided by two EPA documents. The first is *USEPA Contract Laboratory Program National Functional Guidelines for Inorganic Data Review* (EPA-540/R-94/013, PB94-963502), and the second is *USEPA Contract Laboratory National Functional Guidelines for Organic Data Review* (EPA-540/R-94/012, PB94-963501). Both of these are available from NTIS. These guides are very well written and embody a considerable amount of common sense. They can be used for evaluation of any data and should be part of the reference material of any QA department.

A laboratory that submits a bid under a CLP SOW does so for a set maximum number of samples during a specified time period. Each type of sample has contract-specified maximum holding times before the sample preparation and the sample analysis parts of the procedure are accomplished. CLP laboratories tend to have cyclical business; when they have a contract they feast, otherwise it's famine with high overhead. Where laboratories get into trouble is giving in to the temptation of bidding at the maximum sample capacity of the laboratory based on a required minimum number of instruments in the lab. Murphy's Law always holds (Unexpected difficulties always arise at the most inopportune times.), and the laboratory is suddenly faced with too many samples and not enough people or instrument time to meet the holding times. Rather than give the samples back to the agency and not win the next contract, some laboratories have submitted backdated results to appear to meet holding times. When the deception is discovered by the EPA during the next audit, the responsible persons have been prosecuted and awarded jail time instead of the next contract.

VI. OTHER GOVERMENT CONTRACT AGENCIES

Other government agencies, besides the EPA, contract out analytical work. These include the Department of Energy (DOE) Hazardous Wastes Remediation Actions Program (HAZWRAP, administered by Lockheed-Martin), the Department of Defense (DOD), the U.S. Army Corps of Engineers (USACE), the U.S. Army Environmental Center Agency (USAEC formerly USATHAMA), the U.S. Navy Environmental

Energy Support Activity (NEESA), the U.S. Air Force Center for Environmental Excellence (AFCEE), and NASA to name but a few. All of these organizations have just as strict laboratory validation requirements as the EPA CLP, but none have the glamour...or the notoriety.

Direct access to these government contracts is limited to engineering firms (often referred to as "prime contractor" or simply "primes") that submit bids for remediation services. Candidate laboratories are nominated/sponsored by the engineering firm as a subcontractor for analytical services. The laboratories are certified/validated by the government contractor based on an evaluation of the QA manual, performance of PE samples, and, finally, an on-site visit.

The Corps of Engineers has the most developed laboratory validation program of the Department of Defense agencies. The program is detailed in *Validation of Analytical Chemistry Laboratories*, publication EM-200-1-1, 1 July, 1994.

Examples of the TCL and TAL for U.S. Army Corps of Engineers contracts are presented in Tables 4-32 through 4-35. Although largely based on the related lists from the CLP, there are differences. In the volatile TCL the USACE has added vinyl acetate and 2-chloroethylvinyl ether as analytes while dropping 1,1,2-trichloroethane. In the semi-volatile TCL benzoic acid and benzyl alcohol are added, and carbazole is dropped. In the pesticide/PCB TCL technical chlordane replaces alpha- and gamma-chlordane, and endrin ketone is dropped. USACE also specifies a number of anions (chloride, fluoride, bromide, nitrate, nitrite, phosphate and sulfate) on the inorganic TAL, which are performed by either ion chromatography (EPA Method 300.0) or standard wet chemical methods. Other contracted analyses of USACE include dioxins, explosives residues, chemical warfare agent residues, and chlorinated acid herbicides. Required detection levels for the various analytes and matrices are often job specific but in general water analyses, especially groundwater samples, require drinking water detection limits.

Table 4-32. USACE VOA Target Compound List (TCL)[45]

Chloromethane	Bromomethane	Vinyl chloride
Chloroethane	Methylene chloride	Acetone
Carbon disulfide	1,1-Dichloroethene	1,1-Dichloroethane
1,2-Dichloroethene	Chloroform	1,2-Dichloroethane
2-Butanone	1,1,1-Trichloroethane	Carbon tetrachloride
Vinyl acetate	Bromodichloromethane	1,2-Dichloropropane
cis-1,3-Dichloropropene	Trichloroethene	Dibromochloromethane
Benzene	*trans*-1,3-Dichloropropene	Bromoform
2-Chloroethylvinylether	4-Methyl-2-pentanone	2-Hexanone
Tetrachloroethene	Toluene	1,1,2,2-Tetrachloroethane
Chlorobenzene	Ethyl benzene	Styrene
Xylenes (total)		

---

[45] Table D-4, USACE ER 1110-1-263.

Table 4-33. USACE BNA Semi-volatile Target Compound List (TCL)[46]

Phenol	Bis(2-chloroethyl)ether	2-Chlorophenol
1,3-Dichlorobenzene	1,4-Dichlorobenzene	Benzyl alcohol
1,2-Dichlorobenzene	2-Methylphenol	Bis(2-chloroisopropyl)ether
4-Methylphenol	N-Nitroso-di-n-propylamine	Hexachloroethane
Nitrobenzene	Isophorone	2-Nitrophenol
2,4-Dimethylphenol	Benzoic acid	Bis(2-chloroethoxy)methane
2,4-Dichlorophenol	1,2,4-Trichlorobenzene	Naphthalene
4-Chloroaniline	Hexachlorobutadiene	4-Chloro-3-methylphenol
2-Methylnaphthalene	Hexachlorocyclopentadiene	2,4,6-Trichlorophenol
2,4,5-Trichlorophenol	2-Chloronaphthalene	2-Nitroaniline
Dimethylphthalate	Acenaphthylene	2,6-Dinitrotoluene
3-Nitroaniline	Acenaphthene	2,4-Dinitrophenol
4-Nitrophenol	Dibenzofuran	2,4-Dinitrotoluene
Diethylphthalate	4-Chlorophenylphenyl ether	Fluorene
4-Nitroaniline	4,6-Dinitro-2-methylphenol	N-Nitrosodiphenylamine
4-Bromophenylphenyl ether	Hexachlorobenzene	Pentachlorophenol
Phenanthrene	Anthracene	Di-n-butylphthalate
Fluoranthene	Pyrene	Butylbenzylphthalate
3,3'-Dichlorobenzidine	Benzo(a)anthracene	Chrysene
Bis(2-ethylhexyl)phthalate	Di-n-octylphthalate	Benzo(b)fluoranthene
Benzo(k)fluoranthene	Benzo(a)pyrene	Indeno(123cd)pyrene
Dibenzo(ah)anthracene	Benzo(ghi)perylene	

Table 4-34. USACE Pesticide/PCB Target Compound List (TCL)[47]

Aldrin	α-BHC	β-BHC
δ-BHC	γ-BHC (Lindane)	Chlordane
4,4'-DDD	4,4'-DDE	4,4'-DDT
Dieldrin	Endosulfan I	Endosulfan II
Endosulfan sulfate	Endrin	Endrin aldehyde
Heptachlor	Heptachlor epoxide	Methoxychlor
Toxaphene	Aroclor-1016	Aroclor-1221
Aroclor-1232	Aroclor-1242	Aroclor-1248
Aroclor-1254	Aroclor-1260	

---

[46] Table D-5, USACE ER 1110-1-263.
[47] Table D-6, USACE ER 1110-1-263.

Table 4-35. Target Analyte List (TAL) for metals under USACE[48]

Metal	Technique[49]	Soil/Sediment	Groundwater[50]	Surface Water
Antimony	DA	CLP[51]//7040	3005/7040	204.1
	GF	CLP/7041	3020/7041	204.2
	ICP	CLP/6010	3005/6010	200.7
Arsenic	GF	3050/7060	7060	206.2
	H	7061	7061	206.3
Barium	DA	3050/7080	3005/7080	208.1
	GF	3050/7081	3020/7081	208.2
	ICP	3050/6010	3005/6010	200.7
Beryllium	DA	3050/7090	3005/7090	210.1
	GF	3050/7091	3020/7091	210.2
	ICP	3050/6010	3005/6010	200.7
Cadmium	DA	3050/7130	3005/7130	213.1
	GF	3050/7131	3020/7131	213.2
	ICP	3050/6010	3005/6010	200.7
Calcium	DA	3050/7140	3005/7140	215.1
	ICP	3050/6010	3005/6010	200.7
Chromium	DA	3050/7190	3005/7190	218.1
	GF	3050/7191	3020/7191	218.2
	ICP	3050/6010	3005/6010	200.7
Copper	DA	3050/7210	3005/7210	220.1
	GF	3050/7211	3020/7211	220.2
	ICP	3050/6010	3005/6010	200.7
Iron	DA	3050/7380	3005/7380	236.1
	GF	3050/7381	3020/7381	236.2
	ICP	3050/6010	3005/6010	200.7
Lead	DA	3050/7420	3005/7420	239.1
	GF	3050/7421	3020/7421	239.2
	ICP	3050/6010	3005/6010	200.7
Manganese	DA	3050/7460	3005/7460	243.1
	GF	3050/7461	3020/7461	243.2
	ICP	3050/6010	3005/6010	200.7
Mercury	CV	7471	7470	245.1
Nickel	DA	3050/7520	3005/7520	249.1
	GF	-	-	249.2
	ICP	3050/6010	3005/6010	200.7

Continued on next page.

---

[48] Table D-2, USACE ER 1110-1-263, 1 Oct. 90. Engineering and Design Chemical Data Quality Management for Hazardous Waste Remediation Activities.

[49] DA = Direct Aspiration; GF = Graphite Furnace; H = Hydride; CV = Cold Vapor; ICP = Inductively Coupled Plasma

[50] Any water sample may be analyzed by the groundwater techniques. Groundwater samples must be analyzed by these techniques. Surface water and other water samples may be analyzed by the 200-series or SW-846 methods.

[51] Follow CLP sample preparation guidance. Existing data in SW-846 is inadequate.

Table 4-35. Target Analyte List (TAL) for metals under USACE[52], *continued*

Metal	Technique[53]	Soil/Sediment	Groundwater[54]	Surface Water
Selenium	GF	3050/7740	7740	270.2
	H	7741	7741	270.3
Silver	DA	3050/7760	7760	272.1
	GF	3050/7761	7761	272.2
	ICP	3050/6010	3005/6010	200.7
Sodium	DA	3050/7770	3005/7770	273.1
	GF	-	-	273.2
	ICP	3050/6010	3005/6010	200.7
Thallium	DA	3050/7840	3005/7840	279.1
	GF	3050/7841	3020/7841	279.2
	ICP	3050/6010	3005/6010	200.7
Zinc	DA	3050/7950	3005/7950	289.1
	GF	3050/7951	3020/7951	289.2
	ICP	3050/6010	3005/6010	200.7

Beginning with USACE PE samples in 1994, aluminum, cobalt, magnesium, potassium, and vanadium were included as target analytes. With the addition of these TAL metals the USACE list is identical to that of the most recent CLP-SOW for inorganics (ILM03).

The USACE developed and began distributing in December, 1998 a document for data evaluation. This is called "Shell for Analytical Chemistry Requirements" and includes information on the laboratory QA program in addition to contractor data review guidelines. It is available from the Validation Coordinator, USACE MRD, Omaha NE 402-697-2569.

The Corps of Engineers is responsible for the development and maintenance of the nation's waterways. The dredging of harbors and other shipping areas generates tremendous volumes of solid material that is normally disposed in open water. The EPA and the USACE have published two manuals for the evaluation of the dredged materials prior to disposal. They are *Ecological Evaluation of Proposed Discharge of Dredged Materials into Ocean Waters* (the Green Book), and *Evaluation of Dredged Material Proposed for Discharge in Waters of the US -Testing Manual* (EPA 823-B-98-004, the Inland Testing Manual). The bulk of the testing described in the manuals is for direct determination of sediment toxicity and toxicity impact of sediments on water columns. Both manuals are available at the EPA Website (www.epa.gov/ost)

Other government programs defer specifically to the CLP methods, analyte lists and reporting forms. The HAZWRAP is somewhat unique in having 5 different reporting and methodology levels, depending on the exact project.

---

[52] Table D-2, USACE ER 1110-1-263, 1 Oct. 90. Engineering and Design Chemical Data Quality Management for Hazardous Waste Remediation Activities.

[53] DA = Direct Aspiration; GF = Graphite Furnace; H = Hydride; CV = Cold Vapor; ICP = Inductively Coupled Plasma

[54] Any water sample may be analyzed by the groundwater techniques. Groundwater samples must be analyzed by these techniques. Surface water and other water samples may be analyzed by the 200-series or SW-846 methods.

Level A - Qualitative or semiquantitative analysis, indicator parameters, immediate response in the field. Requires no formal final report; the only deliverables are sample results. The daily single point calibration must be kept on file.

Level B - Semiquantitative or quantitative analysis, compound specific, rapid turnaround in the field. Deliverables include sample results, method blanks, three-point calibration, and continuing calibration checks.

Level C - Quantitative analysis with technically defensible data on major remediation sites or site near populated areas. See Table 4-36 for deliverables.

Level D - Quantitative analysis with legally defensible data from sites on the National Priorities List or sites near populated areas that are likely to be litigated. A full CLP data package is required. Deliverables include the summary package and remainder of the data package, including initial and continuing calibration, matrix spikes, matrix spike duplicates, blanks, duplicates, surrogate recoveries, chromatograms, mass spectra, and absorbance data. For methods not defined by the CLP, calibration information, method blanks, blank/spikes, chromatograms, absorbance, matrix spikes, and matrix spike duplicates are reported. Plotted control charts associated with the LCS are presented with the data.

Level E - Qualitative to quantitative analysis that is non-standard method specific to unique matrices (pure waste, air, biota, explosives, etc.). May involve method development along with determination of precision and accuracy. The minimum information to be submitted includes: sample results, method blank data, initial and continuing calibration data, and control charts from the LCS data. Exact deliverables will be stated in the work plan.

Table 4-36. HAZWRAP Level C deliverables

Analyte Group	Method requirements	Deliverables[55]
All methods	Holding times information and method requested	Signed chain-of-custody forms
	Discussion of lab problems	Case narrative
	LCS with results on control charts run with each batch of samples	Control chart copies
Organics	Sample results	CLP form 1
	Surrogate recoveries	CLP form 2
	Matrix spike/Matrix spike duplicate	CLP form 3
	Method blank	CLP form 4
	GC/MS tune	CLP form 5
	GC/MS initial calibration	CLP form 6
	GC initial and continuing calibration	CLP form 8D and 9
	GC/MS continuing calibration	CLP form 7
	GC/MS internal standard area	CLP form 8
	Second column confirmation	CLP form 10 and copies of chromatograms

Continued on next page.

---

55 If alternate forms are used, copies must be submitted to HAZWRAP Project Manager for approval prior to initiating work.

Table 4-36. HAZWRAP Level C deliverables, *continued*

Analyte Group	Method requirements	Deliverables[56]
Metals	Sample results	CLP form 1
	Initial and continuing calibration	CLP form 2
	Method blank	CLP form 3
	ICP interference check	CLP form 4
	Spike sample recovery	CLP form 5A
	PDS spike recovery for ICP	CLP form 5B
	PDS for GFAA	Recovery noted on raw data
	Duplicates	CLP form 6
	LCS	CLP form 7
	Standard addition	CLP form 8
	Holding times	CLP form 10
Wet chemistry	LCS	Control chart copy
	Method blank	Report result
	Sample results	Report result
	Spike/spike duplicate and/or calibration	Report result
	Calibration check	Report RPD

Under HAZWRAP, SW-846, CLP, or other EPA methods are used for most analyses in Levels C and E; however, all semivolatile and volatile organic analyses by GC/MS are to be performed by the most recent CLP-SOW.

On the other hand, the AFCEE requirements allow SW-846 methods and analyte lists for the most part, but specify PQL and MQO for water and soil samples for each of the common SW-846 methods. There are extensive lists of analytical acceptance criteria, formatted as standard corrective action responses and procedures. All these data are presented in the AFCEE Quality Assurance Project Plan (QAPP), version 3.0, available electronically from the Internet. The QAPP is an essential reference for all data evaluators and other persons responsible for Quality Assurance programs.

A number of documents are available as either hardcopy or as downloads from the Internet related to AFCEE. These include:

1. *Handbook to Support the Installation Restoration Program (IRP) Statement of Work for Remedial Investigation/Feasibility Studies (RI/FS)* May, 1987 (Version 1.2), April, 1988 (version 2.0), and May, 1989 (version 3.0)

2. *Handbook to Support the Installation Restoration Program (IRP) Statement of Work, Volume 1 Remedial Investigation/Feasibility Studies,* 5/91.

3. *Handbook for the Installation Restoration Program (IRP) Remedial Investigations and Feasibility Studies (RI/FS),* published by AFCEE September, 1993

4. *Quality Assurance Project Plan (QAPP),* version 3.0, March, 1998

5. *Guidance for AFCEE Quality Assurance/Quality Control (QA/QC) Audits of Installation Restoration Program Contact Laboratories,* October, 1991

---

[56] If alternate forms are used, copies must be submitted to HAZWRAP Project Manager for approval prior to initiating work.

The Internet address for AFCEE is http://www.afcee.brooks.af.mil. A more complete discussion of AFCEE is presented in a recent book[57].

Table 4-37. Contents of AFCEE QAPP version 3.0

Section	Title
1.0	Introduction
2.0	Project Description
3.0	Project Organization and Responsibility
4.0	Quality Program and Data Quality Objectives
4.1	Data categories
4.2	Precision, accuracy, representativeness, completeness, and comparability
4.3	Method detection limits, reporting limits and instrument calibration requirements
4.4	Elements of quality control
4.5	Quality control procedures
5.0	Sampling Procedures
6.0	Screening Analytical Methods
6.1	Analytical screening method descriptions
6.2	Calibration and QC procedures for screening methods
7.0	Definitive Data Analytical Methods and Procedures
7.1	Preparation methods
7.2	Analytical procedures
	SW8011
	SW8015
	SW8021
	SW8070
	SW8081
	SW8082
	SW8141
	SW8151
	SW8260B
	SW8270C
	SW8280
	SW8290
	SW8310
	SW8330
	SW6010B
	SW6020
	SW7041
	SW7060

Continued on next page.

---

57 Berger, W., H. McCarty and R.-K. Smith, 1996. *Environmental Laboratory Data Evaluation*, Genium Publishing, Schenectady, NY 12304.

Table 4-37. Contents of AFCEE QAPP version 3.0

Section	Title
	SW7131
	SW7191
	SW7196
	SW7421
	SW7470/7471
	SW7521
	SW7740
	SW7841
	SW7911
	SW9010/9012
	SW9056
	TO-14
8.0	Data Reduction, Review, Verification, Reporting, Validation, and Recordkeeping
9.0	System and Performance Audits, Performance Evaluation Programs, Magnetic Tape Audits, and Training
10.0	Preventive Maintenance
11.0	Corrective Action
12.0	Quality Assurance Reports to Management

For each analytical method there are three tables in the QAPP. The first is the table of reporting limits for soil and water for each method analyte. The second table is a listing of QC acceptance criteria (accuracy and precision, both soil and water) for each method analyte. The third table is a summary of calibration and QC procedures along with corrective action measures for each QC non-attainment.

VII. MIXED WASTE

The term "mixed waste" refers to samples that are both hazardous and radioactive. In general the hazardous waste part of the analysis is performed by SW-846 methods that have been modified to protect the instrument and the technician from the radioactive nature of the waste. This may involve performing all or part of the analysis in a hood, a hot cell, or a glove box, depending on the nature and level of the radioactivity. The mixed waste methods have been collected into the DOE analytical procedures database, which is available on-line. The majority of the methods are for measuring the radioactive part of the waste rather than the hazardous part. Contact with the database can be initiated by calling Brian O'Malley at 505-667-0089 at Los Alamos National Laboratory and requesting access information and a password. The DOE also published the *DOE Methods for Evaluating Environmental and Waste Management Samples*, document DOE/EM-0089T, as a guide to mixed waste sampling and analysis. This compilation of methods has become comerciallized and is being updated by Battelle Press. A 1997 edition is available; for information call 800-451-3543.

Radioactive materials contain atoms that are unstable and are prone to breakdown accompanied by emission of either particles or energy. The common emission products are alpha particles (2 protons and 2 neutrons with a mass of 4 amu and a charge of +2), beta particles (an electron, 1/2000 of the mass of a proton and a -1 charge), gamma rays (no mass and no charge but high energy) and neutron particles (1 amu mass and no charge). Neutrons are further characterized as thermal (low energy) or fast (high energy).

Table 4-38. Characteristics of Radioactivity

Particle	Range	Bio hazard	Shielding
alpha	1-2 inches in air	external none, internal very hazardous QF = 20	few cm of air, sheet of paper, layer of dead skin
beta	10 ft in air	external skin and eyes, internal hazardous QF = 1	plastic, glass, metal foil or safety glasses
gamma	several hundred feet in air	external/internal hazard QF = 1	concrete, lead or steel
neutron	several hundred feet in air	external/internal hazard QF varies with energy	water or plastic

Materials that are radioactive are undergoing active generation of radiation through disintegration, however the effect of the radiation depends on its exact type. Items and people exposed to radiation do not become radioactive. This occurs only if the actual radioactive material is incorporated into the item or ingested/inhaled by the person.

A. Units of radiation measure

Roentgen (R) - amount of gamma rays necessary to produce one electrostatic unit of electric charge in 1 cc of dry air or 2.58×10^{-4} coulombs/kilogram air. A coulomb is equal to 1 amp/sec.

RAD (Radiation absorbed dose) - energy deposited on a material from a radioactive source: 1 RAD is equal to 100 erg/gram or 0.01 joule/kilogram. A RAD is not a biological measure. The SI unit of measure is the Gray, which is equal to 1 joule/kilogram absorbed energy. 1 Gray is equal to 100 RAD.

REM (Roentgen equivalent man) - energy absorbed by a human multiplied by the Quality factor to give an estimated biological effect. 1000 mREM = 1 REM. The SI unit is the Sievert, and 1 Sv is equal to 100 REM.

Curie (Ci) - amount of material that emits radioactivity equal to 2.2×10^{12} disintegrations per minute (dpm) or 3.7×10^{10} disintegrations per second (dps). A microcurie (μCi) is 1/1,000,000 Curies. A Becquerel (Bq) is the SI unit for a disintegration per second.

Quality Factor (QF) - a multiplier that converts RAD to REM. The QF depends on the type of radiation and on the energy content. The energy content of neutrons is expressed as mega electron volts (MeV). An electron volt is the energy imparted to an electron when it is accelerated in a 1 volt potential, also equal to 1.60×10^{-19} joules. A MeV is then 1.60×10^{-13} joules.

B. Acute Radiation Dosage Results

< 10,000 mREM essentially no effect, average background exposure: comic rays 28 mREM/year, terrestrial radiation 28 mREM/year, internally ingested natural radionuclides (^{40}K) 40 mREM/year, medical X-rays 40 mREM/year, nuclear testing atmospheric residues 1 mREM/year, consumer products 10 mREM/year. A maximum dose of 500 mREM over the 9 months of a pregnancy is allowed by NCRP.

10,000 - 50,000 mREM	slight blood changes
100,000 mREM	radiation sickness (nausea, hair loss, delirium, vomiting) in some people
>200,000 mREM	general radiation sickness
450,000 mREM	50% of exposed persons die within 30 days
>500,000 mREM	recovery problematic (30 firefighters at Chernobyl received in excess of 800,000 mREM and all died)

DOE exposure limits for whole body under normal conditions are 5,000 mREM/year, and the administrative control level is 2,000 mREM.

C. Radiation Quality Factors

As shown in Table 4-39 the alpha particles are the most biological damaging form of radiation. Radon presents a significant hazard for 3 reasons: (1) it is a gas, which means it readily enters the body; (2) second, it decays rapidly giving off an alpha particle; and (3), the decay products are solids and stick in the lungs, rapidly decaying to generate more alpha particles, as shown in Table 4-40.

Table 4-39. Quality factors for radiation types

Radiation type	Quality Factor
X-ray, gamma ray, beta particles and high speed electrons	1
Alpha particles, multiply charged particles, fission fragments	20
High-energy protons	10
Unknown neutrons	10
$<1 \times 10^{-3}$ MeV neutrons	2
1×10^{-2} MeV neutrons	2.5
0.1 MeV neutrons	7.5
0.5 to 1 MeV neutrons	11
2.5 MeV neutrons	9
5 MeV neutrons	8
7 MeV neutrons	7
10 MeV neutrons	6.5
14 MeV neutrons	7.5
20 MeV neutrons	8
40 MeV neutrons	7
60 MeV neutrons	5.5
100 MeV neutrons	4
>200 MeV neutrons	3.5

Table 4-40. Uranium decay series

Nuclide	Product particle	Nuclide half-life
Uranium 238 ↓ decays to	alpha	4.61×10^9 years
Thorium 234 ↓ decays to	beta	24.1 days
Protactinium 234 ↓ decays to	beta	6.75 hours
Uranium 234 ↓ decays to	alpha	2.48×10^5 years
Thorium 230 ↓ decays to	alpha	8.0×10^4 years
Radium 226 ↓ decays to	alpha	1.62×10^3 years
Radon 222 ↓ decays to	alpha	3.82 days
Polonium 218 ↓ decays to	alpha	3.1 minutes
Lead 214 ↓ decays to	beta	26.8 minutes
Bismuth 214 ↓ decays to	beta	19.7 minutes
Polonium 214 ↓ decays to	alpha	1.6×10^{-4} seconds
Lead 210 ↓ decays to	beta	20.4 years
Bismuth 210 ↓ decays to	beta	5.0 days
Polonium 210 ↓ decays to	alpha	138.4 days
Lead 210		Stable

Table 4-41. DOE Methods[58]

Method	Description
Sampling Methods	
SA010	Sampling headspace gas for volatile organic compounds within a TRU waste drum with a sampling manifold
SA011	Sampling headspace gas within a TRU waste drum with SUMMA® canisters for volatile organic compounds
SD010R	Collecting samples from TRU waste drum containing solid process residues and soils
SO010R	Collection of liquid samples for effluent monitoring of operations facilities
ST010	General method for sampling liquids and solids in low-level waste storage tanks
ST011R	General method for sampling liquids and solids in high-level waste storage tanks
SW010R	Core samples in cement solidified low-level liquid waste
Organic Methods	
OC010R	Preparation and cleanup of hydrocarbon-containing samples for the analysis of volatile organic compounds
OG015R	Major nonhalogenated volatile organics in radioactive aqueous liquids analyzed by direct aqueous injection gas chromatography (DAI-GC)
OG081R	Analysis of PCBs as Aroclors in solid radioactive mixed wastes, Rev 1
OH100R	Direct analysis of TCLP acidic semivolatile compounds in radioactive liquid wastes or leachates using HPLC and UV
OM100R	Analysis of semivolatile organic compounds using capillary gas chromatography with ion trap mass spectrometer detection
OM500R	Qualitative analysis of low molecular weight organic acids in mixed hazardous waste samples by thermospray LC-MS
OM510R	Determination of chelators and their degradation products in mixed hazardous waste samples by derivatization GC/MS
OP010R	Remote purge and trap-gas chromatography of volatile organics in high-level radioactive wastes
OP020R	Ultrasonic solvent extraction for volatile organic analysis of solid RMW
OP030R	Purge and trap in a glove box
OP040R	Reduced-scale zero headspace extraction for TCLP volatiles in shielded or contaminant conditions
OP100R	PCBs in aqueous radioactive mixed wastes using solid phase extraction disks and GC-ECD
OP120R	Reduced scale liquid-liquid extraction of semivolatile organic compounds
OP130R	Analysis of TCLP semivolatiles and pesticides in radioactive mixed waste sludges
OP550R	Ultrasonic extraction
OS010	Total organic chlorine in oil, field test kit method
OS020	Immunoassay for polychlorinated biphenyls (PCBs) in soils
OS030	A photoacoustic infrared method for the detection of selected chlorinated volatile organic compounds (VOCs) in water
OS040	Rapid determination of volatile organic contaminants in water and soils by direct purge mass spectrometry
OS050	Supercritical fluid extraction for the analysis of contaminated soils
OS060	Immunoassay for petroleum fuel hydrocarbons in soil

Continued on next page.

---

[58] *DOE Methods for Evaluating Environmental and Waste Management Samples*, 1997, Battelle Press, Columbus, OH. E-mail press@battelle.org

Table 4-41. DOE Methods[59], *continued*

Method	Description
	Inorganic methods
MB100	Immunoassay for mercury in soils
MM100	Inductively coupled plasma mass spectrometry for radionuclide analysis
MM210	ICP-MS of 99Tc, 230Th and 234U using flow injection preconcentration
MM800	Ion chromatography and ICP-MS determination of uranium concentration isotopic abundance in groundwater and drinking water
MP100R	Solvent extraction of uranium and thorium from radioactive liquid wastes
MP110R	Cleanup of transuranic liquid wastes using extraction chromatgraphy
MS100R	A reflectometry based instrument for reading colorimetric test strips
MS110	An indicator strip-based colorimetric test for chromate ions ($CrO_4{}^{2-}$) in aqueous samples
MS210	An indicator strip based colorimetric test for lead (Pb^{2+}) in water
MS310	An indicator strip based colorimetric test for nitrate ions (NO_3) in water and soil
MS410	An indicator strip-based colorimetric test for nickel (Ni^{2+}) in aqueous samples
MU012R	Total cyanide by remote microdistillation and argentometric titration
MU016	Alkaline digestion procedure for the extraction of hexavalent chromium
	Radiological methods
RA010	Method for utilization of alpha track detectors for characterization of gross alpha emission from indoor surfaces
RA020	Method for utilization of Electret ionization chambers for characterization of gross alpha emission from indoor surfaces
RI010	Gamma-ray spectrometry
RI100	Liquid scintillation instrumentation method
RP230	Iodine-129 analysis in aqueous solutions
RP280	Determination of Lead-210 in water using extraction chromatography
RP300	Nickel-59 and nickel-63 determination in aqueous samples
RP330	Separation of niobium for niobium-94 and niobium-93m determination
RP450	Determination of Radium-226 in aqueous samples
RP500	Purification of strontium in water before strontium-89/strontium-90 measurement
RP501	Determination of total radioactive strontium in high-level samples using extraction chromatography
RP510	Determination of strontium-90 in dissolved environmental samples using Chelex-100
RP515	Rapid determination of Radiostrontium using Empore Strontium RAD Disks
RP520	Determination of strontium-90 in soil, water and filter samples
RP530	Determination of selenium-79 in aqueous samples
RP550	Technetium-99 analysis using extraction chromatography
RP570	Radiochemical determination of thorium isotopes in aqueous samples
RP580	Water distillation from soil and aqueous matrices using a Lachat Microdist™ System for tritium determination
RP710	Laboratory method for gross alpha and beta activity determinations
RP720	Rapid determination of gross alpha, gross beta and gross tritium in water using liquid scintillation counter
RP725	Group actinide screening using extraction chromatography
RP730	Gross gamma screening for environmental matrices

Continued on next page.

---

[59] *DOE Methods for Evaluating Environmental and Waste Management Samples*, 1997, Battelle Press, Columbus, OH. E-mail press@battelle.org

---

Table 4-41. DOE Methods[60], *continued*

Method	Description
	Radiological methods, *continued*
RP735	Determination of total fissile content by neutron activation followed by delayed neutron counting
RP800	Sequential separation of americium and plutonium by extraction chromatography
RS100	In-situ analysis of gamma-ray emitting radionuclides by borehole logging
RS551	Rapid isolation and measurement of Tc-99 using anion exchange filter membranes

VIII. FIELD ANALYTICAL METHODS

The ability of a laboratory to perform tests on the site of a remediation of a spill or hazardous materials dump is a great asset. As the site is being dug, the quick analysis of the excavated material serves to guide the efforts to the most contaminated areas and determine when the work is finished. Several alternatives exist to the laboratory. The first is to place all the normal laboratory equipment in a large van and essentially take the lab to the site. The transportation of GC, GC-MS and metals analytical instruments (GFAA or ICP) is the ultimate in the mobile lab and can be worth the effort in some cases. The data obtained from such a facility can be of any desired level of quality, with even CLP packages being generated. Drawbacks are that the instruments are not designed to be moved and require more frequent maintenance and repair efforts. The power, gas and water consumption can be quite large and limit the siting of the van. Further, the waste disposal problems are identical to those occurring in a fixed-base laboratory.

Another alternative is to purchase portable analytical instruments and place them at the site or very close by in a motel room, small van or outbuilding. The advantage of portable instruments such as GCs is that they are built ruggedly to withstand the constant moving about and can be operated on normal 120 V current and small cylinders of helium, compressed air and hydrogen. The portable laboratory instruments usually generate level 2 to level 3 quality data. The disadvantages of the portable GCs is that they have limited oven temperature ranges and stability and normally only have the capacity for a single column and one or two detectors in series. The use of portable GCs for volatiles analysis is an ideal application, however semivolatile organic compound analysis stretches their capability. The analysis of a single sample by portable GC takes approximately the same amount of time as that required by a full sized instrument (30 to 55 minutes per sample). Also, use of organic solvents for sample extraction, even in the modified forms of microextractions, can be somewhat hard to justify in a motel room.

EPA is preparing a compendium of field analytical methods. This compendium is built upon a publication from September, 1988 (Field Screening Methods Catalog, EPA/540/2-88/005, PB 89134159) that reviewed, without detail, field analysis procedures in use within the Regions. Containing 154 methods, the Field Methods Compendium was made available as a draft in March, 1994. Obtained from the various regional EPA offices, the methods are written in a common format but present a wide range of performance evaluation data, from none to slight modifications of fully validated methods. Some methods in the compendium are simply outdated while others are in need of consolidation, however, taken as a whole the document is extremely useful. The contents of the compendium are presented in Table 4-42.

---

[60] *DOE Methods for Evaluating Environmental and Waste Management Samples*, 1997, Battelle Press, Columbus, OH. E-mail press@battelle.org

---

**Table 4-42. Contents of EPA Field Methods Compendium (Draft),
OERR-9285.2-11, February, 1994**

Method	Title
VW-001	Volatile organics in water by purge and trap
-002	Volatile organics in water by automated headspace - external standard method
-003	Volatile organics in water by automated headspace - internal standard method
-004	Volatile organics in water by manual headspace
-005	VOA water/pentane extraction GC-ECD
-006	VOA water/carbon disulfide extraction GC-FID
-007	VOA water/headspace GC-PID
-008	Field screening of target purgeable volatile organic compounds (aqueous matrix)
-009	Method for field screening of volatile organic compounds in water and soil by headspace analysis using the HNu 301P gas chromatograph
-010	Method for field screening of volatile organic compounds in water and soil by headspace analysis using the Photovac 10S10 gas chromatograph
-011	VOA water, soil, sediment/methanol, water extraction GC-PID/ELCD
-012	Volatile organic compound verification by purge and trap with PID/ELCD detection
-013	Volatile organic screening by heated headspace with FID detection
-014	Analysis of volatile organic compounds in water by purge and trap
VS-001	Volatile organics in soil/sediment by purge and trap
-002	Volatile organics in soil/sediment by automated headspace - external standard method
-003	VOA soil/pentane extraction GC-ECD
-004	VOA soil/carbon disulfide extraction GC-FID
-005	VOA soil/headspace GC-PID
-006	Field screening of target purgeable volatile organic compounds (solid matrix)
-007	Analysis of halogenated and aromatic volatile organic compounds in soil and water by purge and trap gas chromatograph
VG-001	Volatile organics in soil gas - adsorbent tube method
-002	Volatile organics in soil gas using electrolytic conductivity detector - direct analysis
-003	Halogenated volatile organics in soil gas using electron capture detector - direct analysis
-004	VOA soil gas charcoal GC-ECD
-005	VOA soil gas canisters GC-PID
-006	Field screening analysis of volatile contaminants in soil gas matrix
-007	Analysis of halogenated and aromatic volatile compounds in air and soil gas by thermal desorption gas chromatograph
-008	Volatile organics in soil gas
-009	Field method for volatile indicator parameters in soil gas samples using Photovac GC-PID
-010	Sampling and field gas chromatographic analysis for volatile organics in soil gas
-011	Analysis of halogenated and aromatic volatile organics compounds in whole gas samples by purge and trap gas chromatograph

Continued on next page.

**Table 4-42. Contents of EPA Field Methods Compendium (Draft),
OERR-9285.2-11, February, 1994,** *continued*

Method	Title
VA-001	Volatile organics in air - adsorbent tube method
-002	Halogenated volatile organics in air using electrolytic conductivity detector - direct analysis
-003	Volatile organics in air - portable direct analysis
-004	Volatile organics in air using electron capture detector - direct analysis
-005	Field screening analysis of ambient air
-006	Manual analysis of ambient air for selected volatile organic compounds by a portable gas chromatograph
-007	Standard operating procedure for the analysis of ambient air for selected volatile organic compounds by a portable gas chromatograph
-008	Automated analysis of ambient air for selected volatile organic compounds by a portable gas chromatograph
S-001	SV water/carbon disulfide extraction GC-FID
-002	Field screening of target semivolatile organic compounds (aqueous matrix)
-003	SV soil/methylene chloride extraction GC-FID
-004	Field screening of target semivolatile organic compounds (solid matrix)
P-001	Chlorinated pesticides in soil
-002	Field screening of organochlorine pesticides (solid matrix)
-003	Chlorinated pesticides in water
-004	Field screening of organochlorine pesticides (aqueous matrix)
-005	Organophosphorous pesticides in water
-006	Organophosphorous pesticides in soil/sediment
-007	Phenoxyherbicides in soil/sediment
-008	Phenoxyherbicides in water
-009	CLP pesticide/PCB analysis by gas chromatograph
-010	Preparation of sediment. soil, and water samples for pesticide analysis
-011	Field extraction and analysis of chlorinated pesticides in soil by ECD
PCB-001	Polychlorinated biphenyls (PCB) in oil
-002	Field screening of polychlorinated biphenyls (PCB) compounds (solid matrix)
-003	Polychlorinated biphenyls (PCB) in water
-004	Field screening of polychlorinated biphenyls (PCB) compounds (aqueous matrix)
-005	PCB/Pesticides soil/hexane extraction GC-ECD
-006	PCB soil/solvent extraction perchlorination GC-ECD
-007	Preparation and analysis of samples for polychlorinated biphenyls
-008	Field analysis of PCBs
-009	Polychlorinated biphenyls (PCBs) in soil
PAH-001	Field gas chromatographic analysis for polynuclear aromatic hydrocarbons (in water and soil)
-002	Polynuclear aromatic hydrocarbons (PAH) water/hexane extraction GC-FID
-003	Polynuclear aromatic hydrocarbons (PAH) soil/hexane extraction GC-FID
-004	Total polynuclear aromatic hydrocarbon screening procedure for sediments
-005	Polycyclic aromatic hydrocarbons in soil/sediment

Continued on next page.

Table 4-42. Contents of EPA Field Methods Compendium (Draft), OERR-9285.2-11, February, 1994, *continued*

Method	Title
PAH-006	Polynuclear aromatic hydrocarbons in water
-007	Polynuclear aromatic hydrocarbons in oil
-008	PAH soil/methanol extraction, sonication UV
-009	Analysis of PAH by gas chromatograph
-010	Preparation of sediment soil and water samples for semivolatile compounds: PAH, phenols
-011	Extraction and analysis of PAH in soil by GC/FID
-012	FASP extraction and analysis of PAH by HPLC
O-001	Pentachlorophenol in soil/sediment
-002	TPH soil/freon extraction IR
-003	TPH-G soil/methanol extraction GC-PID, ELCD
-004	TPH-HCID soil/methylene chloride extraction GC-FID
-005	Analysis of phenols by gas chromatograph
-006	Analysis of total petroleum hydrocarbons by headspace gas chromatography
-007	Low level methane analysis of Summa canister gas sample
-008	Extraction and analysis of pentachlorophenol in soil by electron capture
-009	Field extraction and analysis of TPH in soil by FID
I-001	Selected metals in soil/sediment by X-ray fluorescence
-002	Inorganics soil/acid digestion AA-flame
-003	Hexavalent chromium soil/alkaline digestion spectrophotometer
-004	Inorganics water/acid digestion AA-flame
-005	Mercury analysis by cold vapor atomic absorption spectrometry
-006	FASP mercury cold vapor atomic absorption
C-001	Alkalinity/Water/Titration
-002	Chemical Oxygen Demand/Water/Open Reflux
-003	Chloride, Nitrate, and Sulfate Anions/Water/IC
-004	Hardness/Water/EDTA Colorimetric
-005	Oil and Grease/Water/Gravimetric
-006	Total Dissolved Solids/Water/Dried
-007	Total Organic Carbon/Water/Analyzer
-008	Total Suspended Solids/Water/Dried
-009	10-Day Chronic Toxicity Test using *Daphnia Magna or Daphnia Pulex*
-010	Extractable Organics/Soil/Gravimetric
-011	Moisture/Soil/Drying oven
-012	Paint Filter Test/Soil/Paint Filters
-013	pH/Soil/pH Meter
-014	Specific Gravity/Soil
-015	Total Carbon/Soil/Combustion Train
-016	Total, Fixed, and Volatile Solids/Soil
-017	Water Level Measurement
-018	Controlled Pumping Test
-019	Slug Test

Continued on next page.

Table 4-42. Contents of EPA Field Methods Compendium (Draft), OERR-9285.2-11, February, 1994, *continued*

Method	Title
C-020	General Surface Geophysics
-021	7-Day Standard Reference Toxicity Test using *Larval Pimephales Promelas*
-022	24-Hour Rangefinding Test using *Daphnia Magna or Daphnia Pulex*
-023	96-Hour Acute Toxicity Test using *Larval Pimephales Promelas*
-024	24-hour Rangefinding Test using *Larval Pimephales Promelas*
-025	48-Hour Acute Toxicity Test using *Daphnia Magna or Daphnia Pulex*
-026	7-Day Renewal Toxicity Test using *Ceriodaphnia Dubia*
-027	7-Day Static Toxicity Test using *Larval Pimephales Promelas*
-028	96-Hour Static Toxicity Test using *Selenastrum Capricornutum*
K-001	Hazard Categorization
-002	Compatibility Testing
R-001	Radiological/Quality Control for Sample Preparation, Counting, and Data Handling
-002	Radiological/Determination of Gross Alpha/Beta in Soil Samples [simplified methods]
-003	Radiological/Soil Sample Preparation
-004	Radiological/Determination of Gross Alpha/Beta in Water Samples
-005	Radiological/Determination of Gross Alpha/Beta Activity in Water Samples [dot level]
-006	Radiological/Determination of Gross Alpha/Gross Beta in Core Samples, Soil, Bottom Sediments, Sludges, and Silts Samples [high organic samples]
-007	Radiological/Determination of Gross Alpha/Beta in Biota, vegetation/food stuff, [simplified methods]
-008	Determination of Gross Alpha/Beta in Biota [vegetation/food stuff] [extended methods]
IA-001	X-MET 880 Field Portable X-Ray Fluorescence Operating Procedure
IM-002	Operation of the X-MET 880 X-Ray Fluorescence Spectrometer
-003	Field Flame Atomic Absorption Analysis SOP
OA-001	Sentax Scentograph Gas Chromatograph Field Use
-002	GC/MS Analysis of Tenax/CMS Cartridges and Summa Canisters
-003	Photonionization Detector (PID) HNU
-004	Photovac 10A10 Portable Gas Chromatograph Operation
-005	Photovac 10S50, 10S55, and 10S70 Gas Chromatograph Operation
-006	Photovac GC Analysis for Soil, Water, and Air/Soil Gas
RA-001	Radiological/Determination of Detection Levels for Gross Alpha and Gross Beta Analysis
-002	Radiological/Radiochemical Analysis Efficiency, Background, and Recovery Standards (Counter) Preparation
-003	Radiological Operation of the LB5100 Gas Proportional Counter
-004	Radiological/Setup and Operation of the Counter Top Centrifuge
SM-001	Sample Equipment Decontamination
SWSS-001	Surface Water Sampling
-002	Sediment Sampling
WS-001	Drum Sampling

Continued on next page.

Table 4-42. Contents of EPA Field Methods Compendium (Draft), OERR-9285.2-11, February, 1994, *continued*

Method	Title
WS-002	Tank Sampling
-003	Chip, Wipe, and Sweep Sampling
-004	Waste Pile Sampling
SS-001	Soil Sampling
-002	Soil Gas Sampling
GWS-001	Groundwater Well Sampling
GS-001	Collection of Gaseous Samples by using Tedlar Bags
QA-001	Quality Assurance/Quality Control Samples

A. Immunoassay Kits

The introduction of immunoassay kits as field screening tests for a variety of analytes is another alternative available to the laboratory. EPA has looked at methods for pentachlorophenol (4010), 2,4-D (4015), PCBs (4020), TPH (4030), BTEX (4031), PAH (4035), Toxaphene (4040), Chlordane (4041), DDT (4042), TNT (4050 and 8515), and RDX (4051) by immunoassay, which are in a variety of stages of the acceptance process for inclusion in SW-846. There is also an immunoassay kit for mercury in the inorganic form. The chemistry of the kits allow them to be very selective and gives the technician the ability to perform many analyses in a relatively short period of time. All consumables are included in the kit, and if the colorimeter is battery powered, there are few limitations as to where the test station can be set up. The basis for the test begins with an enzyme-catalyzed reaction of a substrate to give a colored product. One example is the horseradish peroxidase catalyzed reaction of tetramethylbenzidine with hydrogen peroxide, which forms a blue-colored product from the colorless substrate[61]. The enzyme is modified to chemically attach a portion or all of the target molecule to it, in such a fashion so that the enzyme catalytic ability is not affected. To make the antibodies, a larger molecule such as albumin, hemocyanin or thyroglobulin is derivatized with the analyte molecule and then injected into vertebrate host animals (rabbits or horses) to stimulate the immune response[62]. The antibodies are isolated and purified, then used without further processing in the polyclonal method. The monoclonal antibody method uses hybridoma technology to fuse the antibody-producing cells from the spleen with myeloma cells, then culture the resulting progeny cells to produce large amounts of the antibody[63]. Regardless of the source, the antibodies are used to coat either the insides of small test tubes or wells in a 96 well test plate or covalently bound to small superparamagnetic particles. In the test a diluted extract of the analyte (aqueous DMSO, isopropanol or methanol[64]) is mixed with the antibody, forming the antibody-analyte complex. Analyte-modified enzyme (enzyme conjugate) is added, which forms a

---

[61] Carter, K. "The Performance of Immunoassay-Based Field Methods for Pentachlorophenol and Polychlorinated Biphenyls." *Proceedings of the Fifteenth Annual EPA Conference on Analysis of Pollutants in the Environment.* May 6-7, 1992. pp 389-424.

[62] Friedman, S.B. "Immunoassay Methods for Environmental Field Screening." *Proceedings of the 8th Annual Waste Testing and Quality Assurance Symposium,* July 13-17, 1992. pp 43-57.

[63] Swift, R.P., J.R. Leavell, and C.W. Brandenburg. "Evaluation of the ENSYS PAH-RISc® Test Kit." *Proceedings of the 9th Annual Waste Testing & Quality Assurance Symposium.* July 12-16, 1993. pp 484-499.

[64] Harrison, R.O. and R.E. Carlson. "Analysis of PCB's by Enzyme Immunoassay." *Proceedings of the 8th Annual Waste Testing and Quality Assurance Symposium* July 13-17, 1992. pp. 120-128.

complex with the rest of the available antibody. The test tube is then washed out with detergent, removing any uncomplexed analyte modified enzyme. The antibody complexes are left immobilized on either the sides of the test tube or on the magnetic particles, which are held by another magnet in the bottom of the tube. Substrate is added and the enzymatic reaction allowed to proceed for a period of time, terminated by addition of a stop solution, such as acid, to denature the enzyme, and then the intensity of the colored product is determined on a colorimeter. A blank is run with the samples to determine the maximum amount of color formed when no target analyte is present. Any target analyte in the sample will decrease the amount of remaining enzyme and decrease the amount of colored product formed from the substrate. The color decrease is calibrated by running standard concentrations of target analyte in each batch.

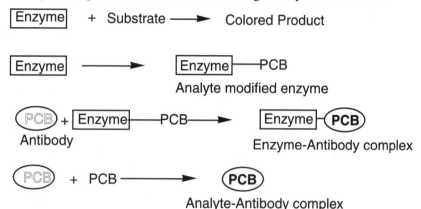

Figure 4-3.   Interaction of enzyme, substrate, antibody and PCB target analyte.

The EPA is currently evaluating the immunoassay kits as pass-fail procedures for a regulatory action level, for instance 20 ppm for PCB in soil on remediation sites. Future evaluations may include quantitative abilities. The kits are designed to minimize the number of false negatives (ideally zero), however there can be up to 10% false positives. For fixed laboratory confirmation purposes, EPA recommends confirmation of all positive immunoassay readings and 10% of the negatives.

The validation package for consideration of a new method for inclusion in SW-846 or for adaptation of an existing method for a new matrix consists of the following information[65]:

1. Cross reactivity with similar analytes

2. Cross reactivity with dissimilar analytes

3. False negative/false positive rates

4. Extraction efficiency for solid matrices

5. Performance data on spiked samples compared with standard SW-846 lab methods

6. Performance data on real samples compared with standard SW-846 lab methods.

[65] Lesnik, B. "Immunoassay Methods: the EPA Approach." *Environmental Lab*. June/July, 1994. pp. 37-44.

In addition to the EPA draft methods for immunoassay kits, there are a large number of other assays commercially available. These include atrazine (triazine pesticides), alaclor, cyanazine, metolachlor, benomyl/carbendazim, aldicarb, carbofuran, captan, cyclodienes, methoprene, procymidone, metalaxyl, isoproturon, paraquat, DDT and others. Some kits are almost entirely selective for the target analyte, such as the 2,4-D kits, while others are cross-reactive to a number of related compounds such as general triazine pesticides in the atrazine test, and 4,4'-DDT, 4,4'-DDE and 4,4'-DDD in the DDT kit. Immunoassays for metals have also been reported[66].

B. Qualitative Screening Tests

At least once a week a client comes to the laboratory with a sample and asks, "What is it?" or "What's in it?" Although it is possible to run a large battery of specific tests on the sample for metals, organics, and inorganic non-metallic parameters, frequently these test results are negative, expensive, and lead to mistaken or no conclusions about the sample. Through judicious choice of a few simple qualitative test procedures, enough information can be obtained to lead directly to a suitable answer[67].

An initial physical examination can often be useful. The smell or lack of smell of the sample may direct you in specific analytical directions. For liquid samples determination of whether the liquid is water or not is easily accomplished by mixing a drop with water and then mixing another drop with methylene chloride. It's going to be soluble in one or the other. An approximation of the density is also obtained by observing whether the drop floats or sinks in the insoluble mixture. Determining the solubility of solid samples is accomplished the same way.

Burning a small portion of the sample on the tip of a stainless steel spatula with a match flame is informative. Most organic materials will rapidly burn while inorganic materials will not. In either case observe the color of the match flame. Green indicates the presence of copper or boron, red is lithium or strontium, orange-red is calcium, yellow is sodium, and violet is potassium. If a copper loop is used to hold the sample while burning, the Bielstein test for halogen is performed. A distinct green color indicates the presence of halogen in the sample. Consult Feigl and Anger for a more complete flame test analysis.

If the sample is a stain or tightly adhered to the surface of a larger item, exposing the sample to the flame of a tightly focused propane torch or placing the item in a 550 °C muffle furnace can help determine whether the stain is organic or not.

Oxidizers - A rapid test for the substantial presence of oxidizers can be performed by testing a small portion of the sample on a potassium iodide-starch paper that has been moistened with acetic acid. An intense blue to black stain on the paper indicates that oxidizers are present. A more sensitive test consists of addition of four drops $0.5M$ KI to four drops of the sample acidified with four drops $3M$ HCl, then shaking with ten drops of chloroform. This extracts any formed I_2 as an intense purple color into the chloroform. An alternate is to treat four drops of the sample with two drops of $12M$

66 Chakrabarti, P., F.M. Hatcher, R.C. Blake, P.A. Ladd and D.A. Blake. "Enzyme Immunoassay to Determine Heavy Metals Using Antibodies to Specific Metal-EDTA Complexes: Optimization and Validation of an Immunoassay for Soluble Indium." *Analytical Biochemistry* 217:70-75; 17th Annual EPA Conference on Analysis of Pollutants in the Environment, May 3-5, 1994, Norfolk VA.

67 Feigl, F., and V. Anger, 1972. *Spot Tests in Inorganic Analysis*, Elsevier; New York, NY; Feigl, F, and V. Anger, *Spot Tests in Organic Analysis*, Elsevier, NY, New York, www.elsevier.com.

HCl, then add four drops of saturated $MnCl_2$ in $12M$ HCl. Heat in boiling water for two minutes then look for the formation of a deep brown to black coloration ($MnCl_3$). The $MnCl_3$ is unstable and may produce a precipitate of MnO_2 on standing.

Reducers - To test for reducing agents, mix a drop of weak iodine-potassium iodide solution (see *Standard Methods* 4500-Cl C.3.h) with the sample. If the brown color of the test solution is bleached, the presence of reducing agents is indicated. Decolorization of the orange color of a weak potassium dichromate solution can also be used to indicate the presence of reducing agents. Permanganate decolorization is also useful. To four drops of the sample add five drops water and six drops $3M$ H_2SO_4. Insure that the solution is acidic. Add two drops $0.01M$ $KMnO_4$ solution and observe for decolorization. If the solution is still purple, heat in boiling water for several minutes.

An alternate test for reducing agents is to prepare a test reagent by mixing two drops of $0.1M$ $Fe(NO_3)_3$, two drops of $0.1M$ $K_3Fe(CN)_6$, and four drops of $3M$ HNO_3 and dilution to 1 mL with water. Addition of four drops of the test solution will generate a dark blue precipitate of Prussian Blue if reducers are present. Any blue or green coloration to the test reagent after addition of the sample should be viewed as a positive.

Sodium fusion test - The sodium fusion test has a long history of use in qualitative analysis, and just because it was discovered back in the 1800s doesn't mean it's not useful now. The test consists of carefully heating a small portion (1 g) of the sample with a small piece of sodium in a test tube. After any initial reaction subsides, alcohol is very cautiously added to quench any unreacted sodium. The mixture is then dissolved in water, with heating if necessary. Sulfur in the sample is detected by addition of 5 mL of the water solution to three drops of 10% lead acetate solution in 2 mL of 10% sodium hydroxide. A black precipitate is a positive for sulfur. Nitrogen is detected by heating 2 mL of the water solution, then adding five drops of 10% sodium hydroxide followed by five drops of 10% ferrous sulfate. After the solution returns to room temperature the suspension is just acidified with 10% hydrochloric acid. A blue or green solution or a blue precipitate is a positive for the presence of nitrogen. Chlorine is determined by acidification of 5 mL of the water solution with nitric acid, then addition of several drops of 10% silver nitrate. A white precipitate indicates chlorine presence. Phosphorus is determined by heating 5 mL of the water solution with 3 mL concentrated nitric acid, then addition of 10 mL of 10% ammonium molybdate. The sample is heated to 60 °C for a few minutes, then allowed to sit. A yellow precipitate indicates the presence of phosphorus.

Cations and anions - Metals in the sample are most economically identified by digesting a portion of the sample in acid and analyzing the digestate by ICP (see Section 2-H). The traditional cation qualitative analysis scheme is not cost effective unless a complete metals identification is necessary, and even then sending the sample off for X-ray diffraction testing is a less expensive means of analysis.

On the other hand, unless one has access to an ion chromatograph or a capillary ion electrophoresis instrument, spot testing for the common anions is very cost effective. Several manufacturers have dip-stick spot tests that can be used to screen samples. Other procedures use addition of one or two drops of a reagent to one or two drops of a sample. Often these tests are the same as the quantitative EPA procedure run in a yes-no manner. Thus if addition of a drop of barium chloride solution results in a white precipitate, this can be indication of the presence of sulfate. Silver nitrate addition can indicate chlorine, bromine or iodine in the sample if a white precipitate is formed. If reaction of a drop of the sample with sulfanillic acid-NED reagent generates a red color, the presence of nitrite is indicated. However, these tests may be subject to interferences unless suitable pre-treatment of the sample has been performed.

For a systematic evaluation of the sample the traditional anion analytical scheme can be very informative and quick[68]. There are four groups of anions in the traditional scheme. They are:

1. *Acid-volatized anions - carbonate, sulfite, thiosulfate, sulfide and nitrite –* Cyanide may be included in this group. A small portion of the sample (six drops) is treated dropwise with four drops $3M$ sulfuric acid and the sample is observed for gas evolution. The sample may be warmed but not heated. The evolved gases could be CO_2 from carbonate, SO_2 from sulfite or thiosulfate, H_2S from sulfide, HCN from cyanide, or NO_2 from nitrite. The creation of a white or yellow precipitate along with gas evolution is probably elemental sulfur from thiosulfate. If the evolved gas is brown, nitrite was probably present. If cyanide is suspected, addition of an iron salt ($Fe[NO_3]_3$) can create ferricyanide and hold it in the sample until Group 3. Addition of hydrogen peroxide to another portion of the sample (to oxidize any sulfite to sulfate) and repeating the acid addition and bubbling the evolved gas into saturated $Ba(OH)_2$ solution will generate a white precipitate in the trap solution if the gas is CO_2. If the gas is not CO_2, use of a hydrogen peroxide/$Ba(OH)_2$ trap on the gas from the acidified sample can verify SO_2 evolution. H_2S can be detected by the smell or darkening of lead acetate paper or solution. Use of zinc acetate or cadmium nitrate solution in a trap will indicate H_2S through formation of a precipitate. HCN can be trapped in NaOH solution and spot tested with pyridine-barbituric acid reagent.

2. *Non-volatized anions precipitated as barium or calcium salts from dilute ammonia solution - sulfate, borate, phosphate, chromate, fluoride, oxalate, arsenite and arsenate –* To the acid treated solution from group 1, add dropwise, $3M$ NH_3 solution until basic. Then add three drops of $0.3M$ $Ba(NO_3)_2$. Formation of a precipitate indicates $BaSO_4$, $Ba(BO_2)_2$, $Ba_3(PO_4)_2$, and/or $BaCrO_4$ formation. After complete precipitation, the sample can be centrifuged and the supernatent is treated with three drops $0.5M$ $Ca(NO_3)_2$. Formation of a precipitate indicates CaF_2, CaC_2O_4, $Ca_3(AsO_3)_2$ and/or $Ca_3(AsO_4)_2$. Addition of 15 drops $3M$ HCl to the barium precipitate will not dissolve $BaSO_4$; the other possibilities are soluble in acid.

3. *Non-volatized anions precipitated as silver salts from dilute nitric acid solution - chloride, bromide, iodide, thiocyanate, ferrocyanide and ferricyanide –* Acidify 6 drops of the sample solution with four drops $3M$ HNO_3, then add 2 drops $0.5M$ $AgNO_3$. Any formed precipitate could consist of AgCl, AgBr, AgI, AgSCN, $Ag_4Fe(CN)_6$, and/or $Ag_3Fe(CN)_6$.

4. *Non-volatized anions of the "soluble" group - nitrate –* To test for nitrate, the brown-ring procedure is appropriate. First, nitrite must be removed. To an eight drop portion of the sample add 15 mg powdered urea, then acidify with three drops $3M$ H_2SO_4. Add six drops water, then heat in a boiling water bath until

68 Margolis, E.J., 1962. *Qualitative Anion-Cation Analysis*, John Wiley & Sons, New York, NY.

gas evolution ceases. Second, other interferring anions must be removed through addition of five drops of a saturated Ag_2SO_4 solution. If any precipitate is formed it is removed through centrifuging the sample. To the clear supernatent in a clean test tube add six drops freshly prepared $0.2M$ $FeSO_4$ and stir well. Using a pipet carefully add a one-half inch thick layer of concentrated H_2SO_4 to the bottom of the test tube without any mixing into the other solution. Allow the tube to sit undisturbed for several minutes, then look for the formation of an intense brown ring at the interface between the two layers. The brown ring $[Fe(NO)^+]$ confirms the presence of nitrate ion.

Another test for nitrate is to add nitron acetate (1,5-diphenylanilodihydrotriazol acetate), which forms a crystalline precipitate with nitrate[69]. Other anions also form precipitates with nitron, and thus should be absent from the sample.

In the traditional procedure, acetate is included with nitrate as a soluble anion determined by steam distillation of the acidified solution followed by smelling for a vinegar odor. Steam distillation is a fairly good isolation procedure, however modern techniques suggest subsequent determination by direct injection GC-FID. Use of GC would also determine other organic anions such as the phenols and other organic acids.

These tests are performed sequentially on an aqueous sample. Combined with the information obtained with an ICP scan, very fast identification of samples can be performed.

[69] Wolff, J.-C., P.D.P. Taylor and P. de Bievre. "Traceable Values for Nitrate in Water Samples by Isotopic Dilution Analysis using a Small Thermionic Quadrupole Mass Spectrometer." *Anal. Chem.* 68(18). pp. 3231-3237

Air Pollution and Monitoring

One of the more interesting phone calls an environmental laboratory will receive is from an existing or potential client who says, "We have an odor down here, and we need to know what it is." After an extended game of 20 questions, the Project Manager will forward the client's problem to the technical manager for air analysis and the game will be repeated. The lab's objective is to intelligently guess exactly what is causing the problem, then go to the site and take a sample for an analysis that will confirm the guess.

I. SAMPLING

The proper method of air sampling depends to a great extent on the desired target analytes, the test method chosen and the tested object. The EPA has published methods for testing outdoor ambient air, indoor air, motor vehicle exhausts, and stationary sources. The latter are point sources of atmospheric effluent for industries, most often referred to as stacks. The EPA also has methods for testing volatile emissions from painted or coated items. Some analytes can be directly quantitated in the gas phase, and transportation of the instrument to the sampling site becomes part of the preferred sampling method. However, most analytes cannot be directly measured and must be trapped on a solid adsorbent or in a liquid before transportation to the laboratory and analysis. In general the analytes directly measured in the field depend on gas phase chemistry, while the solution- or solid-trapped analytes are determined by techniques similar to those already discussed for analysis of water or solid samples.

The most complete collection of reliable air sampling and analysis methods is that published by NIOSH. The contents of the manual are presented in Section 1.II. Whereas EPA has concentrated for the most part upon development of multi-analyte sampling and analysis methods, the individual NIOSH procedures are focused upon a single specific analyte. The result is that the sampling technique is optimized for a single target analyte. Most of the NIOSH procedures will specify an absorbent media and the desorption solvent/technique for the analyte, and the results are quite reliable. However, if the target analyte is not specified, the NIOSH procedures become very tedious, as a multitude of absorbent tubes must be taken to the site for sampling

A. Filter Cassette

A common and easy form of sampling is the filter cassette. This consists of an appropriate filter of paper, polymer membrane, or glass fibers backed with a support in a holder. The filters can have a range of random pore sizes as in the glass fiber filters or be very consistent with 5.0 μm to 0.8 μm sizes common in the polymer membranes. The filter may be uncoated, which results in the trapping of particulate matter, or it may be treated chemically for the preferential trapping of selected analytes, which may be in the form of a gas, liquid aerosol, or solid particles. The filter holder can be plastic, either acrylic or polycarbonate, for use at room temperature, or it may be of stainless steel for use at elevated temperature such as 120 °C in stack testing. The cassette works by attaching a metered pump to one side of the cassettes and sucking air through the filter. The open end of the cassette may consist of a small hole or be completely open faced. Intended for sampling tiny particles, cassettes fail miserably when used for sampling large particles such as visible airborne wood, glass, metal, or plastic fibers generated from grinding machines and lathes. The reason may lie in the presence of static charges on the particles and the cassette, which prevent the trapping of the particles on the filter. Most filter cassettes have limited maximum flows, on the order of 1 or 2 liters per minute.

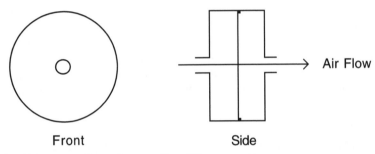

Front　　　　　　　Side

Figure 5-1.　Diagram of an air sampling filter cassette.

B. Annular Denuder

Annular denuders are constructed of metal or plastic concentric tubes coated with an absorbent or reactive chemical layer to trap target analytes from rapid air streams. Flows on the order of several hundred liters per minute can be handled by the large model denuders with very good trapping efficiencies.

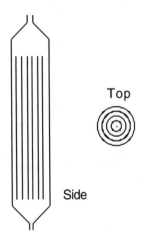

Figure 5-2.　Diagram of an annular denuder.

Table 5-1.   Coating materials used on annular denuders

Coating Material	Target Analyte
Oxalic acid	NH_3, aniline
Oleic acid	SO_3
H_3PO_4	NH_3
K_2CO_3	SO_2, H_2S
Na_2CO_3	SO_2, HCl, HNO_3, HNO_2
$CuSO_4$	NH_3
PbO_2	SO_2, H_2S
WO_3	NH_3, HNO_3
MgO	HNO_3
NaF	HNO_3
NaOH + guaiacol	NO_2
HSO_3^- + triethanolamine	CH_2O
Nylon	SO_2, HNO_3
Powdered Tenax	Halocarbons
Silica gel	Aniline
ICl	R_4Pb

C. Impinger

Impingers are used for trapping airborne target analytes into a liquid solution, which is then analyzed. The trapping solution can be one of a wide variety of solvent/derivatization media for both particulates and specific target analytes. Midget impingers can hold up to 20-25 mL of trapping solution, while larger models are available to handle liters of solution. The maximum flow through the midget impingers is 1 to 2 liters per minute limited by blowing the liquid solution out of the device. Larger impingers can handle much higher flows. See Figure 5-5 for an example.

Table 5-2.   Trapping solutions used in impingers

Target Analyte	Trapping Solution
Acetaldehyde	Water
Acetates	Ethanol
Acetic acid	Glycerol/water
Acetonitrile	Permanganate solution
Acrolein	Hexylresorcinol solution
Aldehydes	MBTH solution
Amines	HCl/isopropanol
Ammonia/aniline	dilute H_2SO_4
Butanol	Water
Carbon disulfide	Copper salt/diethylamine
Chlorine	Methyl Orange solution
Formaldehyde	Bisulfite solution
Mercaptans	$Hg(OAc)_2$ solution
Phenol	NaOH solution
SO_2	Tetrachloromercurate solution

D. Adsorbent Trap

Adsorbent traps can be as simple as glass tubes filled with Tenax, activated charcoal, C_{18} reversed phase media, silica gel, or cold traps (liquid N_2, or solid CO_2), etc. for trapping target analytes from air streams. If volatile, the analytes can be thermally desorbed directly into the analytical instrument. Another method uses solvent desorption of the analytes, followed by further sample processing and analysis.

A different type of adsorbent trap is used for semivolatile analytes. These have been found to be effectively trapped by a combination of a piece of polyurethane foam (PUF) backed by an adsorbent Amberlite® resin such as XAD-2. The sampling adsorbents are exhaustively extracted with a 9:1 combination of diethyl ether : hexane in a soxhlet apparatus for at least 16 hours at 4 cycles per hour prior to use. Normally 273 m^3 of air are drawn through the device at 6 cubic feet (0.17 m^3) per minute.

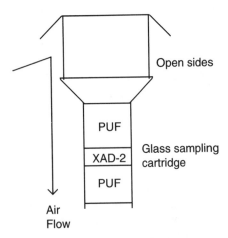

Figure 5-3. Diagram of a hi-flow semivolatiles sampler.

E. Grab Sample

Various types of grab samples for volatile organic analysis can be obtained. They range from an inflatable inert plastic bag called a Tedlar® bag of 0.6- to 10-liter capacity, to an evacuated 1 liter glass flask closed with stopcocks at either end, or a stainless steel 6- or 12-liter capacity ball that is specially polished on the inside with the SUMMA® process. The Tedlar® bag requires a sample pump to fill it, while the SUMMA® canister and the glass flask are filled by simply opening the stopcock or valve and allowing the container to come to atmospheric pressure, then closing the valve or stopcock.

F. Bulk Sample

Bulk samples are commonly obtained with cyclones, electrostatic precipitators, venturi scrubbers, baghouse filters, dust-fall buckets, etc. These techniques are used on the industrial scale for removal of contaminants from air prior to venting to the atmosphere and often provide massive quantities of material for sampling.

G. Cascade Impactor

Particulates come in a variety of sizes. The larger sizes captured by a gauze mask are the particles that would normally be trapped by the mucus membranes and hairs in the nasal passages. Of more concern are the very tiny particles on the order of 0.1 to 1.0 μm in length that will easily pass through the nasal passages and gauze filters and become lodged deep in the lungs. Particles of this order of size are termed "respirable" and present the greatest health hazard. To test for respirable particles a Cascade impactor is used that allows separation of particulates by size. Impactor plates are often coated with a grease or oil to enhance trapping.

Air Flow

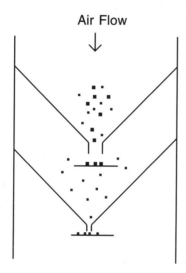

Figure 5-4.   Diagram of a cascade impactor.

H. Colorimetric Indicator Tubes

Sampling events are not always planned, particularly in the case of transportation accidents or warehouse fires. Quick information is needed about the presence of hazardous materials in the air surrounding the site, and nothing can really match the use of colorimetric indicator tubes in these cases. Designed for detection of a limited number of analytes in a very short period of time, one or two operators of the calibrated hand pumps with a series of the tubes can rapidly determine what hazards are present and which are not. Two companies supply the tubes, Sensidyne and Dragger. Both provide handbooks on the chemistry of the tubes and kits and procedures for rapid assessment of hazardous sites. The calibrated pumps sold by the two companies are not interchangeable. For general purpose monitoring the EPA has approved the use of colorimetric tubes for NH_3, CO_2, CO, Cl_2, HCN, H_2S, and SO_2.

I. Stack Testing

Monitoring industrial effluents from stacks is described in detail in 40 CFR part 60, Appendix A, and requires placing permanent sampling ports (nipples) in the sides of the stack in an area with limited turbulence. Sampling is accomplished at many points over the cross-section of the stack. The number and placement of the points is set by the geometry and size of the stack (Method 1). The air velocity of the stack must be determined, and a pitot tube is used for this purpose (Method 2 - 2D). The gas sample can be routed directly from the pitot tube to an instrument analyzer for direct read-out of target analytes, or it may be directed into a sampling train, that is used for most of the chemical methods with appropriate solutions in the traps.

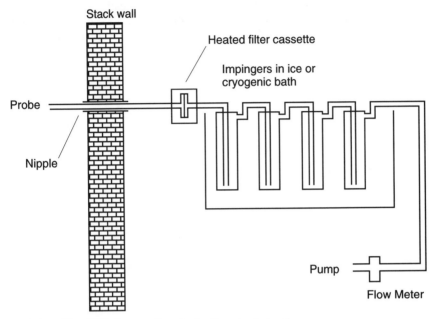

Figure 5-5. Simplified sampling train for stack testing.

II. REPORTING RESULTS

Both ppm and mg/m^3 are commonly found in reports, however the ppm value is actually a partial pressure result rather than being similar to the mass/volume or mass/mass units found in soil and water analysis. The partial pressure depends upon the ideal gas relationship, PV = nRT, where R = 0.0821 L x Atm/mol x K if P is measured in atmospheres, V is measured in liters, n is in moles and T is in Kelvin. The trick lies in the number of moles, which depends on the measured mass of analyte and its molecular mass. For example 1.0 mg of chloromethane and 1.0 mg of carbon tetrachloride in a cubic meter of air give very different ppm values, 0.49 and 0.16 respectfully. An equation relating the two units for air analysis is given in Figure 5-6.

$$\text{ppm} = \frac{24.6 \times \text{mg/m}^3}{\text{Mwt}} \quad \text{at STP conditions (T = 0 °C, P = 1.00 atm)}$$

Figure 5-6. Relationship between ppm and mg/m^3 for reporting air results.

Safety has not been stressed very much in this handbook; however, all chemists, technicians, and chemical workers should be aware of the Material Safety Data Sheets available for their information and protection in working with chemicals. One of the characterizations on the MSDS is the evaporation rate, which is a relative scale based on the vapor pressure of butyl acetate at 20 °C (10 mm Hg). Although alternate reference materials are cited on some MSDSs, butyl acetate is the most common. Values listed in the MSDS physical characteristics section are derived from the equation in Figure 5-7. Values less than 1.0 indicate that the substance is less volatile than butyl acetate; values greater than 1.0 mean the material is more volatile than butyl acetate.

$$\text{Evaporation rate} = \frac{\text{vapor pressure of cmpd at 20 °C}}{10 \text{ mmHg}}$$

Figure 5-7.   Equation for the evaporation rate.

III. SPECIFIC METHODOLOGIES

A natural method for monitoring contaminants in air is infrared spectroscopy. This is because the analysis is most conveniently performed in the gas phase, the infrared analysis region extends from 3700 cm[-1] to 500 cm[-1], and almost all molecules display a spectrum in that range. Recent advances using folded path lengths, Fourier transform IR (FTIR), and liquid-nitrogen-cooled photodetectors have pushed the detection limits for many field sampled analytes to or below the ppb level[1]. The sun has been used as the light source for monitoring the atmosphere by long-path IR. Other long distance techniques use a mirror to bounce the IR light beam back to the source for measurement at a single station where an interferometer obtains a frequency spectrum of a range of wavelengths at one instant then converts the signal to a wavelength spectrum using Fourier transforms. Measuring target analytes can be both qualitative and quantitative, with the biggest interferences being carbon dioxide and water vapor. The reference lists over 130 specific compounds with MDLs for which methods have been developed.

A. Carbon Oxides

1. CO_2 and CO

CO is most easily monitored real-time by Fourier transform long-path IR by detecting absorption at 2165 - 2183 cm[-1]. One set-up uses a path length of 25 m, i.e., the width of a road. CO_2 is also monitored by the same system at 2342 cm[-1]. Coupled to a video system this allows spot checking of on-road vehicle emissions[2].

Another instrument for CO monitoring uses non-dispersive IR (NDIR). The instrument relies on lasers, or selective bandwidth filters and/or detectors for isolation of absorption signals rather than prisms or gratings. One device uses a carbon-monoxide-filled cell as a specific detector and measures the decrease in signal between the clean air reference cell and the sample cell. The difference is proportional to CO concentration in the sample cell. Most IR energy absorbed by carbon monoxide is transferred into heat. Measuring the temperature increase in the sample cell compared to the reference cell is another detection method in NDIR. Non-dispersive instruments are target-analyte-specific.

---

[1]   Hanst, P.L. and S.T. Hanst, *Gas Measurement in the Fundamental Infrared Region*, Volume I. Infrared Analysis, Inc., 11629 Deborah Dr., Potomac, MD 20854. (301) 299-9751.
[2]   Bishop, G. A., and D. F. Stedman. "On-road Carbon Monoxide Emission Measurement Comparisons for the 1988 - 1989 Colorado Oxy-fuels Program." *Environ. Sci. Technol.* 1990. 24(6). pp. 843-847.

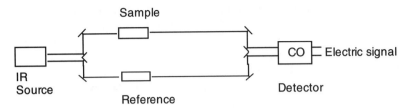

Figure 5-8. **Diagram of a non-dispersive IR instrument for measuring carbon monoxide.**

2. Method 10. Carbon Monoxide

Method 10 is for on-site stack testing using a NDIR. Method 10A requires passing the gas through an alkaline permanganate solution to remove sulfur and nitrogen oxides, followed by collection of the sample in a Tedlar® bag. Carbon monoxide is determined by reaction with *p*-sulfaminobenzoic acid and silver nitrate in basic solution followed by colorimetric determination[3]. Method 10B assays the carbon monoxide trapped in the Tedlar® bag from method 10A by gas chromatography followed by catalytic reduction on nickel at 400 °C to methane and then assay of the methane by FID. The method in 40 CFR 50, App. C, is also NDIR as is method IP-3A. Carbon monoxide is determined in method IP-3C with electrochemical oxidation. The detector is an electrochemical cell consisting of a membrane with a sensor and a counter electrode attached to either side. The counter electrode side is filled with deionized water. The CO-containing air contacts the saturated membrane and reacts with the water.

$$CO + H_2O \longrightarrow CO_2 + 2H^+ + 2e^-$$

The hydrogen ions pass through the membrane, and the other cell reaction occurs.

$$2H^+ + 2e^- + 1/2\ O_2 \longrightarrow H_2O$$

The electrons are detected as they pass through the circuit connecting the sensor and counter electrodes. The net reaction is oxidation of CO to CO_2.

3. Method 6A. Carbon Dioxide

This is a gravimetric method that depends on the absorption of carbon dioxide on Ascarite II, which is a sodium hydroxide coated silica, 8- to 20-mesh size. Method 6B allows substitution of 5 Å molecular sieves. Carbon dioxide can be determined by gas chromatography followed by reduction to methane and passage of the effluent through an FID.

---

3   Lambert, J.L. and R.E. Weins. "Induced Colorimetric Method for Carbon Monoxide." *Anal. Chem.* 1974. 46(7). pp. 929-930; Levaggi, D.A. and M. Feldstein, "The Colorimetric Determination of Low Concentrations of Carbon Monoxide." *Industrial Hygiene Jour.* 1964. 25. pp. 64-66. (Jan.-Feb.).

B. Organic Analytes

Hydrocarbons and other volatile organic compounds can be determined by IR; however, the more common technique is to obtain either a grab sample in a Tedlar® bag or a SUMMA® canister for direct introduction into a GC with specific detector or a GC/MS, or to collect an adsorbed sample on Tenax or activated charcoal for thermal or solvent desorption and analysis. Semivolatiles are collected on adsorbents such as XAD-2 or PUF, solvent desorbed, then analyzed by either capillary column GC-FID, GC-ECD or GC/MS, depending on the exact analytes. These techniques have rather high detection limits, but are very flexible in the compounds that can be detected. The air CLP SOW specifies these types of methods. For the lowest detection limits, the sampling and analysis must be restricted to a specific target analyte.

1. Method 40 CFR 50, App. E. Hydrocarbons

The air sample is passed into an FID to determine the total hydrocarbon content (THC). A sample is next passed through a stripper column, which removes water, CO_2, and hydrocarbons other than methane. Direct introduction of this effluent into a GC separates the carbon monoxide from the methane. Detection is with a catalytic reducer to methane followed by an FID. The difference between the THC and the methane-alone value gives the value for the non-methane hydrocarbons (NMHC). A variation on the procedure gives a measurement method (Method 25) for non-methane organic compounds (NMOC). The whole gas sample is trapped in a dry-ice-cooled condenser, then passed through a gas chromatographic column, which separates carbon monoxide, carbon dioxide, and methane from the gas stream. The residual organic materials are back flushed into an oxidizer made from 19% chromia on alumina pellets at 650 °C, which converts everything to carbon dioxide. The effluent then passes into a reducer packed with nickel at 400 °C, which reduces the carbon dioxide into methane. Final analysis is by FID. Method TO-12 relies on a liquid-argon-cooled (-186 °C) trap to pass methane without retention. Thermal desorption of the trap contents into an FID gives NMOC (CO and CO_2 give no FID response.). Method 25A passes the whole trapped sample through a flame ionization analyzer without the GC column to give a total organic value. Method 25B uses a NDIR for determination of total organics.

2. MASA 116. Formaldehyde[*]

Aldehydes, and formaldehyde in particular, are irreversibly adsorbed to most traps. Most of these compounds present distinct health hazards in low-to-modest air concentrations and must be monitored. The most sensitive determinations of formaldehyde and other aldehydes use specific derivatization processes and colorimetric or instrument analysis of the derivative. The oldest method for formaldehyde is the chromotropic acid procedure. After years of misrepresentation, the reaction mechanism and product have recently been elucidated[4].

---

[*] Methods for Air Sampling and Analysis (MASA). Sources of this and other methods can be found in Section 1.II.

[4] Georghiou, P.E. and C.K. Ho. "The Chemistry of the Chromotropic Acid Method for the Analysis of Formaldehyde." *Can. J. Chem.* 1989. 67. pp. 971-876.

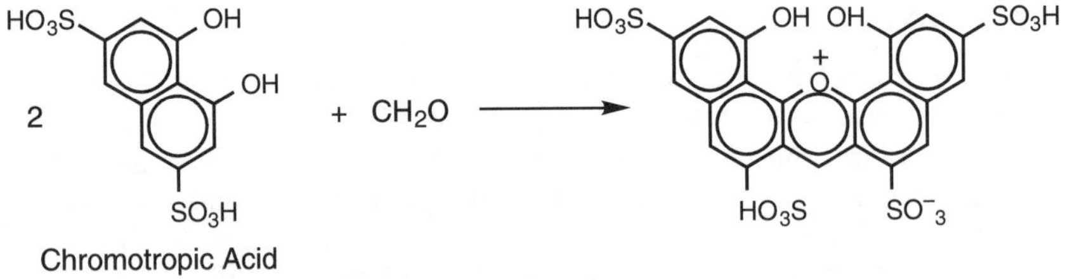

Chromotropic Acid

Figure 5-9. Reaction of chromotropic acid with formaldehyde.

The reaction with bisulfite and para-Rosaniline, has recently been used for determination of formaldehyde[5]. Method IP-6B uses this chemistry for continuous monitoring of formaldehyde through a 550 nm photodetector.

Formaldehyde, and aldehydes in general, react with 2,4-dinitrophenylhydrazine (DNPH) under mildly acidic conditions in water to form very stable hydrazones. This reaction has been used for over a hundred years to prepare solid derivatives of aldehydes for melting point characterization and identification. These derivatives are very strong UV absorbers and can be determined by direct injection HPLC. A more sensitive analysis results from extraction and concentration of the hydrazones followed by either HPLC or GC analysis. Method TO-5 uses the solvent extraction with HPLC determination. Methods TO-11 and IP-6A use a DNPH-coated solid absorbent for sampling. The hydrazones are eluted with acetonitrile and determined by HPLC. Method IP-6C uses a passive DNPH-loaded sampler followed by elution with acetonitrile and HPLC detection for formaldehyde.

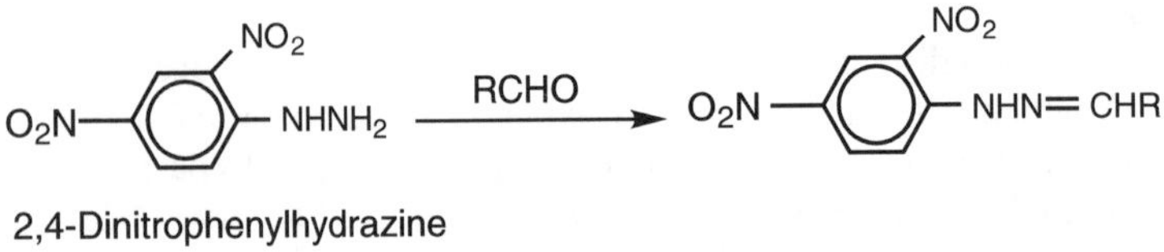

2,4-Dinitrophenylhydrazine

Figure 5-10. Reaction of DNPH with aldehydes.

The reaction of formaldehyde with benzothiazolinon hydrazone (MBTH) is very similar to that with DNPH, and the utility of the derivative is similar.

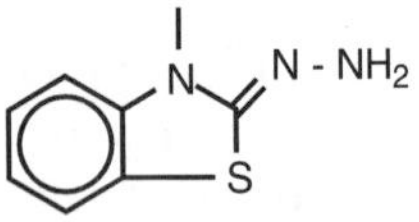

Figure 5-11. Structure of MBTH.

Aldehydes in general react with dansylhydrazine to give a hydrazone that is easily analyzed by HPLC with either fluorescent or chemiluminescent detection[6]. Either detec-

5   Groah, W.J., J. Bradfield, G. Gramp, R. Rudzinski and G. Heroux. "Comparative Response of Reconstituted Wood Products to European and North American Test Methods for Determining Formaldehyde Emissions." *Environ. Sci. Technol.* 1991. 25(1). pp. 117-122.

6   Nondek, L. D.R. Rodler and J.W. Birks. "Measurement of Sub-ppbv Concentrations of Aldehydes in a Forest Atmosphere Using a New HPLC Technique." *Environ. Sci. Technol.* 1992. 26(6) pp. 1174-1178.

tion technique can lower the detection limits by a factor of 100 to 10,000 over those seen with UV detection. A follow-up report on the method[7] offers significant improvement in the removal of interferences.

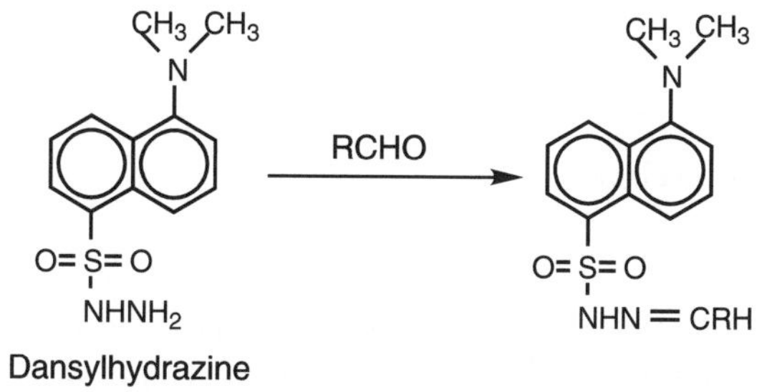

Dansylhydrazine

Figure 5-12. Reaction of aldehydes with dansylhydrazine.

3. Formic acid

Formic acid (HCO_2H) is the next oxidation step from formaldehyde toward carbon dioxide. It is one of the major contributing organic acids to the acidic soup formed in municipal landfills as a product of anaerobic bacterial decomposition of organic materials. Formic acid vapors can be analyzed in-situ by FTIR long-path at 1105 cm[-1]. Samples collected for laboratory analysis can be obtained on KOH-impregnated 47 mm glass fiber filters in forced air samplers followed by HPLC on size exclusion columns with dilute H_2SO_4 eluant and UV detection[8].

4. MASA 114. Acrolein

Acrolein (CH_2=CHCHO) is an important industrial monomer aldehyde used for the formation of many polymers. It is highly reactive. It can be analyzed by many of the above methods for aldehydes A highly specific procedure for acrolein begins with collection of an air sample in an impinger containing 1% $NaHSO_3$. The initial bisulfite addition product is reacted with 4-hexyl resorcinol and $HgCl_2$ in a trichloroacetic acid-ethanol solution to form an intense blue product that is read at 605 nm. The product is not well characterized[9].

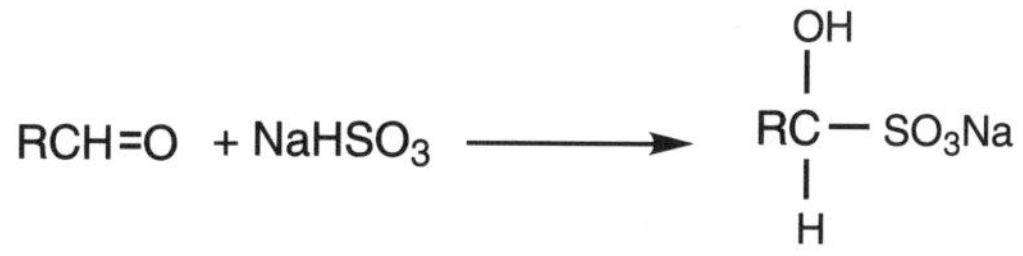

Figure 5-13. Reaction of aldehydes with bisulfite.

[7] Rodler, D.R., L. Nondek and J.W. Birks. "Evaluation of Ozone and Water Vapor Interferences in the Derivatization of Atmospheric Aldehydes with Dansylhydrazine." *Environ. Sci. Technol.* 1993. 27(13). pp. 2814-2820.

[8] Grosjean, D., E. C. Tuazon and E. Fujita. "Ambient Formic Acid in Southern California Air: A Comparison of Two Methods, Fourier Transform Infrared Spectroscopy and Alkaline Trap-liquid Chromatography with UV Detection." *Environ. Sci. Technol.* 1990. 24(1) pp. 144-146

[9] Cohen, I.R., and A.P. Altshuller. "A New Spectrophotometric Method for the Determination of Acrolein in Combustion Gases and in the Atmosphere." *Analytical Chemistry.* 1961. 33(6) pp. 726-733.

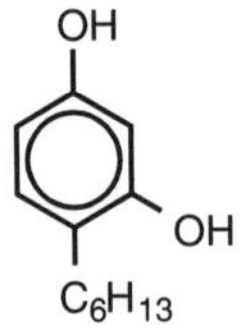

Figure 5-14. Structure of 4-hexyl-resorcinol.

5. Halocarbons

IR or capillary column GC-ECD or GC-MS are most often used for halocarbon analysis, as appropriate. A portable monitor for halocarbons passes the sample air into a cell containing an AC arc between copper and platinum electrodes. When halide vapors are present, a bright line spectrum of copper appears, the intensity of which is proportional to the halocarbon concentration.

C. Inorganic Analytes

1. MASA 202. Free Atmospheric Chlorine

Free atmospheric chlorine is a very hazardous, but transient, species, and it is best monitored on site with a colorimetric tube. Being a symmetrical molecule, it is not detected by IR, although it is feasible to determine it by Raman spectroscopy. A wet chemical method involves the instantaneous bleaching of the primary standard methyl orange at pH 3.0. The reduction of methyl orange in the impinger can be measured colorimetrically or by comparison with color standards. The bleaching reaction is highly specific for chlorine.

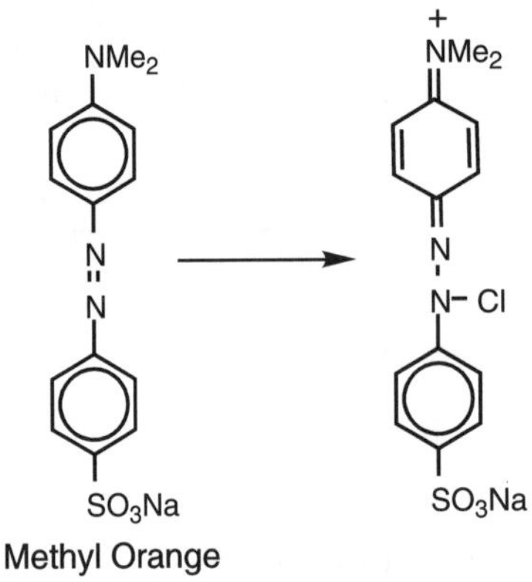

Figure 5-15. Proposed first step for the bleaching reaction of methyl orange with chlorine.

2. Sulfur Compounds

Inorganic sulfur exists in the atmosphere as hydrogen sulfide, carbonyl sulfide (COS), carbon disulfide, sulfur dioxide, and sulfuric acid. Organic sulfur can be present as mercaptans (RSH), thioethers (R_2S), sulfoxides (R_2SO), sulfones (R_2SO_2), and sulfates (R_2SO_4). Other more complex forms are dithio ethers, thiophenes, thio acids, dithio acids, and a host of others. All can be monitored by IR. A general method for total sulfur involves chemiluminescent detection of sulfur species[10]. The sulfur compound is combusted to form SO, which reacts with ozone to form an excited sulfur dioxide. Relaxation of the excited species is accompanied by emission of light.

$$\text{"S"} + \text{Hydrogen flame} \longrightarrow SO \text{ — } O_3 \longrightarrow SO^*_2 + O_2$$
$$SO^*_2 \longrightarrow SO_2 + h\nu$$

Figure 5-16. Chemiluminescent detection of sulfur compounds.

Mercaptans (RSH) can be selectively determined by trapping in an impinger as mercuric sulfide, then treating with DPD and ferric chloride to give a colorimetric reaction. The product is probably similar to methylene blue with the "R" group from the mercaptan still hanging off the sulfur. Hydrogen sulfide can be determined in a similar fashion by trapping as cadmium sulfide then reacting to form methylene blue.

$$RSH + Hg(OAc)_2 \text{ — impinger} \longrightarrow HgS$$
$$HgS + DPD + H^+ + FeCl_3 \longrightarrow \text{Lambert-Beers Law red color (500 nm)}$$

Figure 5-17. Determination of mercaptans.

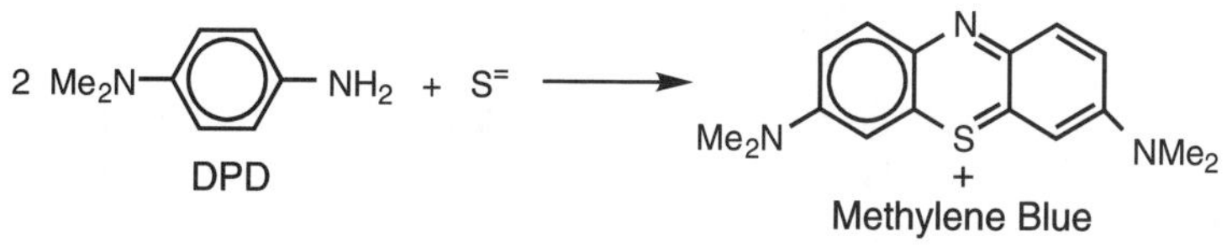

Figure 5-18. Formation of methylene blue from sulfide.

Hydrogen sulfide is determined in method 11 by trapping in a cadmium sulfate solution at pH 3 to form cadmium sulfide, addition of an excess known amount of iodine solution, then iodometric titration with sodium thiosulfate or PAO and starch indicator to determine the excess iodine.

$$S^{-2} + I_2 \longrightarrow S^\circ + 2I^-$$
$$I_{2(excess)} + 2Na_2S_2O_3 \longrightarrow 2I^- + 2Na^+ + Na_2S_4O_6$$

Figure 5-19. Iodometric determination of sulfide.

Hydrogen sulfide, carbonyl sulfide, and carbon disulfide are known as total reduced sulfur (TRS), along with mercaptans, thioethers and dithioethers, and are determined in methods 15 and 16 by gas chromatographic separation of the compounds with an FPD in the sulfur mode. Methods 15A and 16A mix the sampled gas stream with air, remove interfering sulfur dioxide with a citrate buffer scrubber, pass it through an oxidizing combustion chamber at 1100 °C, then trap the produced SO_2 in a peroxide impinger where it is oxidized to sulfate. The sulfate is determined by the barium perchlorate -

---

10 Benner, R. L., and D. H. Stedman. "Field Evaluation of the Sulfur Chemiluminescence Detector." *Environ. Sci. Technol.* 1990. 24(10) pp. 1592-1596.

thorin titration as in method 6. Method 16B is similar in that TRS is oxidized to sulfur dioxide, but the determination is by GC-FPD in the sulfur mode.

3. Sulfur Dioxide

Sulfur dioxide is a primary atmospheric contaminant arising from the burning of soft coal and other low-grade fossil fuels. Another source is the production of metals from ores, which are often metal sulfides. A wide variety of detection methods are available. Sulfur dioxide is amenable to IR monitoring at 1361 cm^{-1} with a 100-meter path length detection limit of 2.0 ppb. Another method uses pulsed fluorescence. Sulfur dioxide irradiated with narrow band (46 nm wide) UV light with a maximum of 216 nm will emit fluorescence over the range 240 - 420 nm, which is detected with a photomultiplier tube. The relationship between emitted intensity and concentration is linear. SO_2 can also be determined by its UV absorbance. All these instrumental techniques are allowed in 40 CFR 60, App. A, Method 6C.

There are also a variety of wet chemical methods for SO_2. Impinger collection with tetrachloromercurate or formaldehyde results in oxidation to sulfite or bisulfite.

$$SO_2 + K_2HgCl_4 + H_2O \longrightarrow HgCl_2SO_3^{-2} + 2HCl$$

$$SO_2 + CH_2O + H_2O \longrightarrow HOCH_2SO_3H$$

Figure 5-20. Impinger collection of sulfur dioxide.

Analysis of the trapped formaldehyde-bisulfite is accomplished by reaction with *p*-rosaniline to form *p*-rosanilinemethylsulfonic acid. This forms the basis for method 40 CFR 50, Appendix A.

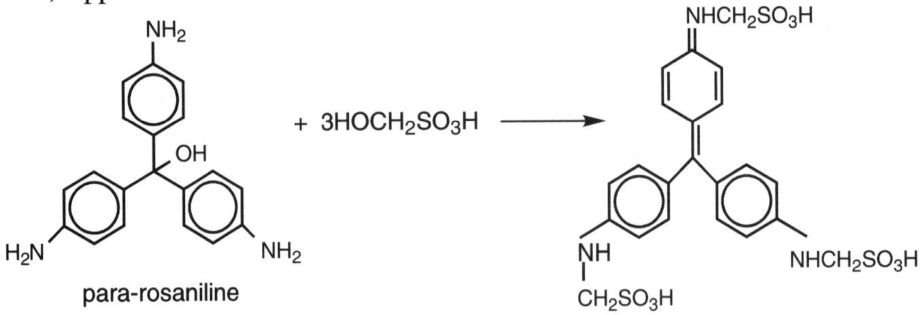

Figure 5-21. Reaction of formaldehyde-bisulfite with *p*-rosaniline.

Another method involves impinger collection of SO_2 in H_2O_2 with resulting oxidation to sulfate followed by analysis for sulfate. Gravimetric analysis with barium is time honored, but not very sensitive. Turbidimetric analysis of barium sulfate is more sensitive.

$$SO_2 + H_2O_2 \longrightarrow H_2SO_4$$

$$SO_4^{-2} + Ba^{+2} \longrightarrow BaSO_4 \text{ (turbidimetric analysis)}$$

Figure 5-22. Oxidation of sulfur dioxide with peroxide to sulfate.

Barium methylthymol blue method (MASA 720C) is a variation where a standard solution of barium methylthymol blue dye is mixed with SO_4^{-2} solution. The barium is removed from the dye complex by precipitation as $BaSO_4$. The reduction in dye absorbance is linear with SO_4^{-2} concentration. The barium methylthymol blue has a maximum absorbance at 608 nm. The free MTB has maximum absorbance at 460 nm, so either can be read. This technique lends itself nicely to automation.

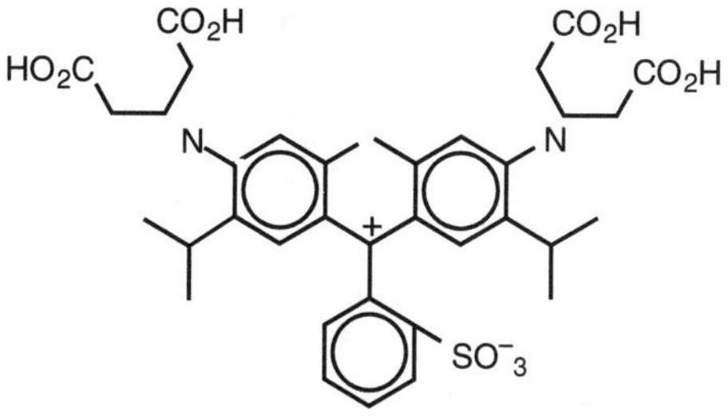

Figure 5-23. Structure of methylthymol blue.

A titration method using $Ba(ClO_4)_2$ and a thorin indicator is useful for moderate SO_4^{-2} levels (>2.5 µg/mL). The free yellow color of thorin changes to a pink when complexed with Ba^{+2}. This is the determinative procedure of 40 CFR 60, App. A, Methods 6, 6A, 6B, and 8.

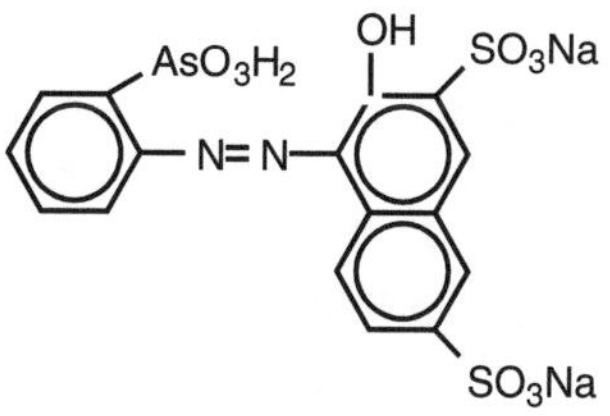

Figure 5-24. Structure of thorin.

A spectroscopic method uses barium chloranilate (MASA 720F). Addition to a sample solution containing SO_4^{-2} gives the insoluble $BaSO_4$ and hydrogenchloranilate, which is read at 312 nm.

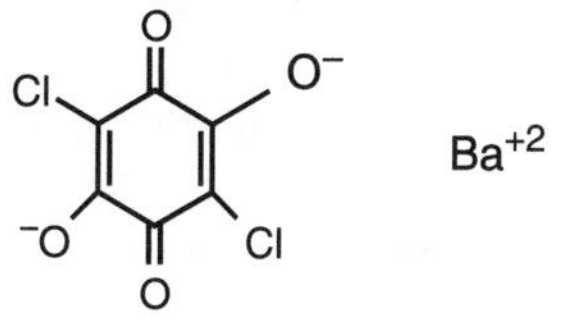

Figure 5-25. Structure of barium chloranilate.

4. Nitrogen Oxides

Table 5-3. Nitrogen oxides

Compound	Name	Comment
N_2O	Nitrous oxide	laughing gas
NO	Nitric oxide	reacts readily with oxygen
NO_2	Nitrogen dioxide	toxic, dimerizes to N_2O_4
N_2O_3	Dinitrogen trioxide	decomposes below room temperature
N_2O_4	Dinitogen tetroxide	dimer of NO_2
N_2O_5	Nitrogen pentoxide	highly reactive

A large number of nitrogen oxides exist, ranging from nitrous oxide (N_2O), the historic laughing gas, to nitrogen dioxide, a brown, choking, toxic gas and an important component of smog. (NO) and nitrogen dioxide are pollutants that arise from the high temperature direct combination of N_2 and O_2 in internal combustion engines. Nitric oxide is determined by IR at 1920-1870 cm^{-1} with a 4.0 ppb detection limit in a 100 meter path length or by chemiluminescence resulting from reaction with O_3. Nitrogen dioxide can be determined in the same instrument by pretreatment reduction to nitric oxide. These techniques are described in 40 CFR 50, Appendix F.

$$NO + O_3 \longrightarrow NO^*_2 + O_2 \; ; NO^*_2 \longrightarrow NO_2 + h\nu$$

$$2NO_2 + Mo \text{ (or Carbon)} - 200 \text{ °C} \longrightarrow 2NO$$

Figure 5-26. Chemiluminescent reaction of nitric oxide with ozone.

Method 7 and MASA 407 are for the determination of nitrogen oxides. Nitrogen oxides (except N_2O) are trapped in an impinger with sulfuric acid-hydrogen peroxide by oxidation to nitric acid. The nitric acid is reacted with phenoldisulfonic acid (formed from phenol and fuming sulfuric acid) to form a product that is determined colorimetrically at 400-415 nm.

Method 7A uses the same trapping solution, with determination by ion chromatography. Method 7B determines the formed nitric acid by UV spectrophotometry.

Methods 7C and 7D use an alkaline-permanganate trapping solution that oxidizes the nitrogen oxides to nitrate ion. Method 7C then reduces the nitrate to nitrite with a cadmium column and determines the nitrite with sulfanilic acid and *N*-naphthyl-ethylenediamine as in Method 352. Method 7D uses ion chromatography for the detection of nitrate.

Method IP-5B traps NO_2 on triethanolamine, then determines the nitrite by colorimetric reaction with sulfanilamide and *N*-1-naphthylethylene diamine. Method IP-5C again traps the NO_2 on triethanolamine but performs the determination by ion chromatography.

Method IP-5A determines nitrogen dioxide in a continuous mode by reaction with 5-amino-2,3-dihydro-1,4-phthalazine dione (Luminol) in base solution to produce light, which is detected by a photodetector.

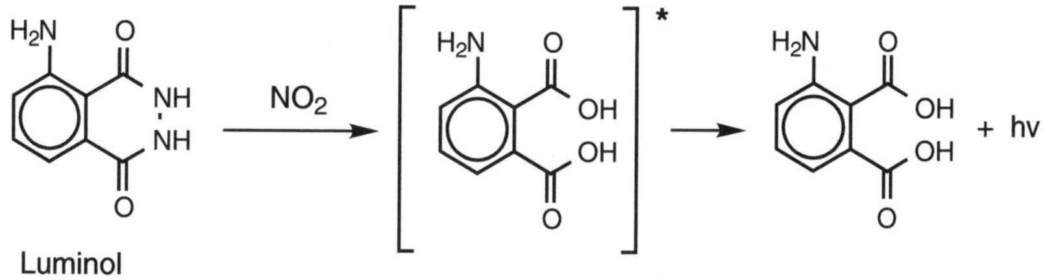

Figure 5-27. Luminol reaction with nitrogen dioxide.

5. Ozone

Ozone can be measured by IR at 1045 cm^{-1} with a 2.0 ppb detection limit in a 100 meter path length. It is also determined by chemiluminescent reaction with $CH_2=CH_2$ (Method 40 CFR 50, App. D) or nitric oxide. Ozone has a UV absorption at 254 nm, which has been used for analysis.

6. Metals

Most metals exist in the atmosphere attached to particulates, although mercury can exist as the elemental vapor. Collection is performed with air sampling cassettes, the filter acid digested, and metals assayed by AA (Method 40 CFR 50, App. G and Method 12 for lead, Method 104 for beryllium, and Method 108 for arsenic) or ICP. Several different types and pore sizes of membrane filters are available. The mixed cellulose ester membrane (MCE) is easily digested overnight in nitric acid at room temperature and preferred for metals analysis. Use of the polyethylene, PVC, or Teflon membranes leaves a gooey mess upon attempted digestion.

Mercury is sampled in acidic iodine monochloride (ICl) solution, then determined by cold vapor AA in methods 101 and 102. Method 101A is similar except the mercury collection is in an acidic permanganate solution.

7. Particulates

Gravimetric assay of filter trapable particulates in a cassette from a high-volume forced-air system is the easiest to perform; however, the detection limit is quite high. A more sensitive analysis measures the optical density of transparent filter tape to measure particulate haze.

8. Asbestos

Asbestos is a family of silicates with a variety of other minerals that form long flexible fibers. Two general groups are recognized, the serpentine, and amphibole asbestos. The serpentines are acid labile while the amphiboles are acid resistant. Both are fire resistant fibers. Asbestos generally exists as 0.1 to 1.0 µm fibers, which are invisible to the eye, and can be suspended in air, which results in their easy inhalation.

The most widely occurring serpentine is chrysotile (White asbestos) $Mg_6(Si_4O_{10})(OH)_8$. Amphiboles are divided into five distinct chemical types. Ascarite is a NaOH-treated asbestos used for CO_2 absorption in combustion analysis.

Table 5-4. Amphibole asbestos

anthophyllite - $(Mg, Fe)_7(Si_8O_{22})(OH)_2$ low iron content

amosite - $Fe_5Mg_2(Si_8O_{22})(OH)_2$

actinolite - $Ca_2(Mg, Fe)_5(Si_8O_{22})(OH)_2$

tremolite - $Ca_2Mg_5(Si_8O_{22})(OH)_2$

crocidolite - $Na_2Fe_5(Si_8O_{22})(OH)_2$ (blue asbestos)

An EPA method for analysis is covered in *Analytical Method for Determination of Asbestos Fibers in Water*, US EPA Environmental Research Laboratory, Athens, GA 30613. September, 1983. EPA 600/4-83-043. It is available from NTIS as publication number PB-83260471. The method requires prior oxidation with ozone and UV light to remove organic materials, filtration with a fine pore membrane (0.1 μm pore size) followed by fixing the surface with carbon vacuum deposition and transmission electron microscopic examination. Selected area electron diffraction is used to determine the crystal structure, and element composition is accomplished by energy dispersive X-ray analysis.

Other asbestos analysis methods are found in Title 40 CFR in the TSCA regulations. 40 CFR 763, Subpart E (follows 763.99), Appendix A contains mandatory and non-mandatory transmission electron miscroscopy procedures for analysis of asbestos fibers on air filters. Part 763, Subpart F (follows 763.119), Appendix A, Section 1 contains a polarized light microscopy method for determination of asbestos in bulk insulation samples, while Section 2 contains an X-ray powder diffraction method. Part 763.121, Appendices A and B contain reference EPA/OSHA methods for air sampling and analysis of asbestos fibers by positive phase contrast microscopy. The majority of environmental laboratories subcontract this work to the few labs that specialize in it.

IV. EPA METHODS

Most of the following methods are available online from the EPA Research Triangle Park service center at www.rtpnc.epa.gov. The website also contains a large number of downloadable draft and proposed methods that have yet to be finalized. Any of these methods may be usable regardless of promulgation status in light of the *Federal Register* notice of Monday, 24 February, 1997, pp 8314-8328, concerning use of alternate methods as credible evidence in compliance monitoring situations for air programs.

Table 5-5. EPA Air Program Methods found in 40 CFR

40 CFR Part	Appendix	Method No.	Method Description
50	A	–	Reference method for the determination of sulfur dioxide in the atmosphere (Pararosaniline method)
50	B	–	Reference method for the determination of suspended particulate matter in the atmosphere (High-Volume method)
50	C	–	Measurement principle and calibration procedure for the measurement of carbon monoxide in the atmosphere by non-dispersive IR

Continued on next page.

Table 5-5.   EPA Air Program Methods found in 40 CFR, *continued*

40 CFR Part	Appendix	Method No.	Method Description
50	D	–	Measurement principle and calibration procedure for the measurement of ozone in the atmosphere
50	E	–	Reference method for determination of hydrocarbons corrected for methane
50	F	–	Measurement principle and calibration procedure for the measurement of nitrogen dioxide in the atmosphere (Gas Phase Chemiluminescence)
50	G	–	Reference method for the determination of lead in suspended particulate matter collected from ambient air
50	H	–	Interpretation of National Ambient Air Quality Standards for ozone
50	J	–	Reference method for the determination of particulate matter as PM_{10} in the atmosphere
51	M	201	Determination of PM_{10} emissions (Exhaust Gas Recycle procedure)
51	M	201A	Determination of PM_{10} emissions (Constant Sampling Rate procedure)
51	M	202	Determination of condensible particulate emissions from stationary sources
52	D	-	Sulfur dioxide emissions from stationary sources by continuous monitors
60.47	I	-	Determination of sulfur dioxide emissions from fossil fuel fired combustion sources (continuous bubbler method)
60.648	-	-	Optional procedure for measuring hydrogen sulfide in acid gas - Tutwiler procedure
60	A	1	Sample and velocity transverses for stationary sources
60	A	1A	Sample and velocity traverses for stationary sources with small stacks or ducts
60	A	2	Determination of stack gas velocity and volumetric flow (type S pitot tube)
60	A	2A	Direct measurement of gas volume through pipes and small ducts
60	A	2B	Determination of exhaust gas volume flow from gasoline vapor incinerators
60	A	2C	Determination of stack gas velocity and volumetric flow rate in small stacks
60	A	2D	Measurement of gas volumetric flows in small pipes
60	A	2E	Landfill gas production flow rate
60	A	3	Gas analysis for the determination of dry molecular weight
60	A	3A	Determination of oxygen and carbon dioxide concentrations in emissions from stationary sources
60	A	3B	Gas analysis for the determination of the emission rate correction factor or excess air
60	A	3C	CO_2, CH_4, N_2, O_2 by TCD
60	A	4	Determination of moisture content in stack gases
60	A	5	Determination of particulate emissions from stationary sources
60	A	5A	Particulate emissions from asphalt
60	A	5B	Non-sulfuric acid particulates from stationary sources

Continued on next page.

Table 5-5. EPA Air Program Methods found in 40 CFR, *continued*

40 CFR Part	Appendix	Method No.	Method Description
60	A	5D	Particulate emissions from positive pressure fabric filters
60	A	5E	Particulate emission from wool fiberglass insulation manufacturing industry
60	A	5F	Determination of non-sulfate particulate matter from stationary sources
60	A	5G	Particulate emissions from wood heaters from a dilution tunnel sampling location.
60	A	5H	Determination of particulate emissions from wood heaters from a stack location
60	A	6	SO_2 from stationary sources
60	A	6A	SO_2, moisture, and CO_2 from fossil fuel combustion sources
60	A	6B	Determination of sulfur dioxide and carbon dioxide daily average emissions from fossil fuel combustion sources.
60	A	6C	Determination of sulfur dioxide emissions from stationary sources (Instrumental Analyzer procedure)
60	A	7	NO_2 from stationary sources
60	A	7A	Determination of nitrogen oxide emissions from stationary sources - ion chromatography method
60	A	7B	Determination of nitrogen oxide emissions from stationary sources (ultraviolet spectrophotometry)
60	A	7C	Determination of nitrogen oxide emissions from stationary sources - alkaline-permanganate/colorimetric method
60	A	7D	Determination of nitrogen oxide emissions from stationary sources - alkaline-permanganate/ion chromatographic method
60	A	7E	Determination of nitrogen oxide emissions from stationary sources (Instrumental Analyzer procedure)
60	A	8	Determination of sulfuric acid mist and SO_2 emissions from stationary sources
60	A	9	Visual determination of the opacity of emissions from stationary sources
60	A	9 Alternate Method 1	Determination of the opacity of emissions from stationary sources remotely by LIDAR
60	A	10	Determination of carbon monoxide emissions from stationary sources
60	A	10A	Determination of carbon monoxide emissions in certifying continuous emission monitoring systems at petroleum refineries
60	A	10B	Determination of carbon monoxide emissions from stationary sources
60	A	11	H_2S of fuel gas streams in petroleum refineries
60	A	12	Inorganic lead emissions from stationary sources
60	A	13A	Total fluoride emissions from stationary sources (SPADNS Zirconium Lake method)
60	A	13B	Total fluoride emissions from stationary sources (Specific Ion Electrode method)

Continued on next page.

Table 5-5.   EPA Air Program Methods found in 40 CFR, *continued*

40 CFR Part	Appendix	Method No.	Method Description
60	A	14	Fluoride emissions from potroom roof monitors for aluminum plants
-	-	14A	Total fluoride emissions from selected sources at primary aluminum plants (proposed)
60	A	15	H_2S, COS, and CS_2 emissions from stationary sources
60	A	15A	Determination of total reduced sulfur emissions from sulfur recovery plants in petroleum refineries
60	A	16	Semi-continuous determination of sulfur emissions from stationary sources
60	A	16A	Determination of total reduced sulfur emissions from stationary sources (Impinger technique)
60	A	16B	Determination of total reduced sulfur emissions from stationary sources
60	A	17	Particulate emissions from stationary sources
60	A	18	Gaseous organic compound emissions by gas chromatography[11]
60	A	19	SO_2 removal efficiency and particulate, SO_2, and NO_x emission rates
60	A	20	NO_x, SO_2, and diluent emissions from gas turbines
60	A	21	Determination of volatile organic compound leaks
60	A	22	Visual determination of fugitive emissions from material sources and smoke emissions from flares
60	A	23	Determination of polychlorinated dibenzo-p-dioxins and polychlorinated dibenzofurans from stationary sources
60	A	24	Volatile matter content, water content, density, volume of solids, and weight of solids of surface coatings
60	A	24A	Determination of volatile matter content and density of printing inks and related coatings
60	A	25	Total gaseous nonmethane organic emissions as carbon
60	A	25A	Determination of total gaseous organic concentration using a flame ionization analyzer
60	A	25B	Determination of total gaseous organic concentration using a non-dispersive infrared analyzer
60	A	25C	NMOC in landfill gas
60	A	25D	Determination of the volatile organic concentration of waste samples[12]
60	A	25E	Determination of vapor phase organic concentration in waste samples
60	A	26	Determination of hydrogen halide emissions from stationary sources - midget impinger method[13]

Continued on next page.

[11] Modified in *Federal Register*, Volume 59, pp. 19306 to 19401, Friday, 22 April 1994.
[12] *Federal Register*, Friday, 22 April 1994. Volume 59, pp. 19306 to 19323.
[13] Same as footnote 12.

Table 5-5.   EPA Air Program Methods found in 40 CFR, *continued*

40 CFR Part	Appendix	Method No.	Method Description
60	A	26A	Determination of hydrogen halide and halogen emissions from stationary sources - isokinetic method[14]
60	A	27	Vapor tightness of gasoline delivery tank using pressure-vacuum test
60	A	28	Certification and auditing of wood heaters
60	A	28A	Measurement of air to fuel ratio and minimum achievable burn ratios for wood-fired appliances
60	A	29	Metals emissions from stationary sources
61	B	101	Determination of particulate and gaseous mercury emissions from chlor-alkali plants - air streams
61	B	101A	Determination of particulate and gaseous mercury emissions from sewage sludge incinerators
61	B	102	Determination of particulate and gaseous mercury emissions from chlor-alkali plants - hydrogen streams
61	B	103	Beryllium screening method
61	B	104	Determination of beryllium emissions from stationary sources
61	B	105	Determination of mercury in wastewater treatment plant sewage sludge
61	B	106	Determination of vinyl chloride from stationary sources
61	B	107	Determination of vinyl chloride content of in-process wastewater samples and vinyl chloride content of polyvinyl chloride resin, slurry, wet cakes and latex samples
61	B	107A	Determination of vinyl chloride content of solvents, resin-solvent solution, polyvinyl chloride resin, resin slurry, wet resin, and latex samples
61	B	108	Determination of particulate and gaseous arsenic emissions
61	B	108A	Determination of arsenic content in ore samples from nonferrous smelters
61	B	108B	Determination of arsenic content in ore samples from nonferrous smelters
61	B	108C	Determination of arsenic content in ore samples from nonferrous smelters
61	B	111	Polonium-210 emissions from stationary sources
61	B	114	Test methods for measuring radionuclide emissions from stationary sources
61	B	115	Monitoring for Radon-222 emissions
-	-	201	Instack PM_{10}
-	-	201A	Instack PM_{10} CRS
-	-	202	Condensible particulate matter
-	-	203	Continuous opacity monitoring for compliance (proposed)
-	-	203A	Time averaged visual opacity (proposed)
-	-	203B	Time-exception visual opacity (proposed)

Continued on next page.

---

[14] Same as footnote 12.

Table 5-5. EPA Air Program Methods found in 40 CFR, *continued*

40 CFR Part	Appendix	Method No.	Method Description
-	-	203C	Instantaneous limitation visual opacity (proposed)
-	-	204	Permanent or temporary total enclosure for determining capture efficiency
-	-	204A	VOCs in liquid input stream
-	-	204B	VOCs in captured stream
-	-	204C	VOCs in captured stream dilution technique
-	-	204D	Fugitive VOCs from temporary total enclosure
-	-	204E	Fugitive VOCs from building enclosure
-	-	204F	VOCs in liquid input stream distillation
-	-	205	Gas dilution calibration
63	A	301	Field validation of pollutant measurement methods from various waste media
-	-	303	By-product coke oven batteries
-	-	303A	Nonrecovery coke oven batteries
63	A	304	Method for determination of biodegradation rates of organic compounds [15]
-	-	304A	Vent option biodegradation rates
-	-	304B	Scrubber option biodegradation rates
63	A	305	Method for measurement of individual volatile organics in wastewater [16]
-	-	306	Chromium emissions
-	-	306A	Chromium emissions (mason jar method)
-	-	306B	Surface tension
-	-	307	Emissions from solvent vapor cleaners
-	-	308	Procedure for methanol emissions (proposed)
-	-	310A	Residual hexane
-	-	310B	Residual solvent
-	-	310C	Residual hexane in EPDM crumb rubber
-	-	311	HAPS in paints & coatings
-	-	312A	Styrene in SBR latex (GC)
-	-	312B	Styrene in SBR latx by capillary GC
-	-	312C	Styrene in SBR latex produced by emulsion polymerization
-	-	313A	Residual hydrocarbons in crumb rubber
-	-	313B	Residual HC in rubber crumb by capillary GC
-	-	315	PM and MCEM from aluminum production facilities (proposed)
-	-	316	Sample & analysis for formaldehyde emissions in the mineral wool & wool fiberglass industries (proposed)
-	-	318	Extractive FTIR method for measurement of emissions from the mineral wool and wool fiberglass industries (proposed)

Continued on next page.

---

[15] *Federal Register*, Thursday, 31 December, 1992. Volume 57, Number 252. pp. 62785-62797. Finalized in Federal Register, Friday, 22 April, 1994. Volume 59, pp. 19402-19625.

[16] Same as footnote 15.

Table 5-5.   EPA Air Program Methods found in 40 CFR, *continued*

40 CFR Part	Appendix	Method No.	Method Description
-	-	319	Filtration efficiency for paint overspray arrestors (proposed)
-	-	320	Vapor phase organic & inorganic emissions by extractive FTIR (proposed)
-	-	321	Gaseous HCl emissions at Portland cement kilns by FTIR (proposed)
-	-	322	HCl emissions from Portland cement kilns by GFCIR (proposed)
80	A		Test for the determination of phosphorus in gasoline
80	B	1	Standard method test for lead in gasoline by atomic absorption spectrometry
80	B	2	Automated method test for lead in gasoline by atomic absorption spectrometry
80	B	3	Test for lead in gasoline by X-ray spectrometry
80	D		Sampling procedures for fuel volatility
80	E	3	Test for determining Reid vapor pressure (RVP) of gasoline and gasoline-oxygenate blends. Method 3 - Evacuated chamber method
80	F	1	Test for determining the quantity of alcohol in gasoline. Method 1 - Water extraction method
80	F	2	Test method for determination of C_1 to C_4 alcohols and MTBE in gasoline by gas chromatography
80	G		Sampling procedures for diesel fuel

Table 5-6.   Methods for compliance with burning hazardous wastes in boilers and industrial furnaces (BIF) regulations

40 CFR Part	Appendix	Method No.	Method Description
266	IX	3.1	Methodology for the determination of metals emissions in exhaust gases from hazardous waste incineration and similar combustion processes
		3.2	Determination of hexavalent chromium emissions from stationary sources (Method Cr^{+6})
		3.3.1	Isokinetic HCl/Cl_2 emission sampling train (Method 0050)
		3.3.2	Midget impinger HCl/Cl_2 emission sampling train (Method 0051)
		3.3.3	Protocols for analysis of samples from HCl/Cl_2 emission sampling train (Method 9057)
		3.4	Determination of polychlorinated dibenzo-p-dioxins (PCDDs) and polychlorinated dibenzofurans (PCDF) from stationary sources (Method 23)
		3.5	Sampling for aldehyde and ketone emissions from stationary sources (Method 0011)
		3.6	Analysis for aldehydes and ketones by HPLC (Method 0011A)

Table 5-7.   Compendium of Methods for the determination of Toxic Organic Compounds in ambient air[17], Second Edition, 1999

Method	Description
TO1	Determination of volatile organic compounds in ambient air using Tenax adsorption and gas chromatography (GC-MS)
TO2	Determination of volatile organic compounds in ambient air by carbon molecular sieve adsorption and GC-MS
TO3	Determination of volatile organic compounds in ambient air using cryogenic preconcentration techniques and gas chromatography with FID and ECD
TO4A	Determination of organochlorine pesticides and polychlorinated biphenyls in ambient air
TO5	Determination of aldehydes and ketones in ambient air using HPLC
TO6	Determination of phosgene in ambient air using HPLC
TO7	Determination of n-nitrosodimethylamine in ambient air using GC
TO8	Determination of phenol and methylphenols (cresols) in ambient air using HPLC
TO9A	Determination of polychlorinated dibenzo-p-dioxins (PCDD) in ambient air using high resolution GC - high resolution MS
TO10A	Determination of organochlorine pesticides in ambient air using low-volume polyurethane foam (PUF) sampling with GC/ECD
TO11A	Determination of formaldehyde in ambient air using adsorbent cartridge followed by HPLC
TO12	Determination of non-methane organic compounds (NMOC) in ambient air using cryogenic preconcentration and direct flame ionization detection
TO13A	Determination of polyaromatic hydrocarbons (PAHs) in ambient air using high volume sampling with GC-MS and high resolution liquid chromatography analysis
TO14A	Determination of volatile organic compounds in ambient air using SUMMA polished canister sampling and GC analysis
TO15	SUMMA passivated canister sampling with GC coupled to a MS or ion trap for polar and non-polar VOC
TO16	VOC by real-time monitoring by FTIR
TO17	VOC by real-time or solid adsorbent sampling followed by GC-FID or GC-MS

Table 5-8.   Compendium of Methods for the determination of Inorganic Compounds in ambient air[18]

Method	Description
IO-1	Continuous measurement of suspended particulate matter (SPM) in ambient air
IO-1.1	Continuous monitoring of ambient PM_{10} concentration using the Graseby Anderson PM_{10} Attenuation Monitor
IO-1.2	Continuous monitoring of PM_{10} in ambient air using the Wedding and Associates Beta Gauge Automated Particle Sampler
IO-1.3	Determination of PM_{10} in ambient air using a continuous TEOM Particular Sampler
IO-2	Integrated sampling of suspended particulate matter (SPM)
IO-2.1	Sampling of ambient air for SPM using high volume sampler
IO-2.2	Sampling for SPM in ambient air using a dichotomous sampler
IO-2.3	Sampling of ambient air for SPM <10um (PM_{10}) using a low volume Partisol sampler

Continued on next page.

---

[17] Available from the Internet at website http://www.epa.gov/ttn/amtic/airtox.html
[18] Available from the Internet at www.epa.gov/ttn/amtic

Table 5-8. **Compendium of Methods for the determination of Inorganic Compounds in ambient air**[19], *continued*

Method	Description
IO-2.4	Calculations, standard volume
IO-3	Chemical species analysis of filter collected SPM
IO-3.1	Selection, preparation and extraction of filter material
IO-3.2	Determination of toxic metals in ambient particulate matter using AA
IO-3.3	Determination of elements captured on filter material and analyzed by XRF
IO-3.4	Determination of metals captured on glass fiber filter and analyzed by ICP
IO-3.5	Determination of metals captured on glass fiber filter and analyzed by ICP-MS
IO-3.6	Analysis of ambient air particles for metals using PIXE spectroscopy
IO-3.7	Determination of elements captured on glass fiber filters and analyzed by neutron activation spectroscopy
IO-4	Determination of reactive acidic and basic gases and strong acidity of atmospheric fine particles in ambient air using annular denuder technology
IO-4.1	Determination of strong acidity of atmospheric fine particles <2.5 um using annular denuder technology
IO-4.2	Determination of reactive acidic and basic gases and strong acidity of atmospheric fine particles in ambient air using annular denuder technology
IO-5	Sampling and analysis for atmospheric mercury
IO-5.1	Sampling and analysis of vapor and particle phase mercury in ambient air utilizing cold vapor atomic fluorescence spectrometry

Table 5-9. **Quality Assurance Handbook for Air Pollution Measurement Systems**

Volume	Description
I	Field Guide to Environmental Quality Assurance EPA/600/R-94/038A
II	Ambient Air Methods EPA/600/R-94/038b
III	Stationary Source-Specific Methods EPA/600/R-94/038c, September, 1994
IV	Meteorological Measurements EPA/6--/R-94/038d, March, 1995
Va	QA Manual for Precipitation Measurement Systems
Vb	Operations and Maintenance for Precipitation Measurement Systems

---

[19] Available from the Internet at www.epa.gov/ttn/amtic

Table 5-10. Compendium of Methods for the determination of Air Pollutants in indoor air

Method	Description
IP-1A	Determination of volatile organic compounds (VOCs) in indoor air using stainless steel canisters
IP-1B	Determination of volatile organic compounds (VOCs) in indoor air using solid absorbent tubes
IP-2A[20]	Determination of nicotine in indoor air using XAD-4 sorbent tubes
IP-2B	Determination of nicotine in indoor air using treated filter cassettes
IP-3A	Determination of carbon monoxide (CO) or carbon dioxide (CO_2) in indoor air using nondispersive infrared (NDIR)
IP-3B	Determination of carbon monoxide (CO) or carbon dioxide (CO_2) in indoor air using gas filter correlation
IP-3C	Determination of carbon monoxide in indoor air using electrochemical oxidation
IP-4A	Determination of air exchange rate in indoor air using perfluorocarbon tracer (PFT)
IP-4B	Determination of air exchange rate in indoor air using tracer gas
IP-5A	Determination of nitrogen dioxide (NO_2) in indoor air using a continuous luminox monitor
IP-5B	Determination of nitrogen dioxide (NO_2) in indoor air using Palmes diffusion tubes
IP-5C	Determination of nitrogen dioxide (NO_2) in indoor air using passive sampling device
IP-6A	Determination of formaldehyde and other aldehydes in indoor air using a solid adsorbent cartridge
IP-6B	Determination of formaldehyde and other aldehydes in indoor air using a continuous colorimetric analyzer
IP-6C	Determination of formaldehyde and other aldehydes in indoor air using a passive sampling device
IP-7	Determination of benzo(a)pyrene [B(a)P] and other polynuclear aromatic hydrocarbons (PAHs) in indoor air
IP-8	Determination of organochlorine pesticides in indoor air
IP-9	Determination of reactive acidic and basic gases and particulate matter in indoor air (annular denuder technique)
IP-10A	Determination of respirable particulate matter in indoor air using size specific impaction
IP-10B	Determination of respirable particulate matter in indoor air using a continuous particulate monitor

Table 5-11. CLP Draft Statement of Work for Air Analysis at CERCLA Sites

Section	Description
1	Analytical method for the determination of volatile organic compounds (VOCs) in air collected in SUMMA canisters and analyzed by GC/MS
2	Analytical method for the determination of volatile organic compounds (VOCs) in air collected on tenax and analyzed by GC/MS
3	Analytical method for the determination of semivolatiles collected by PUF/XAD-2 and analyzed by GC/MS
4	Analytical methods for the determination of inorganic compounds collected on Hi-Vol filters and analyzed by inductively coupled plasma (ICP) atomic emission spectrometry or graphite furnace atomic absorption (GFAA) spectrometry

[20] An article by Nelson, P.R., D.L. Heavner, B.B. Collie, K.C. Maliolo and M.W. Ogden. "Effect of Ventilation and Sampling Time on Environmental Tobacco Smoke Component Ratios." *Environ. Sci. Technol.* 1992. 26(10) pp. 1909-1915, suggests that 3-ethenylpyridine may be a more appropriate indicator of tobacco smoke than nicotine. The analysis is similar.

List of Analytes

Table A-1. Halogenated Volatile Organic Target Analytes

Target Analyte	CAS No.	Structure
Bromodichloromethane	75-27-4	$BrCl_2CH$
Bromochloromethane	74-97-5	$BrCH_2Cl$
Bromoform	75-25-2	Br_3CH
Bromomethane	74-83-9	$BrCH_3$
Carbon tetrachloride	56-23-5	CCl_4
Chlorobenzene	108-90-7	
Chloroethane	75-00-3	$ClCH_2CH_3$
2-Chloroethylvinyl ether	100-75-8	
Chloroform	67-66-3	$CHCl_3$
Chloromethane	74-87-3	CH_3Cl
Dibromomethane	74-95-3	Br_2CH_2
Dibromochloromethane	124-48-1	Br_2ClCH
1,2-Dichlorobenzene	95-50-1	
1,3-Dichlorobenzene	541-73-1	
1,4-Dichlorobenzene	106-46-7	
Dichlorodifluoromethane	75-71-8	CCl_2F_2

Continued on next page.

Table A-1. Halogenated Volatile Organic Target Analytes, *continued*

Target Analyte	CAS No.	Structure
1,1-Dichloroethane	75-34-3	Cl_2CHCH_3
1,2-Dichloroethane	107-06-2	$ClCH_2CH_2Cl$
1,1-Dichloroethene	75-35-4	$Cl_2C=CH_2$
cis-1,2-Dichloroethene	156-59-4	
trans-1,2-Dichloroethene	156-60-5	
1,2-Dichloropropane	78-87-5	$ClCH_2CHClCH_3$
cis-1,3-Dichloropropene	10061-01-5	
trans-1,3-Dichloropropene	10061-02-6	
DBCP Dibromochloropropane	96-12-8	$BrCH_2CH_2BrCH_2Cl$
EDB Ethylenedibromide	106-93-4	$BrCH_2CH_2Br$
Hexachlorobutadiene	87-68-3	$Cl_2C=CCl-CCl=CCl_2$
Methylene chloride	75-09-2	CH_2Cl_2
1,1,2,2-Tetrachloroethane	79-34-5	$Cl_2CHCHCl_2$
Tetrachloroethene	127-18-4	$Cl_2C=CCl_2$
1,1,1-Trichloroethane	71-55-6	Cl_3CCH_3
1,1,2-Trichloroethane	79-00-5	Cl_2CHCH_2Cl
Trichloroethene	79-01-6	$Cl_2C=CHCl$
Trichlorofluoromethane	75-69-4	CCl_3F
Vinyl chloride	75-01-4	$ClHC=CH_2$

Table A-2. Aromatic Volatile Organic Target Analytes

Target Analyte	CAS No.	Structure
Benzene	71-43-2	
Toluene	108-88-3	
Ethylbenzene	100-41-4	
Chlorobenzene	108-90-7	
1,2-Dichlorobenzene	95-50-1	
1,3-Dichlorobenzene	541-73-1	
1,4-Dichlorobenzene	106-46-7	
n-Butylbenzene	104-51-8	
s-Butylbenzene	135-98-8	
tert-Butylbenzene	98-06-6	
4-Isopropyltoluene	99-87-6	
Styrene	100-42-5	
m-Xylene	108-38-3	
o-Xylene	95-47-6	
p-Xylene	106-42-3	

Table A-3. Other Common Volatile Analytes

Target Analyte	CAS No.	Structure
Acetone	67-64-1	$CH_3C(=O)CH_3$
Acetonitrile	75-05-8	CH_3CN
Acrolein	107-02-8	$CH_2=CHCHO$
Acrylonitrile	107-13-1	$CH_2=CHCN$
Ethyl ether	60-29-7	$CH_3CH_2OCH_2CH_3$
p-Dioxane	123-91-1	
Methyl ethyl ketone (MEK)	78-93-3	$CH_3CH_2C(=O)CH_3$
Methyl isobutyl ketone (MIBK)	108-10-1	$(CH_3)_2CHCH_2C(=O)CH_3$
2-Hexanone	591-78-6	$CH_3CH_2CH_2CH_2C(=O)CH_3$
Allyl alcohol	107-18-6	$CH_2=CHCH_2OH$
Carbon disulfide	75-15-0	$S=C=S$
Ethanol	64-10-5	CH_3CH_2OH
Ethylene oxide	75-21-8	
Ethylmethacrylate	97-63-2	$CH_3CH=CHCO_2CH_2CH_3$
Methylmethacrylate	80-62-6	$CH_3CH=CHCO_2CH_3$
Propargyl alcohol	107-19-7	$HCCCH_2OH$
Vinyl acetate	108-05-4	$CH_2=CHO_2CCH_3$

Table A-4. Basic Semivolatile Organic Target Analytes

Target Analyte	CAS No.	Structure
4-Aminobiphenyl	92-67-1	
Aniline	62-53-3	
Benzidine	92-87-5	
4-Chloroaniline	106-47-8	
3,3'-Dichlorobenzidine	91-94-1	
Dimethylaminoazobenzene	60-11-7	
α,α-Dimethylphenethylamine	122-09-8	

Continued on next page.

Table A-4. Basic Semivolatile Organic Target Analytes, *continued*

Target Analyte	CAS No.	Structure
Diphenylamine	122-39-4	
1,2-Diphenylhydrazine	122-66-7	
1-Naphthylamine	134-32-7	
2-Naphthylamine	91-59-8	
2-Nitroaniline	88-77-4	
3-Nitroaniline	99-09-2	
4-Nitroaniline	100-01-6	
2-Picoline	109-06-89	
Pyridine	129-00-0	

Table A-5. Neutral Semivolatile Organic Target Analytes

Target Analyte	CAS No.	Structure
Acenaphthene	83-32-9	
Acenaphthylene	208-96-8	
Acetophenone	98-86-2	

Continued on next page.

Table A-5. Neutral Semivolatile Organic Target Analytes, *continued*

Target Analyte	CAS No.	Structure
Alachlor	15972-60-8	
Aldrin	309-00-2	
Anthracene	120-12-7	
Aroclor (PCBs)[*]		Cl_{1-10}
1016	12674-11-2	Cl_2-Cl_3
1221	11104-28-2	$Cl-Cl_2$
1232	11141-16-5	$Cl-Cl_3$
1242	53469-21-9	Cl_2-Cl_4
1248	12672-29-6	Cl_3-Cl_5
1254	11097-69-1	Cl_4-Cl_6
1260	11096-82-5	Cl_5-Cl_8
1262	37324-23-5	Cl_5-Cl_8
Atrazine	1912-24-9	
Benz(a)anthracene	56-55-3	
Benzo(a)pyrene	50-32-8	

Continued on next page.

[*] Aroclor is the tradename for polychlorinated biphenyls (PCBs). They are a mixture of compounds. The trade number gives the percentage by mass of chlorine in the mixture. For instance Aroclor 1242 contains 42% by weight chlorine. PCBs from the former Soviet Union have been correlated to the Aroclors as Sovol = Aroclor 1254 and trichlorodiphenyl = Aroclor 1242. Ivanov and Sandell, *Environ. Sci. Technol.* 26(10) pp. 2012-2017.

Table A-5. Neutral Semivolatile Organic Target Analytes, *continued*

Target Analyte	CAS No.	Structure
Benzo(b)fluoranthene	205-99-2	
Benzo(ghi)perylene	191-24-2	
Benzo(k)fluoranthene	207-08-9	
Benzyl alcohol	100-51-6	CH_2OH
BHC ** γ-BHC (Lindane)	58-89-8	Cl Cl Cl Cl Cl Cl
Bis(2-chloroethoxy)methane	111-91-1	$ClCH_2CH_2OCH_2OCH_2CH_2Cl$
Bis(2-chloroethyl) ether	111-44-4	$ClCH_2CH_2OCH_2CH_2Cl$
Bis(2-chloroisopropyl) ether	108-60-1	$ClCH_2(CH_3)CHOCH(CH_3)CH_2Cl$
Bis(2-ethylhexyl) phthalate	117-81-7	$CO_2CH_2CH(CH_2CH_3)CH_2CH_2CH_2CH_3$ $CO_2CH_2CH(CH_2CH_3)CH_2CH_2CH_2CH_3$
Bis(2-ethylhexyl)adipate	103-23-1	$C_4H_9(C_2H_5)CHCH_2O_2C(C_4H_8)CO_2CH_2CH(C_2H_5)C_4H_9$
Butyl benzyl phthalate	85-68-7	CO_2CH_2 $CO_2(CH_2)_3CH_3$

Continued on next page.

** BHC are the initials from the incorrect name benzene hexachloride; the correct name is 1,2,3,4,5,6-Hexachlorocyclohexane. Eight well-described isomers are known, which are indicated by greek letters. γ-BHC is the insecticide Lindane, specifically 1α,2α,3β,4α,5α,6β–Hexachlorocyclohexane.

Table A-5. Neutral Semivolatile Organic Target Analytes, *continued*

Target Analyte	CAS No.	Structure
Chlordane ***	57-74-9	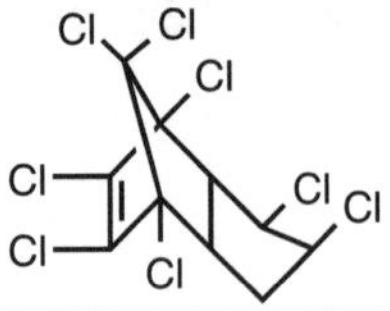
Chrysene	218-01-9	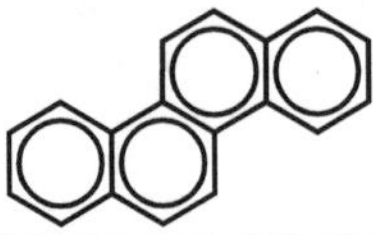
Di-*n*-butyl phthalate	84-74-2	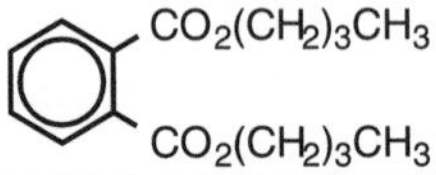 $CO_2(CH_2)_3CH_3$ / $CO_2(CH_2)_3CH_3$
Di-*n*-octyl phthalate	117-84-0	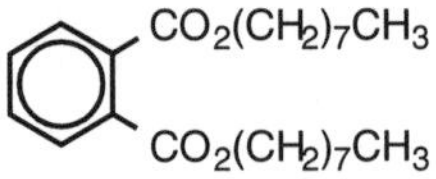 $CO_2(CH_2)_7CH_3$ / $CO_2(CH_2)_7CH_3$
Dibenz(a,h)anthracene	53-70-3	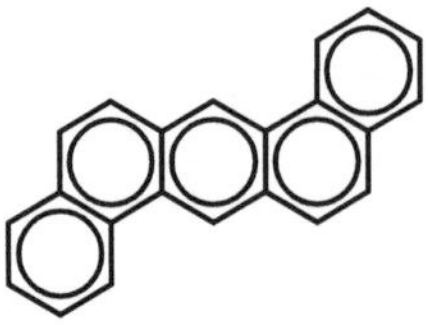
Dibenzofuran	132-64-9	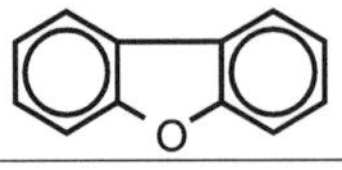
Dibutylchlorendate	1770-80-5	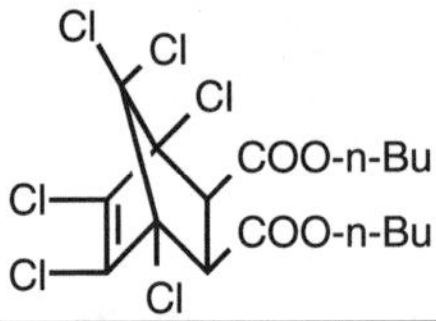 COO-n-Bu / COO-n-Bu
Dieldrin	60-57-1	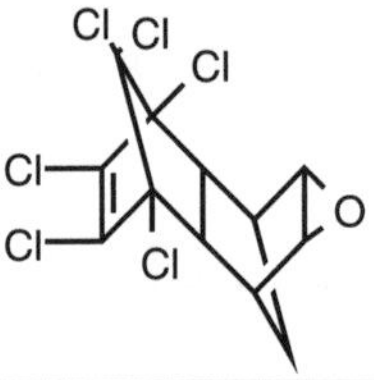
Diethyl phthalate	84-66-2	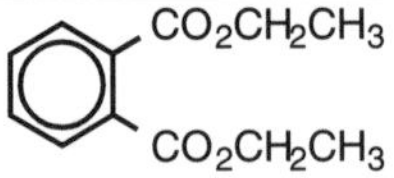 $CO_2CH_2CH_3$ / $CO_2CH_2CH_3$
Dimethyl phthalate	131-11-3	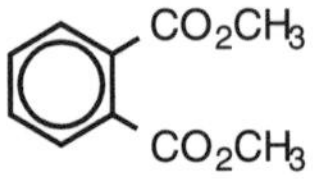 CO_2CH_3 / CO_2CH_3

Continued on next page.

*** Chlordane is a mixture of positionally chlorinated insecticide compounds derived from cyclopentadiene dimer. Heptachlor is one of the components.

Table A-5. Neutral Semivolatile Organic Target Analytes, *continued*

Target Analyte	CAS No.	Structure
Endosulfan I	959-98-8	
Endosulfan II	33212-65-9	
Endosulfan sulfate	1031-07-8	
Endrin	72-20-8	
Endrin aldehyde	7421-93-4	
Endrin ketone	53494-70-5	
Ethyl methanesulfonate	62-50-0	$CH_3SO_2OCH_2CH_3$
Fluoranthene	206-44-0	
Fluorene	86-73-7	
Halowax (Polychlorinated naphthalenes)		$Cl\text{-}Cl_8$
1000	58718-66-4	26% Cl $Cl\text{-}Cl_4$
1001	58718-67-5	50% Cl $Cl\text{-}Cl_4$

Continued on next page.

Table A-5. Neutral Semivolatile Organic Target Analytes, *continued*

Target Analyte	CAS No.	Structure
1013	12616-35-2	56% Cl Cl_3-Cl_6
1014	12616-36-3	62% Cl Cl_3-Cl_7
1051	2234-13-1	70% Cl Cl_7-Cl_8
1099	39450-05-0	52% Cl Cl-Cl_4
Heptachlor	76-44-8	
Heptachlor epoxide	1024-57-3	
Hexachlorobenzene	118-74-1	
Hexachlorobutadiene	87-68-3	$Cl_2C=CClCCl=CCL_2$
Hexachlorocyclo-pentadiene	77-47-4	
Hexachloroethane	67-72-1	Cl_3CCCl_3
Indeno(1,2,3-cd)pyrene	193-39-5	
Isophorone	78-59-1	
Methoxychlor	72-43-5	
Methyl methanesulfonate	66-27-3	$CH_3SO_2OCH_3$

Continued on next page.

Table A-5. Neutral Semivolatile Organic Target Analytes, *continued*

Target Analyte	CAS No.	Structure
N-Nitrosodi-n-propylamine	621-64-7	$(n\text{-}C_3H_7)_2N\text{-}NO$
N-Nitrosodibutylamine	924-16-3	$(C_4H_9)_2N\text{-}NO$
N-Nitrosodimethylamine	62-75-9	$(CH_3)_2N\text{-}NO$
N-Nitrosodiphenylamine	86-30-6	$(C_6H_5)_2N\text{-}NO$
N-Nitrosopiperidine	100-75-4	
Naphthalene	91-20-3	
Nitrobenzene	98-95-3	
Pentachlorobenzene	608-93-5	
Pentachloronitrobenzene	82-68-8	
Phenacetin	62-44-2	
Phenanthrene	85-01-8	
Pronamide	23950-58-5	
Pyrene	129-00-0	
Simazene	122-34-9	

Continued on next page.

Table A-5. Neutral Semivolatile Organic Target Analytes, *continued*

Target Analyte	CAS No.	Structure
Toxaphene ****	8001-35-2	
1-Chloronaphthalene	90-13-1	
2-Chloronaphthalene	91-58-7	
2-Methylnaphthalene	91-57-6	
3-Methylcholanthrene	56-49-5	
4-Bromophenyl phenyl ether	101-55-3	
4-Chlorophenyl phenyl ether	7005-72-3	
4,4'-DDD	72-54-8	
4,4'-DDE	72-55-9	
4,4'-DDT	50-29-3	
2,4-Dinitrotoluene	121-14-2	

Continued on next page.

**** Toxaphene is a mixture of compounds derived from the chlorination of camphene. It contains 67-69% chlorine by weight.

Table A-5. Neutral Semivolatile Organic Target Analytes, *continued*

Target Analyte	CAS No.	Structure
2,6-Dinitrotoluene	606-20-2	
1,2,4-Trichlorobenzene	120-82-1	
7,12-Dimethyl-benz(a)anthracene	57-97-6	
1,2,4,5-Tetrachlorobenzene	95-94-3	
2,3,7,8-Tetrachlorobenzodioxin (2,3,7,8-TCDD)	1746-01-6	

Table A-6. Acidic Semivolatile Organic Target Analytes

Target Analyte	CAS No.	Structure
Benzoic acid	65-85-0	
4-Chloro-3-methylphenol	59-50-7	
2-Chlorophenol	95-57-8	
2,4-Dichlorophenol	120-83-2	
2,6-Dichlorophenol	87-65-0	

Continued on next page.

Table A-6. Acidic Semivolatile Organic Target Analytes, *continued*

Target Analyte	CAS No.	Structure
2,4-Dimethylphenol	105-67-9	
2,4-Dinitrophenol	51-28-5	
2-Methyl-4,6-dinitrophenol	534-52-1	
2-Methylphenol	95-48-7	
4-Methylphenol	106-44-5	
2-Nitrophenol	88-75-5	
4-Nitrophenol	100-02-7	
Pentachlorophenol	87-86-5	
Phenol	108-95-2	
2,3,4,6-Tetrachlorophenol	58-90-2	
2,4,5-Trichlorophenol	95-95-4	
2,4,6-Trichlorophenol	88-06-2	

Table A-7. Herbicide Analytes

Target Analyte	CAS No.	Structure
Dalapon	75-99-0	CH_3CCl_2COOH
2,4-D	133-90-4	
Dinoseb	88-85-7	
Picloram	1918-02-1	
2,4,5-T	93-76-5	
2,4,5-TP (Silvex)	93-72-1	
Dicamba	1918-00-9	
Dichlorprop	120-36-5	
MCPA	94-74-6	
MCPP	7085-19-0	

Table A-8. Organic Disinfection Byproducts

Target Analyte	CAS No.	Structure
Bromochloroacetonitrile	83463-62-1	$BrClCHCN$
Chloral hydrate	75-87-6	$Cl_3CC(OH)_2$
Chloropicrin	76-06-2	Cl_3CNO_2
Dibromoacetonitrile	3252-43-5	Br_2CHCN
Dichloroacetonitrile	3018-12-0	Cl_2CHCN
Trichloroacetonitrile	545-06-2	Cl_3CCN
1,1,1-Trichloropropanone	918-00-3	$Cl_3CC(=O)CH_3$
1,1-Dichloropropanone	513-88-2	$Cl_2CHC(=O)CH_3$
Monobromoacetic acid (MBAA)	79-08-3	$BrCH_2COOH$
Monochloroacetic acid (MCAA)	79-11-8	$ClCH_2COOH$
Dibromoacetic acid (DBAA)	631-64-1	$Br_2CHCOOH$
Dichloroacetic acid (DCAA)	79-43-6	$Cl_2CHCOOH$
Bromochloroacetic acid (BCAA)	5589-96-3	$BrClCHCOOH$
Trichloroacetic acid (TCAA)	76-03-9	Cl_3CCOOH
Dalapon	75-99-0	CH_3CCl_2COOH

Table A-9. Nitrogen-Phosphorous Pesticides Determined by NPD-GC

Target Analyte	CAS No.	Structure
Famphur	52-85-7	Me₂NS(=O)(=O)—C₆H₄—OP(=S)(OMe)₂
Asulam	3337-71-1	NH₂—C₆H₄—SO₂NHCO₂CH₃
Dichlorvos	62-73-7	$(CH_3O)_2P(=O)OCH=CCl_2$
Dimethoate	60-51-5	$(CH_3O)_2P(=S)SCH_2C(=O)NHCH_3$
Disulfoton	298-04-4	$(CH_3CH_2O)_2P(=S)SCH_2CH_2SCH_2CH_3$
Fensulfothion	115-90-2	MeS—C₆H₄—OP(=O)(OEt)₂
Merphos	150-50-5	$(n\text{-}CH_3CH_2CH_2CH_2)_3P$
Methyl parathion	298-00-0	O₂N—C₆H₄—OP(=S)(OMe)₂
Monocrotophos	919-44-8	$(CH_3O)_2P(=O)O(CH_3)C=CHC(=O)NHCH_3$
Naled	300-76-5	$(CH_3O)_2P(=O)OCHBrCBrCl_2$
Phorate	298-02-2	$(CH_3CH_2O)_2P(=S)SCH_2SCH_2CH_3$
Trichlorfon	52-68-6	$(CH_3O)_2P(=O)OCHOHCCl_3$

Continued on next page.

Table A-9. Nitrogen-Phosphorous Pesticides Determined by NPD-GC, *continued*

Target Analyte	CAS No.	Structure
Thiofanox	39196-18-4	$(CH_3)_3C(CH_3SCH_2)C=NOC(=O)NHCH_3$
tris-(2,3-Dibromopropyl) phosphate	126-72-7	$(CH_2BrCHBrCH_2O)_3P=O$
Diazinon	333-41-5	
Bolstar (Sulprofos)	35400-43-2	
Chlorpyrifos	2921-88-2	
Demeton-O	8065-48-3	$(EtO)_2P(=S)OCH_2CH_2SEt$
Demeton-S	8065-48-3	$(EtO)_2P(=O)SCH_2CH_2SEt$
Coumaphos	56-72-4	
Azinphos Methyl	86-50-0	
Ethoprop	13194-48-4	$(n-Pr-S)_2P(=S)OEt$
Fenthion	55-38-9	
Mevinphos	7786-34-7	

Continued on next page.

Table A-9. Nitrogen-Phosphorous Pesticides Determined by NPD-GC, *continued*

Target Analyte	CAS No.	Structure
Ronnel	299-84-3	
Stirophos	22248-79-9	
Tokuthion	34643-46-4	
Trichloronate	327-98-0	
EPN	2104-64-5	
Parathion	56-38-2	
Sulfotepp	3698-24-5	
Malathion	121-75-5	
TEPP	21646-99-1	

Table A-10. Target Analytes Assayed by HPLC

Target Analyte	CAS No.	Structure
Aldicarb (Temik)	116-06-3	$CH_3SC(CH_3)_2CH=NOC(O)NHCH_3$
Aldicarb sulfone	1646-88-4	$CH_3S(O)_2C(CH_3)_2CH=NOC(O)NHCH_3$
Aldicarb sulfoxide	1646-87-3	$CH_3S(O)C(CH_3)_2CH=NOC(O)NHCH_3$
Baygon (Propoxur)	114-26-1	
Carbaryl (Sevin)	63-25-2	
Carbofuran (Furadan)	1563-66-2	
Dioxacarb	6988-21-2	
3-Hydroxycarbofuran	16655-82-6	
Methiocarb (Mesurol)	2032-65-7	
Methomyl (Lannate)	16752-77-5	$CH_3(CH_3S)C=NOC(O)NHCH_3$
Oxamyl (Vydate)	23135-22-0	$(CH_3)_2NCO(CH_3S)C=NOC(O)NHCH_3$
Promecarb	2631-37-0	

Continued on next page.

Table A-10. Target Analytes Assayed by HPLC, *continued*

Target Analyte	CAS No.	Structure
Formaldehyde	50-00-0	H_2CO
Acetaldehyde	75-07-0	H_3CCHO
Acrylamide	79-06-1	$H_2C=CHCONH_2$
Acrylonitrile	107-13-1	$H_2C=CHCN$
Acrolein	107-02-8	$H_2C=CHCHO$
Miscellaneous		
Caffeine	58-08-2	
Nicotine	54-11-5	

Common Acronyms

AA. atomic absorption

ATP. adenosine triphosphate

BAT. best available technology

BDL. below detection limit

BDMC. 4-bromo-3,5-dimethylphenyl -N-methylcarbamate

BFB. 4-bromofluorobenzene

BHC. 1,2,3,4,5,6-hexachlorocyclo-hexane

BN. base neutral

BNA. base neutral and acid

BOD. biochemical oxygen demand

BTEX. benzene, toluene, ethyl benzene and xylene

CBOD. carbonaceous biochemical oxygen demand

CCC. calibration check compounds

CCV. continuing calibration verification

CERCLA. Comprehensive Environmental Response, Compensation & Liability Act

CFR. Code of Federal Regulations

CLP. contract laboratory program

CNCl. cyanogen chloride

CND. 1-chloro-2,4-dinitrobenzene

CNS. central nervous system

COD. chemical oxygen demand

CTAS. cobalt thiocyanate active substances

CWA. Clean Water Act

DAD. diode array detector

DBC. dibutylchlorendate

DBUB. 4,4-dibromooctafluoro-biphenyl

DCPA. 3,5-dichlorophenylacetic acid

DDD. 2,2-bis(4-chlorophenyl)-1,1-dichloroethane

DDE. 2,2-bis(4-chlorophenyl)-1,1-dichloroethene

DDT. 2,2-bis(4-chlorophenyl)-1,1,1-trichloroethane

DER. Department of Environmental Regulation

DFTPP. decafluorotriphenylphosphine

DI. deionized

DMR. discharge monitoring report

DNA. deoxyribonucleic acid

DNPH. 2,4-dinitrophenylhydrazine

DO. dissolved oxygen

DOC. dissolved organic carbon

DOE. Department of Energy

DPD. N,N-diethylphenylene diamine

DQO. data quality objective

DRO. diesel range organics

EC. effective concentration

ECD. electron capture detector

EDTA. disodium ethylenediaminetetra-acetic acid

ELCD. electrolytic conductivity detector

EPP. electronic pressure programming

EPA. Environmental Protection Agency

EQL. estimated quantitation limit

FACTS. free available chlorine test, syringaldazine

FAS. ferrous ammonium sulfate

FC. fecal coliform

FDA. Food and Drug Administration

FDCA. Food, Drug and Cosmetic Act

FFAP. free fatty acids polyester

FID. flame ionization detector

FIFRA. Federal Insecticide, Fungicide and Rodenticide Act

FPD. flame photometric detector

FTIR. fourier transform infrared

GC. gas chromatography

GC/FTIR. gas chromatograph/fourier transform infrared

GC/MS. gas chromatograph/mass spectrometer

GFAA. graphite furnace atomic absorption

GPC. gel permeation chromatography

GRO. gasoline range organics

GWP. global warming potential

H-P. Hewlett-Packard

HBr. hydrogen bromide

HCN. hydrogen cyanide

HDPE. high density polyethylene

HEPES. 4-[2-hydroxyethyl]-1-piperazine ethanesulfonic acid

HPLC. high pressure liquid chromatography

HPLC-DAD. high pressure liquid chromatography-diode array detector

HPLC/MS. high pressure liquid chromatography/mass spectroscopy

HSL. Hazardous Substance List

IC. inorganic carbon

ICAP. inductively coupled argon plasma

ICP. inductively coupled plasma

ICV. initial calibration verification

ID. inside diameter

IDL. instrument detection limit

IR. infrared

IR-TPH. infrared - total petroleum hydrocarbons

IS. internal standard

JTU. Jackson turbidity unit

K-D. Kuderna-Danish concentrator

KBr. potassium bromide

KF. Karl Fisher

KHP. potassium hydrogen phthalate

KOH. potassium hydroxide

LAS. linear alkylbenzene sulfonate

LC. lethal concentration

LCV. leuco crystal violet

LD. lethal dose

LIMS. laboratory information management system

LUST. leaking underground storage tank

M-FC. membrane - fecal coliform

M/Z. mass/charge

MBAS. methylene blue active substance

MBTH. N-methylbenzothiazolinon hydrazine

MC. method code

MCE. mixed cellulose ester

MCL. maximum contaminant levels

MDL. method detection limits

MMO-MUG. minimal media o-nitrophenyl-ß-D-galactopyranoside/4-methylumbelliferyl-ß-D-glucuronide

MTB. methyl thymol blue

MUG. 4-methylumbelliferyl-ß-D-glucuronide

NDIR. non-dispersive infrared

NDOC. non-dissolved organic carbon

NED. N-napthyl ethylenediamine dichloride

NIST. National Institute for Standards and Technology

NMHC. non-methane hydrocarbons

NMOC. non-methane organic compounds

NMR. nuclear magnetic resonance

NORM. naturally occuring radioactive materials

NPDES. National Pollutant Discharge Elimination System

NPL. National Priority List

ONP. *o*-nitrophenol

ONPG. *o*-nitrophenyl-ß-D-galactopyranoside

OPA. *o*-phthalaldehyde

OV. Ohio Valley

P-A. presence-absence

PAH. polycyclic aromatic hydrocarbons

PAO. phenyl arsineoxide

PCB. polychlorinated biphenyl

PCDD. polychlorinated dibenzo-p-dioxins

PCE. perchloroethene

PDS. post digestion spikes

PE. performance evaluation

PEG. polyethylene glycol

PES. post extraction spikes

PFTBA. perfluorotributylamine

PID. photo ionization detector

POC. purgeable organic carbon

POTW. publicly owned treatment works

PQL. practical quantitation levels

PUF. polyurethane foam

PVC. polyvinyl chloride

QA. quality assurance

QC. quality control

RCRA. Resource Conservation and Recovery Act

RF. response factors

RNA. ribonucleic acid

RPD. relative percent difference

RSD. relative standard deviation

RSH. mercaptans

RT. retention time

SARA. Superfund Amendments and Reauthorization Act

SD. standard deviation

SDWA. Safe Drinking Water Act

SFE. supercritical fluid extraction

SM. Standard Methods for the Examination of Water and Wastewater

SOW. statement of work

SPADNS. sodium 2-(parasulfophenyl-azo)-1,8-dihydroxy-3,6-naphthalene disulfonate

SPCC. system performance check compounds

SPE. solid phase extraction

STP. standard temperature and pressure

SVI. sludge volume index

TAL. target analyte list

TC. total carbon

TCDD. tetrachlorodibenzodioxin

TCE. trichloroethene

TCL. target compound list

TCLP. toxic characteristic leaching procedure

TCMP. 2-chloro-6-trichloromethyl pyridine

TDS. total dissolved solids

THC. total hydrocarbons content

THM. trihalomethane

TIC. tentatively identified compounds

TJA. Thermal Jerrol Ash

TOC. total organic carbon

TPH. total petroleum hydrocarbons

TRS. total reduced sulfur

TS. total solids

TSCA. Toxic Substances Control Act

TSD. treatment, storage, and disposal

TSS. total suspended solids

TTHM. total trihalomethanes

TV. true value

TVDS. total volatile dissolved solids

TVS. total volatile solids

TVSS. total volatile suspended solids

USACE. U.S. Army Corps of Engineers

UST. underground storage tanks

UVDAD. ultra violet diode array detector

VOA. volatile organic analysis

VOC. volatile organic compounds

WP. water pollution

WS. water supply

ZHE. zero headspace extraction

Specialized Laboratory Glassware

In the environmental laboratory there are a number of very specialized pieces of glassware not found in other laboratories. They are for the most part used in the organics sample preparation area. The thick lines on the diagrams represent assembly points, which may be Teflon® lined threaded joints or ground glass joints (linear or ball design).

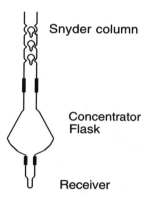

Figure C-1. Kuderna-Danish concentrator.

The Kuderna-Danish (K-D) concentrator is used to reduce the volume of organic solvent sample extracts. Boiling chips (Teflon® is prefered, but a variety of materials is used.) are placed in the tip of the receiver, the extract is added, and the apparatus is heated on a steam table. Clean solvent is added to the top of the Snyder column to wet the balls. The sample is concentrated until 3-4 mL remain in the receiver, then removed from the heat source and allowed to cool. The extract is transfered to a volumetric flask[1] for final concentration to an appropriate volume under a gentle stream of nitrogen gas. The volume graduations on the receiver are only approximate

---

[1] A very useful procedure is to obtain 2 mL Class A volumetric tubes with ground glass stoppers and calibrate them at the 1.000 mL level with an etch mark on the glass. The tubes hold about 4 mL of extract and are very easy to monitor as the solvent level drops to the 1 mL level during nitrogen blowdown. Internal standards can then be added and the contents of the tube shaken with the stopper in place before final transfer to an autosampler vial.

and should never be used as the final volume determination prior to analysis. Care must be taken to avoid reducing the volume of the extract below 1 mL to avoid target analyte and surrogate loss.

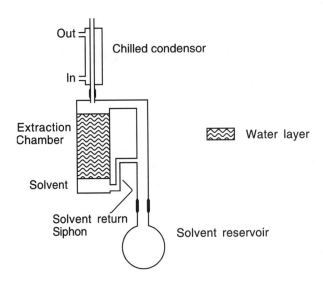

Figure C-2. Continuous liquid-liquid extractor for heavier than water solvents.

The continuous liquid-liquid extractor is used when intractable emulsions form on shaking the sample with organic solvents during the separatory funnel liquid-liquid extraction procedure. The sample is placed in the extraction chamber, which already contains about 100 mL of solvent. Extraction solvent is placed in the reservoir and heated to boiling. Solvent condenses in the chilled condensor and drips down through the aqueous sample. The analytes are partitioned into the solvent layer and slowly siphoned into the solvent reservoir. After 18-24 hours operation the unit is allowed to cool, and the solvent is dried with anhydrous sodium sulfate and concentrated in a K-D concentrator. If a BNA extraction is being performed the sample is first acidified and extracted for 18-24 hours, then basified and extraction continued for another 18-24 hours, a lengthy process. A one-piece extraction chamber is illustrated, however commercially available modular units are easier to clean and less prone to breakage. A shut-off valve in the solvent return siphon is very useful. Continuous liquid-liquid extractors are available that incorporate a K-D concentrator in the design as illustrated in Figure C-3. Other modifications include a water-jacketed receiver/concentrator flask for use with heated water circulators.

The use of the siphon tube allows water to become entrained in the extracting solvent, and, on solvent removal, the major part of the resulting concentrate can be water. A recent technology advance adds a hydrophobic membrane to the bottom of the sample chamber. This allows rapid and efficient separation of the extraction solvent from the water sample and immediate return of the solvent to the concentrator reservoir[2]. The elimination of the solvent pool at the bottom of the extraction chamber shortens the extraction time to 4-6 hours, reduces solvent usage to less than 100 mL, and makes the technique more time efficient and competitive with separatory funnel methods. A further advantage is elimination of water from the sample concentrate without further sample manipulation.

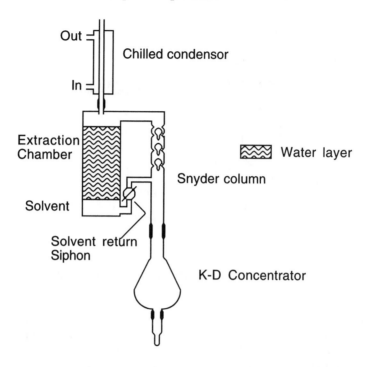

Figure C-3. Continuous liquid-liquid extractor with built-in K-D concentrator.

---

[2] Accelerated One-Step™ Extractor-Concentrator, Corning Glassworks, Corning, NY. One-Step is a registered trademark of Corning Glassworks.

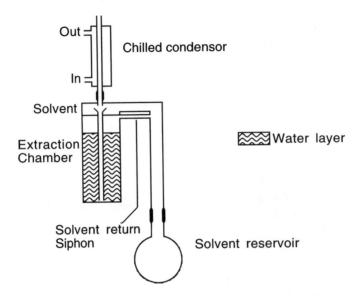

Figure C-4. Continuous liquid-liquid extractor for use with lighter-than-water solvents.

A continuous liquid-liquid extractor for use with lighter-than-water solvents is illustrated in Figure C-4. The drops of solvent from the condensor fall into a tube that opens at the bottom of the extraction chamber. Solvent exiting from the tube percolates upward through the aqueous sample and collects at the top of the chamber. It then drains through an upper siphon into the solvent reservoir.

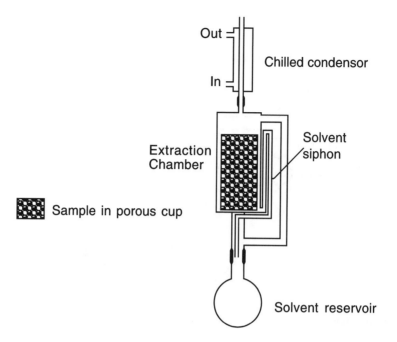

Figure C-5. Soxhlet extractor.

The soxhlet extractor is designed for removal of extractable materials from solid matrices. It can be operated with any solvent, even water, due to the batchwise extraction mechanism. The sample is placed in a porous container, either glass with a fritted bottom or a totally porous cup made of cellulose or cotton. For organic extractions the sample is commonly mixed with a drying agent (anhydrous sodium sulfate or magnesium sulfate monohydrate, depending on the method) prior to placement in the cup. A glasswool plug is commonly placed on top of the solid in the cup when the sample has a lower density than the solvent. This prevents the solid from floating out of the cup and being siphoned into the solvent reservoir. Boiling solvent drips from the condensor into the extraction chamber containing the sample until the chamber fills to the top of the siphon, at which time the solvent drains almost completely back into the solvent reservoir. The fill and drain cycle is allowed to continue for 4 to 24 hours, depending on the method.

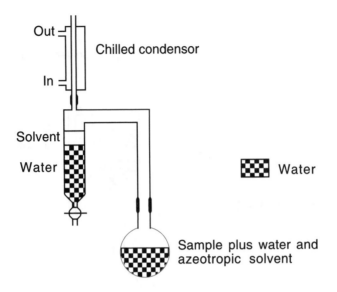

Figure C-6. Dean-Starke trap.

The Dean-Starke trap is used to separate water from a sample by distillation as the azeotrope with an appropriate lighter-than-water solvent, commonly toluene. The layers separate in the trap, and the upper toluene layer returns to the heated flask. The toluene-water azeotrope is approximately 12% water, while toluene is only soluble to the extent of 0.067% in water.

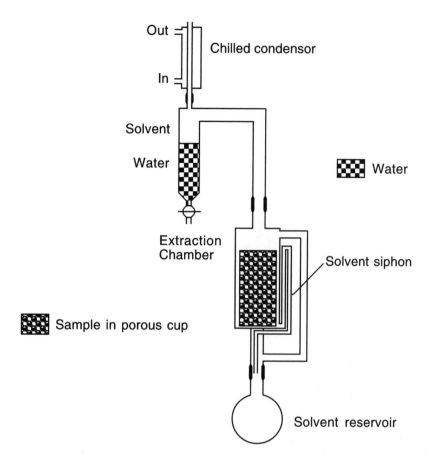

Figure C-7. Soxhlet/Dean-Starke extractor.

A soxhlet extractor has been combined with a Dean-Starke trap, as illustrated in Figure C-7, which eliminates the need to mix the sample with a drying agent prior to extraction.

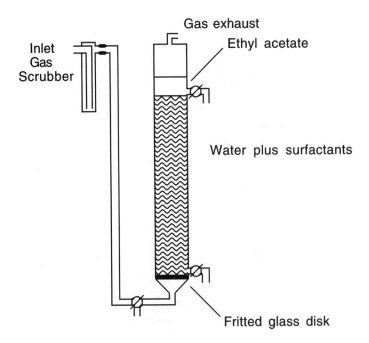

Figure C-8. Sublation apparatus.

The sublation apparatus (Figure C-8) is used to separate surfactants from aqueous samples. A stream of nitrogen is bubbled up through the water sample, forming surfactant micelles. On contact of the micelles with the upper layer of ethyl acetate, the surfactants dissolve into the organic solvent. After operation for 5 minutes at 1 L/min flow rate, the ethyl acetate layer is drained, fresh ethyl acetate added, and the extraction continued. The combined ethyl acetate layers are concentrated to dryness, leaving the surfactants as a solid residue for further analysis.

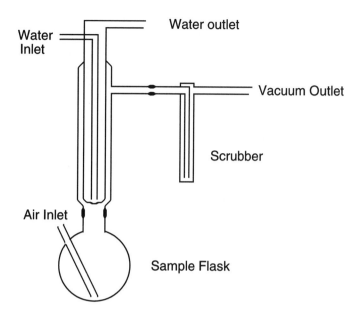

Figure C-9. Distillation apparatus for cyanide or sulfide.

Cyanide and sulfide analyses are subject to many interferences. To remove interferences, the samples are strongly acidified in the sample flask of Figure C-9, generating HCN or H_2S. Vigorous boiling of the sample transfers the cyanide or sulfide acids to the gas phase, and they are swept out of the sample flask by the air stream generated by application of a vacuum at the outlet. Water is removed from the air stream by the condensor and the target analytes trapped in the scrubber by an appropriate absorbing solution; sodium hydroxide for cyanide, and zinc acetate for sulfide.

References

I. QUALITY ASSURANCE

Berger, W, H. McCarty, and R.-K. Smith, 1996. *Environmental Laboratory Data Evaluation*, Genium Publishing, Schenectady NY.

Birkes, D. and Y. Dodge, *Alternative Methods of Regression.* 1993. Wiley Interscience, New York, NY. ISBN 0-471-56881-3.

Garfield, F.M., *Quality Assurance Principles for Analytical Laboratories.* AOAC, Arlington, VA, 1984.

Gautier, M.A. and E.S. Gladney, "A quality assurance program for health and environmental chemistry." *American Laboratory* July, 1987.

Guidance on Evaluation, Resolution and Documentation of Analytical Problems Associated with Compliance Monitoring. USEPA, Office of Water, Engineering and Analysis Division, Washington DC 20460, EPA 821-B-93-001, June 1993.

Handbook for Analytical Quality Control in Water and Wastewater. EPA 600/4-79-019. March 1979. NTIS number PB-297 451.

Keith, L.H., 1995. *Principles of Environmental Sampling*, Second Edition American Chemical Society, Washington, DC.

Manual for Analytical Quality Control for Pesticides and Related Compounds in Human and Environmental Samples. EPA 600/1-79-009. 1979.

Manual for the Certification of Laboratories Analyzing Drinking Water. Criteria and Procedures Quality Assurance. 4th Edition. EPA 815-B-97-001, March, 1997.

Manual for the Evaluation of Laboratories Performing Aquatic Toxicity Tests. EPA/600/4-90/031. NTIS number PB91-148353.

Taylor, J.K., *Principles of Quality Assurance of Chemical Measurements*, U.S. Department of Commerce, February, 1985.

Taylor, J.K., *Quality Assurance of Chemical Measurements.* Orlando Fla.: Lewis Publishers. 1987.

Western Electric Co., Inc. 1956. *Statistical Quality Control Handbook.* Western Electric Co. Inc., Newark, NJ.

USAF, AFCEE, 1997. *Quality Assurance Project Plan*, Version 3.0. www.afcee.brooks.af.mil.

US Army Corps of Engineers, 10 October, 1997. *Chemical Quality Assurance for HTRW Projects*, EM-200-1-6, USACE, Laboratory Validation Coordinator, 12565 West Center Road, Omaha, NE 68144-3869.

II. TECHNICAL

AFCEE Handbook for the Installation Restoration Program (IRP) Remedial Investigations and Feasibility Studies (RI/FS), September, 1993.

Air Sampling Instruments for Evaluation of Atmospheric Contaminants. American Conference of Governmental Industrial Hygienists, 7th Edition, S.V. Hering Editor, Cincinnati, Ohio, 1989.

Analytical method for the determination of asbestos fibers in water, September, 1983 NTIS PB83-260471; *Determination of asbestos structure over 10 um in length in drinking water*, June 1994, EPA 600/R-94-134, NTIS PB94-201902.

Analytical Methods for the Determination of Pollutants in Pharmaceutical Manufacturing Industry Wastewater (EPA-821-94-001) February, 1995.

Analytical Methods for the Determination of Pollutants in Pulp and Paper Industry Wastewater, EPA 821-R-93-017 (PB94-107059), October, 1993.

Analytical Methods for the National Sewage Sludge Survey, EPA Office of Water (WH-585), September, 1990.

Annual Book of ASTM Standards. Vol 11.01 and 11.02 (Water I and II). American Society for Testing and Materials. Latest Edition.

Biological Criteria: Technical Guidance for Streams and Small Rivers, May 1996. USEPA Office of Water 822-B-96-001.

Bruno, T.J. *Handbook for the Analysis and Identification of Alternate Refrigerants*. CRC Press, Boca Raton, FL. ISBN 0-8493-3926-X. 1995.

Characterization of Chronically Toxic Effluents. Phase I EPA/600/6-91/005F.

Compendium of Chemical and Biological Biosolid Methods, EPA 1998 draft.

Compendium of Methods for the Determination of Air Pollutants in Indoor Air. EPA, April 1990. (NTIS PB90-200288).

Compendium of Methods for the Determination of Toxic Organic Compounds in Ambient Air. EPA, June 1988. (NTIS PB90-127374).

Cross, J. *Nonionic Surfactants: Chemical Analysis*. 1987. Marcel Dekker, NY.

DOE Methods for Evaluating Environmental and Waste Management Samples, 1997, Battelle Press, Columbus, OH. E-mail press@battelle.org.

Environmental Compliance Branch Standard Operating Procedures and Quality Assurance Manual. U.S. EPA Region IV Environmental Services Division. February, 1996.

Erickson, M.D. *Analytical Chemistry of PCBs*. 2nd Edition, 1997. CRC Press, Boca Raton, FL.

Georgia Modified Standard Method: Hazardous Waste Management Program Groundwater Testing Appendix IX. Environmental Protection Division, Georgia Department of Natural Resources, February 1991.

Guidelines establishing test procedures for the analysis of Pollutants, 40 CFR, Part 136., EPA/GPO.

Guidelines for Testing of Chemicals, through the 10th Supplement, OECD , October, 1998.

Handbook on Reference Methods for Soil Analysis, Soil and Plant Analysis Council, Inc. 1992.

Industrial user inspection and sampling manual for POTW's. EPA 831-B-94-001, April, 1994.

Kingston, H.M., and C.B. Jassie. *Introduction to Microwave Sample Preparation Theory and Practice*. American Chemical Soc. Washington, DC. 1988. ISBN -0-8412-1450-6.

Klute, A. *Methods of Soil Analysis, Part 1 Physical and Mineralogical Methods*, 2nd Edition. 1986. ASA and SSSA, Madison, WI.

Kostecki, P.T. and E.J. Calabrese. *Hydrocarbon Contaminated Soils* Volumes 1 and 2. Chelsea, MI. Lewis Publishers, 1991.

Leichnitz, K. *Detector Tube Handbook*. National Draeger, Inc. 412-787-8383, Drägerwerk, AG PO Box 1339 D-24 Lübeck FDR, 6th Edition, 1985.

Lodge, J.P., Jr. *Methods for Air Sampling and Analysis*. 3rd Edition, Intersociety Committee APCA, ACS, AIChE, APWA, ASME, AOAC, HPS & ISA, Chelsea, MI; Lewis Publishers, 1989.

Margolis, E.J., 1962. *Qualitative Anion-Cation Analysis*, John Wiley & Sons, New York, NY.

Mahin, E.G., 1929. *Introduction to Quantitative Analysis,* McGraw-Hill Book Company, New York, NY.

Methods for Aquatic Toxicity Identification Evaluations. Phase I EPA/600/6-91/003; *Phase II* EPA/600/3-88/035; *Phase III* EPA/600/3-88/036.

Methods for assessing the toxicity of sediment-associated contaminants with estuarine and marine amphipods, EPA 600/R-94/025, June, 1994.

Methods for Chemical Analysis of Water and Wastes. EPA 600/4-79-020, Revised March, 1983. NTIS number PB84-128677.

Methods for Collection and Analysis of Aquatic Biological and Microbiological Samples, Book 5, Chapter A4. U.S. Geological Survey, 1977.

Methods for the determination of chemical substances in marine and estuarine environmental samples (EPA/600/R-92/121), November 1992; Second Edition EPA/600/R-97/072.

Methods for the determination of diesel, mineral, and crude oils in offshore oil and gas industry discharges, December, 1992, EPA 821-R-92-008, PB 93-166932.

Methods for the determination of inorganic substances in environmental samples 1993 EPA 600/R-93/100.

Methods for Determination of Inorganic Substances in Water and Fluvial Sediments, Book 5, Chapter A1. U.S. Geological Survey, 1979.

Methods for the Determination of Metals in Environmental Samples, 1991 EPA 600/4-91/010; *Methods for the Determination of Metals in Environmental Samples* Supplement I, 1994 EPA-600/R-94/111.

Methods for the Determination of Nonconventional Pesticides in Municipal and Industrial Wastewater. EPA 821RR-92-002. April, 1992.

Methods for the Determination of Organic Compounds in Drinking Water (EPA-600/4-88/039) 1988; Supplement I (EPA 600/4-90/020) 1990; Supplement II (EPA 600/R-92/129) 1992; and Supplement III (EPA 600/R-95/131) 1995.

Methods for the Determination of Organic Substances in Water and Fluvial Sediments, Book 5, Chapter A3. U.S. Geological Survey, 1983.

Methods for Measuring the Acute Toxicity of Effluents to Freshwater and Marine Organisms, 3rd Edition. EPA 600/4-85/019, 1985. NTIS number PB85-205383.

Methods for Measuring the Acute Toxicity of Effluents and Receiving Water Freshwater and Marine Organisms. 4th Edition. EPA/60/4-90/027. NTIS number PB91-167650.

Methods of Soil Analysis: Part 2 - Chemical and Microbiological Properties, 2nd Edition, American Society of Agronomy Soil Science Society of America, Madison, WI. 1982.

Microbiological Methods for Monitoring the Environment. EPA 600/8-78-017. 1978.

Midwidsky, B, and D.M. Gabriel. *Detergent Analysis*. 1982. Halstead Press, NY.

Moeller, T., 1958. *Qualitative Analysis*, McGraw-Hill Book Company, Inc., New York, NY.

NIOSH Manual of Analytical Methods U.S. Department of Health and Human Services, 3rd Edition, 15 February, 1984. 2nd Supplement, 15 August, 1987.

Official Methods of Analysis of the Association of Official Analytical Chemists. 15th Edition, AOAC 1986.

POTW Sludge Sampling and Analysis Guidance Document , USEPA August 1989.

Precision Gas Detector System Manual. Sensidyne, Inc. 12345 Starkey Rd., Largo FL 33453. 1985. Tel 800-451-9444.

Prescribed Procedures for Measurement of Radioactivity in Drinking Water, EPA-600/4-80-032 1980.

Procedures for Handling and Chemical Analysis of Sediments and Water Samples. EPA/Corps of Engineers CE-81-1. March, 1981.

RCRA Groundwater Monitoring Technical Enforcement Guidance Document, (TEGD). EPA OSWER-9950.1. September, 1986.

Short-term Methods for Estimating the Chronic Toxicity of Effluents and Receiving Water to Freshwater Organisms, Third Edition, July, 1994. EPA-600-4-91-002.

Short-term Methods for Estimating the Chronic Toxicity of Effluents and Receiving Water to Marine and Estuarine Organisms, Second Edition, July, 1994 EPA-600-4-91-003.

Soil Sampling and Methods of Analysis, M.R. Carter (Ed), Canadian Society of Soil Science. 1993, CRC Press, Boca Raton FL.

Specifications and Guidance for Contaminant-free Sample Containers. USEPA Office of Solid Waste and Emergency Response. December, 1992. (EPA 540/R-93/051, PB93-963316).

Standard Methods for the Examination of Water and Wastewater, 16th Edition. APHA, AWWA, & WEF 1985, 6666 West Quincy Avenue, Denver, CO 80235.

Standard Methods for the Examination of Water and Wastewater, 17th Edition. APHA, AWWA, & WEF 1989, 6666 West Quincy Avenue, Denver, CO 80235.

Standard Methods for the Examination of Water and Wastewater, 18th Edition. APHA, AWWA, & WEF 1992, 6666 West Quincy Avenue, Denver, CO 80235.

Standard Methods for the Examination of Water and Wastewater, 19th Edition. APHA, AWWA, & WEF 1995, 6666 West Quincy Avenue, Denver, CO 80235.

Standard Methods for the Examination of Water and Wastewater, 20th Edition. APHA, AWWA, & WEF 1998, 6666 West Quincy Avenue, Denver, CO 80235.

Sulcek, Z and P. Povondra 1989 *Methods for Decomposition in Inorganic Analysis* CRC Press, Boca Raton FL, ISBN 0-8493-4963-X.

Swisher, R.D., *Surfactant Biodegradation*, 2nd Ed, 1987. Marcel Dekker, NY.

Talmage, S.S. *Environmental and Human Safety of Major Surfactants*, Lewis Publishers, Boca Raton, FL. 1994. ISBN 1-56670-017-5.

Test methods for Eschericia coli and Enterococci in Water by the Membrane Filter Procedure, EPA 600/4-85-076 1985, NTIS PB86-158052.

Test Methods for Evaluating Solid Waste - Physical/Chemical Methods, EPA/SW-846, 3rd Edition, 1986, Update 1, July, 1992, Updates II and IIa, 1994, Update III, 1996, and proposed Updates IVa and IVb, 1998.

Textile dyes and dyeing equipment classification, properties and environmental aspects. EPA-600/2-85-010, February, 1995, PB85-173771.

US EPA Contract Laboratory Program Statement of Work for Inorganic Analysis, EPA SOW ILM03.0, 1993.

US EPA Contract Laboratory Program Statement of Work for Organic Analysis, EPA SOW OLMO2.1, 1994.

US EPA Contract Laboratory Program Statement of Work for Analysis of Air Toxics from Superfund Sites.

Winegardner, D.L. *Introduction to Soils for Environmental Professionals.* 1996. CRC Press, Boca Raton, FL.

Wisconsin Procedures for Soil Testing, Plant Analysis and Feed & Forage Analysis, Department of Soil Science, College of Agricultural and Life Sciences, University of Wisconsin-Extension-Madison. 1987.

III. GENERAL

Benefield, L.D., J.F. Judkins and B.L. Weand. *Process Chemistry for Water and Wastewater Treatment.* Englewood Cliffs, NJ: Prentice-Hall, 1982.

Bunce, N. *Environmental Chemistry.* Winnipeg, Canada: Wuerz Publishing, 1990.

Colborn, T., D. Dumanoski and J.P. Myers. *Our Stolen Future.* 1996. Penguin Books, New York, NY.

Cotton, F.A., and G. Wilkinson *Advanced Inorganic Chemistry,* 5th Edition, New York, NY Wiley & Sons. 1988.

Feigl, F., and V. Anger, 1972. *Spot Tests in Inorganic Analysis,* Elsevier, New York, NY.

Feigl, F, and V. Anger, *Spot Tests in Organic Analysis,* Elsevier, NY, New York, www.elsevier.com.

Hunt, D.T.E. and A.L. Wilson. *The Chemical Analysis of Water.* 2nd Edition, Royal Society of Chemistry, London, 1986.

Kaufman, J.A. *Waste Disposal in Academic Institutions.* Chelsea, MI: Lewis Publishers, 1990.

Manahan, S.E. *Environmental Chemistry,* 5th Edition, Chelsea, MI: Lewis Publishers, 1991.

March, J. *Advanced Organic Chemistry,* 4th Edition, New York, NY: Wiley & Sons, 1992.

Reife, A. and H.S. Freeman, 1996. *Environmental Chemistry of Dyes and Pigments.* John Wiley & Sons, New York, NY.

Sawyer, C.N., P.L. McCarty and G.F. Parkin. *Chemistry for Environmental Engineering,* 4th Edition. 1994. McGraw-Hill, Inc. New York, NY.

Smith, R.-K., 1999. *Lectures on Wastewater Analysis and Interpretation*, Genium Publishing, Schenectady, NY.

Smith, R.-K., 1995. *Water and Wastewater Laboratory Techniques.* Water Environment Federation, Alexandria, VA.

Snoeyink, V.L. and D. Jenkins. *Water Chemistry.* New York, NY: John Wiley & Sons, 1980.

Stumm, W., and J.J. Morgan, 1996. *Aquatic Chemistry, Third Edition.* John Wiley & Sons, New York, NY.

Wagner, R.E. *Guide to Environmental Analytical Methods*, 3rd Edition, Schenectady, NY: Genium Publishing Corporation, 1996. 1-800-243-6486.

Water Pollution Control Federation. *The Clean Water Act of 1987.* WPCF 601 Wythe St, Alexandria, Va. 22314, 1987, WPCF No. P0070JR.

Wentz, C.A. *Hazardous Waste Management.* New York, NY: McGraw-Hill Book Company, 1989.

Vendors

I. ANALYTICAL STANDARDS

NSI Environmental Solutions, P.O. Box 12313, Research Triangle Park, NC 27709. 800-234-7837

AccuStandard, Inc., 25 Science Park, Box 1, New Haven, CT 06511. 203-786-5290

Analytical Products Group, Inc., 2730 Washington Blvd., Belpre, OH 45714. 800-272-4442 (PET Program)

Ultra Scientific, 250 Smith Street, North Kingston RI 02852. 401-294-9400

SPEX CertiPrep, 203 Norcross Avenue, Metchen NJ 08840. 800-522-7739 or 908-549-7144.

Environmental Resource Associates, 5540 Marshall Street, Arvada, Colorado 80002. 800-372-0122 (PET Program)

Chem Service, 660 Tower Lane, P.O. Box 599, West Chester, PA 19381-0599. 610-692-3026

Plasma-Chem Corporation, 5142 West Hurley Pond Rd., Farmingdale, NJ 07727. 800-343-0437

American Type Culture Collection, 12301 Parklawn Dr., Rockville, MD 20852. 800-638-6597

Fisher Scientific, 2775 Pacific Drive, Norcross, GA 30091. 770-449-5050

VWR Scientific Products, P.O. Box 626, Bridgeport, NJ 08014. 800-234-5227

Protocol Analytical Supplies, Inc., 472 Lincoln Blvd., Middlesex, NJ 08846. 800-862-0080

Standard Reference Materials, National Institute of Standards and Technology, Building 202, Room 204, Gaithersburg, MD 20899. 301-975-6776

Radian International LLC, P.O. Box 201088, Austin TX 78720-1088, 1-800-848-7837

Restek Corporation, 110 Benner Cir. Bellefonte PA 16823-8812, 1-800-356-1688

Analytical Standards, Inc., P.O. Box 183, 6331 Emerson Avenue, Parkersburg, WV 26102-0183, (304) 442-4274

II. PRE-CLEANED SAMPLE CONTAINERS

Eagle Picher Environmental Services, 36 B.J. Tunnell Blvd. East, Miami, OK
74354-3300. 800-331-7425

Industrial Glassware, 130 Bogden Blvd., Millville, NJ 08332. 609-327-2688

I-Chem, 2 Bolden Circle, New Castle, DE 19720. 800-443-1689

Qorpak, 1195 Washington Pike, Bridgeville, PA 15017. 412-257-3100

Cleaning Protocols

Organic and metals glass sample containers
- Wash with laboratory grade non-phosphate detergent
- Rinse 3 times with distilled water
- Rinse with 1:1 nitric acid
- Rinse 3 times with ASTM Type 1 organic free water
- Oven dry for 1 hour
- Rinse with hexane, methylene chloride, acetone or methanol
- Oven dry for 1 hour

Volatile organic glass sample containers
- Wash with laboratory grade non-phosphate detergent
- Rinse 3 times with distilled water
- Rinse 3 times with ASTM Type 1 organic free water
- (optional methanol rinse)
- Oven dry 1 hour

Metals plastic sample containers
- Wash with laboratory grade non-phosphate detergent
- Rinse 3 times with distilled water
- Rinse with 1:1 nitric acid
- Rinse 3 times with ASTM Type 1 organic free water
- Air dry

Plastic sample containers for other nutrients and demands
- Rinse three times with deionized water
- Fill with deionized water and let sit 48 hours
- Empty and air dry

Suitable non-phosphate detergents include Liquinox or Alconox for organics, Liquinox
for inorganic anions, and Liquinox, Acationox or Micro for inorganic cations

Regulatory Contact Directory

NATIONAL AND REGIONAL CONTACTS

ENVIRONMENTAL HOTLINES

Asbestos & Small Business Ombudsman Office
All except VA .... (800) 368-5888
VA only .... (703) 557-1938
TDD machine .... (703) 557-2824
Provides information to the public sector, including individual citizens and community services on the handling and abatement of asbestos in schools, the workplace and the home.

Chemical Manufacturers Association Hotlines
National .... (703) 741-5000
Non-emergency information on chemicals
Chemical Referral Center (CRC)
Chemtree Non-emergency .... (800) 262-8200
Provides Chemical Emergency Information.

CHEMTREC
National .... (800) 424-9300
Dist. of Columbia .... (202) 887-4620

Consumer Product Safety Commission Hotline
National .... (800) 638-2772

Emergency Planning and Community Right-to-Know (Title III SARA) Hotline
National .... (800) 535-0202
Virginia .... (703) 920-9877
Provides regulatory, policy and technical assistance to federal agencies, local and state governments, the public and regulated community in response to questions related to the Emergency Planning and Community Right-to-Know Act (Title III of SARA). Information on reporting of hazardous substances for community planning purposes.

EPA Hotline .... (800) 438-2474

EPA Superfund (Region II Investigative Hotline)
Restricted area codes as follows: 809, 201, 609, 908, 906, 212, 315, 516, 518, 607, 716, 718, 914 .... (800) 245-2738
Enables the Superfund Civil Investigators to receive information relevant to specific Superfund Site Enforcement Investigations.

TSCA Assistance Information Services
.... (202) 554-1404
Provides technical assistance and information about the Toxic Substances Control Act (TSCA), the Asbestos School Hazard Abatement Act (ASHAA), the Asbestos Hazard Emergency Response Act (AHERA), the Asbestos School Hazard Abatement Reauthorization Act (ASHARA), the Residential Lead-based Pain Hazard Reduction Act, and the Pollution Prevention Act (PPA), and 33/50 Program.

Mercury Hotline
National .... (800) 833-3505
Provides answers to questions. No emergency Service

National Pesticides Telecommunications Network
National, incl. US, PR,
    and Virgin Island .... (800) 858-7378
FAX: .... (541) 737-0761
Provides the medical, veterinary, professional communities and general public with information on: pesticides and herbicides product information, recognition and management of pesticide poisonings, toxicology and symptomatic reviews, safety information, health and environmental effects, clean-up and disposal procedures.

National Radon Hotline

National.................................(800) 767-7236
Radon testing information. A message records names and addresses of callers and a brochure on radon is sent via 1st class mail.

National Response Center - US Coast Guard Oil and Hazardous Material Spills

National except DC ....(800) 424-8802
DC and outside US ....(202) 267-2675
For reporting of oil and hazardous material spills. NOTE: Please have ready as much relevant data as possible when calling.

Occupational Safety and Health Administration Referral Service

National.................................(800) 321-6742
24-hour access line to report unsafe and hazardous work practices.

Office of the Inspector General - Public Information

Washington, DC.............................(202) 619-1142
Office of Special Council for Whistle
   Blower............................(800) 872-9855

RCRA/Superfund/Community Right-to-Know (Title III) Hotline

International ....(800) 424-9346
TDD machine...................(800) 553-7672
Answers factual questions from the regulated community, other interested parties and the public about EPA's RCRA regulations and policies; referrals for obtaining related documents. RCRA, Underground Storage Tanks (USTs), Superfund/CERCLA and Pollution Prevention/Waste Minimization.

Risk Communication Hotline

.................................(202) 260-5606
Responds to questions from EPA program offices and regions, and external inquiries as time permits, regarding the EPA's Risk Communication Program and risk communication issues.

Safe Drinking Water Hotline

National.................................(800) 426-4791
Provides assistance and regulatory knowledge to the regulated community (public water systems) and the public on the regulations and programs developed in response to the Safe Drinking Water Act Amendments of 1986.

Substance Identification Hotline

National.................................(800) 848-6538
Identifies chemical by CAS number or Name

US Dept of Transportation (US DOT)

National.................................(202) 366-4488
Information of DOT CFR-49 regulations.

OTHER REGIONAL AND NATIONAL CONTACTS

Centers for Disease Control (CDC)

National.................................(404) 639-3535
Answers technical and public questions.

Environmental Export Council (EEC)

National.................................(202) 466-6933

EPA Assistant Administrator for Enforcement and Compliance Monitoring

National.................................(202) 564-2440
Provides direction for the review and enforcement of compliance activities.

EPA Assistant Administrator for Research and Development

National.................................(202) 260-7676
Provides technical information for the EPA administrator on scientific and technical issues.

EPA General Information

National.................................(617) 565-3420
Referral service to appropriate program office.

EPA General Information - Environmental Issues

.................................(303) 312-6312
General information - environmental issues.

EPA Public Center

National.................................(202) 260-7751
Provides guidance about general environmental information for the public.

Center for Hazardous Materials (CHMR)

.................................(412) 826-5320
Regulatory, toxic waste minimization, pollution prevention, publications and referrals.

Center for International Env. Law

National.................................(202) 332-4840

Food and Drug Administration (FDA) Hazardous Waste Ombudsman

National ....(800) 262-7937
The hazardous waste management program established under RCRA is a highly complex regulatory program developed by EPA. It assists the public and regulated community in resolving problems concerning any program or requirement under the Hazardous Waste

Program. The ombudsman handles complaints from citizens and the regulated community, obtains facts, sorts information, and substantiates policy.

Mobile Sources
National...(313) 668-4200
Complaints regarding auto emission tampering, emission, auto warranty, recall notices, fuel issues, CSC recycling, auto air conditioning.

National Institute for Occupational Safety and Health (NIOSH)
National..(800) 356-4674

National Institute of Standards and Technology (NIST)
National...(301) 975-2000
Previously the National Bureau of Standards (NBS).

National Technical Information Service (NTIS)
National...(703) 487-4600
....(800) 553-6847
Source of information services (technical documents and databases) and documents from federal agencies, industries, and universities.

Nuclear Regulatory Commission
....(800) 368-5642
NRC provides information about technical questions and documents regarding hazardous materials and wastes.

Public Health Service
National..(301) 443-2403

Water and Waste Water Information (600-series methods)
National...(202) 260-7120
Provides information on testing methods for water and waste water (600-series methods) contained in CFR-40 part 136.

Wetlands Protection
National, VI and Guam.................(800) 832-7828
Responsive to public interest, questions and requests for information about the values and functions of wetlands and options for their protection. Provides referrals to callers when necessary.

ENVIRONMENTAL DATABASE AND COMPUTER CONTACTS

CERCLIS - Helpline
National ....(703) 908-2066
Answering machine for all off-hour callers. Technical Support and referrals to the users of CERCLIS database, Waste LAN and Clean LAN.

EPA Office of Research and Development Electronic Bulletin Board (ORD BBS)
National (1200 & 2400 baud).....(513) 569-7610
(9600 baud).....................................(513) 569-7700

STORET
National ....(800) 424-9067
....(202) 260-8161
Technical support for STORET users.

Solid Waste Information Clearinghouse Hotline (SWICH)
National ....(800) 424-9346
Online service, modem. SWICH computer system. All aspects of solid waste management, including: source reduction, recycling, composting, planning education and training, public participation, legislation and regulation, waste combustion, collection, transfer, disposal, landfill gas and special waster.

Facility Index System (FINDS)
National ....(800) 908-2493
Technical user support; FINDS users only.

Customer Technical Support National Computer Center (NCC)
National ....(800) 334-2405
NC only ....(919) 541-7862
Provides NCC customers with technical assistance, problem diagnosis, solution and tracking. Supports mainframe IBM.

US EPA Contacts

USEPA Analytical Operations Branch (OS-230)
401 M Street, SW
Room M-2624
Washington, DC 20460
(202) 260-2090

USEPA Contracts Mgmt. Div. (MD-33)
79 Alexander Drive
Research Triangle Park, NC 27711
(919) 541-3699

USEPA Environmental Monitoring Systems Laboratory (EMSL/LV)
944 East Harmon Avenue
Las Vegas, NV 89108

Mailing Address:
P.O. Box 93478
Las Vegas, NV 89193-3478

Data To:
EMSL/LV Executive Center
944 East Harmon Ave.
Las Vegas, NV 89119
Attn: Data Audit Staff

USEPA National Enforcement Investigations Center (NEIC)
Denver Federal Center
Building 53
W1 Entrance, 2nd Floor
Denver, CO 80225
(303) 236-5073

USEPA Environmental Monitoring Systems Laboratory (EMSL/Cincinnati)
26 W. M. L. King Dr.
Cincinnati, OH 45268
(513) 569-7325
(513) 569-7931 for General Info Directory

USEPA PE Studies Coordinator
National Water Quality Assurance Programs Branch
USEPA, EERD
26 W. M.L. King Drive, Room 525
Cincinnati, OH 45268
(513) 569-7196
FAX: (513) 569-7115

USEPA REGION I

USEPA Region I
J.F. Kennedy Federal Bldg.
One Congress Street
Boston, MA 02203-0001
(617) 565-3420
FAX: (617) 565-3660

USEPA Region I, QA Coordinator
Mrs. Denise DePierro
Environmental Services Division
US EPA, Region 1
60 Westview Street
Lexington, MA 02173
(617) 860-4365
FAX: (617) 860-4397

USEPA REGION II

USEPA Region II
290 Broadway
New York, NY 10007-1866
(212) 637-5000
FAX: (212) 637-3526

USEPA Region II, QA Coordinator
Mr. John Bourbon
Monitoring Management Branch, ESD
US EPA, Region 2
2890 Woodbridge Ave., M.S. 103
Edison, NJ 08837
(908) 321-6729
FAX: (908) 906-6824
DMR QA Coordinator (Linda Manuel) for NY, NJ, Puerto Rico and US Virgin Islands
....(908) 321-6766

USEPA REGION III

USEPA Region III
841 Chestnut Building
Philadelphia, PA 19107
(215) 566-5000
FAX: (215) 566-5103

USEPA Region III, QA Coordinator
Mr. Charles Jones, Jr.
Env. Assessment & Protection Div.
US EPA, Region 3
841 Chestnut Building (3EP10)
Philadelphia, PA 19107
(215) 566-2710
FAX: (215) 566-2782

USEPA REGION IV

USEPA Region IV
100 Alabama St. SW
Atlanta, GA 30303
(404) 562-9900
FAX: (404) 562-8174

USEPA Region IV, QA Coordinator
Mr. Ralph Gentry, Office of Quality Assurance
Science & Ecosystem Support Div.
US EPA, Region 4
980 College Station Road
Athens, GA 30605-2720
(706) 355-8553
FAX: (706) 355-8803

USEPA REGION V

USEPA Region V
77 West Jackson Blvd.
Chicago, IL 60604-3507
(312) 353-2000 FAX: (312) 353-4135

USEPA Region V, QA Coordinator
Mr. Robert Gnaedinger
Standards & Applied Science Branch
US EPA, Water Division, Region 5
77 West Jackson Blvd.
Chicago, IL 60604
(312) 353-2975 FAX: (312) 353-4342

USEPA REGION VI

USEPA Region VI
US EPA, Region 6
Fountain Place 12th Floor, Suite 1200
1445 Ross Avenue
Dallas, TX 75202-2733
(214) 665-6444 FAX: (214) 665-7113

USEPA Region VI Laboratory
10625 Fallstone Road
Houston, TX 77099-4303
(713) 983-2100 FAX: (713) 983-2248

USEPA Region VI, QA Coordinator
Mr. Don Johnson
Enforcement and Compliance Div.
US EPA, Region 6
1445 Ross Avenue
Dallas, TX 75202-2733
(214) 665-8343 FAX: (214) 665-2168
Recorded Info: (214) 665-8397

USEPA REGION VII

USEPA Region VII
726 Minnesota Avenue
Kansas City, KS 66101
(913) 551-7000
FAX: (913) 551-7467

USEPA Region VII, QA Coordinator
Mr. Douglas Brune
Environmental Services Division
US EPA, Region 7
25 Funston Road
Kansas City, KS 66115
(913) 551-5180
FAX: (913) 551-5218

USEPA REGION VIII

USEPA Region VIII
999 18th Street, Suite 500
Denver, CO 80202-2466
(303) 312-6312 FAX: (303) 312-6339

USEPA Region VIII, QA Coordinator
Mr. John Manhart (8ES-LB)
US EPA, Region 8, ESD, Lab. Br.
P.O. Box 25366
Denver Federal Center
Bldg. 56, W-1
Denver, CO 80225
(303) 236-7366 FAX: (303) 236-8235

USEPA REGION IX

USEPA Region IX
75 Hawthorne Street
San Francisco, CA 94105
(415) 744-1305 FAX: (415) 744-2499

USEPA Region IX, QA Coordinator
Ms. Carolyn Tambwekar
US EPA, Region 9 Lab, Bldg 201
1337 S. 46th St., P-3-1
Richmond, CA 94804
(510) 412-2383 FAX; (510) 412-2304

USEPA REGION X

USEPA Region X
US EPA, Region 10
1200 Sixth Avenue
Seattle, WA 98101
(206) 553-1200 FAX: (206) 553-0149

USEPA Region X, QA Coordinator
Mr. Arthur Dan Baker
Office of Environmental Assessment
US EPA, Region 10
1200 Sixth Avenue (OEA-095)
Seattle, WA 98101
(206) 553-1692 FAX: (206) 553-8210

Manchester Environmental Lab
7411 Beach Drive East
Port Orchard, WA 98366
(360) 871-0748 FAX: (360) 871-8747

MISCELLANEOUS

Ms. Natalie Murff
US EPA, NERL, EERD, NWQAPB
26 West M. L. King Drive, Room 525
Cincinnati, OH 45268
(513) 569-7196
FAX: (513) 569-7115

MISCELLANEOUS INFORMATION

Federal Information Center
Can provide you with a federal phone number
for any federal agency located in the US.
(800) 688-9889

Cooler Returns
T. Head and Company
950 Herndon Parkway
Suite 230
Herndon, VA 22070
(703) 473-3886

ERT Edison
USEPA Environmental Response Branch
GSA Raritan Depot
Woodbridge Avenue
Edison, NJ 08837
FTS 340-6649, 6689, 6743

EPA Libraries
Research Triangle, North Carolina
(919) 541-2777
Cincinnati, Ohio
(513) 569-7562
(800) 490-9198

OSW Methods Section
(202) 260-4761

ASTM
100 Barr Harbor Drive
West Conshohocken, PA 19428-2959
(610) 832-9585

Government Printing Office
(202) 572-2303

**National Center for Environmental
Publications and Information (NCEPI)**
(513) 489-8190

USGS Books and Open File Publications
Denver Federal Center
Box 25425
Denver, CO 80225
(303) 202-4700 FAX: (303) 202-4693

STATE CONTACTS

State NELAP Accrediting Authorities
www.epa.gov/ttn/nelac

Accrediting Authority	Agency Name	Contact	Telephone FAX e-mail
Arkansas	AR Dept. of Pollution Control & Ecology	Mr. Jeff Ruehr	(501) 682-0955 (501) 682-0891 dc@adeq.state.ar.us
California	Environmental Laboratory Accreditation Program	Dr. George Kulasingam	(510) 540-2800 (510) 849-5106 elapca@pacbell.net
Colorado	CO Dept. of Public Health & Environment	Ms. Judith Donaldson	(303) 692-3090 (303) 344-9965 judith.donaldson@state.co.us
Florida	FL Dept of Health, Bureau of Laboratories	Dr. Stephen Arms	(904) 791-1502 (904) 791-1591 steve_arms@doh.state.fl.us
Idaho	ID Dept of Health and Welfare	Mr. Richard Hudson	(208) 334-2235 (208) 334-2382 —
Illinois	IL EPA, Division of Laboratories, QA Section	Mr. Jim Shaw	(217) 782-6455 (217) 524-0944 epa6109@epa.state.il.us
Kansas	KS Dept. of Health & Environment	Mr. Stan Sutton	(785) 296-1640 (785) 296-1641 uskanhgn@ibmmail.com
Louisiana	LA Dept of Health & Hospitals	Ms. Jeanne Mixon	(504) 568-5375 (504) 568-5393 —
New Hampshire	NH Environmental Lab Accreditation Program	Mr. Charles Dyer	(603) 271-2991 (603) 271-2997 c_dyer@des.state.nh.us
New Jersey	NJ Dept of Environmental Protection	Mr. Joseph Aiello	(609) 292-3950 (609) 777-1774 jaiello@dep.state.nj.us
New York	NY State Dept of Health	Dr. Kenneth Jackson	(518) 485-5570 (518) 485-5568 jackson@wadsworth.org
Oregon	OR Dept of Environmental Quality	Ms. Rae Ann Haynes	(503) 229-5983 (503) 229-6924 haynes.raeann@deq.state.or.us
Oregon	OR State Public Health Laboratory	Dr. Irene Ronning	(503) 229-5882 (503) 229-5682 irene.e.ronning@state.or.us
Pennsylvania	Bureau of Labs, Dept of Environmental Protection	Mr. Richard Sheibley	(717) 783-7150 (717) 783-1502 sheibley.richard@al.dep.state.pa.us
Texas	TX Dept. of Health, Bureau of Labs.	Dr. David Maserang	(512) 458-7381 (512) 458-7294 dmaserang@laba.tdh.state.tx.us
Utah	UT Dept. of Health	Mr. Dave Mendenhall	(801) 584-8470 (801) 584-8501 dmendenh@state.ut.us

Alabama

Alabama Dept. of Environmental Management
Chief, Land Division
1751 W. L. Dickinson Drive
Montgomery, AL 36130
Phone: (205) 271-7730
FAX: (205) 271-7950
PE Studies
DMR: E. John Williford.................(334) 260-2700
WS: Joe Power ....(334) 271-7773

Alaska

Alaska Dept. of Environmental Conservation
Solid and Hazardous Waste Mgt.
Pouch 0
Juneau, AK 99811
Phone: (907) 465-5150
FAX: (907) 456-5362

Alaska Dept. of Environmental Conservation
Chief, Spill Planning and Prevention
Pouch 0
Juneau, AK 99811
Phone: (907) 465-5250

Alaska Dept. of Environmental Conservation
Contaminated Sites Section
Pouch 0
Juneau, AK 99811
Phone: (907) 465-2630
UST Information ....(907) 465-5200
PE Studies
DMR: Karen Hoover (EPA Region X)
....(206) 553-1213

Arizona

Arizona Dept. of Environmental Quality
Assistant Director, Office of Waste Programs
3033 N. Central Avenue, 7th Floor
Phoenix, AZ 85002
Phone: (602) 207-2300
FAX: (602) 257-6874

Arizona Dept. of Environmental Quality
Hazardous Waste Section
3033 N. Central, Room 403C
Phoenix, AZ 85002
Phone: (602) 257-6995
FAX: (602) 257-6948

Environmental Lab Licensure
AZ Dept of Health Services
Phoenix, AZ 85012
PE Studies
DMR: Gary Brussels......................(602) 255-3454
UST Information ....(602) 207-4288

Arkansas

Arkansas Dept. of Poll. Control and Ecology
Chief, Hazardous Waste Division
P.O. Box 8913
Little Rock, AR 72219-8913
Phone: (501) 562-0831 or
              (501) 682-0580
FAX: (501) 682-0880 or
              (501) 682-0707

PE Studies
WP & WS: Jeff Ruhr ....(501) 682-0955
DMR: Dick Cassat ....(501) 682-0744
UST Information ....(501) 562-6533

State Quality Assurance Coordinator
Jeff Ruehr, QA Officer
AR Dept. of Poll. Control & Ecology
Technical Services Division
8001 National Drive
Little Rock, AR 72209
Phone: (501) 682-0955
FAX: (501) 682-0798

California

California Dept. of Toxic Substances Control
Haz. Waste Management Program
P.O. Box 806
Sacramento, CA 95812-0806
Phone: (916) 323-6042
FAX: (916) 372-4495

CA State Water Resources Control Board
Chief, Div. of Clean Water Programs
2014 T Street
Suite 130
Sacramento, CA 95814
Phone: (916) 227-4400
FAX: (916) 227-4349
DMR QA Coordinator (Bill Ray)
....(916) 657-1123

State Quality Assurance Coordinator
Dr. Theodore Belsky
Environmental Lab Accreditation Program
California. Dept. of Health Services
2151 Berkeley Way
Annex #2
Berkeley CA 94704-1011
Phone: (510) 540-2800
FAX: (510) 849-5106
PE Studies WP & WS: Dr. T. Belsky
....(510) 540-2800
DMR: Bill Ray................................(916) 657-1123
UST Information ....(916) 227-4337

Colorado

Colorado Dept. of Health
Hazardous Materials and Waste Mgt. Div.
4300 Cherry Creek Dr. South
Denver, CO 80222-1530
Phone: (303) 692-3300
FAX: (303) 759-4355
UST Information .... (303) 692-3330
PE Studies
WS & WP: Judy Donaldson ...... (303) 692-3290
DMR: Derald Lang .... (303) 692-3561

Public Utilities Commission
Hazardous Materials Transportation Permits
1580 Logan Street, Off. Level 1
Denver, CO 80203
Phone: (303) 894-2000
FAX: (303) 894-2065

State Quality Assurance Coordinator
Judy Donaldson
Supervisor of Certification Unit
Lab CLIA
CO Dept. of Public Health & Environ.
8100 Lowry Blvd.
Denver, CO 80220-6928
Phone: (303) 692-3290
FAX: (303) 344-9989

Connecticut

Connecticut Waste Management Bureau
Bureau Chief
79 Elm Street
Hartford, CT 06106
Phone: (860) 424-3023
FAX: (860) 424-4059
UST Information .... (203) 566-5599

Connecticut Resource Recovery Authority
President
179 Allyn St., Suite 603
Hartford, CT 06103
Phone: (860) 549-6390
FAX: (860) 522-2390

State Quality Assurance Coordinator
Nick Mascelletti, Super. Env. Lab Consultant
State of Connecticut Dept of Public Health
Division of Env. Health, Lab Certification
450 Capitol Ave
MS #51 LAB
PO Box 340308
Hartford, CT 03134
Phone: (860) 509-7367
FAX: (860) 509-7295
PE Studies
WP & WS: Nick Mascelletti..... (860) 509-7386
DMR: Donald Gonyea .... (860) 424-3827

Delaware

Delaware Dept. of Natural Resources and
    Environmental Control
Haz. Waste Management Branch Manager
P.O. Box 1401
89 Kings Highway
Dover, DE 19903
Phone: (302) 739-3689
FAX: (302) 739-5060
PE Studies
DMR: Joe Mulrooney.................... (302) 739-5731
UST Information.............................. (302) 323-4588

District of Columbia

Dept. of Consumer and Regulatory Affairs
Pesticides, Haz. Waste, and Underground
    Storage Tank Division
2100 M. Luther King, Jr. Ave., SE
Suite #203
Washington, DC 20020
Phone: (202) 645-6080
PE Studies
DMR: William Ruby
.... (202) 645-6601, Ext. 3032

Florida

Florida Dept. of Environmental Regulation
Administrator, Solid and Haz. Waste
Twin Towers Office Bldg
2600 Blair Stone Road
Tallahassee, FL 32399-2400
Phone: (904) 488-0300
FAX: (904) 921-8061
PE Studies
WP & WS: Dr. Carl Kircher....... (904) 791-1574
DMR: Carlos Boueres .... (904) 488-2796
UST Information.............................. (904) 488-0190

State Quality Assurance Coordinator
Dr. Stephen Arms
FL DHRS, Lab Services
Water Certification Program
1217 Pearl Street
Jacksonville, FL 32202
Phone: (904) 791-1574
FAX: (904) 791-1591

Georgia

Hazardous Waste Management Branch
Floyd Towers East
205 Butler Street, SE
Atlanta, GA 30334
Phone: (404) 656-2833
FAX: (404) 651-9425
UST Information............................. (404) 362-2687
EPD, DNR

Water Protection Branch
Atlanta Tradeport
4244 International Pkwy Suite 110
Atlanta, GA 30354

Drinking Water Program, EPD
GA Dept. of Nat. Resources
Floyd Towers East, Rm 1362
205 Butler St. SE
Atlanta, GA 30334

PE Studies
WP: Ted Jackson............................ (404) 206-5246
WS: Loretta Lambert......................(404) 651-5164
DMR: Jeff Larsen ....(404) 362-2680

State Quality Assurance Coordinator
Ted Jackson
EPD Lab
GA Dept. of Natural Resources
Technology Park
455 14th Street
Atlanta, GA 30318-7900
Phone: (404) 206-5246
FAX: (404) 206-5268

Hawaii

Hawaii Dept. of Health
Mgr, Solid and Hazardous Waste Branch
919 Ala Moana Blvd.
Room 212
Honolulu, HI 96814
Phone: (808) 586-4226
FAX: (808) 586-7509
UST Information................................(808) 586-4225

Hawaii Dept. of Health
Hazard Evaluation and Emerg. Response
Manager
919 Ala Moana Blvd.
Room 206
Honolulu, HI 96814
Phone: (808) 586-4249
FAX: (808) 586-7537

State Quality Assurance Coordinator
Jodi Nakamura
HI Dept Health
State Labs, Env. Microbio.
2725 Waimano Home Rd
Pearl City, HI 96782
Phone: (808) 453-6678
FAX: (808) 453-6685
PE Studies
WS: Mary Ann Craddock.............(808) 453-6678
DMR & WP: Rendy Chow..........(808) 453-6684

Idaho

Division of Environmental Quality
RCRA Programs
1410 North Hilton Street
Boise, ID 83706
Phone: (208) 373-0502
FAX: (208) 373-0417
PE Studies
DMR: Karen Hoover (EPA Region X)
....(206) 553-1213
UST Information ....(208) 334-5860

Illinois

Illinois Environmental Protection Agency, Dir.
2200 Churchill Road
Springfield, IL 62706
Phone: (217) 782-3397
FAX: (217) 782-9039
PE Studies
WS: Mary Beth Lawhorn.............(217) 785-8508
DMR: Erin Rednour.......................(217) 782-9720
UST Information...............................(217) 782-6761

Illinois Environmental Protection Agency
Public Information Officer
Division of Land Pollution Control
2200 Churchill Road
Springfield, IL 62706
Phone: (217) 782-3397
FAX: (217) 785-7725

Haz. Waste Research and Information Center
Illinois Energy and Natural Resources
David Thomas - Director
1 E. Hazelwood Drive
Champaign, IL 61820
Phone: (217) 333-8941
FAX: (217) 333-8944

Indiana

Indiana Dept. of Environmental Management
Branch Chief, Office of Hazardous Waste Mgt.
Indiana Government Center North
100 N. Senate Ave.
P.O. Box 6015
Indianapolis, IN 46206-6015
Phone: (317) 232-3292
FAX: (317) 232-3403

Laboratory Improvement Branch
Indiana State Dept. of Health
1330 W. Michigan St
Indianapolis, IN 46202-1964
PE Studies
WS: Phillip Zillinger.....................(317) 233-8071
DMR: Steve Kim............................(317) 232-8793
UST Information ....(317) 232-8603

Iowa

State Quality Assurance Coordinator
Stacy Freeburg
University Hygienic Laboratory
102 Oakdale Campus
Iowa City, IA 52242
Phone: (319) 355-4500
FAX: (319) 355-4555

Iowa Dept of Natural Resources
Henry A. Wallace Building
900 E. Grand
Des Moines, IA 50319
PE Studies
WP & WS: Stacy Freeburg........(319) 335-4500
DMR: Charles Furrey....................(515) 281-4067
UST Information..............................(515) 281-8957

Kansas

Bureau of Air and Radiation
Dir., Kansas Dept. of Health and Environment
Forbes Field, Building 283
Topeka, KS 66620
Phone: (913) 296-1593
FAX: (913) 296-1545

Bureau of Waste Management
Dir., Kansas Dept. of Health and Environment
Forbes Field, Building 740
Topeka, KS 66620
Phone: (913) 296-1600
FAX: (913) 296-1592
UST Information..............................(913) 296-1684

State Quality Assurance Coordinator
Jack McKenzie
Kansas Health and Environment Lab
Laboratory Improvement Office
Forbes Field, Building 740
Topeka, KS 66620-0001
Phone: (913) 296-1639
FAX: (913) 296-1641
PE Studies
DMR, WP, & WS: Jack McKenzie
....(785) 296-1639

Kentucky

Kentucky Dept. of Environmental Protection
Director, Div. of Waste Mgt.
Omega Bldg., Ft. Boone Plaza
Frankfort, KY 40601
Phone: (502) 564-6716, Ext. 214
FAX: (502) 564-4049
PE Studies
WP: Gary Levy (DEP)..................(502) 564-3410
WP: John Knafl (Enforcement)
...............................(502) 564-2356, Ext. 712
WS: Scott Bryan............................(502) 564-6120

DMR: Donna Drury......(502) 564-3410, Ext. 461
UST Information..............................(502) 564-6716

Division of Environmental Services
100 Sower Blvd., Rm. 104
Frankfort, KY 40601

State Quality Assurance Coordinator
Gary Levy
Division of Water
Kentucky Dept. of Environmental Protection
14 Reilly Road
Frankfort, KY 40601
Phone: (502) 564-3410
FAX: (502) 564-4245

State Quality Assurance Coordinator
John Knafl
Reclamation & Enforcement - Soap Br.
KY Dept. for Surface Mining
#2 Hudson Hollow Complex
Frankfort, KY 40601
Phone: (502) 564-2356, Ext. 712
FAX: (502) 564-5848

Louisiana

Louisiana Dept. of Environmental Quality
Office of Solid and Hazardous Waste
P.O. Box 82178
Baton Rouge, LA 70884-2178
Phone: (504) 765-0355
FAX: (504) 765-0617
UST Information
....(504) 765-0741

Louisiana Dept. of Environmental Quality
Administrator, Ground Water Protection Div.
P.O. Box 82215
Baton Rouge, LA 70884-2215
Phone: (504) 765-0585
FAX: (504) 765-0602

State Quality Assurance Coordinator
Jeanne Mixon
LA Dept. of Health and Hospitals
325 Loyola Ave
New Orleans, LA 70112
Phone: (504) 568-3455
FAX: (504) 568-5393
PE Studies
WS: Jeanne Mixon.........................(504) 568-3455
DMR: Elaine Sorbet.......................(504) 765-2406

LA Dept of Environmental Quality
Water Pollution Control Division
3501 Shateau Blvd
West Wing Suit 1
Kennere, LA 70065
DMR QA Coordinator (Tom Bradley)
....(504) 471-2800

Maine

Bureau of Hazardous Materials and Solid
  Waste Control
Dir., Maine Dept of Environmental Protection
State House Station #17
Augusta, ME 04333
Phone: (207) 287-2651
FAX: (207) 287-7826
PE Studies
WP & WS: Michael Soldano.....(207) 287-2727
DMR: David Dodge........................(207) 287-7659
UST Information...............................(207) 289-2651

State Quality Assurance Coordinator
Michael Soldano
Maine Dept of Human Services
State House Station #12
Augusta, ME 04333
Phone: (207) 287-2727
FAX: (207) 287-6832

Maryland

Haz. and Solid Waste Management Admin.
Dir., Maryland Dept. of the Environment
2500 Broening Highway
Baltimore, MD 21224
Phone: (301) 631-3304; FAX: (301) 631-3321
UST Information...............................(410) 631-3442

Water Quality Lab
MD Dept. of Health and Mental Hygiene
201 West Preston St
Baltimore, MD 21202
PE Studies
WS: Mary Stancavage..................(410) 767-5074
DMR: Marlene Patillo..................(410) 631-3646

Massachusetts

Massachusetts Dept. of Environmental Affairs
Director, Executive Office
100 Cambridge St., 20th Floor
Boston, MA 02202
Phone: (617) 727-9800
FAX: (617) 727-2754
PE Studies
WP & WS: Anne Marie Allen
....(508) 682-5237, Ext. 333
DMR: Ping Lee.................................(508) 756-7281
UST Information...............................(617) 935-2160

State Quality Assurance Coordinator
Anne Marie Allen
MA Dept of Environ. Protection
Lawrence Experiment Station
37 Shattuck Street
Lawrence, MA 01843
Phone: (508) 682-5237, Ext. 333
FAX: (508) 688-0352

MA Dept of Env. Protection
Div. of Water Pollution Control
Training Center, Route 20
Millbury, MA 01527

Michigan

Waste Management Division
Michigan Dept. of Natural Resources
Chief, Hazardous Waste Permits Section
P.O. Box 30241
Lansing, MI 48909
Phone: (517) 373-2730
FAX: (517) 373-4797
UST Information ....(517) 373-8168

State Quality Assurance Coordinator
Dr. George Su
MI Dept. of Natural Resources
Environ. Response Division Lab
3500 N. Logan Street
Lansing, MI 48909
Phone: (517) 335-9800
FAX: (517) 335-9600
PE Studies
WP: Bob Avery...............................(517) 335-9500
DMR: Clyde Marion (EPA Region V)
....(312) 353-5966
WS: Jon Bloemker......................(517) 335-8319

Minnesota

Minnesota Pollution Control Agency
Director, Hazardous Waste Div.
520 Lafayette Rd. North
St. Paul, MN 55155
Phone: (612) 297-8502
FAX: (612) 297-8676
PE Studies
WP & WS: Al Tupy......................(612) 623-5680
DMR: Kim Sandrock......................(612) 296-7387
UST Information...............................(612) 297-8594

Hazardous Waste Division
Minnesota Pollution Control Agency
Chief, Program Development
520 Lafayette Rd. North
St. Paul, MN 55155
Phone: (612) 297-8355
FAX: (612) 297-8676

Minnesota Tech. Assistance Prog. (MnTAP)
Director
1313 5th Street, SE, Suite 207
Minneapolis, MN 55414
Phone: (612) 627-4646 or (800) 247-0015
FAX: (612) 627-4769

State Quality Assurance Coordinator
Al Tupy
Lab Services Section
MN Dept. of Health
717 Delaware St, SE
Minneapolis, MN 55440
Phone: (612) 623-5680
FAX: (612) 623-5514

Mississippi

Mississippi Dept. of Environmental Quality
Chief, Hazardous Waste Division
P.O. Box 10385
Jackson, MS 39289-0385
Phone: (601) 961-5062
FAX: (601) 961-5741
PE Studies
WP: Earskin Phillips .... (601) 939-8460
WS: Sammie Malone .... (601) 960-7592
DMR: Phillip Bass .... (601) 961-5143
UST Information .... (601) 939-8460

State Quality Assurance Coordinator
Earskin Phillips
Mississippi Dept. of Environmental Quality
P.O. Box 10385
Jackson, MS 39289-0385
Phone: (601) 939-8460
FAX: (601) 939-8479

Bureau of Public Health Labs
MS State Dept of Health
2423 North State St
P.O. Box 1700
Jackson, MS 39215-1700

Missouri

Missouri Dept. of Natural Resources
Dir., Hazardous Waste Program
205 Jefferson St.
P.O. Box 176
Jefferson City, MO 65102
Phone: (573) 751-3176
FAX: (573) 751-7869
Solid Waste Program - (573) 751-5401
PE Studies
DMR: Jack Pate .... (573) 751-1399
UST Information .... (816) 795-8655

Montana

Montana Dept. of Health and Env. Quality
Solid and Hazardous Waste Div.
2209 Phoenix Ave., P.O. Box 200901
Helena, MT 59620-0901
Phone: (406) 444-2821
FAX: (406) 444-1499
UST Information .... (406) 444-5970

State Quality Assurance Coordinator
Dennis Braun
MT Dept. of Public Health and Human Serv.
Chemistry Laboratory, Cogswell Bldg
Helena, MT 59620
Phone: (406) 444-2643
FAX: (406) 444-1802

MT. Dept of Environmental Quality
P.O. Box 200901
1520 E. 6th St.
Helena, MT 59620-0901
PE Studies
WP & WS: Dennis Braun .... (406) 444-2643
DMR: Mike Pasichnyk .... (406) 444-5326

Nebraska

Nebraska Dept. of Environmental Quality
Haz. Waste Section, CERCLA Unit Supervisor
P.O. Box 98922
Lincoln, NE 68509
Phone: (402) 471-2186
FAX: (402) 471-2909
UST Information .... (402) 471-4230

Nebraska Dept. of Environmental Quality
Hazardous Waste Sec., RCRA Unit Supervisor
P.O. Box 98922
Lincoln, NE 68509
Phone: (402) 471-2186
FAX: (402) 471-2909
PE Studies
DMR: Brian Gorman .... (402) 471-4253

Nevada

Division of Environmental Protection
Nevada Dept. of Conserv. and Natural Res.
Chief, Waste Mgt. Bureau, Capitol Complex
123 W. Nye Lane
Carson City, NV 89710
Phone: (702) 687-5872
FAX: (702) 885-0868
PE Studies
WP & WS: Jack Ruckman .... (702) 688-2888
DMR: Wendall McCurry
.... (702) 687-4670, Ext. 3098
UST Information .... (702) 687-5872

NV State Bureau of License & Certification
1475 Terminal Way, Suite D
Reno, NV 89502

State Quality Assurance Coordinator
Robert Vicks - NV State Health Lab
1660 N. Virginia
Reno, NV 89503
Phone: (702) 688-1335
FAX: (702) 688-1460

New Hampshire

New Hampshire Dept. of Environmental Serv.
Dir., Waste Management Division
6 Haven Drive
Concord, NH 03301-6509
Phone: (603) 271-2906
FAX: (603) 271-2456
PE Studies
WP & WS: Charles Dyer.............(603) 271-2991
DMR: Stephanie Larson................(603) 271-1493
UST Information................................(603) 271-3503

State Quality Assurance Coordinator
NH Dept. of Environ. Services
Lab Services Unit
P.O. Box 95, Hazen Drive
Concord, NH 03301
Phone: (603) 271-2991

New Jersey

NJ Dept. of Environmental Protection
Assistant Commissioner
Site Remediation Program
401 E. State Street
CN 028-6th Floor East
Trenton, NJ 08625
Phone: (609) 292-1250
FAX: (609) 633-2360
UST Information...............................(609) 984-3156

NJ Dept. of Env. Protection and Energy
Director
Div. of Responsible Party Site Remediation
401 E. State Street
CN 028-5th Floor East
Trenton, NJ 08625
Phone: (609) 633-1408
FAX: (609) 633-1454

State Quality Assurance Coordinator
Michale DiBalsi
NJ Dept. of Environmental Protection
Office of Quality Assurance
9 Ewing St., CN-424
Trenton, NJ 08625
Phone: (609) 292-3950
FAX: (609) 777-1774
PE Studies
WP & WS: Michale DiBalsi......(609) 292-3950
DMR: Linda Mauel (EPA Region II)
....(732) 321-6766

New Mexico

New Mexico Environment Dept.
Groundwater Quality Bureau
P.O. Box 26110
Santa Fe, NM 87502
Phone: (505) 827-2922

FAX: (505) 827-2965
PE Studies
WS: Barbara Geisler.....................(505) 827-7536
WP & DMR: Patrick Hanson......(505) 827-2799
UST Information..............................(505) 827-0079

State Quality Assurance Coordinator
Pat Hanson
NM Environment Department
Surface Water Quality Bureau
P.O. Box 26110
Santa Fe, NM 87502
Phone: (505) 827-2799
FAX: (505) 827-0160

New Mexico Environment Dept.
Chief
Hazardous and Radioactive Mat'ls Bureau
Physical Location:
2044A Galisteo St
Santa Fe, NM 87505
Phone: (505) 827-1564

Drinking Water Bureau
2052 Gallisto
PO Box 26110
Santa Fe, NM 87505

New York

NYS Dept. of Environmental Conserv.
Div. of Solid and Hazardous Materials
50 Wolf Rd., Room 488
Albany, NY 12233-7250
Phone: (518) 457-6934
FAX: (518) 457-0629
PE Studies
WP & WS: Through Wadsworth Center
DMR: Linda Mauel (EPA Region II)
....(732) 321-6766
UST Information..............................(518) 457-7363

New York State Dept. of Health
Wadsworth Center for Laboratories & Research
Environmental Laboratory Approval Program
P.O. Box 509
Albany, NY 12201-0509
Dr. Ken Jackson...............................(518) 485-5570

North Carolina

N. Carolina Dept. of Env., Health, and Natural
    Resources
Director - Div. of Solid Waste Management
P.O. Box 27687
Raleigh, NC 27611-7687
Phone: (919) 733-4996
FAX: (919) 733-4810
UST Information
....(919) 733-1320

State Quality Assurance Coordinator
William Edwards
DEM/Lab Section - NCDEHNR
4405 Reedy Creek Road
Raleigh, NC 27601
Phone: (919) 733-3908
FAX: (919) 733-6241
PE Studies
WP & DMR: Jim Meyer
....(919) 733-3908, Ext. 243
WS: Don Beesley...........................(919) 733-7308

Div. of Health Services
306 N. Wilmington St.
Raleigh, NC 27611-8047

North Dakota

N. Dakota Dept. of Health and Waste Mgt.
P.O. Box 5520
Bismarck, ND 58506-5520
Phone: (701) 328-5166
FAX: (701) 328-5200
PE Studies
WP & WS: Errol Erickson
....(701) 328-6172
DMR: Jean Pfiefer
....(701) 328-5228
UST Information
....(701) 221-5166

State Quality Assurance Coordinator
Errol Erickson
ND Dept. of Health - Chemistry Division
2635 East Main St.
PO Box 937
Bismarck, ND 58501
Phone: (701) 328-6172
FAX: (701) 328-6145

Ohio

Ohio Environmental Protection Agency
Chief, Div. of Solid and Hazardous Waste Mgt.
1800 Watermark Drive
P.O. Box 1049
Columbus, OH 43266-0149
Phone: (614) 644-2917
FAX: (614) 644-2329
UST Information
....(614) 752-7941

Ohio Dept. of Health Labs
1571 Perry St., PO Box 2568
Columbus, OH 43266-0068
PE Studies
WS: James Dolfi
....(614) 644-4272
DMR: Susan Plank
....(614) 644-4240

Ohio EPA
1571 Perry St
Columbus, OH 43201

Ohio Environmental Protection Agency
Div. of Solid & Infectious Waste Mgt.
2305 Westbrooke Drive
Building C
Columbus, OH 43228-9644
Phone: (614) 644-2621
FAX: (614) 728-5315

Oklahoma

Dept. of Environmental Quality
Waste Mgt. Div. (Hazardous Waste)
1000 Northeast Tenth Street
Oklahoma City, OK 73117-1299
Phone: (405) 702-6100
FAX: (405) 702-1001
PE Studies
WP & WS: Anthony Bright
....(405) 702-1024
DMR: Aaron Milligan
....(405) 702-6100
UST Information
....(405) 702-6100

State Quality Assurance Coordinator
Anthony Bright
OK Dept. of Environ. Quality
State Environ. Lab
1000 NE Tenth St.
Oklahoma City, OK 73117-1212
Phone: (405) 271-5240, Ext. 121
FAX: (405) 271-1836

Oregon

Oregon Dept. of Environmental Quality
Waste Mgt/Environmental Cleanup Div.
811 SW 6th Ave.
Portland, OR 97204
Phone: (503) 229-5913
FAX: (503) 229-6977
UST Information
....(503) 229-6764

Oregon Dept. of Environmental Quality
Administrator, Environmental Cleanup Div.
811 SW 6th Ave.
Portland, OR 97204
Phone: (503) 229-5254
FAX: (503) 229-6124
PE Studies
DMR: Judy Johndohl
....(503) 229-6896

Pennsylvania

Pennsylvania Dept. of Environmental
  Resources
Dir., Bureau of Land Recycling & Waste Mgt.
P.O. Box 2063
Harrisburg, PA 17105-2063
Phone: (717) 783-2388
FAX: (717) 787-1904
UST Information
....(717) 772-5835

Pennsylvania Dept. of Environmental
  Protection
Municipal & Residual Waste
P.O. Box 8472
Harrisburg, PA 17105-8472
Phone: (717) 787-7381
FAX: (717) 787-1904
PE Studies
WP & WS: Richard Scheibley
....(717) 783-7150

DMR: Laurue Wyrick
....(717) 783-2940

State Quality Assurance Coordinator
Ted Lyter
PA DER, Bureau of Labs
Labs Certification Program
3rd & Reilly Sts.
PO Box 1467
Harrisburg, PA 17105-1467
Phone: (717) 783-7150
FAX: (717) 783-1502

Rhode Island

Rhode Island Dept. of Environmental Waste
Dept. of Environment
Waste Management Division.
291 Promenade Street
Providence, RI 02908
Phone: (401) 277-2797
PE Studies
Deborah Dehmel
....(401) 222-4526
DMR QA Coordinator (Ben Lovesky)
.................................(401) 277-3961, Ext. 7268
UST Information
....(401) 277-2234

State Quality Assurance Coordinator
Deborah Dehmel
Div. of Facilities Regulation
Cannon Building, 33 Capitol Hill
Providence, RI 02908
Phone: (401) 277-4526
FAX: (401) 277-3999

South Carolina

S. Carolina Dept. of Health and Env. Control
Chief., Bureau of Solid and Haz. Waste Mgt.

Physical Location:
8901 Farrow Road
Columbia, SC 29203
Phone: (803) 896-4000
FAX: (803) 896-4001
UST Information
....(803) 734-5331

Mailing Address:
2600 Bull St.
Columbia, SC 29400

State Quality Assurance Coordinator
R. Wayne Davis
Lab Certification
SC Dept. of Health & Env. Control
P.O. Box 72
State Park, SC 29147
Phone: (803) 935-6856
FAX: (803) 935-6859
PE Studies
DMR, WP & WS: R. Wayne Davis
....(803) 935-6856

South Dakota

S. Dakota Dept. of Env. and Natural Res.
Office of Waste Mgt.
Joe Foss Building
523 E. Capital Avenue
Pierre, SD 57501-3181
Phone: (605) 773-3153
FAX: (605) 773-6035
PE Studies
WP: Mike Smith.............................(605) 773-3368
DMR: Brian Zenda
....(605) 773-3351
UST Information
....(605) 773-3296

State Quality Assurance Coordinator
Mike Smith
SD Dept. of Health, Lab Services
500 E. Capitol Ave.
Pierre, SD 57501-5093
Phone: (605) 773-3368
FAX: (605) 773-6129

S. Dakota Highway Patrol, Commerce and
  Regulation
320 N. Nicollet
Pierre, SD 57501
Phone: (605) 773-3105; FAX: (605) 773-6046

Tennessee

Tennessee Dept. of Environment and
  Conservation
Director, Div. of Solid Waste Mgt.
401 Church St.
L&C Tower, 5th Floor
Nashville, TN 37243-1535
Phone: (615) 532-0780
UST Information
....(615) 532-0945

TN Dept. of Environment and Conservation
Director, Div. of Superfund
401 Church St.
L&C Tower, 4th Floor
Nashville, TN 37243-1535
Phone: (615) 532-0900
PE Studies
WP & WS: Charles Mickle
....(615) 262-6354
DMR: Pamela Townsend
....(615) 532-0677

Tennessee Dept. of Env. and Conservation
Director, Div. of Superfund
Doctors Bldg, 706 Church Street
Nashville, TN 37243-1538
Phone: (615) 741-6287

State Quality Assurance Coordinator
Charles Mickle
Lab Services
TN Department of Health
630 Ben Allen Rd
Nashville, TN 37247-0801
Phone: (615) 262-6354
FAX: (615) 262-6393

Texas

Texas Water Commission
Dir., Hazardous and Solid Waste Division
P.O. Box 13087, Capitol Station
Austin, TX 78711-3087
Phone: (512) 239-1000
FAX: (512) 463-8408

Texas Dept. of Health
Occupational Safety and Health Division
1100 West 49th Street
Austin, TX 78756-3199
Phone: (512) 834-6600
PE Studies
WP: Burt Harrison...........................(210) 536-5226
WS: Sharon Duboise
....(512) 458-7587
DMR: Mary Stordal
....(281) 457-5229

Texas NRCC
P.O. Box 13087
Capitol Station
Austin, TX 78711
UST Information
....(512) 908-2247

State Quality Assurance Coordinator
Burt Harrison
HQ AFCEE/ERC
3207 North Road E.
Brooks AFB, TX 78235-5357
Phone: (210) 536-5226
FAX: (210) 536-5989

Utah

Utah Dept. of Environmental Quality
Dir., Div. of Solid and Hazardous Waste
288 North 1460 West St.
Salt Lake City, UT 84114-4880
Phone: (801) 538-6170
FAX: (801) 538-6715
PE Studies
WP & WS: Craig Odekirk
....(801) 584-8468
DMR: Mike Herkimer
....(801) 538-6146
UST Information
....(801) 536-4100

State Quality Assurance Coordinator
Craig Odekirk
Bureau of Lab Improvement
Utah State Health Laboratory
46 North Medical Drive
Salt Lake City, UT 84113-1105
Phone: (801) 584-8468

Vermont

Vermont Agency of Natural Resources
Director
Hazardous Mat'ls Mgt. Div.
103 South Main St.
Waterbury, VT 05676
Phone: (802) 241-3888
FAX: (802) 241-3296
UST Information
....(802) 241-3888

Vermont Dept. of Health
Occupations and Radiological Health Div.
Director
108 Cherry Street
Burlington, VT 05402
Phone: (802) 865-7730
FAX: (802) 865-7745

State Quality Assurance Coordinator
Andrew Fish
VT Dept. of Environ. Conservation
WW Management Division
103 South Main St.
Waterbury, VT 05676
Phone: (802) 241-3822
FAX: (802) 241-2596
PE Studies
WP & DMR: Andrew Fish...........(802) 241-3739
WS: Georgia Mills.........................(802) 863-7632

Virginia

Virginia Dept. of Waste Management
Div. of Regulation
629 East Main Street
Richmond, VA 23219
Phone: (804) 225-2667
FAX: (804) 762-4500
UST Information
....(804) 527-5188

State Quality Assurance Coordinator
Alicia Ordona
Div. of Consolidated Labs
Commonwealth of Virginia
1 North 14th Street
Richmond, VA 23219
Phone: (804) 786-3411
FAX: (804) 371-7973
PE Studies
WP & WS: Alicia Ordona 804-786-3411
DMR: Roger Stewart
....(804) 698-4449

Washington

Washington Dept. of Ecology
Mgr., Solid and Hazardous Waste Program
P.O. Box 47600
Olympia, WA 98504
Phone: (360) 407-6000
FAX: (360) 407-6102
UST Information
....(206) 459-6000

State Quality Assurance Coordinator
Stewart Lombard
WA State Dept of Ecology
P.O. Box 488
2350 Colchester
Manchester, WA 98353
Phone: (360) 895-4649
FAX: (360) 895-4648
PE Studies
WP & DMR: Stewart Lombard
....(360) 895-4649

West Virginia

Bureau of Environment
Div. of EP, Office of Waste Management
1356 Hansford St.
Charleston, WV 25301
Phone: (304) 558-5929
FAX: (304) 558-0256
UST Information ....(304) 558-6371

Air Pollution Control Commission
1558 Washington Street, East
Charleston, WV 25311
Phone: (304) 558-4022
Public Information Line: (304) 558-3381

West Virginia Division of Highways
Secretary/Commissioner of Highways
Building 5, Room A-109
Charleston, WV 25305
Phone: (304) 558-3505

WV EPD
Water Resources Office
1201 Greenbriar St.
Charleston, WV 25305
PE Studies
DMR: Don Caldwell......................(304) 558-2108

Wisconsin

Wisconsin Dept. of Natural Resources
Dir., Bureau of Solid and Haz. Waste Mgt.
P.O. Box 7921
Madison, WI 53707
Phone: (608) 266-1327
FAX: (608) 267-2768

State Quality Assurance Coordinator
Mike Kvitrud
WI Dept. of Nat. Resources
101 South Webster
Madison, WI 53707
Phone: (608) 261-8459
FAX: (608) 267-5231
PE Studies
DMR, WP, & WS: Mike Kvitrud
....(608) 621-8459
UST Information ....(608) 267-7560

Wyoming

Wyoming Dept. of Environmental Quality
Solid and Hazardous Waste Div.
122 West 25th St.
Herschler Building
Cheyenne, WY 82002
Phone: (307) 777-7752
FAX: (307) 777-5973
UST Information...........................(307) 777-7096

WY DEQ
Water Quality Division
122 W. 25th St.
Cheyenne, WY 82002
PE Studies
DMR: Edward Mock
....(307) 777-7317

American Somoa
Environmental Quality Commission
American Somoa Government
Pago Pago, AS 96799
DMR QA Coordinator Sheila Wiegman
....(684) 633-2304

Guam
Guam EPA
D-107 Harmon Plaza
130 Rojas St
Harmon, Guam 96911
DMR QA Coordinator Jesus Salas
....(671) 472-8863

Northern Islands
NI Div. of Environmental Quality
Mariana Island
P.O. Box 1304
Saipan, CM 96984
DMR QA Coordinator John Castro
....(670) 234-6950

Puerto Rico
State Quality Assurance Coordinator
Luis Quintero Ocasio, QAO
Puerto Rico Dept. of Health
Institute for Health Labs
Call Box 70184
San Juan, PR 00936-0184
Phone: (809) 274-7711
FAX: (809) 759-6210

Internet Addresses of Interest

EPA Federal Register "listserv"
    listserver@unixmail.rtpnc.epa.gov
to sign on, in the body of the message put
"subscribe [ ] *your name*"
where [ ] can be:

EPA-AIR

EPA-GENERAL

EPA-MEETINGS

EPA-PEST

EPA-PRESS

EPA-SAB

EPA-SPECIES

EPA-TOX

EPA-TRI

EPA-WASTE

EPA-WATER

EPAFR-CONTENTS

EPA Homepage
    http://www.epa.gov

Government Printing Office Pathway Services
    http://www.access.gpo.gov./su_docs/aces/
aces140.html (access to the archives of
Federal Register copies from 1995 on) Water
Environment Federation
    http://www.wef.org

ASTM
    http://www.astm.org

CFR
    http://www.law.house.gov/cfr.htm (out of
date versions and very slow to update)
    http://www.access.gpo.gov/nara/cfr/cfr-
retrive.html#page1 (40 CFR in its most up-to-
date form, but not a lot else. Appendices are
pulled up by requesting the last Section prior to
the Appendix. For example to get 40 CFR 136,
App A-C, request 40 CFR 136.5)

For a more complete listing see:
Schupp, J.F., 1995.
Environmental Guide to the Internet,
Government Institutes, Inc.
4 Research Place, Suite 200
Rockville, MD 20850

Alphabetical Elements List

Element[1]	Symbol	Number	Mass
Actinium	Ac	89	227
Aluminum	Al	13	26.98
Americium	Am	95	243
Antimony	Sb	51	121.8
Argon	Ar	18	39.95
Arsenic	As	33	74.92
Astatine	At	85	210
Barium	Ba	56	137.3
Berkelium	Bk	97	247
Beryllium	Be	4	9.012
Bismuth	Bi	83	209.0
Bohrium (Nielsbohrium)	Bh	107	262
Boron	B	5	10.81
Bromine	Br	35	79.90
Cadmium	Cd	48	112.4
Calcium	Ca	20	40.08
Californium	Cf	98	249
Carbon	C	6	12.01
Cerium	Ce	58	140.1
Cesium	Cs	55	132.9
Chlorine	Cl	17	35.45
Chromium	Cr	24	52.00
Cobalt	Co	27	58.93
Copper	Cu	29	63.55

Continued on next page.

---

[1] ACS names are the same except elements 105 and 107, where the ACS name is in parentheses.

Alphabetical Elements List, *continued*

Element[2]	Symbol	Number	Mass
Curium	Cm	96	247
Dubium (Hahnium)	Db	105	260
Dysprosium	Dy	66	162.5
Einsteinium	Es	99	254
Erbium	Er	68	167.3
Europium	Eu	63	152.0
Fermium	Fm	100	253
Fluorine	F	9	19.00
Francium	Fr	87	223
Gadolinium	Gd	64	157.3
Gallium	Ga	31	69.72
Germanium	Ge	32	72.59
Gold	Au	79	197.0
Hafnium	Hf	72	178.5
Hassium	Hs	108	265
Helium	He	2	4.003
Holmium	Ho	67	164.9
Hydrogen	H	1	1.008
Indium	In	49	114.8
Iodine	I	53	126.9
Iridium	Ir	77	192.2
Iron	Fe	26	55.85
Krypton	Kr	36	83.80
Lanthanum	La	57	138.9
Lawrencium	Lr	103	257
Lead	Pb	82	207.2
Lithium	Li	3	6.941
Lutetium	Lu	71	175.0
Magnesium	Mg	12	24.31
Manganese	Mn	25	54.94
Meitnerium	Mt	109	266
Mendelevium	Md	101	256
Mercury	Hg	80	200.6
Molybdenum	Mo	42	95.94

Continued on next page.

[2] ACS names are the same except elements 105 and 107, where the ACS name is in parentheses.

Alphabetical Elements List, *continued*

Element[3]	Symbol	Number	Mass
Neodymium	Nd	60	144.2
Neon	Ne	10	20.18
Neptunium	Np	93	237
Nickel	Ni	28	58.69
Niobium	Nb	41	92.91
Nitrogen	N	7	14.01
Nobelium	No	102	253
Osmium	Os	76	190.2
Oxygen	O	8	16.00
Palladium	Pd	46	106.4
Phosphorus	P	15	30.97
Platinum	Pt	78	195.1
Plutonium	Pu	94	242
Polonium	Po	84	210
Potassium	K	19	39.10
Praseodymium	Pr	59	140.9
Promethium	Pm	61	147
Protactinium	Pa	91	231
Radium	Ra	88	226
Radon	Rn	86	222
Rhenium	Re	75	186.2
Rhodium	Rh	45	102.9
Rubidium	Rb	37	85.47
Ruthenium	Ru	44	101.1
Rutherfordium	Rf	104	257
Samarium	Sm	62	150.4
Scandium	Sc	21	44.96
Seaborgium	Sg	106	263
Selenium	Se	34	78.96
Silicon	Si	14	28.09
Silver	Ag	47	107.9
Sodium	Na	11	22.99
Strontium	Sr	38	87.62
Sulfur	S	16	32.07

Continued on next page.

[3] ACS names are the same except elements 105 and 107, where the ACS name is in parentheses.

Alphabetical Elements List, *continued*

Element[4]	Symbol	Number	Mass
Tantalum	Ta	73	180.9
Technetium	Tc	43	99
Tellurium	Te	52	127.6
Terbium	Tb	65	158.9
Thallium	Tl	81	204.4
Thorium	Th	90	232.0
Thulium	Tm	69	168.9
Tin	Sn	50	118.7
Titanium	Ti	22	47.88
Tungsten	W	74	183.9
Uranium	U	92	238.0
Vanadium	V	23	50.94
Xenon	Xe	54	131.3
Ytterbium	Yb	70	173.0
Yttrium	Y	39	88.91
Zinc	Zn	30	65.39
Zirconium	Zr	40	91.22

---

[4] ACS names are the same except elements 105 and 107, where the ACS name is in parentheses.

Periodic Chart

1 H 1.008																	2 He 4.003
3 Li 6.941	4 Be 9.01											5 B 10.81	6 C 12.01	7 N 14.01	8 O 16.00	9 F 19.00	10 Ne 20.18
11 Na 22.99	12 Mg 24.31											13 Al 26.98	14 Si 28.09	15 P 30.97	16 S 32.06	17 Cl 35.45	18 Ar 39.95
19 K 39.10	20 Ca 40.08	21 Sc 44.96	22 Ti 47.88	23 V 50.94	24 Cr 52.00	25 Mn 54.94	26 Fe 55.85	27 Co 58.93	28 Ni 58.69	29 Cu 63.55	30 Zn 65.38	31 Ga 69.72	32 Ge 72.59	33 As 74.92	34 Se 78.96	35 Br 79.90	36 Kr 83.80
37 Rb 85.47	38 Sr 87.62	39 Y 88.91	40 Zr 91.22	41 Nb 92.91	42 Mo 95.94	43 Tc 98	44 Ru 101.1	45 Rh 102.9	46 Pd 106.4	47 Ag 107.9	48 Cd 112.4	49 In 114.8	50 Sn 118.7	51 Sb 121.7	52 Te 127.6	53 I 126.9	54 Xe 131.3
55 Cs 132.9	56 Ba 137.3	57 La 138.9	72 Hf 178.5	73 Ta 180.9	74 W 183.8	75 Re 186.2	76 Os 190.2	77 Ir 192.2	78 Pt 195.1	79 Au 197.0	80 Hg 200.6	81 Tl 204.4	82 Pb 207.2	83 Bi 209.0	84 Po 209	85 At 210	86 Rn 222
87 Fr 223	88 Ra 226.0	89 Ac 227.0	104 Unq 257	105 Unp 260	106 Unh 263	107 Uns 262	108 Uno 265	109 Une 266									

58 Ce 140.1	59 Pr 140.9	60 Nd 144.2	61 Pm 145	62 Sm 150.4	63 Eu 152.0	64 Gd 157.3	65 Tb 158.9	66 Dy 162.5	67 Ho 164.9	68 Er 167.3	69 Tm 168.9	70 Yb 173.0	71 Lu 175.0
90 Th 232.0	91 Pa 231.0	92 U 238.0	93 Np 237.0	94 Pu 244	95 Am 243	96 Cm 247	97 Bk 247	98 Cf 251	99 Es 252	100 Fm 257	101 Md 258	102 No 259	103 Lr 260

From the U.S. Government Printing Office via GPO Access [40CFR136.3]

TITLE 40--PROTECTION OF ENVIRONMENT

CHAPTER I--ENVIRONMENTAL PROTECTION AGENCY (CONTINUED)

PART 136--GUIDELINES ESTABLISHING TEST PROCEDURES FOR THE ANALYSIS OF POLLUTANTS--Sec. 136.3 Identification of test procedures.

(a) Parameters or pollutants, for which methods are approved, are listed together with test procedure descriptions and references in Tables IA, IB, IC, ID, and IE. The full text of the referenced test procedures are incorporated by reference into Tables IA, IB, IC, ID, and IE. The references and the sources from which they are available are given in paragraph (b) of this section. These test procedures are incorporated as they exist on the day of approval and a notice of any change in these test procedures will be published in the Federal Register. The discharge parameter values for which reports are required must be determined by one of the standard analytical test procedures incorporated by reference and described in Tables IA, IB, IC, ID, and IE, or by any alternate test procedure which has been approved by the Administrator under the provisions of paragraph (d) of this section and Secs. 136.4 and136.5 of this part 136. Under certain circumstances (Sec. 136.3 (b) or (c) or 40 CFR 401.13) other test procedures may be used that may be more advantageous when such other test procedures have been previously approved by the Regional Administrator of the Region in which the discharge will occur, and providing the Director of the State in which such discharge will occur does not object to the use of such alternate test procedure.

Table IA. List of Approved Biological Methods

Parameter and units	Method [1]	EPA	Standard Methods, 18th Ed.	ASTM	USGS
Bacteria:					
1. Coliform (fecal), number per 100 mL.	Most Probable Number (MPN), 5 tube, 3 dilution, or	p. 132 [3]	9221C E [4]		
	Membrane filter (MF), single step.[2]	p. 124 [3]	9222D [4]	B-0050-85 [5]	
2. Coliform (fecal) in presence of chlorine, number per 100 mL.	MPN, 5 tube, 3 dilution, or	p. 132 [3]	9221C E [4]		
	MF, single step [6].	p. 124 [3]	9222D [4]		
3. Coliform (total), number per 100 mL.	MPN, 5 tube, 3 dilution, or	p. 114 [3]	9221B [4]		
	MF [2] single step or two step.	p. 108 [3]	9222B [4]	B-0025-85 [5]	

Continued on next page.

Table IA. List of Approved Biological Methods, *continued*

Parameter and units	Method [1]	EPA	Standard Methods, 18th Ed.	ASTM	USGS
Bacteria, *continued*					
4. Coliform (total), in presence of chlorine, number per 100 mL.	MPN, 5 tube, 3 dilution, or	p. 114 [3]	9221B [4]		
	MF [2] with enrichment	p. 111 [3]	9222(B+B.5c)[4]		
5. Fecal streptococci, number per 100 mL.	MPN, 5 tube, 3 dilution	p. 139 [3]	9230B [4]		
	MF [2], or	p. 136 [3]	9230C [4]	B-0055-85 [5]	
	Plate count	p. 143 [3]			
Aquatic Toxicity					
6. Toxicity, acute, fresh water organisms, LC$_{50}$, percent effluent	Daphnia, Ceriodaphnia,	Sec. 9 [7]			
	Fathead Minnow, Rainbow Trout, Brook Trout, or Bannerfish Shiner mortality				
7. Toxicity, acute, estuarine and marine organisms, LC$_{50}$, percent effluent	Mysid, Sheepshead Minnow, or Menidia spp. mortality	Sec. 9 [7]			
8. Toxicity, chronic, fresh water organisms, NOEC or IC$_{25}$, percent effluent	Fathead minnow larval survival and growth	1000.0 [8]			
	Fathead minnow embryo-larval survival and teratogenicity	1001.0 [8]			
	Ceriodaphnia survival and reproduction	1002.0 [8]			
	Selenastrum growth	1003.0 [8]			
9. Toxicity, chronic, estuarine and marine organisms, NOEC or IC$_{25}$, percent effluent	Sheepshead minnow larval survival and growth	1004.0 [9]			
	Sheepshead minnow embryo-larval survival and teratogenicity	1005.0 [9]			
	Menidia beryllina larval survival and growth	1006.0 [9]			
	Mysidopsis bahia survival, growth, and fecundity	1007.0 [9]			
	Arbacia punctulata fertilization	1008.0 [9]			
	Champia parvula reproduction	1009.0 [9]			

Notes to Table IA:

[1] The method must be specified when results are reported.

[2] A 0.45 um membrane filter (MF) or other pore size certified by the manufacturer to fully retain organisms to be cultivated and to be free of extractables which could interfere with their growth.

[3] USEPA. 1978. Microbiological Methods for Monitoring the Environment, Water, and Wastes. Environmental Monitoring and Support Laboratory, U.S. Environmental Protection Agency, Cincinnati, Ohio. EPA/600/8-78/017.

Notes continued on next page

Notes to Table IA: *continued*

4 APHA. 1992. Standard Methods for the Examination of Water and Wastewater. American Public Health Association. 18th Edition. Amer. Publ. Hlth. Assoc., Washington, DC.

5 USGS. 1989. U.S. Geological Survey Techniques of Water-Resources Investigations, Book 5, Laboratory Analysis, Chapter A4, Methods for Collection and Analysis of Aquatic Biological and Microbiological Samples, U.S. Geological Survey, U.S. Department of Interior, Reston, Virginia.

6 Because the MF technique usually yields low and variable recovery from chlorinated wastewaters, the Most Probable Number method will be required to resolve any controversies.

7 USEPA. 1993. Methods for Measuring the Acute Toxicity of Effluents to Freshwater and Marine Organisms. Fourth Edition. Environmental Monitoring Systems Laboratory, U.S. Environmental Protection Agency, Cincinnati, Ohio. August 1993, EPA/600/4-90/027F.

8 USEPA. 1994. Short-term Methods for Estimating the Chronic Toxicity of Effluents and Receiving Waters to Freshwater Organisms. Third Edition. Environmental Monitoring Systems Laboratory, U.S. Environmental Protection Agency USEPA. 1994, Cincinnati, Ohio (July 1994, EPA/600/4-91/002).

9 Short-term Methods for Estimating the Chronic Toxicity of Effluents and Receiving Waters to Marine and Estuarine Organisms. Second Edition. Environmental Monitoring Systems Laboratory, U.S. Environmental Protection Agency, Cincinnati, Ohio (July 1994, EPA/600/4-91/003). These methods do not apply to marine waters of the Pacific Ocean.

Table IB. List of Approved Inorganic Test Procedures

Parameter, units and method	Reference (method number or page)				
	EPA [1]	Standard Methods 18th ed.	ASTM	USGS [2]	Other
1. Acidity, as CaCO$_3$/, mg/L:					
Electrometric endpoint or	305.1	2310 B(4a)	D1067-92		
phenolphthalein endpoint					
2. Alkalinity, as CaCO$_3$/, mg/L:					
Electrometric or	310.1	2320 B	D1067-92	I-1030-85	973.43.[3]
Colorimetric titration to pH 4.5, manual or automated	310.2			I-2030-85	
3. Aluminum--Total,[4] mg/L; Digestion [4] followed by:					
AA direct aspiration [36]	202.1	3111 D		I-3051-85	
AA furnace	202.2	3113 B			
Inductively Coupled Plasma [5] Atomic Emission Spectrometry (ICP/AES) [36]	200.7	3120 B			
Direct Current Plasma (DCP) [36]			D4190-82(88)		Note 34
Colorimetric (Eriochrome cyanine R)		3500-Al D			
4. Ammonia (as N), mg/L:					
Manual, distillation (at pH 9.5),[6] followed by:	350.2	4500-NH3/ B			973.49.[3]
Nesslerization	350.2	4500-NH3/ C	D1426-93(A)	I-3520-85	973.49.[3]
Titration	350.2	4500-NH3/ E			
Electrode	350.3	4500-NH3/ F or G	D1426-93(B)		
Automated phenate, or	350.1	4500-NH3/ H		I-4523-85	
Automated electrode					Note 7
5. Antimony-Total,[4] mg/L; Digestion [4] followed by:					
AA direct aspiration [36]	204.1	3111 B			
AA furnace	204.2	3113 B			
ICP/AES [36,5]	200.7	3120 B			

Continued on next page.

Table IB. List of Approved Inorganic Test Procedures, *continued*

Parameter, units and method	EPA [1]	Standard Methods 18th ed.	ASTM	USGS [2]	Other
6. Arsenic-Total,[4] mg/L: Digestion [4] followed by.	206.5				
AA gaseous hydride	206.3	3114 B 4.d	D2972-93(B)	I-3062-85	
AA furnace	206.2	3113 B	D2972-93(C)		
ICP/AES,[36] or	200.7	3120 B			
Colorimetric (SDDC)	206.4	3500-As C	D2972-93(A)	I-3060-85	
7. Barium--Total,[4] mg/L; Digestion [4] followed by:					
AA direct aspiration [36]	208.1	3111 D		I-3084-85	
AA furnace	208.2	3113 B	D4382-91		
ICP/AES [36]	200.7	3120 B			
DCP [36]					Note 34
8. Beryllium--Total,[4] mg/L; Digestion [4] followed by:					
AA direct aspiration	210.1	3111 D	D3645-93(88)(A)	I-3095-85	
AA furnace	210.2	3113 B	D3645-93(88)(B)		
ICP/AES	200.7	3120 B			
DCP, or			D4190-82(88)		Note 34
Colorimetric (aluminon)		3500-Be D			
9. Biochemical oxygen demand (BOD5), mg/L:					
Dissolved Oxygen Depletion	405.1	5210 B		I-1578-78 [8]	973.44,[3] p. 17[9]
10. Boron [37]--Total, mg/L:					
Colorimetric (curcumin)	212.3	4500-B B		I-3112-85	
ICP/AES, or	200.7	3120 B			
DCP			D4190-82(88)		Note 34
11. Bromide, mg/L:					
Titrimetric	320.1		D1246-82(88)(C)	I-1125-85	p. S44[10]
12. Cadmium--Total,[4] mg/L; Digestion [4] followed by:					
AA direct aspiration [36]	213.1	3111 B or C	D3557-90(A or B)	I-3135-85 or I-3136-85	974.27,[3] p. 37[9]
AA furnace	213.2	3113 B	D3557-90(D)		
ICP/AES [36]	200.7	3120 B		I-1472-85	
DCP [36]			D4190-82(88)		Note 34
Voltametry,[11] or			D3557-90(C)		
Colorimetric (Dithizone)		3500-Cd D			
13. Calcium--Total,[4] mg/L; Digestion [4] followed by:					
AA direct aspiration	215.1	3111 B	D511-93(B)	I-3152-85	
ICP/AES	200.7	3120 B			
DCP, or					Note 34
Titrimetric (EDTA)	215.2	3500-Ca D	D511-93(A)		

Continued on next page.

Table IB. List of Approved Inorganic Test Procedures, *continued*

Parameter, units and method	EPA [1]	Standard Methods 18th ed.	ASTM	USGS [2]	Other
14. Carbonaceous biochemical oxygen demand (CBOD5), mg/L [12]:					
Dissolved Oxygen Depletion with nitrification inhibitor		5210 B			
15. Chemical oxygen demand (COD), mg/L;					
Titrimetric, or	410.1 410.2 410.3	5220 C	D1252-88(A)	I-3560-85 I-3562-85	973.46,[3] p. 17[9]
Spectrophotometric, manual or automated	410.4	5220 D	D1252-88(B)	I-3561-85	Notes 13 or 14
16. Chloride, mg/L:					
Titrimetric (silver nitrate) or		4500-Cl- B	D512-89(B)	I-1183-85	
(Mercuric nitrate)	325.3	4500-Cl- C	D512-89(A)	I-1184-85	973.51[3]
Colorimetric, manual or				I-1187-85	
Automated (Ferricyanide)	325.1 325.2	4500-Cl;- E		I-2187-85	
17. Chlorine--Total residual, mg/L; Titrimetric:					
Amperometric direct	330.1	4500-Cl D	D1253-86(92)		
Iodometric direct	330.3	4500-Cl B			
Back titration ether end-point [15] or	330.2	4500-Cl C			
DPD-FAS	330.4	4500-Cl F			
Spectrophotometric, DPD	330.5	4500-Cl G			
Or Electrode					Note 16
18. Chromium VI dissolved, mg/L; 0.45 micron filtration					
AA chelation-extraction or	218.4	3111 C		I-1232-85	
Colorimetric (Diphenylcarbazide)		3500-Cr D	D1687-92(A)	I-1230-85	
19. Chromium--Total,[4] mg/L; Digestion [4] followed by:					
AA direct aspiration [36]	218.1	3111 B	D1687-92(B)	I-3236-85	974.27[3]
AA chelation-extraction	218.3	3111 C			
AA furnace	218.2	3113 B	D1687-92(C)		
ICP/AES [36]	200.7	3120 B			
DCP,[36] or			D4190-82(88)		Note 34
Colorimetric (Diphenylcarbazide)		3500-Cr D			
20. Cobalt--Total,[4] mg/L; Digestion [4] followed by:					
AA direct aspiration	219.1	3111 B or C	D3558-90(A or B)	I-3239-85	p. 37[9]
AA furnace	219.2	3113B	D3558-90(C)		
ICP/AES [5]	200.7	3120 B			
DCP			D4190-82(88)		Note 34
21. Color platinum cobalt units or dominant wavelength, hue, luminance purity:					
Colorimetric (ADMI), or	110.1	2120 E			Note 18
(Platinum cobalt), or	110.2	2120 B		I-1250-85	
Spectrophotometric	110.3	2120 C			

Continued on next page.

Table IB. List of Approved Inorganic Test Procedures, *continued*

Parameter, units and method	EPA [1]	Standard Methods 18th ed.	ASTM	USGS [2]	Other
22. Copper--Total,[4] mg/L; Digestion ;[4] followed by:					
AA direct aspiration [36]	220.1	3111 B or C	D1688-90(A or B)	I-3270-85 or I3271-85	974.27 [3], p. 379[9]
AA furnace	220.2	3113 B	D1688-90(C)		
ICP/AES [36]	200.7	3120 B			
DCP [36] or			D4190-82(88)		Note 34
Colorimetric (Neocuproine) or		3500-Cu D			
(Bicinchoninate)		3500-Cu E			Note 19
23. Cyanide--Total, mg/L: Manual distillation with MgCl$_2$ followed by:		4500-CN C	D2036-91(A)		
Titrimetric, or	335.2	4500-CN D			p. 22[9]
Spectrophotometric, manual [31]		4500-CN E	D2036-91(A)	I-3300-85	
Automated [20, 31]	335.3				
24. Cyanide amenable to chlorination,mg/L Manual distillation with MgCl$_2$ followed by:	335.1	4500-CN G	D2036-91(B)		
Titrimetric or	335.2	4500-CN D			
Spectrophotometric		4500-CN E			
25. Fluoride--Total, mg/L: Manual distillation [6] followed by:		4500-F B			
Electrode, manual or	340.2	4500-F C	D1179-93(B)		
Automated				I-4327-85	
Colorimetric (SPADNS)	340.1	4500-F D	D1179-93(A)		
or Automated complexone	340.3	4500-F E			
26. Gold--Total,[4] mg/L; Digestion [4] followed by:					
AA direct aspiration	231.1	3111 B			
AA furnace, or	231.2				
DCP					Note 34
27. Hardness--Total, as CaCO3/, mg/L					
Automated colorimetric,	130.1				
Titrimetric (EDTA), or Ca plus Mg as their carbonates, by ICP or AA direct aspiration (See Parameters 13 and 33)	130.2	2340 B or C	D1126-86(92)	I-1338-85	973.52B[3]
28. Hydrogen ion (pH), pH units					
Electrometric measurement,	150.1	4500-H+ B	D1293-84(90)(A or B)	I-1586-85	973.41[3]
Automated electrode					Note 21
29. Iridium--Total,[4] mg/L; Digestion [4] followed by:					
AA direct aspiration or	235.1	3111 B			
AA furnace	235.2				
30. Iron--Total,[4] mg/L; Digestion [4] followed by:					
AA direct aspiration [36]	236.1	3111 B or C	D1068-90(A or B)	I-3381-85	974.27[3]
AA furnace	236.2	3113 B	D1068-90(C)		
ICP/AES [36]	200.7	3120 B			

Continued on next page.

Table IB. List of Approved Inorganic Test Procedures, *continued*

Parameter, units and method	EPA [1]	Standard Methods 18th ed.	ASTM	USGS [2]	Other
30. Iron--Total,[4] mg/L; Digestion [4] followed by:					
DCP [36] or			D4190-82(88)		Note 34
Colorimetric (Phenanthroline)		3500-Fe D	D1068-90(D)		Note 22
31. Kjeldahl Nitrogen--Total, (as N), mg/L:					
Digestion and distillation followed by:	351.3	4500-NH3 B or C.	D3590-89(A)		
Titration	351.3	4500-NH3 E	D3590-89(A)		973.48 [3]
Nesslerization	351.3	4500-NH3 C	D3590-89(A)		
Electrode	351.3	4500-NH3 F or G			
Automated phenate colorimetric	351.1			I-4551-88	
Semi-automated block digester colorimetric	351.2		D3590-89(B)		
Manual or block digester potentiometric	351.4		D3590-89(A)		
Block Digester, followed by: Auto distillation and Titration, or					Note 39
Nesslerization					Note 40
Flow injection gas diffusion					Note 41
32. Lead--Total,[4] mg/L; Digestion [4] followed by:					
AA direct aspiration [36]	239.1	3111 B or C	D3559-90(A or B)	I-3399-85.	974.27[3]
AA furnace	239.2	3113 B	D3559-90(D)		
ICP/AES [36]	200.7	3120 B			
DCP [36]			D4190-82(88)		Note 34
Voltametry [11] or			D3559-90(C)		
Colorimetric (Dithizone)		3500-Pb D			
33. Magnesium--Total,[4] mg/L; Digestion [4] followed by:					
AA direct aspiration	242.1	3111 B	D511-93(B)	I-3447-85	974.27[3]
ICP/AES [5]	200.7	3120 B			
DCP, or					Note 34
Gravimetric		3500-Mg D			
34. Manganese--Total,[4] mg/L; Digestion [4] followed by:					
AA direct aspiration [36]	243.1	3111 B.	D858-90(A or B)	I-3454-85	974.27[3]
AA furnace	243.2	3113 B	D858-90(C)		
ICP/AES [36, 5]	200.7	3120 B			
DCP [36] or			D4190-82(88)		Note 34
Colorimetric (Persulfate), or		3500-Mn D			920.203[3]
(Periodate)					Note 23
35. Mercury--Total,[4] mg/L:					
Cold vapor, manual or	245.1	3112 B	D3223-91	I-3462-85	977.22[3]
Automated	245.2				

Continued on next page.

Table IB. List of Approved Inorganic Test Procedures, *continued*

Parameter, units and method	EPA [1]	Standard Methods 18th ed.	ASTM	USGS [2]	Other
36. Molybdenum--Total,[4] mg/L; Digestion [4] followed by:					
AA direct aspiration	246.1	3111 D		I-3490-85	
AA furnace	246.2	3113 B			
ICP/AES[5]	200.7	3120 B			
DCP					Note 34
37. Nickel--Total,[4] mg/L; Digestion [4] followed by:					
AA direct aspiration [36]	249.1	3111 B or C	D1886-90(A or B)	I-3499-85	
AA furnace	249.2	3113 B	D1886-90(C)		
ICP/AES [36, 5]	200.7	3120 B			
DCP [36], or			D4190-82(88)		Note 34
Colorimetric (heptoxime)		3500-Ni D			
38. Nitrate (as N), mg/L:					
Colorimetric (Brucine sulfate), or	352.1				973.50,[3] 419 D,[17]
Nitrate-nitrite N minus Nitrite N (See parameters 39 and 40)					p. 28[9]
39. Nitrate-nitrite (as N), mg/L:					
Cadmium reduction, Manual	353.3	4500-NO3- E	D3867-90(B)		
Automated, or	353.2	4500-NO3- F	D3867-90(A)	I-4545-85	
Automated hydrazine	353.1	4500-NO3- H			
40. Nitrite (as N), mg/L; Spectrophotometric:					
Manual or	354.1	4500-NO2- B			Note 25
Automated (Diazotization)				I-4540-85	
41. Oil and grease--Total recoverable, mg/L:					
Gravimetric (extraction)	413.1	5520 B [38]			
42. Organic carbon--Total (TOC), mg/L:					
Combustion or oxidation	415.1	5310 B, C, or D	D2579-93 (A or B)		973.47,[3] p. 14[24]
43. Organic nitrogen (as N), mg/L:					
Total Kjeldahl N (Parameter 31) minus ammonia N (Parameter 4)					
44. Orthophosphate (as P), mg/L; Ascorbic acid method:					
Automated, or	365.1	4500-P F		I-4601-85	973.56[3]
Manual single reagent	365.2	4500-P E	D515-88(A)		973.55[3]
Manual two reagent	365.3				
45. Osmium--Total,[4] mg/L; Digestion [4] followed by:					
AA direct aspiration	252.1	3111 D			
AA furnace	252.2				
46. Oxygen, dissolved, mg/L:					
Winkler (Azide modification), or	360.2	4500-O C	D888-92(A)	I-1575-78 [8]	973.45B[3]
Electrode	360.1	4500-O G	D888-92(B)	I-1576-78 [8]	

Continued on next page.

Table IB. List of Approved Inorganic Test Procedures, *continued*

Parameter, units and method	EPA [1]	Standard Methods 18th ed.	ASTM	USGS [2]	Other
47. Palladium--Total,[4] mg/L; Digestion [4] followed by:					
AA direct aspiration, or	253.1	3111 B			p. S27[10]
AA furnace	253.2				p. S28[10]
DCP					Note 34
48. Phenols, mg/L:					
Manual distillation [26] followed by:	420.1				Note 27
Colorimetric (4AAP) manual, or	420.1				Note 27
Automated [19]	420.2				
49. Phosphorus (elemental), mg/L:					
Gas-liquid chromatography					Note 28
50. Phosphorus--Total, mg/L:					
Persulfate digestion followed by:	365.2	4500-P B,5			973.55[3]
Manual or	365.2, 365.3	4500-P E	D515-88(A)		
Automated ascorbic acid reduction	365.1	4500-P F		I-4600-85	973.56[3]
Semi-automated block digestor	365.4		D515-88(B)		
51. Platinum--Total,[4] mg/L; Digestion [4] followed by:					
AA direct aspiration	255.1	3111 B			
AA furnace	255.2				
DCP					Note 34
52. Potassium--Total,[4] mg/L; Digestion [4] followed by:					
AA direct aspiration	258.1	3111 B		I-3630-85	973.53[3]
ICP/AES [5]	200.7	3120 B			
Flame photometric, or		3500-K D			
Colorimetric					317 B[17]
53. Residue--Total, mg/L:					
Gravimetric, 103-105 deg	160.3	2540 B		I-3750-85	
54. Residue--filterable, mg/L:					
Gravimetric, 180 deg	160.1	2540 C		I-1750-85	
55. Residue--nonfilterable (TSS), mg/L:					
Gravimetric, 103-105 deg. post washing of residue	160.2	2540 D		I-3765-85	
56. Residue--settleable, mg/L:					
Volumetric, (Imhoff cone), or gravimetric	160.5	2540 F			
57. Residue--Volatile, mg/L:					
Gravimetric, 550 deg	160.4			I-3753-85	
58. Rhodium--Total,[4] mg/L; Digestion [4] followed by:					
AA direct aspiration, or	265.1	3111 B			
AA furnace	265.2				
59. Ruthenium--Total,[4] mg/L; Digestion [4] followed by:					
AA direct aspiration, or	267.1	3111 B			
AA furnace	267.2				
60. Selenium--Total,[4] mg/L; Digestion [4] followed by:					
AA furnace	270.2	3113 B	D3859-93(B)		
ICP/AES[36, 5]	200.7	3120 B			

Continued on next page.

Table IB. List of Approved Inorganic Test Procedures, *continued*

Parameter, units and method	EPA [1]	Standard Methods 18th ed.	ASTM	USGS [2]	Other
60. Selenium--Total,[4] mg/L; Digestion [4] followed by: *Continued*					
AA gaseous hydride		3114 B	D3859-93(A)	I-3667-85	
61. Silica [37]--Dissolved, mg/L; 0.45 micron filtration followed by:					
Colorimetric, Manual or	370.1	4500-Si D	D859-88	I-1700-85	
Automated (Molybdosilicate), or				I-2700-85	
ICP[5]	200.7	3120 B			
62. Silver--Total,[4] mg/L; Digestion[4], [29] followed by:					
AA direct aspiration	272.1	3111 B or C		I-3720-85	974.27,[3] p. 37[9]
AA furnace	272.2	3113 B			
ICP/AES [5]	200.7	3120 B			
DCP					Note 34
63. Sodium--Total,[4] mg/L; Digestion [4] followed by:					
AA direct aspiration	273.1	3111 B		I-3735-85	973.54[3]
ICP/AES[5]	200.7	3120 B			
DCP, or					Note 34
Flame photometric		3500 Na D			
64. Specific conductance, micromhos/cm at 25°C:					
Wheatstone bridge	120.1	2510 B	D1125-91(A)	I-1780-85	973.40[3]
65. Sulfate (as SO$_4$), mg/L:					
Automated colorimetric (barium chloranilate)	375.1				
Gravimetric	375.3	4500-SO$_4$-2 C or D			925.54[3]
Turbidimetric	375.4		D516-90		426C[30]
66. Sulfide (as S), mg/L:					
Titrimetric (iodine), or	376.1	4500-S-2 E		I-3840-85	
Colorimetric (methylene blue)	376.2	4500-S-2 D			
67. Sulfite (as SO$_3$), mg/L:					
Titrimetric (iodine-iodate)	377.1	4500-SO3-2 B			
68. Surfactants, mg/L:					
Colorimetric (methylene blue)	425.1	5540 C	D2330-88		
69. Temperature, deg.C:					
Thermometric	170.1	2550 B			Note 32
70. Thallium--Total,[4] mg/L; Digestion[4] followed by:					
AA direct aspiration	279.1	3111 B			
AA furnace	279.2				
ICP/AES[5]	200.7	3120 B			
71. Tin--Total,[4] mg/L; Digestion[4] followed by:					
AA direct aspiration	282.1	3111 B.		I-3850-78 8	
AA furnace, or	282.2	3113 B			
ICP/AES [5]	200.7				

Continued on next page.

Table IB. List of Approved Inorganic Test Procedures, *continued*

Parameter, units and method	EPA [1]	Standard Methods 18th ed.	ASTM	USGS [2]	Other
72. Titanium--Total,[4] mg/L; Digestion[4] followed by:					
AA direct aspiration	283.1	3111 D			
AA furnace	283.2				
DCP					Note 34
73. Turbidity, NTU:					
Nephelometric	180.1	2130 B	D1889-88(A)	I-3860-85	
74. Vanadium--Total,[4] mg/L; Digestion[4] followed by:					
AA direct aspiration	286.1	3111 D			
AA furnace	286.2		D3373-93		
ICP/AES[5]	200.7	3120 B			
DCP or			D4190-82(88)		Note 34
Colorimetric (Gallic acid)		3500-V D			
75. Zinc--Total,[4] mg/L; Digestion [4] followed by:				I-3900-85	
AA direct aspiration [36]	289.1	3111 B or C	D1691-90 (A or B)		974.27,[3] p. 379[9]
AA furnace.	289.2				
ICP/AES [36, 5]	200.7	3120 B			
DCP[36] or			D4190-82(88)		Note 34
Colorimetric (Dithizone)		3500-Zn E			
(Zincon)		3500-Zn F			Note 33

Table IB Notes:

[1] "Methods for Chemical Analysis of Water and Wastes," Environmental Protection Agency, Environmental Monitoring Systems Laboratory-Cincinnati (EMSLCI), EPA-600/4-79-020, Revised March 1983 and 1979 where applicable.

[2] Fishman, M.J., et al, "Methods for Analysis of Inorganic Substances in Water and Fluvial Sediments," U.S. Department of the Interior, Techniques of Water--Resource Investigations of the U.S. Geological Survey, Denver, CO, Revised 1989, unless otherwise stated.

[3] "Official Methods of Analysis of the Association of Official Analytical Chemists," methods manual, 15th ed. (1990).

[4] For the determination of total metals the sample is not filtered before processing. A digestion procedure is required to solubilize suspended material and to destroy possible organic-metal complexes. Two digestion procedures are given in "Methods for Chemical Analysis of Water and Wastes, 1979 and 1983". One (section 4.1.3), is a vigorous digestion using nitric acid. A less vigorous digestion using nitric and hydrochloric acids (section 4.1.4) is preferred; however, the analyst should be cautioned that this mild digestion may not suffice for all samples types. Particularly, if a colorimetric procedure is to be employed, it is necessary to ensure that all organo-metallic bonds be broken so that the metal is in a reactive state. In those situations, the vigorous digestion is to be preferred making certain that at no time does the sample go to dryness. Samples containing large amounts of organic materials may also benefit by this vigorous digestion, however, vigorous digestion with concentrated nitric acid will convert antimony and tin to insoluble oxides and render them unavailable for analysis. Use of ICP/AES as well as determinations for certain elements such as antimony, arsenic, the noble metals, mercury, selenium, silver, tin, and titanium require a modified sample digestion procedure and in all cases the method write-up should be consulted for specific instructions and/or cautions.

Note to Table IB Note 4: If the digestion procedure for direct aspiration AA included in one of the other approved references is different than the above, the EPA procedure must be used. Dissolved metals are defined as those constituents which will pass through a 0.45 micron membrane filter. Following filtration of the sample, the referenced procedure for total metals must be followed. Sample digestion of the filtrate for dissolved metals (or digestion of the original sample solution for total metals) may be omitted for AA (direct aspiration or graphite

Notes continued on next page

Table IB Notes: *continued*

furnace) and ICP analyses, provided the sample solution to be analyzed meets the following criteria: **a.** has a low COD (20) **b.** is visibly transparent with a turbidity measurement of 1 NTU or less, **c.** is colorless with no perceptible odor, and. is of one liquid phase and free of particulate or suspended matter following acidification.

5 The full text of Method 200.7, "Inductively Coupled Plasma Atomic Emission Spectrometric Method for Trace Element Analysis of Water and Wastes," is given at Appendix C of this Part 136.

6 Manual distillation is not required if comparability data on representative effluent samples are on company file to show that this preliminary distillation step is not necessary: however, manual distillation will be required to resolve any controversies.

7 Ammonia, Automated Electrode Method, Industrial Method Number 379-75 WE, dated February 19, 1976, (Bran & Luebbe (Technicon) Auto Analyzer II, Bran & Luebbe Analyzing Technologies, Inc., Elmsford, NY 10523.

8 The approved method is that cited in "Methods for Determination of Inorganic Substances in Water and Fluvial Sediments", USGS TWRI, Book 5, Chapter A1 (1979).

9 American National Standard on Photographic Processing Effluents, Apr. 2, 1975. Available from ANSI, 1430 Broadway, New York, NY 10018.

10 "Selected Analytical Methods Approved and Cited by the United States Environmental Protection Agency", Supplement to the Fifteenth Edition of Standard Methods for the Examination of Water and Wastewater (1981).

11 The use of normal and differential pulse voltage ramps to increase sensitivity and resolution is acceptable.

12 Carbonaceous biochemical oxygen demand ($CBOD_5$) must not be confused with the traditional BOD_5 test which measures "total BOD". The addition of the nitrification inhibitor is not a procedural option, but must be included to report the $CBOD_5$ parameter. A discharger whose permit requires reporting the traditional BOD_5 may not use a nitrification inhibitor in the procedure for reporting the results. Only when a discharger's permit specifically states $CBOD_5$ is required can the permittee report data using the nitrification inhibitor.

13 OIC Chemical Oxygen Demand Method, Oceanography International Corporation, 1978, 512 West Loop, P.O. Box 2980, College Station, TX 77840.

14 Chemical Oxygen Demand, Method 8000, Hach Handbook of Water Analysis, 1979, Hach Chemical Company, P.O. Box 389, Loveland, CO 80537.

15 The back titration method will be used to resolve controversy.

16 Orion Research Instruction Manual, Residual Chlorine Electrode Model 97-70, 1977, Orion Research Incorporated, 840 Memorial Drive, Cambridge, MA 02138. The calibration graph for the Orion residual chlorine method must be derived using a reagent blank and three standard solutions, containing 0.2, 1.0, and 5.0 ml 0.00281 N potassium iodate/100 ml solution, respectively.

17 The approved method is that cited in Standard Methods for the Examination of Water and Wastewater, 14th Edition, 1976.

18 National Council of the Paper Industry for Air and Stream Improvement, (Inc.) Technical Bulletin 253, December 1971.

19 Copper, Biocinchoinate Method, Method 8506, Hach Handbook of Water Analysis, 1979, Hach Chemical Company, P.O. Box 389, Loveland, CO 80537.

20 After the manual distillation is completed, the autoanalyzer manifolds in EPA Methods 335.3 (cyanide) or 420.2 (phenols) are simplified by connecting the re-sample line directly to the sampler. When using the mainfold setup shown in Method 335.3, the buffer 6.2 should be replaced with the buffer 7.6 found in Method 335.2.

21 Hydrogen ion (pH) Automated Electrode Method, Industrial Method Number 378-75WA, October 1976, Bran & Luebbe (Technicon) Autoanalyzer II. Bran & Luebbe Analyzing Technologies, Inc., Elmsford, NY 10523.

22 Iron, 1,10-Phenanthroline Method, Method 8008, 1980, Hach Chemical Company, P.O. Box 389, Loveland, CO 80537.

23 Manganese, Periodate Oxidation Method, Method 8034, Hach Handbook of Wastewater Analysis, 1979, pages 2-113 and 2-117, Hach Chemical Company, Loveland, CO 80537.

24 Wershaw, R.L., et al, "Methods for Analysis of Organic Substances in Water," Techniques of Water-Resources Investigation of the U.S. Geological Survey, Book 5, Chapter A3, (1972 Revised 1987) p. 14.

25 Nitrogen, Nitrite, Method 8507, Hach Chemical Company, P.O. Box 389, Loveland, CO 80537.

26 Just prior to distillation, adjust the sulfuric-acid-preserved sample to pH 4 with 1 + 9 NaOH.

27 The approved method is cited in Standard Methods for the Examination of Water and Wastewater, 14th Edition. The colorimetric reaction is conducted at a pH of 10.0 ± 0.2. The approved methods are given on pp 576-81 of the 14th Edition: Method 510A for distillation, Method 510B for the manual colorimetric procedure, or Method 510C for the manual spectophotometric procedure. *Notes continued on next page.*

Table IB Notes: *continued*

[28] R. F. Addison and R.G. Ackman, "Direct Determination of Elemental Phosphorus by Gas-Liquid Chromatography," Journal of Chromatography, vol. 47, No. 3. pp. 421-426, 1970.

[29] Approved methods for the analysis of silver in industrial wastewaters at concentrations of 1 mg/L and above are inadequate where silver exists as an inorganic halide. Silver halides such as the bromide and chloride are relatively insoluble in reagents such as nitric acid but are readily soluble in an aqueous buffer of sodium thiosulfate and sodium hydroxide to pH of 12. Therefore, for levels of silver above 1 mg/L, 20 mL of sample should be diluted to 100 mL by adding 40 mL each of 2 M $Na_2S_2O_3$ and NaOH. Standards should be prepared in the same manner. For levels of silver below 1 mg/L the approved method is satisfactory.

[30] The approved method is that cited in Standard Methods for the Examination of Water and Wastewater, 15th Edition.

[31] EPA Methods 335.2 and 335.3 require the NaOH absorber solution final concentration to be adjusted to 0.25 N before colorimetric determination of total cyanide.

[32] Stevens, H.H., Ficke, J.F., and Smoot, G.F., "Water Temperature--Influential Factors, Field Measurement and Data Presentation", Techniques of Water-Resources Investigations of the U.S. Geological Survey, Book 1, Chapter D1, 1975.

[33] Zinc, Zincon Method, Method 8009, Hach Handbook of Water Analysis, 1979, pages 2-231 and 2-333, Hach Chemical Company, Loveland, CO 80537.

[34] "Direct Current Plasma (DCP) Optical Emission Spectrometric Method for Trace Elemental Analysis of Water and Wastes, Method AES0029," 1986-- Revised 1991, Fison Instruments, Inc., 32 Commerce Center, Cherry Hill Drive, Danvers, MA 01923.

[35] Precision and recovery statements for the atomic absorption direct aspiration and graphite furnace methods, and for the spectrophotometric SDDC method for arsenic are provided in Appendix D of this part titled, "Precision and Recovery Statements for Methods for Measuring Metals".

[36] "Closed Vessel Microwave Digestion of Wastewater Samples for Determination of Metals", CEM Corporation, P.O. Box 200, Matthews, NC 28106-0200, April 16, 1992. Available from the CEM Corporation.

[37] When determining boron and silica, only plastic, PTFE, or quartz laboratory ware may be used from start until completion of analysis.

[38] Only the trichlorofluoromethane extraction solvent is approved.

[39] Nitrogen, Total Kjeldahl, Method PAI-DK01 (Block Digestion, Steam Distillation, Titrimetric Detection), revised 12/22/94, Perstop Analytical Corporation.

[40] Nitrogen, Total Kjeldahl, Method PAI-DK02 (Block Digestion, Steam Distillation, Colorimetric Detection), revised 12/22/94, Perstop Analytical Corporation.

[41] Nitrogen, Total Kjeldahl, Method PAI-DK03 (Block Digestion, Automated FIA Gas Diffusion), revised 12/22/94, Perstop Analytical Corporation.

Table IC. List of Approved Test Procedures for Non-Pesticide Organic Compounds

Parameter [1]	EPA Method No. [27]					
	GC	GC/MS	HPLC	Standard Methods 18th Ed.	ASTM	Other
1. Acenaphthene	610	625, 1625	610	6410 B, 6440 B	D4657-92	
2. Acenaphthylene	610	625, 1625	610	6410 B, 6440 B	D4657-92	
3. Acrolein	603[4]	624, 1624				
4. Acrylonitrile	603[4]	624, 1624	610			
5. Anthracene	610	625, 1625	610	6410 B, 6440 B	D4657-92	
6. Benzene	602	624, 1624		6210 B, 6220 B		
7. Benzidine		625, 1625[5]	605			Note[3], p.1
8. Benzo(a)anthracene	610	625, 1625	610	6410 B, 6440 B	D4657-92	

Continued on next page.

Table IC. List of Approved Test Procedures for Non-Pesticide Organic Compounds, *continued*

| Parameter [1] | EPA Method No. [27] | | | | | |
	GC	GC/MS	HPLC	Standard Methods 18th Ed.	ASTM	Other
9. Benzo(a)pyrene	610	625, 1625	610	6410 B, 6440 B	D4657-92	
10. Benzo(b)fluoranthene	610	625, 1625	610	6410 B, 6440 B	D4657-92	
11. Benzo(g, h, i)perylene	610	625, 1625	610	6410 B, 6440 B	D4657-92	
12. Benzo(k)fluoranthene	610	625, 1625	610	6410 B, 6440 B	D4657-92	
13. Benzyl chloride						Note[3], p. 130: Note[6], p. S102
14. Benzyl butyl phthalate	606	625, 1625		6410 B		
15. Bis(2-chloroethoxy)methane	611	625, 1625		6410 B		
16. Bis(2-chloroethyl) ether	611	625, 1625		6410 B		
17. Bis (2-ethylhexyl)phthalate	606	625, 1625		6410 B, 6230 B		
18. Bromodichloromethane	601	624, 1624		6210 B, 6230 B		
19. Bromoform	601	624, 1624		6210 B, 6230 B		
20. Bromomethane	601	624, 1624		6210 B, 6230 B		
21. 4-Bromophenylphenylether	611	625, 1625		6410 B		
22. Carbon tetrachloride	601	624, 1624		6230 B, 6410 B		Note[3] p.130
23. 4-Chloro-3-methylphenol	604	625, 1625		6410 B, 6420 B		
24. Chlorobenzene	601, 602	624, 1624		6210 B, 6220 B, 6230 B		Note[3] p.130
25. Chloroethane	601	624, 1624		6210 B, 6230 B		
26. 2-Chloroethylvinyl ether	601	624, 1624		6210 B, 6230 B		
27. Chloroform	601	624, 1624		6210 B, 6230 B		Note[3] p.130
28. Chloromethane	601	624, 1624		6210 B. 6230 B		
29. 2-Chloronaphthalene	612	625, 1625		6410 B		
30. 2-Chlorophenol	604	625, 1625		6410 B, 6420 B		
31. 4-Chlorophenylphenylether	611	625, 1625		6410 B		
32. Chrysene	610	625, 1625	610	6410 B, 6440 B	D4657-92	
33. Dibenzo(a,h)anthracene	610	625, 1625	610	6410 B, 6440 B	D4657-92	
34. Dibromochloromethane	601	624, 1624		6210 B, 6230 B		
35. 1, 2-Dichlorobenzene	601,602, 612	624,625,1625		6410 B, 6230 B, 6220 B		
36. 1, 3-Dichlorobenzene	601,602, 612	624,625,1625		6410 B, 6230 B, 6220 B		
37. 1,4-Dichlorobenzene	601,602, 612	624,625,1625		6410 B, 6230 B, 6220 B		
38. 3, 3'-Dichlorobenzidine		625, 1625	605	6410 B		
39. Dichlorodifluoromethane	601			6230 B		
40. 1, 1-Dichloroethane	601	624, 1624		6230 B, 6210 B		
41. 1, 2-Dichloroethane	601	624, 1624		6230 B, 6210 B		
42. 1, 1-Dichloroethene	601	624, 1624		6230 B, 6210 B		
43. *trans*-1, 2-Dichloroethene	601	624, 1624		6230 B, 6210 B		
44. 2, 4-Dichlorophenol	604	625, 1625		6420 B, 6410 B		
45. 1, 2-Dichloropropane	601	624, 1624		6230 B, 6210 B		

Continued on next page.

Table IC. List of Approved Test Procedures for Non-Pesticide Organic Compounds, *continued*

Parameter [1]	EPA Method No. [27]					
	GC	GC/MS	HPLC	Standard Methods 18th Ed.	ASTM	Other
46. *cis*-1, 3-Dichloropropene	601	624, 1624		6230 B, 6210 B		
47. *trans*-1, 3-Dichloropropene	601	624, 1624		6230 B, 6210 B		
48. Diethyl phthalate	606	625, 1625		6410 B		
49. 2, 4-Dimethylphenol	604	625, 1625		6420 B, 6410 B		
50. Dimethyl phthalate	606	625, 1625		6410 B		
51. Di-n-butyl phthalate	606	625, 1625		6410 B		
52. Di-n-octyl phthalate	606	625, 1625		6410 B		
53. 2, 3-Dinitrophenol	604	625, 1625		6420 B, 6410 B		
54. 2,4-Dinitrotoluene	609	625, 1625		6410 B		
55. 2, 6-Dinitrotoluene	609	625, 1625		6410 B		
56. Epichlorohydrin						Note [3], p. 130, Note [6], p. S102
57. Ethylbenzene	602	624, 1624		6220 B, 6210 B		
58. Fluoranthene	610	625, 1625	610	6410 B, 6440 B	D4657-92	
59. Fluorene	610	625, 1625	610	6410 B, 6440 B	D4657-92	
60. Hexachlorobenzene	612	625, 1625		6410 B		
61. Hexachlorobutadiene	612	625, 1625		6410 B		
62. Hexachlorocyclopentadiene	612	[5] 625, 1625		6410 B		
63. Hexachloroethane	616	625, 1625		6410 B		
64. Ideno(1,2,3-cd) pyrene	610	625, 1625	610	6410 B, 6440 B	D4657-92	
65. Isophorone	609	625, 1625		6410 B		
66. Methylene chloride	601	624, 1624		6230 B		Note[3], p. 130
67. 2-Methyl-4,6-dinitrophenol	604	625, 1625		6420 B, 6410 B		
68. Naphthalene	610	625, 1625	610	6410 B, 6440 B		
69. Nitrobenezene	609	625, 1625		6410 B		
70. 2-Nitrophenol	604	625, 1625		6410 B, 6420 B		
71. 4-Nitrophenol	604	625, 1625		6410 B, 6420 B		
72. N-Nitrosodimethylamine	607	625, 1625		6410 B		
73. N-Nitrosodi-n-propylamine	607	625, 1625[5]		6410 B		
74. N-Nitrosodiphenylamine	607	625, 1625[5]		6410 B		
75. 2,2-Oxybis(1-chloropropane)	611	625, 1625		6410 B		
76. PCB-1016	608	625		6410 B		Note[3], p. 43, Note [8]
77. PCB-1221	608	625		6410 B		Note[3], p. 43, Note [8]
78. PCB-1232	608	625		6410 B		Note[3], p. 43, Note [8]
79. PCB-1242	608	625		6410 B		Note[3], p. 43, Note [8]

Continued on next page.

Table IC. List of Approved Test Procedures for Non-Pesticide Organic Compounds, *continued*

80. PCB-1248	608	625		6410 B		Note[3], p. 43, Note [8]
81. PCB-1254	608	625		6410 B		Note[3], p. 43, Note [8]
82. PCB-1260	608	625		6410 B		Note[3], p. 43, Note [8]
83. Pentachlorophenol	604	625, 1625		6410 B, 6630 B		Note[3], p.140
84. Phenanthrene	610	625, 1625	610	6410 B, 6440 B	D4657-92	
85. Phenol	604	625, 1625		6420 B, 6410 B		
86. Pyrene	610	625, 1625	610	6410 B, 6440 B	D4675-92	
87. 2,3,7,8- Tetrachlorodibenzo-p-dioxin		Note [5a], 613				
88. 1,1,2,2-Tetrachloroethane	601	624, 1624		6230 B, 6210 B		Note[3], p. 130
89. Tetrachloroethene	601	624, 1624		6230 B, 6210 B		Note[3], p. 130
90. Toluene	602	624, 1624		6210 B, 6220 B		
91. 1,2,4-Trichlorobenzene	612	625, 1625		6410 B		Note[3], p. 130
92. 1,1,1-Trichloroethane	601	624, 1624		6210 B, 6230 B		
93. 1,1,2-Trichloroethane	601	624, 1624		6230 B, 6210 B		Note[3], p. 130
94. Trichloroethene	601	624, 1624		6230 B, 6210 B		
95. Trichlorofluoromethane	601	624, 1624		6230 B, 6210 B		
96. 2,4,6-Trichlorophenol	604	625, 1625		6410 B, 6240 B		
97. Vinyl chloride	601	624, 1624		6230 B, 6210 B		

Table IC notes:

[1] All parameters are expressed in micrograms per liter (μg/L).

[2] The full text of Methods 601-613, 624, 625, 1624, and 1625, are given at appendix A, "Test Procedures for Analysis of Organic Pollutants," of this part 136. The standardized test procedure to be used to determine the method detection limit (MDL) "Definition and Procedure for the Determination of the Method Detection Limit" of this part 136.

[3] "Methods for Benzidine: Chlorinated Organic Compounds, Pentachlorophenol and Pesticides in Water and Wastewater," U.S. Environmental Protection Agency, September, 1978.

[4] Method 624 may be extended to screen samples for Acrolein and Acrylonitrile. However, when they are known to be present, the preferred method for these two compounds is Method 603 or Method 1624.

[5] Method 625 may be extended to include benzidine, hexachlorocyclopentadiene, N-nitrosodimethylamine, and N-nitrosodiphenylamine. However, when they are known to be present, Methods 605, 607, and 612, or Method 1625, are preferred methods for these compounds.

[5a] 625, Screening only.

[6] "Selected Analytical Methods Approved and Cited by the United States Environmental Protection Agency", Supplement to the Fifteenth Edition of Standard Methods for the Examination of Water and Wastewater (1981).

[7] Each Analyst must make an initial, one-time demonstration of their ability to generate acceptable precision and accuracy with Methods 601-603, 624, 625, 1624, and 1625 (See Appendix A of this Part 136) in accordance with procedures each in section 8.2 of each of these Methods. Additionally, each laboratory, on an on-going basis must spike and analyze 10% (5% for Methods 624 and 625 and 100% for methods 1624 and 1625) of all samples to monitor and evaluate laboratory data quality in accordance with sections 8.3 and 8.4 of these Methods. When the recovery of any parameter falls outside the warning limits, the analytical results for that parameter in the unspiked sample are suspect and cannot be reported to demonstrate regulatory compliance. *Note:* These warning limits are promulgated as an "interim final action with a request for comments."

[8] "Organochlorine Pesticides and PCBs in Wastewater Using Empore TM Disk", 3M Corp. Revised 10/28/94.

Table ID. List of Approved Test Procedures for Pesticides [1]

Parameter	Method	EPA[2 7]	Standard Methods 18th Ed	ASTM	Other
1. Aldrin	GC	608	6630 B & C	D3086-90	Note[3], p. 7; note[4], p. 30; note[8]
	GC/MS	625	6410 B		
2. Ametryn	GC				Note[3], p. 83; Note[6], p. S68
3. Aminocarb	TLC				Note[3], p. 94; Note[6], p. S16
4. Atraton	GC				Note[3], p. 83; Note[6], p. S68
5. Atrazine	GC				Note[3], p. 83; Note[6], p. S68
6. Azinphos methyl	GC				Note[3], p. 25; Note[6], p. S51
7. Barban	TLC				Note[3], p. 104; Note[6], p. S64
8. a-BHC	GC	608	6630 B & C	D3086-90	Note[3], p. 7; Note[8]
	GC/MS	625[5]	6410 B		
9. b-BHC	GC	608	6630 C	D3086-90	Note[8]
	GC/MS	625[5]	6410 B		
10. d-BHC	GC	608	6630 C	D3086-90	Note[8]
	GC/MS	625[5]	6410 B		
11. g-BHC (Lindane)	GC	608	6630 B & C	D3086-90	Note[3], p. 7; note[4], p. 30; note [8]
	GC/MS	625	6410 B		
12. Captan	GC		6630 B	D3086-90	Note[3], p. 7
13. Carbaryl	TLC				Note[3], p. 94: Note[6], p. S60
14. Carbophenothion	GC				Note[4], p. 30; Note[6], p. S73
15. Chlordane	GC	608	6630 B & C	D3086-90	Note[3], p. 7; Note[8]
	GC/MS	625	6410 B		
16. Chloropropham	TLC				Note[3], p. 104; Note [6], p. S64
17. 2,4-D	GC		6640 B		Note[3], p. 115; Note[4], p. 35
18. 4,4'-DDD	GC	608	6630 B & C	D3086-90	Note[3], p. 7; Note[4], p. 30; Note[8]
	GC/MS	625	6410 B		
19. 4,4'-DDE	GC	608	6630 B & C	D3086-90	Note[3], p. 7; Note[4], p. 30; Note[8]
	GC/MS	625	6410 B		
20. 4,4'-DDT	GC	608	6630 B & C	D3086-90	Note[3], p. 7; Note[4], p. 30; Note[8]
	GC/MS	625	6410 B		
21. Demeton-O	GC				Note[3], p. 25; Note[6], p. S51
22. Demeton-S	GC				Note[3], p. 25; Note[6], p. S51
23. Diazinon	GC				Note[3], p. 25; Note[4], p. 30; Note[6], p. S51
24. Dicamba	GC				Note[3], p. 115
25. Dichlofenthion	GC				Note[4], p. 30; Note[6], p. S73
26. Dichloran	GC		6630 B & C		Note[3], p. 7
27. Dicofol	GC			D3086-90	
28. Dieldrin	GC	608	6630 B & C		Note[3], p. 7; Note[4], p. 30; Note[8]
	GC/MS	625	6410 B		
29. Dioxathion	GC				Note[4], p. 30; Note[6], p. S73
30. Disulfoton	GC				Note[3], p. 25; Note[6], p. S51
31. Diuron	TLC				Note[3], p. 104; Note[6], p. S64

Continued on next page.

Table ID. List of Approved Test Procedures for Pesticides [1], *continued*

Parameter	Method	EPA[2][7]	Standard Methods 18th Ed	ASTM	Other
32. Endosulfan I	GC	608	6630 B & C	D3086-90	Note[3], p. 7; Note[8]
	GC/MS	625[5]	6410 B		
33. Endosulfan II	GC	608	6630 B & C	D3086-90	Note[3], p. 7; Note[8]
	GC/MS	625[5]	6410 B		
34. Endosulfan Sulfate	GC	608	6630 C		Note[8]
	GC/MS	625	6410 B		
35. Endrin	GC	608	6630 B & C	D3086-90	Note[3], p. 7; Note[4], p. 30; Note[8]
	GC/MS	625[5]	6410 B		
36. Endrin aldehyde	GC	608			Note[8]
	GC/MS	625			
37. Ethion	GC				Note[4], p. 30; Note[6], p. S73
38. Fenuron	TLC				Note[3], p. 104; Note[6], p. S64
39. Fenuron-TCA	TLC				Note[3], p. 104; Note[6], p. S64
40. Heptachlor	GC	608	6630 B & C	D3086-90	Note[3], p. 7; Note[4], p. 30; Note[8]
	GC/MS	625	6410 B		
41. Heptachlor epoxide	GC	608	6630 B & C	D3086-90	Note[3], p. 7; Note[4], p.30; Note[6], p. S73; Note[8]
	GC/MS	625	6410 B		
42. Isodrin	GC				Note[4], p. 30; Note[6], p. S73
43. Linuron	GC				Note[3], p. 104; Note[6], p. S64
44. Malathion	GC		6630 C		Note[3], p. 25; Note[4], p. 30; Note[6], p. S51
45. Methiocarb	TLC				Note[3], p. 94; Note[6], p. S60
46. Methoxychlor	GC		6630 B & C	D3086-90	Note[3], p. 7; Note[4], p. 30; Note[8]
47. Mexacarbate	TLC				Note[3], p. 94; Note[6], p. S60
48. Mirex	GC		6630 B & C		Note[3], p. 7
49. Monuron	TLC				Note[3], p. 104; Note[6], p. S64
50. Monuron	TLC				Note[3], p. 104; Note[6], p. S64
51. Nuburon	TLC				Note[3], p. 104; Note[6], p. S64
52. Parathion methyl	GC		6630 C		Note[3], p. 25; Note[4], p. 30
53. Parathion ethyl	GC		6630 C		Note[3], p. 25
54. PCNB	GC		6630 B & C		Note[3], p. 7
55. Perthane	GC			D3086-90	
56. Prometron	GC				Note[3], p. 83; Note[6], p. S68
57. Prometryn	GC				Note[3], p. 83; Note[6], p. S68
58. Propazine	GC				Note[3], p. 83; Note[6], p. S68
59. Propham	TLC				Note[3], p. 104; Note[6], p. S64
60. Propoxur	TLC				Note[3], p. 94; Note[6], p. S60
61. Secbumeton	TLC				Note[3], p. 83; Note[6], p. S68
62. Siduron	TLC				Note[3], p. 104; Note[6], p. S64
63. Simazine	GC				Note[3], p. 83; Note[6], p. S68
64. Strobane	GC		6630 B & C		Note[3], p. 7

Continued on next page.

Table ID. List of Approved Test Procedures for Pesticides [1], *continued*

Parameter	Method	EPA[2][7]	Standard Methods 18th Ed	ASTM	Other
65. Swep	TLC				Note[3], p. 104; Note[6], p. S64
66. 2,4,5-T	GC		6640 B		Note[3], p. 115; Note[4], p. 35
67. 2,4,5-TP (Silvex)	GC		6640 B		Note[3], p. 115
68. Terbuthylazine	GC				Note[3], p. 83; Note[6], p. S68
69. Toxaphene	GC	608	6630 B & C	D3086-90	Note[3], p. 7; Note[4], p. 30; Note[8]
	GC/MS	625	6410 B		
70. Trifluralin	GC		6630 B		Note[3], p. 7

Table ID notes:

[1] Pesticides are listed in this table by common name for the convenience of the reader. Additional pesticides may be found under Table 1C, where entries are listed by chemical name.

[2] The full text of Methods 608 and 625 are given at Appendix A. "Test Procedures for Analysis of Organic Pollutants," of this Part 136. The standardized test procedure to be used to determine the method detection limit (MDL) for these test procedures is given at Appendix B. "Definition and Procedure for the Determination of the Method Detection Limit", of this Part 136.

[3] "Methods for Benzidine, Chlorinated Organic Compounds, Pentachlorophenol and Pesticides in Water and Wastewater," U.S. Environmental Protection Agency, September, 1978. This EPA publication includes thin-layer chromatography (TLC) methods.

[4] "Methods for Analysis of Organic Substances in Water and Fluvial Sediments," Techniques of Water-Resources Investigations of the U.S. Geological Survey, Book 5, Chapter A3 (1987).

[5] The method may be extended to include α-BHC, γ-BHC, endosulfan I, endosulfan II, and endrin. However, when they are known to exist, Method 608 is the preferred method.

[6] "Selected Analytical Methods Approved and Cited by the United States Environmental Protection Agency." Supplement to the Fifteenth Edition of Standard Methods for the Examination of Water and Wastewater (1981).

[7] Each analyst must make an initial, one-time, demonstration of their ability to generate acceptable precision and accuracy with Methods 608 and 625 (See Appendix A of this Part 136) in accordance with procedures given in section 8.2 of each of these methods. Additionally, each laboratory, on an on-going basis, must spike and analyze 10% of all samples analyzed with Method 608 or 5% of all samples analyzed with Method 625 to monitor and evaluate laboratory data quality in accordance with Sections 8.3 and 8.4 of these methods. When the recovery of any parameter falls outside the warning limits, the analytical results for that parameter in the unspiked sample are suspect and cannot be reported to demonstrate regulatory compliance. These quality control requirements also apply to the Standard Methods, ASTM Methods, and other Methods cited. *Note:* These warning limits are promulgated as an "Interim final action with a request for comments."

[8] "Organochlorine Pesticides and PCBs in Wastewater Using Empore; TM Disk", 3M Corporation, Revised 10/28/94.

Table IE. List of Approved Radiologic Test Procedures

Parameter	Method	EPA[27]	Standard Methods 18th Ed	ASTM	Other
1. Alpha-Total, pCi per liter	Proportional or scintillation counter	900	7110 B	D1943-90	pp. 75 and 78[3]
2. Alpha-Counting error, pCi per liter	Proportional or scintillation counter	Appendix B	7110 B	D1943-90	P. 79
3. Beta-Total, pCi per liter	Proportional counter	900.0	7110 B	D1890-90	pp. 75 and 78[3]
4. Beta-Counting error, pCi	Proportional counter	Appendix B	7110 B	D1890-90	p. 79
5. (a) Radium Total pCi per liter	Proportional counter	903.0	7500Ra B	D2460-90	
5. (b)Ra, pCi per liter	Scintillation counter	903.1	7500Ra C	D3454-91	p. 81

Table IE notes:

[1] "Prescribed Procedures for Measurement of Radioactivity in Drinking Water," EPA-600/4-80-032 (1980), U.S. Environmental Protection Agency, August 1980.

[2] Fishman, M.J. and Brown, Eugene, "Selected Methods of the U.S. Geological Survey of Analysis of Wastewaters," U.S. Geological Survey, Open-File Report 76-177 (1976).

[3] The method found on p. 75 measures only the dissolved portion while the method on p. 78 measures only the suspended portion. Therefore, the two results must be added to obtain the "total".

(b) The full texts of the methods from the following references which are cited in Tables IA, IB, IC, ID, and IE are incorporated by reference into this regulation and may be obtained from the sources identified. All costs cited are subject to change and must be verified from the indicated sources. The full texts of all the test procedures cited are available for inspection at the Environmental Monitoring Systems Laboratory, Office of Research and Development, U.S. Environmental Protection Agency, 26 West Martin Luther King Dr., Cincinnati, OH 45268 and the Office of the Federal Register, Room 8301, 1110 L Street, NW., Washington, DC 20408.

References, Sources, Costs, and Table Citations Used to Develop These Tables:

(1) The full text of Methods 601-613, 624, 625, 1624, and 1625 are printed in appendix A of this part 136. The full text for determining the method detection limit when using the test procedures is given in appendix B of this part 136. The full text of Method 200.7 is printed in appendix C of this part 136. Cited in: Table IB, Note 5; Table IC, Note 2; and Table ID, Note 2.

(2) USEPA. 1978. Microbiological Methods for Monitoring the Environment, Water, and Wastes. Environmental Monitoring and Support Laboratory, U.S. Environmental Protection Agency, Cincinnati, Ohio. EPA/600/8-78/017. Available from: National Technical Information Service, 5285 Port Royal Road, Springfield, Virginia 22161, Publ. No. PB-290329/AS. Cost: $36.95. Table IA, Note 3

(3) "Methods for Chemical Analysis of Water and Wastes," U.S. Environmental Protection Agency, EPA-600/4-79-020, March 1979, or "Methods for Chemical Analysis of Water and Wastes," U.S. Environmental Protection Agency, EPA-600/4-79-020, Revised March 1983. Available from: ORD Publications, CERI, U.S. Environmental Protection Agency, Cincinnati, Ohio 45268, Table IB, Note 1.

(4) "Methods for Benzidine, Chlorinated Organic Compounds, Pentachlorophenol and Pesticides in Water and Wastewater," U.S. Environmental Protection Agency, 1978. Available from: ORD Publications, CERI, U.S. Environmental Protection Agency, Cincinnati, Ohio 45268, Table IC, Note 3; Table D, Note 3.

(5) "Prescribed Procedures for Measurement of Radioactivity in Drinking Water," U.S. Environmental Protection Agency, EPA-600/4-80032, 1980. Available from: ORD Publications, CERI, U.S. Environmental Protection Agency, Cincinnati, Ohio 45268, Table IE, Note 1.

(6) American Public Health Association. 1992. Standard Methods for the Examination of Water and Wastewater. 18th Edition. Amer. Publ. Hlth. Assoc., 1015 15th Street NW, Washington, DC 20005. Cost: $160.00. Table IA, Note 4.

(7) Ibid, 15th Edition, 1980. Table IB, Note 30; Table ID.

(8) Ibid, 14th Edition, 1975. Table IB, Notes 17 and 27.

(9) "Selected Analytical Methods Approved and Cited by the United States Environmental Protection Agency," Supplement to the 15th Edition of Standard Methods for the Examination of Water and Wastewater, 1981. Available from: American Public Health Association, 1015 Fifteenth Street NW., Washington, DC 20036. Cost available from publisher. Table IB, Note 10; Table IC, Note 6; Table ID, Note 6.

(10) Annual Book of ASTM Standards, Water and Environmental Technology, Section 11, Volumes 11.01 and 11.02, 1994 in 40 CFR 136.3, Tables IB, IC, ID and IE.

References, Sources, Costs, and Table Citations Used to Develop These Tables: *continued*

(11) USGS. 1989. U.S. Geological Survey Techniques of Water-Resources Investigations, Book 5, Laboratory Analysis, Chapter A4, Methods for Collection and Analysis of Aquatic Biological and Microbiological Samples, U.S. Geological Survey, U.S. Dept. of the Interior, Reston, VA. Available from: USGS Books and Open-File Reports Section, Federal Center, Box 25425, Denver, CO 80225. Cost: $18.00. Table IA, Note 5.

(12) "Methods for Determination of Inorganic Substances in Water and Fluvial Sediments," by M.J. Fishman and Linda C. Friedman, Techniques of Water-Resources Investigations of the U.S. Geological Survey, Book 5 Chapter A1 (1989). Available from: U.S. Geological Survey, Denver Federal Center, Box 25425, Denver, CO 80225. Cost: $108.75 (subject to change). Table IB, Note 2.

(13) "Methods for Determination of Inorganic Substances in Water and Fluvial Sediments," N.W. Skougstad and others, editors. Techniques of Water-Resources Investigations of the U.S. Geological Survey, Book 5, Chapter A1 (1979). Available from: U.S. Geological Survey, Denver Federal Center, Box 25425, Denver, CO 80225. Cost: $10.00 (subject to change), Table IB, Note 8.

(14) "Methods for the Determination of Organic Substances in Water and Fluvial Sediments," Wershaw, R.L., et al, Techniques of Water Resources Investigations of the U.S. Geological Survey, Book 5, Chapter A3 (1987). Available from: U.S. Geological Survey, Denver Federal Center, Box 25425, Denver, CO 80225. Cost: $0.90 (subject to change). Table IB, Note 24; Table ID, Note 4.

(15) "Water Temperature--Influential Factors, Field Measurement and Data Presentation," by H.H. Stevens, Jr., J. Ficke, and G.F. Smoot, Techniques of Water-Resources Investigations of the U.S. Geological Survey, Book 1, Chapter D1, 1975. Available from: U.S. Geological Survey, Denver Federal Center, Box 25425, Denver, CO 80225. Cost: $1.60 (subject to change). Table IB, Note 32.

(16) "Selected Methods of the U.S. Geological Survey of Analysis of Wastewaters," by M.J. Fishman and Eugene Brown; U.S. Geological Survey Open File Report 76-77 (1976). Available from: U.S. Geological Survey, Branch of Distribution, 1200 South Eads Street, Arlington, VA 22202. Cost: $13.50 (subject to change). Table IE, Note 2.

(17) "Official Methods of Analysis of the Association of Official Analytical Chemicals", Methods manual, 15th Edition (1990). Price: $240.00. Available from: The Association of Official Analytical Chemists, 2200 Wilson Boulevard, Suite 400, Arlington, VA 22201. Table IB, Note 3.

(18) "American National Standard on Photographic Processing Effluents," April 2, 1975. Available from: American National Standards Institute, 1430 Broadway, New York, New York 10018. Table IB, Note 9.

(19) "An Investigation of Improved Procedures for Measurement of Mill Effluent and Receiving Water Color," NCASI Technical Bulletin No. 253, December 1971. Available from: National Council of the Paper Industry for Air and Stream Improvements, Inc., 260 Madison Avenue, New York, NY 10016. Cost available from publisher. Table IB, Note 18.

(20) Ammonia, Automated Electrode Method, Industrial Method Number 379-75WE, dated February 19, 1976. Technicon Auto Analyzer II. Method and price available from Technicon Industrial Systems, Tarrytown, New York 10591. Table IB, Note 7.

(21) Chemical Oxygen Demand, Method 8000, Hach Handbook of Water Analysis, 1979. Method price available from Hach Chemical Company, P.O. Box 389, Loveland, Colorado 80537. Table IB, Note 14.

(22) OIC Chemical Oxygen Demand Method, 1978. Method and price available from Oceanography International Corporation, 512 West Loop, P.O. Box 2980, College Station, TX 77840. Table IB, Note 13.

(23) ORION Research Instruction Manual, Residual Chlorine Electrode Model 97-70, 1977. Method and price available from ORION Research Inc., 840 Memorial Dr, Cambridge, MA 02138. Table IB, Note 16.

(24) Bicinchoninate Method for Copper. Method 8506, Hach Handbook of Water Analysis, 1979, Method and price available from Hach Chemical Company, P.O. Box 300, Loveland, CO 80537. Table IB, Note 19.

(25) Hydrogen Ion (pH) Automated Electrode Method, Industrial Method Number 378-75WA. October 1976. Bran & Luebbe (Technicon) Auto Analyzer II. Method and price available from Bran & Luebbe Analyzing Technologies, Inc. Elmsford, N.Y. 10523. Table IB, Note 21.

(26) 1,10-Phenanthroline Method using FerroVer Iron Reagent for Water, Hach Method 8008, 1980. Method and price available from Hach Chemical Company, P.O. Box 389 Loveland, CO 80537. Table IB, Note 22.

(27) Periodate Oxidation Method for Manganese, Method 8034, Hach Handbook for Water Analysis, 1979. Method and price available from Hach Chemical Co, P.O. Box 389, Loveland, CO 80537. Table IB, Note 23.

(28) Nitrogen, Nitrite--Low Range, Diazotization Method for Water and Wastewater, Hach Method 8507, 1979. Method and price available from Hach Chemical Co, P.O. Box 389, Loveland, CO 80537. Table IB, Note 25.

(29) Zincon Method for Zinc, Method 8009. Hach Handbook for Water Analysis, 1979. Method and price available from Hach Chemical Company, P.O. Box 389, Loveland, Colorado 80537. Table IB, Note 33.

References, Sources, Costs, and Table Citations Used to Develop These Tables: *continued*

(30) "Direct Determination of Elemental Phosphorus by Gas-Liquid Chromatography," by R.F. Addison and R.G. Ackman, Journal of Chromatography, Volume 47, No. 3, pp. 421-426, 1970. Available in most public libraries. Back volumes of the Journal of Chromatography are available from Elsevier/North-Holland, Inc., Journal Information Center, 52 Vanderbilt Avenue, New York, NY 10164. Cost available from publisher. Table IB, Note 28.

(31) "Direct Current Plasma (DCP) Optical Emission Spectrometric Method for Trace Elemental Analysis of Water and Wastes", Method AES 0029, 1986-Revised 1991, Fison Instruments, Inc., 32 Commerce Center, Cherry Hill Drive, Danvers, MA 01923. Table B, Note 34.

(32) "Closed Vessel Microwave Digestion of Wastewater Samples for Determination of Metals", CEM Corporation, P.O. Box 200, Matthews, North Carolina 28106-0200, April 16, 1992. Available from the CEM Corporation. Table IB, Note 36.

(33) "Organochlorine Pesticides and PCBs in Wastewater Using Empore TM Disk" Test Method 3M 0222, Revised 10/28/94. 3M Corporation, 3M Center Building 220-9E-10, St. Paul, MN 55144-1000. Method available from 3M Corporation. Table IC, Note 8 and Table ID, Note 8.

(34) USEPA. 1993. Methods for Measuring the Acute Toxicity of Effluents to Freshwater and Marine Organisms. Fourth Edition, December 1993. Environmental Monitoring Systems Laboratory, U.S. Environmental Protection Agency, Cincinnati, Ohio (EPA/600/4-90/027F). Available from: National Technical Information Service, 5285 Port Royal Road, Springfield, Virginia 22161, Publ. No. PB-91-167650. Cost: $31.00. Table IA, Note 17. See changes in the manual, listed in Part V of this rule.

(35) "Nitrogen, Total Kjeldahl, Method PAI-DK01 (Block Digestion, Steam Distillation, Titrimetric Detection)", revised 12/22/94. Available from Perstorp Analytical Corporation, 9445 SW Ridder Rd., Suite 310, P.O. Box 648, Wilsonville, OK 97070. Table IB, Note 39.

(36) "Nitrogen, Total Kjeldahl, Method PAI-DK02 (Block Digestion, Steam Distillation, Colorimetric Detection)", revised 12/22/94. Available from Perstorp Analytical Corporation, 9445 SW Ridder Rd., Suite 310, P.O. Box 648, Wilsonville, OK 97070. Table IB, Note 40.

(37) "Nitrogen, Total Kjeldahl, Method PAI-DK03 (Block Digestion, Automated FIA Gas Diffusion)", revised 12/22/94 Available from Perstorp Analytical Corporation, 9445 SW Ridder Rd., Suite 310, P.O. Box 648, Wilsonville, OK 97070. Table IB, Note 41.

(38) USEPA. 1994. Short-term Methods for Estimating the Chronic Toxicity of Effluents and Receiving Waters to Freshwater Organisms. Third Edition. July 1994. Environmental Monitoring Systems Laboratory, U.S. Environmental Protection Agency, Cincinnati, Ohio. (EPA/600/4-91/002). Available from: National Technical Information Service, 5285 Port Royal Road, Springfield, Virginia 22161, Publ. No. PB-92-139492. Cost: $31.00. Table IA, Note 8.

(39) USEPA. 1994. Short-term Methods for Estimating the Chronic Toxicity of Effluents and Receiving Waters to Marine and Estuarine Organisms. Second Edition, July 1994. Environmental Monitoring Systems Laboratory, U.S. Environmental Protection Agency, Cincinnati, Ohio. EPA/600/4-91/003. Available from: National Technical Information Service, 5285 Port Royal Road, Springfield, Virginia 22161, Publ. No. PB-92139484. Cost: $45.00. Table IA, Note 9.

(c) Under certain circumstances the Regional Administrator or the Director in the Region or State where the discharge will occur may determine for a particular discharge that additional parameters or pollutants must be reported. Under such circumstances, additional test procedures for analysis of pollutants may be specified by the Regional Administrator, or the Director upon the recommendation of the Director of the Environmental Monitoring Systems Laboratory--Cincinnati.

(d) Under certain circumstances, the Administrator may approve, upon recommendation by the Director, Environmental Monitoring Systems Laboratory--Cincinnati, additional alternate test procedures for nationwide use.

(e) Sample preservation procedures, container materials, and maximum allowable holding times for parameters cited in Tables IA, IB, IC, ID, and IE are prescribed in Table II. Any person may apply for a variance from the prescribed preservation techniques, container materials, and maximum holding times applicable to samples taken from a specific discharge. Applications for variances may be made by letters to the Regional Administrator in the Region in which the discharge will occur. Sufficient data should be provided to assure such variance does not adversely affect the integrity of the sample. Such data will be forwarded, by the Regional Administrator, to the Director of the Environmental Monitoring Systems Laboratory--Cincinnati, Ohio for technical review and recommendations for action on the variance application. Upon receipt of the recommendations from the Director of the Environmental Monitoring Systems Laboratory, the Regional Administrator may grant a variance applicable to the specific charge to the applicant. A decision to approve or deny a variance will be made within 90 days of receipt of the application by the Regional Administrator.

Table II. Required Containers, Preservation Techniques, and Holding Times

Parameter Number/name	Container [1]	Preservation [2,3]	Maximum holding time [4]
Table IA--Bacteria Tests:			
1-4 Coliform, fecal and total	P,G	Cool, 4°C, 0.008% $Na_2S_2O_3$	6 hours
5 Fecal streptococci	P,G	Cool, 4°C, 0.008% $Na_2S_2O_3$	6 hours
Table IA--Aquatic Toxicity Tests:			
6-10 Toxicity, acute and chronic	P,G	Cool, 4°C [16]	36 hours
Table IB--Inorganic Tests:			
1. Acidity	P, G	Cool, 4°C	14 days
2. Alkalinity	P, G	Cool, 4°C	14 days
4. Ammonia	P, G	Cool, 4°C, H_2SO_4 to pH<2	28 days
9. Biochemical oxygen demand	P, G	Cool, 4°C	48 hours
10. Boron	P, PFTE, or Quartz	HNO_3 to pH<2	6 months
11. Bromide	P, G	None required	28 days
14. Biochemical oxygen demand, carbonaceous	P, G	Cool, 4°C	48 hours
15. Chemical oxygen demand	P, G	Cool, 4°C, H_2SO_4 to pH<2	28 days
16. Chloride	P, G	None required	28 days
17. Chlorine, total residual	P, G	None required	Analyze immediately
21. Color	P, G	Cool, 4°C	48 hours
23-24. Cyanide, total and amenable to chlorination	P, G	Cool, 4°C, NaOH to pH>12, 0.6g ascorbic acid [5]	14 days[6]
25. Fluoride	P	None required.	28 days
27. Hardness	P, G	HNO_3 to pH2, H_2SO_4 to pH<2	6 months
28. Hydrogen ion (pH)	P, G	None required	Analyze immediately
31, 43. Kjeldahl and organic nitrogen	P, G	Cool, 4°C, H_2SO_4 to pH<2	28 days
Metals:[7]			
18. Chromium VI	P, G	Cool, 4°C	24 hours
35. Mercury	P, G	HNO_3 to pH<2	28 days
3, 5-8, 12, 13, 19, 20, 22, 26, 29, 30, 32-34, 36, 37, 45, 47, 51, 52, 58-60, 62, 63, 70-72, 74, 75. Metals,except boron, chromium VI and mercury	P, G	HNO_3 to pH<2	6 months
38. Nitrate	P, G	Cool, 4°C	48 hours
39. Nitrate-nitrite	P, G	Cool, 4°C, H_2SO_4 to pH<2	28 days
40. Nitrite	P, G	Cool, 4°C	48 hours
41. Oil and grease	G	Cool to 4°C, HCl or H_2SO_4 to pH<2	28 days
42. Organic Carbon	P, G	Cool to 4 C HCl or H_2SO_4 or H_3PO_4, to pH<2	28 days
44. Orthophosphate	P, G	Filter immediately, Cool, 4°C	48 hours
46. Oxygen, Dissolved Probe	G Bottle and top	None required	Analyze immediately
47. Winkler	G Bottle and top	Fix on site and store in dark	8 hours
48. Phenols	G only	Cool, 4°C, H2SO4 to pH<2	28 days
49. Phosphorus (elemental)	G	Cool, 4°C	48 hours
50. Phosphorus, total	P, G	Cool, 4°C, H2SO4 to pH<2	28 days

Continued on next page.

Table II. Required Containers, Preservation Techniques, and Holding Times, *continued*

Parameter Number/name	Container [1]	Preservation [2,3]	Maximum holding time [4]
53. Residue, total	P, G	Cool, 4°C	7 days
54. Residue, Filterable	P, G	Cool, 4°C	7 days
55. Residue, Nonfilterable (TSS)	P, G	Cool, 4°C	7 days
56. Residue, Settleable	P, G	Cool, 4°C	48 hours
57. Residue, volatile	P, G	Cool, 4°C	7 days
61. Silica	P, PFTE, or Quartz	Cool, 4°C	28 days
64. Specific conductance	P, G	Cool, 4°C	28 days
65. Sulfate	P, G	Cool, 4°C	28 days
66. Sulfide	P, G	Cool, 4°C add zinc acetate plus sodium hydroxide to pH>9	7 days
67. Sulfite	P, G	None required	Analyze immediately
68. Surfactants	P ,G	Cool, 4°C	48 hours
69. Temperature	P, G	None required	Analyze immediately
73. Turbidity	P, G	Cool, 4°C	48 hours
Table IC. Organic Tests[8]			
13, 18-20, 22, 24-28, 34-37, 39-43, 45-47, 56, 66, 88, 89, 92-95, 97. Purgeable Halocarbons	G, Telflon-lined septum	Cool, 4°C, 0.008% $Na_2S_2O_3$[5]	14 days
6, 57, 90. Purgeable aromatic hydrocarbons	G, Telflon-lined septum	Cool, 4°C, 0.008% $Na_2S_2O_3$[5], HCl to pH<2 [9]	14 days
3, 4, Acrolein and acrylonitrile	G, Telflon-lined septum	Cool, 4°C, 0.008% $Na_2S_2O_3$[5] Adjust pH to 4-5 [10]	14 days
23, 30, 44, 49, 53, 67, 70, 71, 83, 85, 96. Phenols [11]	G, Teflon-lined cap	Cool, 4°C, 0.008% $Na_2S_2O_3$[5]	7 days until extraction, 40 days after extraction
7, 38. Benzidines[11]	G, Teflon-lined cap	Cool, 4°C, 0.008% $Na_2S_2O_3$[5]	7 days until extraction
13, 14, 17, 48, 50-52. Phthalate esters [11]	G, Teflon-lined cap	Cool, 4°C	7 days until extraction, 40 days after extraction
72-74. Nitrosamines [11,14]	G, Teflon-lined cap	Cool, 4°C, store in dark, 0.008% $Na_2S_2O_3$ [5]	7 days until extraction, 40 days after extraction
76-82. PCBs [11]	G, Teflon-lined cap	Cool, 4°C	7 days until extraction, 40 days after extraction
54, 55, 65, 69. Nitroaromatics and isophorone [11]	G, Teflon-lined cap	Cool, 4°C, store in dark, 0.008% $Na_2S_2O_3$[5]	7 days until extraction, 40 days after extraction
1, 2, 5, 8-12, 32, 33, 58, 59, 64, 68, 84, 86. Polynuclear aromatic hydrocarbons[11]	G, Teflon-lined cap	Cool, 4°C, store in dark, 0.008% $Na_2S_2O_3$[5]	7 days until extraction, 40 days after extraction
15, 16, 21, 31, 75 Haloethers[11]	G, Teflon-lined cap	Cool, 4°C, 0.008% $Na_2S_2O_3$[5]	7 days until extraction, 40 days after extraction
29, 35-37, 60-63, 91. Chlorinated hydrocarbons[11]	G, Teflon-lined cap	Cool, 4°C	7 days until extraction, 40 days after extraction

Continued on next page.

Table II. Required Containers, Preservation Techniques, and Holding Times, *continued*

Parameter Number/name	Container [1]	Preservation [2,3]	Maximum holding time [4]
87. TCDD[11]	G, Teflon-lined cap	Cool, 4°C, 0.008% $Na_2S_2O_3$[5]	7 days until extraction, 40 days after extraction
Table ID. Pesticides Tests:			
1-70. Pesticides[11]	G, Teflon-lined cap	Cool, 4°C, pH 5-9[15]	7 days until extraction, 40 days after extraction
Table IE--Radiological Tests:			
1-5. Alpha, beta and radium	P, G	HNO_3 to pH<2	6 months

Table II Notes

1   Polyethylene (P) or glass (G). For microbiology, plastic sample containers must be made of sterilizable materials (polypropylene or other autoclavable plastic).

2   Sample preservation should be performed immediately upon sample collection. For composite chemical samples each aliquot should be preserved at the time of collection. When use of an automated sampler makes it impossible to preserve each aliquot, then chemical samples may be preserved by maintaining at 4°C until compositing and sample splitting is completed.

3   When any sample is to be shipped by common carrier or sent through the United States Mails, it must comply with the Department of Transportation Hazardous Materials Regulations (49 CFR part 172). The person offering such material for transportation is responsible for ensuring such compliance. For the preservation requirements of Table II, the Office of Hazardous Materials, Materials Transportation Bureau, Department of Transportation has determined that the Hazardous Materials Regulations do not apply to the following materials: Hydrochloric acid (HCl) in water solutions at concentrations of 0.04% by weight or less (pH about 1.96 or greater); Nitric acid (HNO3) in water solutions at concentrations of 0.15% by weight or less (pH about 1.62 or greater); Sulfuric acid (H2SO4) in water solutions at concentrations of 0.35% by weight or less (pH about 1.15 or greater); and Sodium hydroxide (NaOH) in water solutions at concentrations of 0.080% by weight or less (pH about 12.30 or less).

4   Samples should be analyzed as soon as possible after collection. The times listed are the maximum times that samples may be held before analysis and still be considered valid. Samples may be held for longer periods only if the permittee, or monitoring laboratory, has data on file to show that for the specific types of samples under study, the analytes are stable for the longer time, and has received a variance from the Regional Administrator under Sec. 136.3/(e). Some samples may not be stable for the maximum time period given in the table. A permittee, or monitoring laboratory, is obligated to hold the sample for a shorter time if knowledge exists to show that this is necessary to maintain sample stability. See Sec. 136.3/(e) for details. The term "analyze immediately" usually means within 15 minutes or less of sample collection.

5   Should only be used in the presence of residual chlorine.

6   Maximum holding time is 24 hours when sulfide is present. Optionally all samples may be tested with lead acetate paper before pH adjustments in order to determine if sulfide is present. If sulfide is present, it can be removed by the addition of cadmium nitrate powder until a negative spot test is obtained. The sample is filtered and then NaOH is added to pH 12.

7   Samples should be filtered immediately on-site before adding preservative for dissolved metals.

8   Guidance applies to samples to be analyzed by GC, LC, or GC/MS for specific compounds.

9   Sample receiving no pH adjustment must be analyzed within seven days of sampling.

10   The pH adjustment is not required if acrolein will not be measured. Samples for acrolein receiving no pH adjustment must be analyzed within 3 days of sampling.

11   When the extractable analytes of concern fall within a single chemical category, the specified preservative and maximum holding times should be observed for optimum safeguard of sample integrity. When the analytes of concern fall within two or more chemical categories, the sample may be preserved by cooling to 4°C, reducing residual chlorine with 0.008% sodium thiosulfate, storing in the dark, and adjusting the pH to 6-9; samples preserved in this manner may be held for seven days before extraction and for forty days after extraction. Exceptions to this optional preservation and holding time procedure are noted in footnote 5 (re: the requirement for thiosulfate reduction of residual chlorine), and footnotes 12, 13 (re: the analysis of benzidine).

12   If 1,2-diphenylhydrazine is likely to be present, adjust the pH of the sample to 4.0 ± 0.2 to prevent rearrangement to benzidine.

Table II Notes, *continued*

13 Extracts may be stored up to 7 days before analysis if storage is conducted under an inert (oxidant-free) atmosphere.

14 For the analysis of diphenylnitrosamine, add 0.008% $Na_2S_2O_3$ and adjust pH to 7-10 with NaOH within 24 hours of sampling.

15 The pH adjustment may be performed upon receipt at the laboratory and may be omitted if the samples are extracted within 72 hours of collection. For the analysis of aldrin, add 0.008% $Na_2S_2O_3$.

16 Sufficient ice should be placed with the samples in the shipping container to ensure that ice is still present when the samples arrive at the laboratory. However, even if ice is present when the samples arrive, it is necessary to immediately measure the temperature of the samples and confirm that the 4°C temperature maximum has not been exceeded. In the isolated cases where it can be documented that this holding temperature can not be met, the permittee can be given the option of on-site testing or can request a variance. The request for a variance should include supportive data which show that the toxicity of the effluent samples is not reduced because of the increased holding temperature.

GLOSSARY

601-602. EPA GC methods for determination of volatile organic compounds by PID Hall detectors in series.

AA. Atomic absorption spectrometric method for metals.

Accuracy. The ability of a test to give the true amount of target analyte.

Acetonitrile partition. A technique for removing fat and oil interference from organic extracts.

Acid digestion. Method for obtaining metal analytes in solution for analysis.

Acid extractables. Organic analytes that are removed from acidified water with methylene chloride.

Acid-base partition. Clean-up technique for organic analysis.

Activated carbon. Carbon heated to 900 °C in the absence of oxygen.

Activated charcoal. Charcoal heated to 900 °C in the absence of oxygen.

Acute. Immediate effects.

Alkalinity. A measure of the acid-neutralizing ability of the sample.

Ames Test. A common screening test for mutagenic properties.

Analyte-free water. Water that has been treated to remove impurities of interest.

Analytical balance. Electronic balance capable of accurate weighings to 0.1 mg.

Analytically valid. Term used to indicate a procedure has been performed with sufficient controls to assure a high degree of confidence in the result.

Appendix I. Municipal landfill leachate monitoring list for detection, 40 CFR 258

Appendix II. Municipal landfill leachate monitoring list for assessment, 40 CFR 258

Appendix VIII. Hazardous substances list, 40 CFR 261

Appendix IX. Groundwater monitoring list, 40 CFR 264

Areal composite sample. Samples taken over an area then mixed to give an overall analysis of the site.

Areal domain. Samples taken at a variety of points within a larger sampling site.

Ascarite. A sodium hydroxide treated asbestos.

Ash. Residue left from a sample after heating to 555 °C.

Atomic absorption. Method of analysis based on atomizing a metal sample in a flame and monitoring the absorption of specific wavelengths of light passed through the flame.

ATP. Adenosine triphosphate, a polyphosphate biochemical.

Audits. Examination of test procedures or other laboratory processes and comparison of the findings to a written standard, may be performed by an internal or external person to the laboratory.

Autotune. A software program that adjusts voltages and currents in a MS analyzer to achieve standard results.

Baghouse filters. Large cloth bags used to filter particulates from industrial air emissions.

Bar code. Optical pattern of narrow and wide bars used for sample tracking.

Base-neutral extractables. Compounds extractable from basic or neutral water solutions with organic solvents.

Bench worksheets. Papers used to record sample preparation and analysis work and notes by the technician as the work is being performed.

BFB. 4-bromofluorobenzene.

BFB tuning requirements. Abundance and mass detection requirements that must be met before analysis of compounds begins.

Biochemical oxygen demand (BOD). Oxygen requirement for bacteria to consume organic matter in a waste stream.

Blank analysis. QC measure that checks for contamination of analyte in reagents used for a test.

Blank preservatives. Analysis of preservatives used for samples to check for contamination.

Blank samples. Reagent water-filled containers prepared in the field and analyzed in the lab.

BN. Base/neutral organic target analytes.

BNA analysis. Base/neutral/acid extractable organics analyzed by GC/MS.

BOD. See biochemical oxygen demand.

BOD bottles. 300 mL bottles with ground glass stopper that is tapered at the bottom so as not to trap air bubbles in the bottle.

BOD5. Biochemical oxygen demand for a 5-day test.

Breakpoint chlorination. Addition of chlorine to water until all the chlorine demand has been satisfied and a residual remains.

Brown Ring Test. Qualitative test for nitrite.

BTEX. Benzene, toluene, ethylbenzene and xylene test.

Buffers. Solutions of a weak acid and a salt of the acid or a weak base and a salt of the base that are capable of maintaining pH on addition of acid or base.

C, H, O pesticides. Carbon-, hydrogen-, and oxygen-containing pesticides.

Calculation Worksheets. Forms filled out by the technician that record the mathematical transformation of raw analytical data into final results.

Calibration Check Compounds. A small group of representative compounds used to check the validity of instrument calibrations for a larger number of analyte compounds.

Calibration Checks. Procedures used to check instrument calibration.

Calibration Curve. Graphical plot of instrument response against amount of analyte in standards. Most often gives a straight line result.

Calibration Factor. Also called a response factor, it is a number used to multiply the instrument response and arrive at the amount of analyte.

California Method. Slang term for the GC-FID determination of diesel fuel.

Carbamates. Polar pesticides characterized by the presence of a urethane function.

Carcinogenesis. Uncontrolled replication of cells in the body resulting in tumors.

Cascade impactor. Device used for the speciation of particulates in air.

CBOD. Carbonaceous biochemical oxygen demand.

CCC. Calibration check compounds.

CCV. Continuing calibration verification.

CERCLA. Comprehensive Environmental Response, Compensation and Liability Act.

Chain of custody. Legal document recording who had the sample and over what period of time as it moves from the sampling point to the laboratory.

Chemiluminescence. Production of light from a chemical process.

Chlorinated acid herbicides. Herbicides structurally related to 2,4-dichloro phenoxyacetic acid.

Chlorinated hydrocarbons. Non-polar poly chlorinated hydrocarbon materials used mainly as pesticides.

Chlorinated pesticides. Non-polar poly chlorinated hydrocarbons.

Chlorination. Addition of chlorine to water for disinfection purposes.

Chlorination disinfection by-products. Chemicals resulting from addition of chlorine to water that contains organic materials.

Chronic. Effects seen over the long-term.

Clean-up methods. Procedures used to reduce interferences in organic sample extracts prior to analysis.

CLP. Contract Laboratory Program.

CLP Deliverables. Required quality control results and analytical documentation that must accompany each sample report on submission to EPA under the CLP.

CLP SOW. Contract Laboratory Program Statement of Work.

Cobalt thiocyanate Active Substances. non-ionic surfactants.

COD. Chemical oxygen demand.

Cold vapor. An AA method used with an optical cell replacing the flame.

Coliform bacteria. Any anaerobic and aerobic, gram negative, non-spore forming, rod-shaped bacteria that ferment lactose within 48 hours at 35 °C to produce carbon dioxide and acid.

Colorimetric indicator tubes. Scaled glass tubes packed with reagents that produce a color on passage of target analyte containing metered amounts of air through the tube.

Composite Samples. Individual samples are mixed together to make a single sample.

Confirmed Test. Second phase test of total or fecal coliform that confirms identification.

Container Blanks. Empty containers that are rinsed with reagent water and tested to insure freedom from target analytes. Generally performed by the lot number of the containers.

Continuing Calibration Verification. Standards are reanalyzed on a daily basis to reconfirm the validity of the instrument calibration.

Continuous liquid-liquid extraction. Device for extraction of organic analytes from water by dripping extraction solvent through the sample.

Control charts. Day-by-day or batch-by-batch plots of accuracy or precision as a process monitor.

Control level. ±3 standard deviations from the mean on a control chart.

Conventional pollutants. BOD$_5$, TSS, pH, and fecal coliform tests standard on most NPDES permits

Correlation coefficient. A mathematical measure of the goodness of fit, ranges from 0 to 1 with 1 being a perfect fit.

CTAS. Cobalt thiocyanate active substances.

DAD. Diode array detector.

Data quality objectives. Statements of the expected performance of the laboratory with respect to accuracy, precision, and MDL of each test procedure for each analyte.

DBCP. 1,2-Dibromo-3-chloropropane.

DBOB. 4,4'-Dibromooctafluorobiphenyl.

DCAA. 2,4-Dichlorophenylacetic acid.

De-tuning. After an MS passes autotune requirements for PFTBA, the voltage and current settings for the MS are changed in a set fashion so that the MS can meet the tune criteria for BFB or DFTPP.

Dean-Starke trap. A glassware device for separation of water from an organic material by azeotropic distillation.

Denuders. Devices for removing target analytes from air.

DFTPP. Decafluorotriphenylphospine.

Diesel range organics. Organic compounds determined by GC-FID that have retention times between decane and pentacosane, often assumed as diesel fuel.

Digestion. Solubilizing of metal analytes through heating with a variety of acids or oxidizers.

Digestion logs. Bound notebooks kept by technicians that record the details of the preparation of metals samples for analysis.

Discharge Monitoring Report. Periodic summaries of analytical results of wastewater effluents required of NPDES permit holders.

DMR. Discharge monitoring report.

DNPH. 2,4-dinitrophenyl hydrazine.

Dose. Dose/response.

DPD. N,N-diethyl phenylenediamine.

DQO. Data quality objectives.

DRO method. Diesel range organics referring to diesel fuel.

EDB. Ethylene dibromide.

ELCD. Electrolytic conductivity detector or Hall detector.

Electrostatic precipitators. Large scale devices that short circuit the static charges on particulates in air streams and result in removal of particulates.

EQL. Estimated quantitation limit.

Equipment blanks. Sampling equipment is rinsed with reagent water that is tested to determine contamination levels on the equipment.

Estimated quantitation limit. A term used to replace MDL when the MDL cannot be determined or is unavailable for the matrix, often 10 to 12 times a determined MDL.

Extraction logs. Logs maintained by the semivolatiles organic extraction technicians that detail everything that was performed on the sample.

F- series. Hazardous wastes from generic industrial sources.

FAS. Ferrous ammonium sulfate.

FDA. Food and Drug Administration.

FDCA. Food, Drug, and Cosmetic Act.

Fecal coliform. Coliform bacteria found in mammalian intestinal tracts.

Field duplicate samples. Duplicate samples obtained in the field and analyzed in the lab to assess field precision in sampling.

Field log book. A bound notebook maintained by the field operators that details every aspect of the sampling event.

FIFRA. Federal Insecticide, Fungicide, and Rodenticide Act.

Filter cassette. Device for holding membrane or glass fiber filters for removal of target analytes from air.

Final analytical report. Summary of the analytical results obtained by the laboratory and sent to the client.

Fixed solids. Another term for ash.

Flash point. Temperature at which a sample creates sufficient vapor to support combustion in air.

Flow domain. Set volumes of sample removed from a stationary sampling location after every set amount of flow.

FPD. Flame photometric detector.

Freon 113. 1,1,2-trichlorotrifluoroethane.

FTIR. Fourier transform infrared spectrophotometer.

Gas chromatography. Separatory technique that uses a solid or liquid absorbent and an inert gas stream as mobile phase - separation mechanisms are vapor pressure and chemical affinity.

Gasoline range organic. All organic materials that elute from a GC with retention times between 2-methyl pentane and trimethylbenzene - assumed to be gasoline fuel.

GC. Gas chromatography.

GC/FTIR. Gas chromatography - fourier transform infrared spectrophotometer interfaced together.

GC/MS. Gas chromatography - mass spectrometer interfaced together.

Gel permeation Column. A clean-up technique that separates compounds based on molecular size.

GFAA. Graphite furnace atomic absorption.

GPC. Gel permeation chromatography.

Grab Sample. A sample obtained in a single instant of time at a single location.

Graphite furnace. A carbon tube that is electrically heated in an AA to replace the flame as the atomization source.

GRO method. Gasoline range organics, used in reference to gasoline analysis.

Groundwater. Subsurface water.

Halowaxes. Polychlorinated derivatives of naphthalene.

Hardness. Dissolved metal content of water, expressed as calcium carbonate.

High performance liquid chromatography. Separation technique that uses a solid absorbent and liquid mobile phase - separation mechanism is chemical partitioning.

Holding times. Elapsed time between moment of sampling and initiation of analysis.

Hotplate Digestion. Open beaker method of acid digestion of metals.

HPLC. High pressure liquid chromatography.

HPLC-DAD. High pressure liquid chromatography with a diode array detector.

HPLC/MS. High pressure liquid chromatography interfaced to a mass spectrometer.

ICAP. Inductively coupled argon plasma emission spectrometer.

ICP. Inductively coupled argon plasma emission spectrometer.

ICV. Initial calibration verification.

IDL. Instrument detection limit.

Immunity. Ability of an organism to develop protecting antibodies to a foreign agent after an initial exposure.

Impingers. Glassware device for passing air through a liquid solution.

Indicators. Chemicals added to a sample that signal an end to a process by a color change.

Inductively Coupled Argon Plasma. 6,000 to 10,000 °C thermal source for excitation of metal atoms in emission spectrometry.

Initial Calibration Verification. Immediate analysis of standards from a different manufacturer than that of the calibration standards to check suitability of a calibration curve.

Instrument Detection Limit. Minimum signal level that can be differentiated from instrument background noise with 99% confidence.

Instrument Maintenance. Regular and nonscheduled procedures required to keep an instrument in top operational condition.

Integrated sample. A variety of different sampling methods used to form an overall picture of the sampling site.

Internal chain of custody. A record of who had the sample over what period of time within the laboratory.

Internal standards. Compounds added to the sample after sample preparation for qualitative and quantitative instrument analysis - the compounds serve to give a standard of retention time and response, which is invariant from run-to-run with the instruments.

Ion chromatography. Instrument very similar to an HPLC used for analysis of anions or cations.

IR. Infrared spectrophotometric.

IR-TPH. Infrared determination of total petroleum hydrocarbons.

IRIS. Plasma emission spectrometer that uses a photodetector to simultaneously record all the emission lines of a sample.

Isotope dilution. Addition of isotopically labeled analytes to a sample to assess sample preparation and serve as internal standard for analysis.

K-D concentrator. Kuderna-Danish concentrator - glassware device for removal of solvents from an organic extract.

K-series. Listed hazardous wastes from specific industrial processes.

KHP. Potassium hydrogen phthalate.

Kuderna-Danish concentrator. Glassware device for removal of solvents from an organic extract.

Laboratory control sample. Known amounts of target analytes are added to reagent water and analyzed. Serves as a quality control on the sample preparation process.

Landfill leachate. Liquid that drains from the bottom of the site into the ground.

Langelier's Index. An analytical measure of the corrosivity of water.

LAS. Linear alkylbenzene sulfonate.

Lauric acid value. Standardization procedure for Florosil.

LC. Lethal concentration.

LD5. Lethal dose for 5% of the test subjects.

LD50. Lethal dose for 50% of the test subjects.

Legally defensible. Analytical results supported by the necessary documentation to withstand challenge in a US court of law.

Lethal concentration. Amount of substance in water solution that the test organism was exposed to that resulted in the death.

LIMS. Laboratory information management system.

LUST. Leaking underground storage tanks remediation program.

MASA Methods. Methods of Air Sampling and Analysis, Lodge, 3rd Edition.

Matrix spikes. Target analyte added to a sample in known amount to determine recovery for the specific matrix..

Maximum Contaminant Levels. Regulatory action levels for primary drinking water analytes.

MBAS. Methylene blue active substances.

MBTH. N-Methyl benzothiazolinon hydrazone.

MCE. Mixed cellulose ester membrane for metals analysis of air samples.

MDL. Method detection limits.

Method Detection Limits. Minimum level of a target analyte that can be determined with 99% confidence.

Methylene Blue Active Substances. Anionic surfactants that can be extracted into chloroform solution by a ion-pairing mechanism with methylene blue.

MSDS. Material safety data sheets.

MTB. Methyl thymol blue.

MUG. 4-Methylumbelliferyl-ß-D-glucuronide.

Multiple Sampling. More than one sample taken from a site to assess pollution.

Mutagenesis. Inheritable damage to DNA of an organism caused by a foreign chemical or agent.

N & P Pesticides. Nitrogen and/or phosphorous-containing pesticides.

NDIR. Non-dispersive infrared analyzer.

NED. N-Napthyl-ethylenediamine dichloride.

Nipples. Permanent sampling ports in the sides of smoke stacks.

Nitrogen Inhibition. Chemicals added to BOD test to eliminate nitrogen oxidation demand on the results.

NMHC. Non-methane hydrocarbons.

NMOC. Non-methane organic compounds.

Non-conventional pollutants. Nitrogen forms, phosphorous, chloride, sulfate and other substances that may endanger water quality while not necessarily being toxic.

NPDES. National Pollutant Discharge Elimination System.

NTU. Nephelometric turbidity unit.

ONPG. o-Nitrophenyl-ß-D-galactopyranoside.

OPA. Ortho phthalaldehyde.

P-A. Presence-absence of total or fecal coliforms.

P-series. Acutely hazardous wastes from commercial chemical products, intermediates and residues.

PAH. Polynuclear aromatic hydrocarbons.

PAO. Phenylarsine oxide.

Pathogenic bacteria. Disease causing bacteria.

PCBs. Polychlorinated biphenyls.

PDS. Post digestion spike - independently checks the calibration of the AA, GFAA, or ICP instrument.

PE Samples. Performance evaluation samples.

Performance evaluation. Blind samples sent to the laboratory by outside parties for evaluation of qualitative and quantitative accuracy.

PES. Post extraction spike - a solution of extraction solvent containing surrogates, matrix spikes and internal standards for evaluating instrument calibration.

PFTBA. Perfluorotributylamine

pH. The negative log of the activity of the hydrogen ion.

Phenoxy-acid herbicides. See chlorinated acid herbicides.

Phthalate esters. As a group they are the most common form of laboratory contamination.

Pitot. Sampling tube for stack gas analysis.

Post column derivatization. Chemical procedure for derivatization of compounds after they elute from the separation column and before they enter the detector.

POTW. Publicly owned treatment works.

ppm. Parts per million.

ppt. Parts per trillion.

PQL. Practical quantitation levels.

Practical Quantitation Levels. Some randomly selected multiple, often 10 or 12, of the same sample.

Precision. The closeness of agreement between two or more analyses of the same sample.

Presence-absence. Qualitative test for total or fecal coliforms.

Preservatives. Chemical or physical treatment of the sample to assure continued presence of the target analytes at the same level as when the sample was first taken.

Primary standard. Analytical standard compounds that are stable solids, easy to purify to a known and reproducible level.

PUF. Polyurethane foam used as a trapping material for sampling of semivolatile organic compounds from air.

QC check standards. Analytical standards obtained from a different source than the manufacturer of the calibration standards, used as an independent check on the calibration.

Qualified data. Data derived from a sample analysis where something about the sample, the sampling procedure, or the analysis is not in accordance with specifications.

Qualitative analysis. The analytical process to determine what is in the sample.

Quality assurance program. The written overall program in the laboratory that details all the steps and procedures used to produce data of a known and stated quality.

Quality control. An individual procedure used in the quality assurance program. A matrix spike performed on a metals sample is a quality control, the use of matrix spikes in all procedures in the laboratory is quality assurance.

Quantitative analysis. After an analyte is identified in the sample, quantitative analysis is used to determine how much is there.

r. Regression coefficient with values between 0 to 1 - a value of 1.00 is perfect correlation of the points to the equation.

Raw data. Unprocessed data from the analysis.

Reagent blanks. An analyte-free sample of water, air or solid is processed with all the reagents in the procedure, then analyzed to discover any interference from the reagents used in the batch.

Relative percent difference. The difference between two values divided by the average of the values, expressed as a percent.

Representative sample. The degree to which a single sample of the whole can give results identical to analysis of the whole.

Residues. Remainder after removal of water or other liquids, see solids and total solids.

Resistance. Ability of a single organism, due to a genetic difference, to survive challenge by a toxic material that would be fatal to most of the rest of the population of the organism.

Respirable. Particles that pass the nasal membranes and hairs to lodge deep in the lungs.

Response factors. Multiplication factors for converting instrument response to mass of analyte.

Retention time. Elapsed time between injection of sample to elution on the chromatogram.

RF. Response factor.

RPD. Relative percent difference.

RT. Retention time.

Run logs. A bound logbook for each instrument listing consecutively what was run, when, by whom, how much was analyzed, and what file name the raw data is filed under.

Sample container logs. A written account of either the in-house cleaning of sample containers and results of blank analyses, or a record of receipt of pre-cleaned containers along with manu-facturers' certificates and results of blank analyses by lot.

Sample disposition logs. A written record of how samples were disposed after the required post-analysis holding times.

Sample duplicate. Analysis of two aliquots of sample in the same analytical batch to assess precision.

Sample preparation logs. Written record of the preparation of standards including weights, dilutions, and person performing the work.

Sample receipt logbooks. Written records of when samples were received, description of the samples, client name, date sampled, requested analyses, and person performing the log-in.

Sample result worksheets. Also described as work orders, these are sheets that give the analyst basic information about what tests are requested for the samples and may also provide space for entry of sample analysis results.

Sample splits. A single sample is divided into two containers that are sent to different labs for analysis.

Secondary Drinking Water Standards. Includes materials which affect the taste, odor, color and other non-health related qualities of water and collectively serve as a suggested list for states to act upon.

Sequential samples. A series of identical samples obtained under time or flow domain that are analyzed as a separate samples.

SFE. Supercritical fluid extraction, normally of solids.

SOW. Contract Laboratory Program Statement of Work, in essence a request for bid for services to EPA.

SPCC. System performance check compounds.

Stacks. Points of discharge of air from industrial processes to the atmosphere.

Standard receipt logs. Written record of the receipt of standards, including date, manufacturer's certificate of analysis, person logging standards, etc.

Surrogates. Compounds added to the sample prior to preparation, then monitored after analysis to detect problems in the sample preparation procedure.

SVI. Sludge volume index.

TAL. Target analyte list.

TCDD. 2,3,7,8-Tetrachloro-dibenzodioxin.

TCL. Target compound list.

TCLP. Toxic characteristic leaching procedure.

TCMP. 2-Chloro-6-trichloromethylpyridine.

TDS. Total dissolved solids.

Temperature monitoring logs. Written logs that record the twice daily checking of temperature on refrigerators, ovens and incubators, along with repair notes.

Teratogenesis. Birth defects caused by chemical exposure.

THC. Total hydrocarbon content.

THM. Trihalomethanes.

TIC. Tentatively identified compounds.

Time domain. Identical samples obtained at the same location at set intervals of time.

TOC. Total organic carbon.

TOX. Total organic halide.

TPH. Total petroleum hydrocarbon.

Trip blanks. VOC sample containers assembled with reagent water at the laboratory, then taken to the field and back to the lab, analyzed to reveal contamination that occurs by passage of volatile compounds through the septum into the container.

TRS. Total reduced sulfur.

TS. Total solids.

TSCA. Toxic Substances Control Act.

TSD. Treatment, storage and disposal facility for hazardous waste.

TSS. Total suspended solids.

TTHM. Total trihalomethanes.

TVDS. Total volatile dissolved solids.

TVS. Total volatile solids.

TVSS. Total volatile suspended solids.

U-series. Hazardous waste of a general nature from commercial chemical products, intermediates, or residues.

UST. Underground storage tanks.

Vertical composite sample. Grab samples at a variety of depths at one sampling location that are mixed together to form a single sample representing the water column.

VOA. Volatile organic analysis.

VOC. Volatile organic compounds.

Warning Level. ± 2 standard deviations from the mean on a control chart.

Work assignments. Printouts of samples that require the same test by a worker for processing as a batch.

WP. Biannual performance evaluation samples sent out by EPA in support of the water pollution programs under the Clean Water Act.

WP analytes. A list of the analytes in the WP studies.

WS. Biannual performance evaluation samples sent out by EPA in support of the water supply programs under the Safe Drinking Water Act.

XAD-2. Insoluble, porous, non-polar polystyrene Amberlite resin used for isolation of organic materials from air streams.

ZHE. Zero headspace extractor.

INDEX

EPA Methods, *continued*

505	**324**	632.1	**353**	
506	**325**	633	**353**	
507	**325**	633.1	**353**	
508A	**327**	634	**354**	
510.1	**258**	635	**354**	
513	**327**	636	**354**	
515.1	**328**	641	**355**	
515.2	**328**	645	**355**	
524.2	**308**	646	**355**	
525	**330**	1311	**438**	
531.1	**332**	1312	**442**	
547	**332**	1624	**313**	
548	**332**	1625	**356**	
549	**333**	1656	**356**	
549.1	**333**	1657	**357**	
550	**334**	1658	**359**	
551	**334**	1659	**359**	
552	**335**	1660	**359**	
601-602	**302, 317, 323**	1661	**360**	
601	**310**	3005	**243**	
602	**311**	3010	**243**	
604	**335**	3015	**244**	
604.1	**336**	3050	**243**	
605	**336**	3051	**244, 246**	
606	**337**	3510	**360**	
607	**337**	3520	**361**	
608	**337**	3540	**361**	
608.1	**338**	3541	**362**	
608.2	**338**	3550	**362**	
609	**339**	3560	**362**	
610	**339**	3580	**363**	
611	**340**	3600	**364**	
612	**340**	3610	**364**	
613	**341**	3611	**364**	
614	**341**	3620	**364**	
614.1	**341**	3630	**365**	
615	**341**	3640	**365**	
616	**342**	3650	**366**	
617	**342**	3660	**366**	
618	**343**	3665	**366**	
619	**343**	8015	**316**	
622	**343**	8021	**317**	
624	**311**	8032	**366**	
627	**351**	8040	**367**	
629	**351**	8081	**369, 370**	
630.1	**352**	8260	**318**	
631	**352**	8270	**378**	
632	**352**	8275	**384**	
		8315	**386**	